Howard H. B

PROBABILITY AND ITS ENGINEERING USES. *By* THORNTON C. FRY.

ELEMENTARY DIFFERENTIAL EQUATIONS. *By* THORNTON C. FRY. Second Edition.

TRANSMISSION CIRCUITS FOR TELEPHONIC COMMUNICATION. METHODS OF ANALYSIS AND DESIGN. *By* K. S. JOHNSON.

TRANSMISSION NETWORKS AND WAVE FILTERS. *By* T. E. SHEA.

ECONOMIC CONTROL OF QUALITY OF MANUFACTURED PRODUCT. *By* W. A. SHEWHART.

ELECTROMECHANICAL TRANSDUCERS AND WAVE FILTERS. *By* WARREN P. MASON. Second Edition.

RHOMBIC ANTENNA DESIGN. *By* A. E. HARPER.

POISSON'S EXPONENTIAL BINOMIAL LIMIT. *By* E. C. MOLINA.

ELECTROMAGNETIC WAVES. *By* S. A. SCHELKUNOFF.

NETWORK ANALYSIS AND FEEDBACK AMPLIFIER DESIGN. *By* HENDRICK W. BODE.

SERVOMECHANISMS. *By* LEROY A. MACCOLL.

QUARTZ CRYSTALS FOR ELECTRICAL CIRCUITS. *By* R. A. HEISING.

CAPACITORS—THEIR USE IN ELECTRONIC CIRCUITS. *By* M. BROTHERTON.

FOURIER INTEGRALS FOR PRACTICAL APPLICATIONS. *By* GEORGE A. CAMPBELL AND RONALD M. FOSTER.

VISIBLE SPEECH. *By* RALPH K. POTTER, GEORGE A. KOPP, AND HARRIET C. GREEN

APPLIED MATHEMATICS FOR ENGINEERS AND SCIENTISTS. *By* S. A. SCHELKUNOFF.

EARTH CONDUCTION EFFECTS IN TRANSMISSION SYSTEMS. *By* ERLING D. SUNDE.

RADAR SYSTEMS AND COMPONENTS. *By* MEMBERS OF THE STAFF OF THE BELL TELEPHONE LABORATORIES; Introduction by M. J. KELLY.

THEORY AND DESIGN OF ELECTRON BEAMS. *By* J. R. PIERCE.

PIEZOELECTRIC CRYSTALS AND THEIR APPLICATION TO ULTRASONICS. *By* WARREN P. MASON.

MICROWAVE ELECTRONICS. *By* JOHN C. SLATER.

PRINCIPLES AND APPLICATIONS OF WAVEGUIDE TRANSMISSION. *By* GEORGE C. SOUTHWORTH.

TRAVELING-WAVE TUBES. *By* J. R. PIERCE.

ELECTRONS AND HOLES IN SEMICONDUCTORS. *By* WILLIAM SHOCKLEY.

FERROMAGNETISM. *By* RICHARD M. BOZORTH.

THE DESIGN OF SWITCHING CIRCUITS. *By* WILLIAM KEISTER, ALASTAIR E. RITCHIE, AND SETH H. WASHBURN.

SPEECH AND HEARING IN COMMUNICATION. *By* HARVEY FLETCHER. Second Edition.

Network Analysis and Feedback Amplifier Design

Network Analysis and Feedback Amplifier Design

By

HENDRIK W. BODE, Ph.D.,

Research Mathematician,

BELL TELEPHONE LABORATORIES, INC.

NINTH PRINTING

D. VAN NOSTRAND COMPANY, INC.

TORONTO NEW YORK LONDON

NEW YORK
D. Van Nostrand Company, Inc., 250 Fourth Avenue, New York 3

TORONTO
D. Van Nostrand Company (Canada), Ltd., 25 Hollinger Road, Toronto

LONDON
Macmillan & Company, Ltd., St. Martin's Street, London, W.C. 2

First Published September 1945
Reprinted January 1946, February 1947
October 1947, April 1949, October 1950
September 1951, July 1952, December 1953

Produced by
TECHNICAL COMPOSITION CO.
BOSTON, MASS.

PRINTED IN THE UNITED STATES OF AMERICA

PREFACE

This book was originally written as an informal mimeographed text for one of the so-called "Out-of-Hour" courses at Bell Telephone Laboratories. The bulk of the material was prepared in 1938 and 1939 and was given in course form to my colleagues there in the winters of 1939–40 and 1940–41. During the war, however, the text has also been supplied as a reference work to a considerable number of other laboratories engaged in war research. The demand for the text on this basis was unexpectedly heavy and quickly exhausted the original supply of mimeographed copies. It has consequently been decided to make the text more widely available through regular channels of publication.

In revising the material for publication, the original theoretical discussion has been supplemented by footnote references to other books and papers appearing both before and after the text was first written. In addition, an effort has been made to simplify the theoretical treatment in Chapter IV, and minor editorial changes have been made at a number of points elsewhere. Otherwise, however, the text is as it was originally written.

The book was first planned as a text exclusively on the design of feedback amplifiers. It shortly became apparent, however, that an extensive preliminary development of electrical network theory would be necessary before the feedback problem could be discussed satisfactorily. With the addition of other logically related chapters, this has made the book primarily a treatise on general network theory. The feedback problem is still conspicuous, but the book also contains material on the design of non-feedback as well as feedback amplifiers, particularly those of wide band type, and on miscellaneous transmission problems arising in wide band systems generally. Much of this is material which has not hitherto appeared in previous texts on network theory. On the other hand, transmission line and filter theory, which are the primary concerns of most earlier network texts, are omitted.

Two further explanatory remarks may be helpful in understanding the book. The first is the fact that, although the feedback amplifiers envisaged in most of the discussion are of the conventional single loop, absolutely stable type, the original plan for the text called for two final chapters on design methods appropriate for multiple loop and conditionally stable circuits. Invincible fatigue set in before these chapters could be written. In anticipation of these chapters, however, the preliminary analysis in the early portions of the book was carried forward in more general terms than would otherwise have been necessary. In Chapters IV–VI, particularly, this appreciably complicates the discussion, and the reader interested only in conventional feedback amplifiers can afford to omit the more difficult portions of these chapters.

The second general remark concerns the apparently unnecessary refinement to which the design methods described in the book are sometimes carried. This is explained by the fact that the amplifiers of particular interest to the class for which the notes were originally prepared were those used as repeaters in long distance telephone systems. Since a long system may include many repeater points, the cumulative effect of even quite small imperfections in individual amplifiers may be serious. Thus, the amplifier design requires more care than might be justified in an ordinary engineering application.

Under the circumstances in which the text was originally prepared, it naturally benefited by suggestions from many sources. I am indebted for such help to too many of my colleagues to enumerate individually. Special mention should, however, be made of Mrs. S. P. Mead for her assistance in the final preparation of the material for publication. It is a particular pleasure also to express my thanks to Dr. Thornton C. Fry, without whose support and encouragement the book could scarcely have been written.

H. W. Bode

Bell Telephone Laboratories, Inc.
New York City
April 1945

CONTENTS

LIST OF SYMBOLS

NOTE: Asterisks indicate relatively unimportant symbols or subsidiary meanings restricted to one section of the book.

Symbol	Meaning	Page
A	real component of θ	230, 278
$*A, B, C, \cdots$	nodes	1
A_m	maximum obtainable feedback, under different assumptions	466, 477, 484
A_t	circuit loss	477
A_0	loop feedback in the useful band	455
B	imaginary component of θ	230, 278
$*B$	number of branches in a network	3
C	generic symbol for capacity	1
D	generic symbol for stiffness or reciprocal capacity	2
$*D_a, D_b, D_c, \cdots$	branch stiffnesses	2
D_{ij}	mutual stiffness, $i \neq j$	4
D_{ij}	self-stiffness, $i = j$	4
E	generic symbol for voltage	2, 12
$*E_A, E_B, E_C, \cdots$	node voltages	2
E_R	output voltage	32
E_i	impressed voltage in mesh i, $i = 1, 2, \cdots, n$	4
E_i	response voltage on node i, $i = 1, 2, \cdots, n$	10
E_0	input voltage	22, 32
$*E_1$	output voltage, of tube	404
$*E_1$	" returned " voltage	32
$*E_\beta$	β-circuit output voltage	385
$*E_\mu$	μ-circuit input voltage	385
F	return difference or feedback	47
$F(k)$	return difference of an element W, when $W = k$	50
$F_k(W)$	return difference of W for reference k	47

Symbol	Meaning	Page
$F(0)$	return difference of W, when a given pair of terminals in the network is short-circuited	67
$F(\infty)$	return difference of W, when the given pair of terminals is open-circuited	67
$*F$	dissipation function	127
$*F(a)$ or F_a	value of dissipation function obtained by using real components of complex current coefficients as instantaneous physical currents	133, 171
$*F(b)$ or F_b	value of dissipation function obtained by using imaginary components of complex current coefficients as instantaneous physical currents	133, 171
$*F_{av}$	average value of dissipation function with respect to time	130
G	generic symbol for conductance	13
G_m	transconductance, equal to μ/R_0	14
G_{ij}	mutual conductance	13
I	generic symbol for current	19
I_R	output or receiver current	385
$*I_a, I_b, I_c, \cdots$	instantaneous branch currents	2
I_i	response current in mesh i, $i = 1, 2, \cdots, n$	4
I_i	impressed current on node i, $i = 1, 2, \cdots, n$	11
I_j	steady-state mesh current in mesh j; coefficient of exp $(i\omega t)$	8
$*I_{ja}$	real component of I_j	129
$*I_{jb}$	imaginary component of I_j	129
I_0	input current	22
$*I_1$	plate current	404
$*I_\beta$	β-circuit input current	385
$*I_\mu$	μ-circuit output current	385
L	generic symbol for inductance	1
$*L_a, L_b, L_c, \cdots$	branch inductances	2
L_{ij}	mutual inductance, $i \neq j$	4
L_{ij}	self-inductance, $i = j$	4
$*N$	number of nodes in a network	3
$*N$	number of zeros within a contour	148
$*P$	number of poles within a contour	148
Q	reactance-resistance ratio	219, 367

		Page
R	generic symbol for resistance	1
R_T	transfer resistance, real component of Z_T	433
$^*R_a, R_b, R_c, \cdots$	branch resistances	2
R_p and R_g	plate and grid resistances, respectively	404
R_{ij}	mutual resistance, $i \neq j$	4
R_{ij}	self-resistance, $i = j$	4
R_0	image impedance of a constant-R network	241
R_0	internal tube resistance	14
$^*R_0$	terminating resistance	385
R_1 and R_2	terminating resistances	227
S	sensitivity	52
S'	relative sensitivity	63
$^*S_m$	transconductance	156
T	return ratio	48
$^*T$	stored magnetic energy function	127
$^*T(a)$ or T_a	value of stored magnetic energy function obtained by using real components of complex current coefficients as instantaneous physical currents	133, 171
$^*T(b)$ or T_b	value of stored magnetic energy function obtained by using imaginary components of complex current coefficients as instantaneous physical currents	133, 171
$^*T_{av}$	average value of stored magnetic energy function with respect to time	130
$^*V$	stored electric energy function	127
$^*V(a)$ or V_a	value of stored electric energy function obtained by using real components of complex current coefficients as instantaneous physical currents	133, 171
$^*V(b)$ or V_b	value of stored electric energy function obtained by using imaginary components of complex current coefficients as instantaneous physical currents	133, 171
$^*V_{av}$	average value of stored electric energy function with respect to time	133, 171
W	generic symbol for immittance; symbol for a selected unilateral or bilateral element in the network	15, 48, 51
W_R	output immittance	53

		Page
W_T	transfer immittance	25
W_0	reference value of an element W	61
W'	$W - W_0$, the effective value of W	62
X	generic symbol for reactance	206
Y	generic symbol for admittance	15
Y_T	transfer admittance	15
Y_{jk}	mutual admittance, $j \neq k$	11
Y_{jk}	self-admittance, $j = k$	11
Z	generic symbol for impedance	8
Z_I	image impedance	231
Z_T	transfer impedance	9
Z_g	grid impedance	6
*Z_n	arbitrary impedance added to the nth mesh	68
Z_x and $\mathbf{Z_y}$	branch impedances of the lattice	231
Z_{jk}	mutual impedance, $j \neq k$	4
Z_{jk}	self-impedance, $j = k$	4
Z_0	circuit impedance, when a prescribed element vanishes	67
*$a, b, c, \cdots$	branches	1
a_i	zeros of Z_T, $i = 1, 2, \cdots, n$	230
b_i	poles of Z_T, $i = 1, 2, \cdots, n$	230
*e	voltage Z_gI across the grid	6
e, e_n	instantaneous voltage in an element	126
f	frequency in cycles per second	22
f_a and f_b	horizontal step frequencies in loop cutoff characteristic	465
f_c and f_d	horizontal step frequencies with gain and phase margins	467
f_0	frequency at edge of useful band	455
f_p	frequency at which excess phase for feedback loop is equal to $2n/\pi$ radians	484
*f_r	frequency of equal resistance and reactance in a capacity-resistance network	511
f_t	figure of merit frequency	477
i, i_n	instantaneous current	126
k	filter type	373
k	arbitrary reference value of W	49
*k_1 and k_1'	volume performance characteristics	385
*k_2 and k_2'	contributions of input and output circuits to loop transmission characteristic	385

		Page
*k_3 and k_3'	transmission characteristics between β circuit and input and output lines, respectively	385
m	parameter in filter theory	373
n	slope of asymptote in units of 6 db per octave	459
p and $1/p$	differential and integral operators, respectively	2
p	$2\pi if$	22
*p_n and p_n'	zeros and poles of immittance, respectively	25
q, q_n	charge on condenser	126
t	time	8
x	gain margin in db	453
y	phase margin, expressed as a fraction of π radians	453
*α	transmission characteristic of subsidiary feedback path	158
β	transmission characteristic of backward or feedback path or the backward circuit itself	31
*γ_1, γ_2, γ_3, γ_4	transmission characteristics of tube circuit with tube dead	78
θ	generic symbol for complex quantity representing transmission, i. e. loss (or gain) and phase shift. By extension, symbol for a general complex network function ($=A + iB$)	45, 53, 278
θ	transfer loss and phase; image transfer constant (of a constant-resistance structure)	230, 231
*θ	phase angle of driving-point impedance	171
θ_F	fractionated gain, $W = 0$	81
θ_F'	fractionated gain, $W = W_0$	87
*θ_{AB}	gain from point A to point B	100
θ_0	direct transmission gain	53
*λ	ratio of number of stages to the optimum number of stages in a feedback amplifier	478
μ	amplification ratio of a vacuum tube	14
μ	transmission characteristic of forward circuit or the forward circuit itself	32

		Page
ρ	reflection coefficient	364
ϕ	frequency variable, $\sin^{-1} \omega/\omega_0$	415
ϕ'	frequency variable, $\sin^{-1} \omega_0/\omega$	419
ω	angular velocity, $2\pi f$	8
$^*\Gamma_{ij}$	reciprocal inductance	13
Δ	determinant of the mesh equations	8
Δ^k	value of Δ when $W = k$	50
Δ^0	value of Δ when $W = 0$	48
Δ'	value of Δ when $W' = 0$ or $W = W_0$	62
$^*\Delta'$	determinant of the nodal equations	15
Δ_{ij}, Δ_{ijkl}, etc.	cofactors of Δ	8–10
$^*\Phi$	analytic function, $A + iB$, representing some network characteristic	218
$^*\Phi_0$	value of Φ when dissipation is neglected	219
$\int_C$	integration in the complex plane, over a contour C	140
$\int_0$	integration in the complex plane, around a circle	141
$\oint$	integration around a semicircle in the right half-plane, centered at the origin and terminating on the imaginary axis	144
$\oint$	integration around the closed path consisting of the semicircle above and the included portion of the imaginary axis (with indentations if necessary to exclude singularities on the imaginary axis)	144

CHAPTER I

Mesh and Nodal Equations for an Active Circuit

1.1 *Introduction*

The networks to be considered consist of ordinary lumped inductances, resistances, and capacities, together with vacuum tubes. The accessible terminals of the vacuum tubes will be taken as the grid, plate, and cathode. Auxiliary electrodes, such as a suppressor or screen grid, are thus ignored, and the analysis assumes, in effect, that they are grounded to the cathode at signal frequencies. For purposes of discussion the tubes will be replaced by equivalent structures consisting of ordinary circuit elements connected between the accessible terminals, together with a source of current or voltage to represent the amplification of the tube. This ignores such effects as transit time and distributed inductance in the wires inside the tube envelope, which may appear in physical tubes at sufficiently high frequencies.

It will be assumed throughout that all the elements are linear. This chapter is intended principally as a recapitulation of the conventional theory for networks including vacuum tubes in a form which can be used as a foundation for the chapters to follow.*

1.2. *Branch Equations for a Passive Circuit*

It is simplest to begin by ignoring the active elements in the circuit. The network can then be regarded as an arrangement of individual branches, which may include any combination of the elements R, C, and L in series, connected together at various junctions or nodes. An example is shown by Fig. 1.1. The circuit contains six branches, as indicated by the subscripts $a \cdots f$, and four nodes represented by the points $A \cdots D$. Generators to furnish the driving forces on the circuit are shown in three of the branches.

* A good general reference to the mesh analysis of passive networks is Guillemin "Communication Networks," Vol. I. See also Shea "Transmission Networks and Wave Filters" for a brief discussion emphasizing the stock theorems, such as the superposition theorem, reciprocity theorem, and Thévenin's theorem, which follow readily from the mesh analysis. The theorem on the use of an equivalent plate generator to represent the amplification of a vacuum tube, on which the extension of the mesh analysis to active circuits depends, is described in most books on radio engineering. See, e.g., Terman "Radio Engineering" or "Radio Engineer's Handbook," or Everitt "Communication Engineering."

The condensers are specified in units of stiffness, or reciprocal capacity, $D = 1/C$, in order to simplify later equations. Each branch has been shown as including all three types of elements but in an actual network many of the elements might, of course, be omitted.

Fundamental expressions for the analysis of such a network can be set up by equating the instantaneous voltage drops in each branch of the network to the voltage applied to that branch. For example, if I_a represents

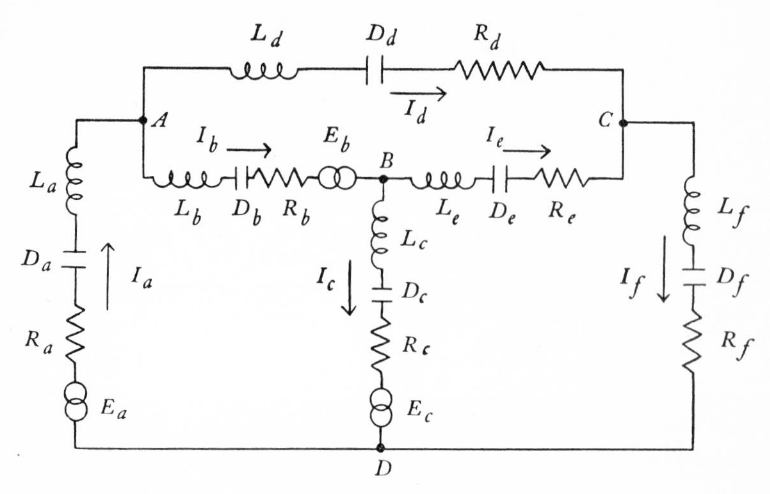

FIG. 1.1

the instantaneous current in the first branch of Fig. 1.1, the voltages across the individual elements of that branch are $R_a I_a$, $pL_a I_a$, and $(1/p)D_a I_a$, where p and $1/p$ represent respectively differentiation and integration with respect to time. The sum of the voltage drops through these three elements must be equal to the voltage of the generator E_a plus the difference between the voltages at the nodes A and D at which the branch terminates. If we let E_A and E_D represent the node voltages, we therefore have

$$\left(pL_a + R_a + \frac{1}{p}D_a\right) I_a = E_a + E_D - E_A. \tag{1-1}$$

There will be one equation similar to (1–1) for each branch of the network, or B equations in all if B represents the number of branches. In addition to these equations, however, further equations follow from the fact that, since no electrical charge can accumulate at any node, *the sum of the instantaneous currents leaving each node must be equal to the sum of the currents entering it.* In Fig. 1.1, for example, this leads to the condition $I_a = I_b + I_d$. There is one such equation for each node. One of the equations, however, is superfluous, since if the law of conservation of charge is satisfied at all but one of the nodes, it will automatically be satisfied at the last one also.* If the number of nodes is represented by N, there will then be $N - 1$ current equations. The original branch equations included, in addition to the branch currents, the N nodal voltages. One of these voltages, however, can be chosen arbitrarily, since the branch equations involve only voltage differences. There are thus $B + N - 1$ unknowns to be determined, and the $N - 1$ current equations together with the original B branch equations are just sufficient to permit a solution.

The $N - 1$ conditions at the nodes allow us to express $N - 1$ of the branch currents in terms of the others so that a corresponding number of the branch voltage equations similar to (1–1) can be eliminated. This reduction becomes particularly easy if we follow the familiar device of regarding the remaining branch currents as flowing through complete closed loops in the network. The assumption of closed loops or meshes has two advantages. In the first place it evidently leads to automatic satisfaction of the condition of conservation of charge at each node, since in each mesh as much current flows away from any node as flows into it. In the second place, it eliminates the differences in node voltages which appeared in the original branch equations, since the sum of all such voltage differences around a complete loop must be zero. We may also notice that, since there were originally B branch currents and $N - 1$ of them have been eliminated, the number of remaining currents or meshes is given by the

Theorem: In any conductively united network the number of independent closed meshes or loops is one greater than the difference between the number of branches and the number of nodes.

An illustration of the reduction from branch to mesh currents is furnished by Fig. 1.2, which shows a choice of mesh currents which is appropriate for the circuit of Fig. 1.1. The independent branch currents in terms of which the other currents are expressed are those flowing through branches a, d, and f, each of which is included in only one mesh. There are three meshes since the circuit contains six branches and four nodes.

It is apparent that in general the meshes can be chosen in a variety of ways. Thus in Fig. 1.2 the independent branch currents might be chosen as those flowing through, for example, a, d, and e, or a, b, and c. These

* This analysis neglects mutual inductance couplings as a matter of simplicity. If the network consists of a number of isolated fragments connected only by mutual inductance, there is evidently one superfluous condition of this sort for each conductively separate fragment of the network

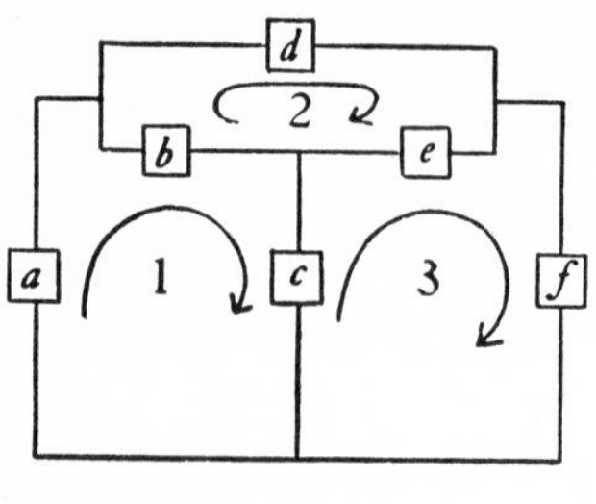

FIG. 1.2

possibilities are useful since they allow us to assign branches in which we may have particular interest, such as the generator or receiver impedances, to individual meshes. In a given physical circuit such assignments cannot be made with unlimited freedom. In Figs. 1.1 and 1.2, for example, it is not possible to assign branches a, b, and d to three separate meshes because the corresponding branch currents are related by the condition at node A and are not independent variables. For purposes of future analysis, however, it will be assumed that there are no restrictions on the choice of meshes, since an adequate mesh system can always be obtained by the addition of ideal transformers or other elements of vanishing physical importance.

1.3. *Mesh Equations for a Passive Circuit*

It is evident that each mesh equation can be obtained by adding together the branch voltage equations around the complete loop and at the same time eliminating the superfluous branch currents by means of the nodal current conditions. Since this introduces only linear combinations of the coefficients in the original branch equations, the resulting system of equations must be in the general form

$$\begin{aligned} Z_{11}I_1 + Z_{12}I_2 + \cdots + Z_{1n}I_n &= E_1 \\ Z_{21}I_1 + Z_{22}I_2 + \cdots + Z_{2n}I_n &= E_2 \\ \cdots\cdots\cdots\cdots\cdots\cdots\cdots \\ \cdots\cdots\cdots\cdots\cdots\cdots\cdots \\ Z_{n1}I_1 + Z_{n2}I_2 + \cdots + Z_{nn}I_n &= E_n \end{aligned} \qquad (1\text{–}2)$$

where the Z's in the left-hand side are of the form

$$Z_{ij} = pL_{ij} + R_{ij} + \frac{1}{p} D_{ij}$$

and p still represents d/dt.

The mesh currents are indicated by numbered subscripts to distinguish them from the branch currents. The coefficients Z_{11}, Z_{22}, etc., will be called the *self-impedances* of the various meshes and the coefficients Z_{12}, Z_{13}, Z_{23}, etc., the *mutual* or *coupling* impedances between meshes.

The mesh equations are expressions of voltage equilibrium. They express, in other words, the fact that the sum of the driving voltages around a closed loop must be equal to the sum of the voltage drops in the loop. This makes it easy to evaluate the E's and Z's in the equations. In the first mesh equation, for example, let it be supposed that we set $I_2 = I_3 = \cdots = I_n = 0$. This can be done without disturbing the first mesh by inserting sufficiently high impedances in each of the other meshes. The first mesh equation then reduces to

$$\left(pL_{11} + R_{11} + \frac{1}{p} D_{11}\right) I_1 = E_1. \tag{1-3}$$

Since there are no other currents flowing in the structure, the left-hand side of this expression evidently represents the voltage drop due to the flow of the current I_1 through all of the elements in the first mesh. The coefficients L_{11}, R_{11}, and D_{11} thus represent respectively the sum of the inductances, resistances and stiffnesses in the first mesh. Correspondingly, E_1 on the right-hand side represents the sum of the generator voltages in this mesh. Now, if we allow I_2 to flow, an additional voltage drop $Z_{12}I_2$ appears in the first mesh. This must evidently be due to the flow of I_2 through the elements which are shared by the first and second meshes. Similarly, Z_{13} represents the elements which are common to the first and third mesh, etc.

The coefficients in the equations for the other meshes can be determined in analogous fashion. In the purely passive circuits now under consideration, the coefficients representing a coupling between two meshes must be the same in each mesh equation. In other words, Z_{ij} in the ith equation must be the same as Z_{ji} in the jth equation, since either quantity merely represents the elements which are common to the two meshes.

The determination of the coefficients in the mesh equations can be illustrated by reference to the structure of Figs. 1.1 and 1.2. The self-impedance Z_{11} of the first mesh is equal to the sum of the impedances around that mesh. We thus have $L_{11} = L_a + L_b + L_c$, $R_{11} = R_a + R_b + R_c$, and $D_{11} = D_a + D_b + D_c$. Similarly, the voltage E_1 is equal to the total voltage $E_a + E_b + E_c$ of all the generators in this mesh. The impedances Z_{12} and Z_{13} represent the elements which the first mesh shares respectively with the second and third. As Fig. 1.1 is drawn, however, the positive direction of the first mesh current opposes that of the second and third mesh currents in each common branch. The coupling elements must therefore be taken negatively to account for the fact that the voltage drops across them due to the flow of the second and third mesh currents are opposite to those produced by the flow of the first mesh current. We thus have $L_{12} = -L_b$, $R_{12} = -R_b$, etc. The terms appearing in the other mesh equations can be determined in a similar fashion.

1.4. *Mesh Equations for an Active Circuit*

To generalize equation (1–2) to fit a circuit containing vacuum tubes, we may suppose that only one of the E's on the right-hand side of (1–2) is an actual driving voltage and that the remaining E's are apparent plate generators representing the amplifications of the tubes. For example, in one particular tube, let us suppose that the jth mesh current flows from grid to cathode and the kth mesh current from cathode to plate as shown by

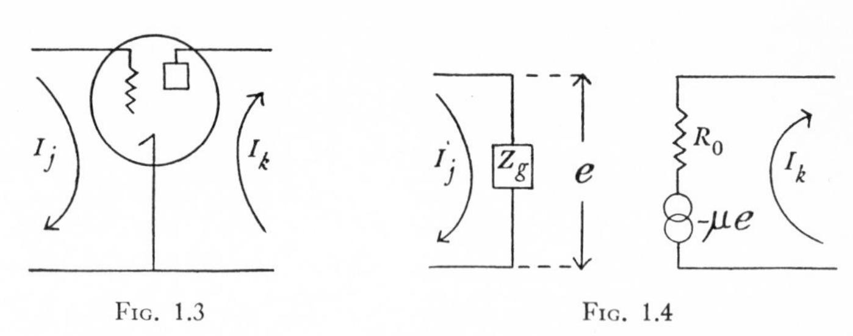

FIG. 1.3 FIG. 1.4

Fig. 1.3. Following the usual assumptions, the amplification of the tube can then be represented by inserting an equivalent generator $-\mu e$ in series with the plate impedance R_0, where e is the grid voltage, as shown by Fig. 1.4. The passive impedances of the tube can be incorporated as part of the passive circuit and play no part in this analysis.

Since $e = Z_g I_j$ in Fig. 1.4, the equivalent plate generator voltage can also be written as $-\mu Z_g I_j$. The kth of equations (1–2) can therefore be written as

$$Z_{k1}I_1 + \cdots + Z_{kj}I_j + \cdots + Z_{kn}I_n = -\mu Z_g I_j$$

or

$$Z_{k1}I_1 + \cdots + (Z_{kj} + \mu Z_g)I_j + \cdots + Z_{kn}I_n = 0 \qquad (1\text{–}4)$$

where Z_{kj} is the passive coupling between the two meshes. It is obvious that the equation is still in the same form as the original kth equation of (1–2) provided we redefine Z_{kj} to include the added quantity μZ_g. This is the familiar result that the amplifications of the tubes can be represented by modifications in the various coupling terms in the mesh equations. So far as the general form of the equations goes, the only distinction between active and passive structures is the fact that we can no longer assume in general that the principle of reciprocity holds. In other words, we can no longer assume that $Z_{ij} = Z_{ji}$. The quantity μZ_g will be called the *mutual impedance* or *transimpedance* of the tube, after the analogy with transconductance in the following discussion.

In order to prevent future confusion with signs, it is important to notice here the convention adopted in Fig. 1.3 for the positive direction of grid and plate currents. It has been so chosen that the transimpedances in the left sides of the mesh equations will be positive when the μ's are positive, as they are in normal tubes, and also so that a uniform convention of sign can be adopted for a number of tubes in tandem coupled by ordinary interstage networks. With this choice, however, the equivalent plate generator voltage is negative, so that *successive tubes in an amplifying circuit give successive phase reversals*, in addition to any phase shifts which may be ascribed to the purely passive elements of the circuit. Similar remarks apply to the nodal analysis given later.

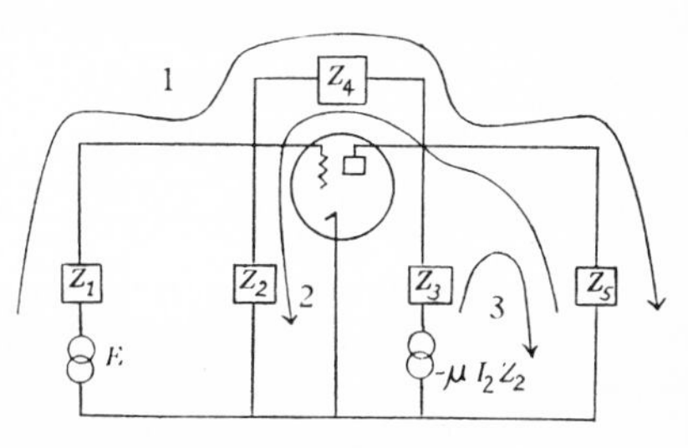

Fig. 1.5

As an example of the processes indicated by (1–4) we may consider the mesh equations for the circuit of Fig. 1.5. The structure represents broadly one stage of an amplifier with grid plate coupling. The coupling is indicated by the impedance Z_4 and the preceding and following interstages by the impedances Z_1 and Z_5. Z_2 is the grid cathode capacity of the tube and Z_3 represents its plate impedance.

The circuit has three meshes. They are chosen in the form shown by Fig. 1.5 in order to assign the generator impedance, the grid impedance and the plate impedance each to only one mesh. If we assume for the moment that the tube has no amplification the mesh equations are readily set up in the form

$$\begin{aligned} (Z_1 + Z_4 + Z_5)I_1 - (Z_4 + Z_5)I_2 + Z_5I_3 &= E \\ -(Z_4 + Z_5)I_1 + (Z_2 + Z_4 + Z_5)I_2 - Z_5I_3 &= 0 \\ Z_5I_1 - Z_5I_2 + (Z_3 + Z_5)I_3 &= 0. \end{aligned} \tag{1–5}$$

Since the voltage across the grid is $+I_2Z_2$ when the currents are taken in the directions shown in Fig. 1.5, the equivalent generator in the plate circuit is $-\mu Z_2 I_2$. This appears as an effective voltage in the third mesh equation. When this term is transposed to the left side of the equation in the manner described previously, the third equation thus becomes

$$Z_5I_1 + (\mu Z_2 - Z_5)I_2 + (Z_3 + Z_5)I_3 = 0 \tag{1–6}$$

the other mesh equations remaining unaffected.

1.5. *Steady State Solution for the Mesh Equations*

As the mesh equations have been developed thus far, they have always represented differential equations for the circuit. Thus, for example, in

(1–2) the E's and I's represent instantaneous values of voltages and currents and p represents differentiation with respect to time. In order to find the response of the circuit when one of the E's is a voltage varying sinusoidally with time, therefore, we should, strictly speaking, substitute $\sin \omega t$ or $\cos \omega t$ for the appropriate E and attempt to find expressions for the I's as sums of sine and cosine terms in a form which would satisfy the set of differential equations.

In accordance with the usual practice, this procedure can be much simplified if we represent a physical sinusoid by the exponential $e^{i\omega t}$.* The currents and voltages in the system are then written in the form $I_j e^{i\omega t}$ and $E_j e^{i\omega t}$, where the I's and E's are now merely constants instead of being quantities varying with time as they were in (1–2). The advantage of this substitution results from the fact that differentiating or integrating $e^{i\omega t}$ with respect to time merely multiplies or divides the exponential by $i\omega$. Thus, any quantities of the form $pe^{i\omega t}$ or $(1/p)e^{i\omega t}$ which result when the currents $Ie^{i\omega t}$ are substituted for the original currents in (1–2) become simply $i\omega e^{i\omega t}$ and $(1/i\omega)e^{i\omega t}$ when the differentiation and integration symbolized by p and $1/p$ are carried out. Each p on the left-hand side of (1–2) is then replaced by $i\omega$. The time factors $e^{i\omega t}$ in the current and voltage expressions are unchanged, and can be divided out of the final equations.

1.6. *Driving Point and Transfer Impedance*

It follows from the considerations just advanced that the differential equations (1–2) can also be regarded as a solution for the steady state response of the network to sinusoidal voltages of frequency $\omega/2\pi$ provided p is replaced by $i\omega$ and that we regard the I's and E's as representing merely the constant coefficients in the general current and voltage expressions $Ie^{i\omega t}$ and $Ee^{i\omega t}$. With this understanding, the determination of any particular current flowing in response to a particular voltage is equivalent to the solution of a set of ordinary linear equations. As an example, the current $I_1 e^{i\omega t}$ in the first mesh flowing in response to the voltage $E_1 e^{i\omega t}$ also in that mesh is given by

$$I_1 e^{i\omega t} = \frac{\Delta_{11}}{\Delta} E_1 e^{i\omega t} \tag{1–7}$$

where Δ is the determinant of the coefficients in the left-hand side of (1–2) and Δ_{11} is the determinant obtained when the first row and the first column of Δ are omitted.

The *driving point impedance* Z in the first mesh is by definition the ratio

* A discussion of the physical meaning of this substitution is avoided here, since the subject is taken up again in the next chapter.

of the voltage to the current in equation (1–7). It is given in other words by

$$Z = \frac{E_1}{I_1} = \frac{\Delta}{\Delta_{11}}. \tag{1–8}$$

In a similar fashion the equations can be solved to determine the current in any other mesh in response to this same voltage. For example, the current in the second mesh is given by

$$I_2 e^{i\omega t} = \frac{\Delta_{12}}{\Delta} E_1 e^{i\omega t} \tag{1–9}$$

where Δ_{12} is the determinant of the coefficients in the left-hand side of (1–2) after the elements in the first row and second column have been omitted.*

The ratio between the voltage E_1 and the current I_2 will be called the *transfer impedance*, Z_T, from the first to the second mesh. It is given by

$$Z_T = \frac{E_1}{I_2} = \frac{\Delta}{\Delta_{12}}. \tag{1–10}$$

1.7. *Z and Z_T as Functions of a Single Element*

In future discussion, we will have frequent occasion to study the dependence of the driving point and transfer impedance upon a single element in the network. Let it be supposed, for example, that we are interested in the variation of Z with respect to a bilateral impedance z in the jth mesh.† This can be investigated by examining the way in which z enters the determinants Δ and Δ_{11} of (1–8).

In general, any determinant can be regarded as the sum, with appropriate signs, of all possible products formed by multiplying together elements of the determinant, when each product includes just one element from each row and column of the determinant. Since z is in the jth row and column of Δ, it must therefore be multiplied by all possible products of elements taken from every row and column of Δ except the jth. These, however, evidently form the minor Δ_{jj} of the original determinant. Similarly, in

* Strictly speaking, the symbols Δ_{11}, Δ_{12}, etc., represent cofactors here. In other words, they are the determinants as defined in the text multiplied by $+1$ or -1 in accordance with the usual rules of determinant theory. In particular, Δ_{12} is negative. This may be ignored for theoretical analysis, however, since it is only necessary to treat the symbols as cofactors consistently.

†It is assumed here, in other words, that z is found in the jth mesh and in none of the others so that it is a constituent of only the self-impedance Z_{jj} in (1–2).

forming Δ_{11} the terms by which z is multiplied must be the minor Δ_{11jj} obtained by omitting both the first and jth rows and columns. If we let Δ^0 and Δ_{11}^0 represent, respectively, Δ and Δ_{11} when $z = 0$, therefore, we have

$$Z = \frac{\Delta^0 + z\Delta_{jj}}{\Delta_{11}^0 + z\Delta_{11jj}}. \tag{1–11}$$

Since Δ_{jj} and Δ_{11jj} are evidently independent of z they can equally well be written as Δ_{jj}^0 and Δ_{11jj}^0. This will occasionally be done in later analysis in order to facilitate further transformations.

The relation between Z_T and z can be found in similar fashion. It is given by

$$Z_T = \frac{\Delta^0 + z\Delta_{jj}}{\Delta_{12}^0 + z\Delta_{12jj}}. \tag{1–12}$$

If z represents a unilateral coupling term, instead of a bilateral element, the expansion is essentially the same. Thus, if we suppose that z is a part of Z_{ij} in the original determinant, we readily find

$$Z = \frac{\Delta^0 + z\Delta_{ij}}{\Delta_{11}^0 + z\Delta_{11ij}} \tag{1–13}$$

and

$$Z_T = \frac{\Delta^0 + z\Delta_{ij}}{\Delta_{12}^0 + z\Delta_{12ij}}. \tag{1–14}$$

1.8. *Nodal Equations for a Passive Circuit**

In the mesh equation formulation, the driving sources are regarded as voltages. The dependent variables, whose determination constitutes the solution of the structure, are the currents in the several closed loops or meshes. There is one equation for each mesh and each equation represents the fact that it is physically necessary for all the meshes to be in voltage equilibrium.

As we might expect, it is also possible to set up a system of equations in reciprocal form with the activating forces taken as currents and their responses as voltages. In this case, the nodes replace the closed loops in the mesh equation analysis. Figure 1.6 shows the form which such an analysis may take. The driving sources are the currents $I_1 \cdots I_n$ impressed on the nodes $1 \cdots n$ from some outside sources. The responses are the voltages $E_1 \cdots E_n$ for the individual nodes. Each voltage is sup-

* The writer is indebted to Prof. R. M. Foster, of the Polytechnic Institute of Brooklyn, for pointing out the superiority of the nodal analysis.

posed to be measured with reference to some particular node which is chosen as ground.

The fundamental equations in the nodal system are expressions of current equilibrium. They represent, in other words, the fact that the driving current flowing into any node from the outside must be equal to the total current flowing away from that node into the rest of the network, just as

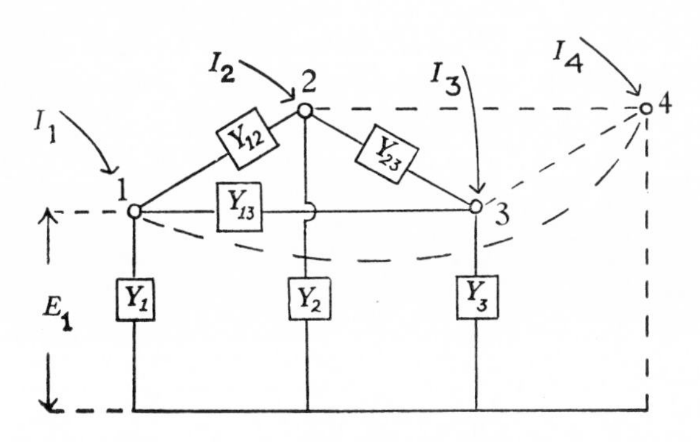

Fig. 1.6

the mesh equations represent an equilibrium between driving voltages and voltage drops in any mesh. In Fig. 1.6, for example, the current flowing into the first node from the outside is I_1. The current flowing from that node directly to ground must be Y_1E_1. The current flowing from that node to the second node must be $Y_{12}(E_1 - E_2)$, etc. The complete equation is therefore

$$Y_1E_1 + Y_{12}(E_1 - E_2) + \cdots + Y_{1n}(E_1 - E_n) = I_1 \qquad (1\text{–}15)$$

which can evidently be written as

$$Y_{11}E_1 - Y_{12}E_2 - Y_{13}E_3 - \cdots - Y_{1n}E_n = I_1 \qquad (1\text{–}16)$$

where

$$Y_{11} = Y_1 + Y_{12} + Y_{13} + \cdots + Y_{1n}. \qquad (1\text{–}17)$$

In equation (1–17) Y_{11} is obviously the total admittance between the first node and all the others when the others are shorted together. It will be called the *self-admittance* of the node and is evidently analogous to the self-impedance of a mesh, which can be defined as the impedance of the mesh when all other meshes are opened. Similarly, the terms Y_{1j} are *mutual admittances* corresponding to the mutual impedances appearing in a set of mesh equations.

Since an equation analogous to (1–16) can be written for each node, the complete system of equations becomes

$$
\begin{aligned}
Y_{11}E_1 - Y_{12}E_2 - \cdots - Y_{1n}E_n &= I_1 \\
-Y_{21}E_1 + Y_{22}E_2 - \cdots - Y_{2n}E_n &= I_2 \\
\cdots\cdots\cdots\cdots\cdots\cdots\cdots\cdots & \\
\cdots\cdots\cdots\cdots\cdots\cdots\cdots\cdots & \\
-Y_{n1}E_1 - Y_{n2}E_2 - \cdots + Y_{nn}E_n &= I_n.
\end{aligned}
\tag{1-18}
$$

It is not necessary to write a separate equation for the last or " ground " node. Since as much current must leave the network as a whole as enters it, the condition of current continuity will automatically be satisfied for this node if it is satisfied for each of the others. We thus have the

Theorem: In any conductively united network the number of independent nodal equations is one less than the total number of nodes.

At first sight, it might appear that the cases in which we can regard the energizing sources as constant current generators or, in other words, as generators with infinite internal impedances would be rather rare. In the mesh equation analysis, however, we seldom deal with generators having zero internal impedance and it is customary to allow for this by adding the

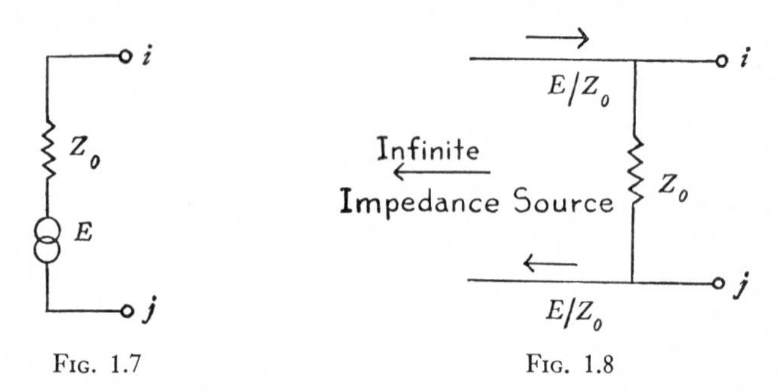

FIG. 1.7 FIG. 1.8

internal impedance of the generator to the impedance of the mesh in which it appears. When consideration is given to this fact the two methods stand on an absolute parity.

To show this, let us suppose that the actual driving source is a generator of internal emf E and internal impedance Z_0 connected between terminals i and j as shown by Fig. 1.7. It is easy to see that this must be equivalent to the circuit shown in Fig. 1.8 for any connections between i and j. In other words, the source shown in Fig. 1.7 can be represented in the nodal admittance analysis merely by choosing the energizing currents I_i and I_j

as E/Z_0 and $-E/Z_0$, respectively, and adding the admittance $1/Z_0$ across terminals i and j.

In this discussion we are concerned with the use of current rather than voltage sources only to establish the broad possibility of writing network equations in the general form given by (1–18). It is interesting to note, however, that the formal symmetry between the current and voltage methods of analysis can also be extended to the individual terms in these equations. This follows from the fact that the current and voltage relations for a resistance or conductance can be written as $E = RI$ and $I = GE$, while the corresponding expressions for a capacity or inductance are $E = LpI$ and $I = CpE$, where p may be either $i\omega$ or d/dt.

It is obvious from the symmetry of these expressions that we can erect a set of nodal equations formally identical with a given set of mesh equations by interchanging R and G and L and C wherever they appear. In other words, the general term $Z_{ij} = pL_{ij} + R_{ij} + D_{ij}/p$ in (1–2) is replaced by $Y_{ij} = pC_{ij} + G_{ij} + \Gamma_{ij}/p$ in (1–18), where Γ stands for a reciprocal inductance, just as D represents a reciprocal capacity. The two sets of equations will evidently be equal, term for term, provided we set $L_{ij} = C_{ij}$, $R_{ij} = G_{ij}$, and $D_{ij} = \Gamma_{ij}$.

The recognition of these general possibilities constitutes the so-called *principle of duality* in network theory.* If the mesh equations for one network correspond, term for term, with the nodal equations for another, the two networks are called *inverse* structures. It is not always possible to obtain the exact inverse of a given structure. There are difficulties, for example, with networks including mutual inductance coupling, since the capacitance dual of a coupling between coils does not exist. The inverse may also fail because the inverse set of equations does not correspond to any conceivable arrangement of impedance branches. In most of these instances, however, it is possible to obtain a network which will behave like the desired inverse so far as external connections are concerned, though it may have a different internal structure. The detailed discussion of these possibilities is beyond the scope of this chapter. The subject is resumed in Chapter X.

1.9. *Nodal Equations for an Active Network*

The modifications which are necessary in order to include vacuum tubes in a nodal admittance analysis are essentially similar to those we have already made in the mesh analysis. Suppose, for example, that the grid,

* Good general discussions are given in Guillemin "Communication Networks," Vol. II, and Gardner and Barnes "Transients in Linear Systems," Vol. I. The latter reference may also be cited for its detailed description of the method of setting up a system of nodal equations, especially in circuits containing mutual inductance.

plate, and cathode of a given vacuum tube are respectively nodes j, k, and m of the complete network. The voltage between grid and cathode is then $E_j - E_m$, and in accordance with our preceding discussion the effect of the amplification of the tube can be represented by introducing an equivalent generator $-\mu(E_j - E_m)$ in the plate circuit. It follows from Figs. 1.7 and 1.8, however, that this equivalent generator can in turn be replaced by two current sources of strengths $-\mu(E_j - E_m)/R_0$ and $\mu(E_j - E_m)/R_0$ applied to the plate and cathode, respectively, where R_0 is the internal resistance of the tube, provided the admittance $1/R_0$ between plate and cathode is incorporated as part of the network.

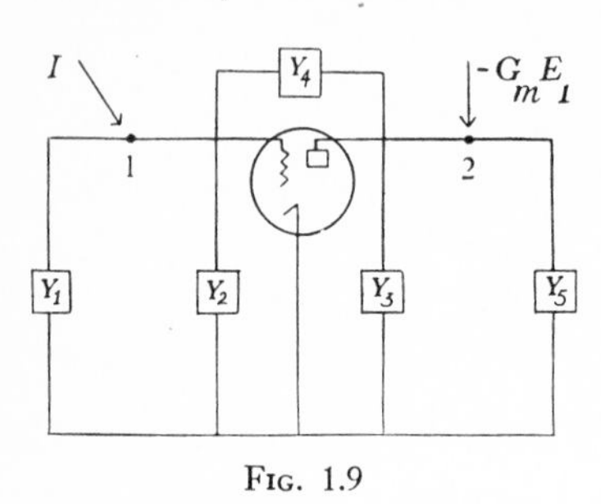

FIG. 1.9

With the application of these two current sources, the kth and mth nodal equations become

$$-Y_{k1}E_1 - Y_{k2}E_2 - \cdots - Y_{kn}E_n = \frac{-\mu(E_j - E_m)}{R_0}$$
$$(1\text{–}19)$$
$$-Y_{m1}E_1 - Y_{m2}E_2 - \cdots - Y_{mn}E_n = \frac{\mu(E_j - E_m)}{R_0}.$$

The terms on the right-hand side can now be transposed and incorporated as part of the mutual admittance terms appearing in the left-hand side. In most cases, the mth or cathode node will be at ground. If we make this assumption, which corresponds to the assumption made in connection with Fig. 1.3, that the grid and plate circuits are in separate meshes, the second of equations (1–19) can be ignored. The first equation then becomes

$$-Y_{k1}E_1 - Y_{k2}E_2 - \cdots - (Y_{kj} - G_m)E_j - \cdots - Y_{kn}E_n = 0 \quad (1\text{–}20)$$

where $G_m = \mu/R_0$ and is the quantity usually described as the *transconductance* of the tube. As in the mesh analysis, the effect of adding vacuum tubes is not to change the form of the equations but merely to destroy the reciprocity condition $Y_{ij} = Y_{ji}$.

As an illustration of these processes, nodal equations will be developed for the circuit shown in Fig. 1.9. This is the same network as the one previously shown by Fig. 1.5, redrawn to suit the nodal analysis. Since the bottom or cathode node can be taken as ground, there are two equations. If we suppose initially that the apparent current generator $-G_mE_1$ in the plate circuit is zero, the equations are readily found to be

$$(Y_1 + Y_2 + Y_4)E_1 - Y_4E_2 = I$$

$$-Y_4E_1 + (Y_3 + Y_4 + Y_5)E_2 = 0. \tag{1-21}$$

The introduction of the plate generator is equivalent to adding $-G_mE_1$ to the right-hand side of the second of these equations. After this term is transposed to the left-hand side, this equation becomes

$$-(Y_4 - G_m)E_1 + (Y_3 + Y_4 + Y_5)E_2 = 0 \tag{1-22}$$

the first of equations (1–21) remaining unchanged.

A solution of the nodal equations to find the steady state voltages corresponding to any given set of sinusoidal driving currents can evidently be obtained by the processes already used for mesh equations. For example, the *driving point admittance* Y between the first node and ground will be defined as the ratio between the driving current entering that node and the resulting voltage at the node. It is evidently given by

$$Y = \frac{I_1}{E_1} = \frac{\Delta'}{\Delta'_{11}} \tag{1-23}$$

where the primes are used to indicate that the determinants refer to the system of equations given by (1–18). Similarly, the *transfer admittance* Y_T between the first and second node will be defined as the ratio of current applied at the first node to the resulting voltage at the second node. It can be written as

$$Y_T = \frac{I_1}{E_2} = \frac{\Delta'}{\Delta'_{12}}. \tag{1-24}$$

In view of the obvious analogy between the mesh and nodal methods of analyzing a circuit, the two methods will be used indifferently in most of the following discussion. The primes, which were used in equations (1–23) and (1–24) to distinguish the nodal determinants from those obtained from the mesh equations, will ordinarily be omitted. The determinant Δ will thus be used to refer to either system unless there is some particular reason for distinguishing between them. The symbol W, which may perhaps be called an "*adpedance*" or "*immittance*," will be used to refer to an element in either system.

1.10. *Choice between Mesh and Nodal Analysis*

The above discussion has emphasized the fact that mesh and nodal equations can be used symmetrically in a general theoretical analysis.

The reader is cautioned, however, against concluding from this that the choice between the two systems is a matter of indifference when one is dealing with a definite physical circuit. In most circumstances the nodal analysis will be found appreciably more convenient.

The advantages of the nodal analysis may be traced to several causes. The most obvious is, of course, the fact that many circuits contain screen grid tubes having a very high plate resistance. Since such tubes are very nearly constant current devices, circuits containing them can evidently be analyzed more conveniently on the nodal than on the mesh basis.

Another advantage of the nodal formulation results from the fact that the equations can be more directly correlated with the physical structure of the network than is possible with the mesh formulation. The nodal equations can be written down directly, but to use the mesh analysis it is at least necessary to begin by selecting a suitable system of closed loops. In a complicated circuit, this may not be as easy a problem as it appears. The difference becomes particularly conspicuous in the inverse situation, when one has been given a set of equations and wishes to determine a corresponding physical structure. It is evident that the corresponding structure can be written down directly if we use nodal equations. If we begin with mesh equations, on the other hand, the process may be quite difficult. In fact, it is theoretically possible to write down a plausible looking set of " mesh equations " for which no corresponding circuit configuration exists.

The final consideration is the fact that, although either mesh or nodal equations can be used in analyzing any given circuit, it is not necessarily true that the two formulations will require the same number of equations. The preceding discussion gives the required number of equations as $B - (N - 1)$ for the mesh system and as $N - 1$ for the nodal system. In order to compare these expressions, suppose that the network is originally very simple and is built up to its final form by the addition of one node at a time. Obviously, each new node must be connected with the original circuit with at least two new branches if the node is to be an operative part of the structure. We may expect therefore that B will be at least twice as great as $N - 1$, so that in general the number of mesh equations will not be less than the number of nodal equations and may be much greater if the circuit is complicated.* For example, it required three mesh equations and only two nodal equations to analyze the structure shown by Figs. 1.5

* These conclusions are true only " in general " because of the possibility of simultaneously creating two new nodes by means of a cross-connection between them, so that one branch serves for both. An example is furnished by a balanced ladder line, the cross-connections being the shunt branches. These, however, are exceptional cases which are not representative of ordinary physical circuits.

and 1.9. In general, the nodal analysis appears to be particularly adapted to complicated high frequency circuits where we must consider many capacities to ground. Evidently, ground capacities from any of the existing nodes will not greatly complicate the nodal equations, but they may considerably increase the number of meshes in the circuit.

CHAPTER II

The Complex Frequency Plane

2.1. *Introduction*

In actual engineering applications we are concerned with the response of a circuit only to currents and voltages at real frequencies, that is, to ordinary sinusoids. For purposes of analysis, however, it is often necessary to give attention also to the response of the circuit to driving forces whose frequencies are complex. This chapter will consider the physical meaning which may be assigned to the term " complex frequency " and some of the elementary ways in which the conception of complex frequencies may be used in describing circuit characteristics.

2.2. *The Single Resonant Circuit*

It will be recalled that the general circuit equations in the last chapter were first developed in differential form, and that integrated or " steady-state " solutions for sinusoidal driving forces were obtained by supposing that the exponential $e^{i\omega t}$ could be substituted for a physical sinusoid. The meaning of a complex frequency can be understood most easily if we return for a moment to this last step. It will be sufficient to examine the solution for the single resonant circuit consisting of resistance, inductance, and stiffness in series, as shown by Fig. 2.1.

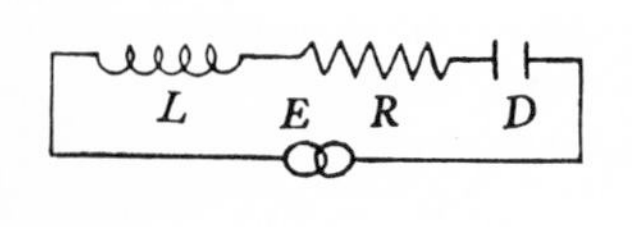

Fig. 2.1

Let the sinusoidal driving voltage be written as $E_0 \cos \omega t$. If q represents the charge on the condenser, so that the current $I = dq/dt$, the differential equation of the circuit is

$$L\frac{d^2q}{dt^2} + R\frac{dq}{dt} + Dq = E_0 \cos \omega t. \tag{2-1}$$

We may assume that the solution of this equation can be written in the general form

$$q = A \cos \omega t + B \sin \omega t \tag{2-2}$$

or

$$I = \frac{dq}{dt} = -A\omega \sin \omega t + B\omega \cos \omega t \tag{2-3}$$

where A and B are constants still to be determined.

The substitution of the assumed form (2–2) for q in (2–1) gives

$$-AL\omega^2 \cos \omega t - BL\omega^2 \sin \omega t - AR\omega \sin \omega t + BR\omega \cos \omega t + AD \cos \omega t + BD \sin \omega t = E_0 \cos \omega t. \quad (2\text{–}4)$$

This equation must hold for all values of t. In particular, it must hold for values of t at which $\sin \omega t$ is zero and also at values of t for which $\cos \omega t$ is zero. But when the sine terms are zero (2–4) becomes

$$-AL\omega^2 + BR\omega + AD = E_0 \quad (2\text{–}5)$$

and when the cosine terms are zero it becomes

$$-BL\omega^2 - AR\omega + BD = 0. \quad (2\text{–}6)$$

These equations can be solved simultaneously for A and B. This gives

$$A = \frac{(D - L\omega^2)E_0}{(R\omega)^2 + (D - L\omega^2)^2} \quad (2\text{–}7)$$

$$B = \frac{(R\omega)E_0}{(R\omega)^2 + (D - L\omega^2)^2} \quad (2\text{–}8)$$

from which the assumed solution for q becomes

$$q = E_0\left[\frac{(D - L\omega^2)}{(R\omega)^2 + (D - L\omega^2)^2} \cos \omega t + \frac{R\omega}{(R\omega)^2 + (D - L\omega^2)^2} \sin \omega t\right] \quad (2\text{–}9)$$

or

$$I = E_0\left[\frac{R}{R^2 + (L\omega - D/\omega)^2} \cos \omega t + \frac{L\omega - D/\omega}{R^2 + (L\omega - D/\omega)^2} \sin \omega t\right]. \quad (2\text{–}10)$$

The fact that these are correct solutions is easily established by direct substitution in equation (2–1). The coefficients in equation (2–10) are, of course, the familiar expressions for the in-phase and quadrature components of the total current.

2.3. *Exponential Representation of Physical Sinusoids**

The expression given by (2–10) is evidently the true physical current which would flow in response to the assumed sinusoidal driving voltage.

*The use of the exponential solution in electric circuit theory goes back at least as far as Heaviside, " Electromagnetic Theory." For later discussions see G. A. Campbell, " Cisoidal Oscillations," Trans. A.I.E.E., April, 1911; J. R. Carson, " Electric Circuit Theory and Operational Calculus," 1926 (Bibliography); T. C. Fry, " Elementary Differential Equations," 1929. The last reference gives a particularly complete discussion.

The method required to derive (2–10), however, is cumbersome and laborious and these objections would appear still more forcefully if we had dealt with a multi-mesh system. The use of the exponential $e^{i\omega t}$ to represent the actual physical sinusoid provides a way of analyzing the circuit much more expeditiously.

The justification for the use of $e^{i\omega t}$ in place of a physical sinusoid depends upon the principle of superposition. It depends, in other words, upon the fact that in a linear system such as (2–1) the current flowing in response to two driving forces acting together is the sum of the currents which would flow in response to the two separately. Thus, in (2–1), if $q_1(t)$ is the response of the network to $E_1(t)$ so that

$$L\frac{d^2q_1}{dt^2} + R\frac{dq_1}{dt} + Dq_1 = E_1(t) \tag{2–11}$$

and $q_2(t)$ is the response to $E_2(t)$ so that

$$L\frac{d^2q_2}{dt^2} + R\frac{dq_2}{dt} + Dq_2 = E_2(t) \tag{2–12}$$

then

$$L\frac{d^2(q_1 + q_2)}{dt^2} + R\frac{d(q_1 + q_2)}{dt} + D(q_1 + q_2) = E_1(t) + E_2(t) \tag{2–13}$$

follows obviously from simple addition of equations (2–11) and (2–12).

This principle is usually applied to find the response to $E_1(t) + E_2(t)$ from the responses to $E_1(t)$ and $E_2(t)$ separately. In this application, however, the principle is made to work backward to give the responses to $E_1(t)$ and $E_2(t)$ separately when the response to $E_1(t) + E_2(t)$ is known. Obviously, it is not always possible to do this, since the knowledge merely of the sum $q_1(t) + q_2(t)$ does not necessarily tell us how much is $q_1(t)$ and how much is $q_2(t)$. The decomposition can, however, be effected without ambiguity if $E_1(t)$ is real while $E_2(t)$ is a pure imaginary quantity, since it follows from the fact that the coefficients of (2–1) are real quantities that the corresponding $q_1(t)$ and $q_2(t)$ must then be real and pure imaginary, respectively. In this special case, therefore, we can work backward from equation (2–13) to equations (2–11) and (2–12) merely by picking out the real and imaginary components of the q which is a solution of (2–13).

In the present application, we have $e^{i\omega t} = \cos \omega t + i \sin \omega t$. The real and imaginary components of the q which corresponds to the driving voltage $e^{i\omega t}$ must therefore be the q's which would correspond respectively to the voltages $\cos \omega t$ and $i \sin \omega t$. For example, let q_1 and iq_2 be the solutions which would correspond to the voltages $E_0 \cos \omega t$ and $iE_0 \sin \omega t$ in (2–1).

and let $q = q_1 + iq_2$. We then have

$$L\frac{d^2q_1}{dt^2} + R\frac{dq_1}{dt} + Dq_1 = E_0 \cos \omega t \tag{2-14}$$

$$L\frac{d^2(iq_2)}{dt^2} + R\frac{d(iq_2)}{dt} + D(iq_2) = iE_0 \sin \omega t. \tag{2-15}$$

Adding (2–14) and (2–15) together gives us

$$L\frac{d^2q}{dt^2} + R\frac{dq}{dt} + Dq = E_0e^{i\omega t} = E_0e^{pt} \tag{2-16}$$

where p has been written for $i\omega$. By the previous argument, the real component of the q which satisfies this equation will be the q_1 which satisfies equation (2–14). Upon assuming that $q = q_0e^{pt}$ we find readily

$$q_0(p^2L + pR + D)e^{pt} = E_0e^{pt}. \tag{2-17}$$

It follows that

$$q_0 = \frac{E_0}{p^2L + pR + D} \tag{2-18}$$

or

$$I = \frac{pE_0e^{pt}}{p^2L + pR + D}. \tag{2-19}$$

Upon substituting $i\omega$ for p in (2–19) we secure

$$I = \frac{E_0(\cos \omega t + i \sin \omega t)}{R + i\left(\omega L - \frac{1}{\omega}D\right)}. \tag{2-20}$$

The real component of (2–20) should be the current flowing in response to the voltage $E_0 \cos \omega t$. It turns out to be

$$I_{\text{real}} = E_0\left[\frac{R \cos \omega t}{R^2 + \left(\omega L - \frac{1}{\omega}D\right)^2} + \frac{\left(\omega L - \frac{1}{\omega}D\right)\sin \omega t}{R^2 + \left(\omega L - \frac{1}{\omega}D\right)^2}\right] \tag{2-21}$$

which agrees with equation (2–10). The method also gives as a by-product the current which will flow in response to the voltage $E_0 \sin \omega t$. We have merely to take the imaginary component of (2–20), discarding the i.

This gives

$$I_{\text{imag}} = E_0 \left[\frac{R \sin \omega t}{R^2 + \left(\omega L - \frac{1}{\omega} D\right)^2} - \frac{\left(\omega L - \frac{1}{\omega} D\right) \cos \omega t}{R^2 + \left(\omega L - \frac{1}{\omega} D\right)^2} \right]. \quad (2\text{–}22)$$

This process can evidently be extended directly to multi-mesh circuits. If we begin with a driving voltage Ee^{pt} the solution of the circuit equations for any one of the currents will appear in the general form Ie^{pt}, and if the real component of Ee^{pt} is taken as the true physical voltage the real component of Ie^{pt} will be the physical current.

It will be convenient to summarize this discussion in a form in which it appears as a set of definitions of the meanings we shall ascribe to the terms "frequency" and "impedance." Thus

(1) A voltage of frequency f will be written as $E_0 e^{pt}$ where $p = 2\pi i f$. Physically, we shall interpret such an expression by taking only its real component. E_0, which was taken as a real quantity in the previous example, may in general be complex. The use of a complex value of E_0 amounts simply to a shift in the phase of the physical voltage, as we can readily see by taking the real component of $(E_{01} + iE_{02})e^{pt}$.

(2) We shall take as the current in any mesh the quantity which satisfies the differential equations of the circuit with the voltage of (1) as the driving force. It will appear in the form $I_0 e^{pt}$ where I_0 is another complex constant. The actual physical current corresponding to the actual physical voltage will be the real component of this expression. For brevity, the constants E_0 and I_0 alone will sometimes be spoken of as "voltage" and "current."

(3) The self- or transfer impedance, depending upon whether the current and voltage are in the same or different meshes, will be defined as the ratio $E_0 : I_0$ of the constants in the voltage and current expressions of (1) and (2).

(4) The impedance is obtained as an algebraic quantity from the solution of the set of linear equations which result when the differential operator d/dt is replaced by $p = i\omega$ in the differential equations of the circuit.

2.4. *The Complex Frequency Plane*

The definitions of frequency and impedance which have just been given were developed on the assumption that the driving force would be a simple sine wave. The frequency f is then a real quantity and the new variable p is a pure imaginary. Quite evidently, however, the definitions can be extended formally to situations in which both f and p are complex. The physical meaning of such an assumption is easily determined. Suppose, for example, that we are dealing with the driving voltage E_0e^{pt}. Let E_0 and p be, respectively, $E_{01} + iE_{02}$ and $p_1 + ip_2$. The voltage can then be written as

$$(E_{01} + iE_{02})e^{(p_1+ip_2)t} = (E_{01} \cos p_2t - E_{02} \sin p_2t)e^{p_1t} + i(E_{01} \sin p_2t + E_{02} \cos p_2t)e^{p_1t}. \quad (2\text{–}23)$$

By the definitions just established the physical voltage is the real component of this expression or, in other words, $(E_{01} \cos p_2t - E_{02} \sin p_2t)e^{p_1t}$. It is obviously a sinusoidal oscillation with positive or negative damping depending upon whether p_1 is negative or positive. The physical current

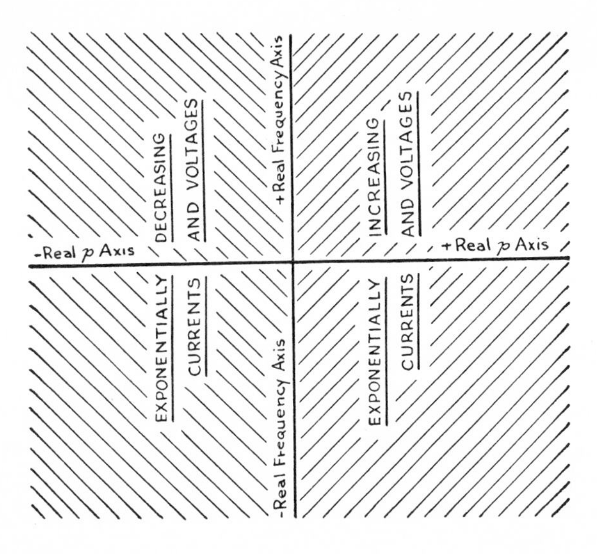

Fig. 2.2

corresponding to this voltage is obtained by dividing the complex voltage by the impedance and taking the real component of the result. It will evidently be a damped sinusoid with the same frequency and damping as the driving voltage.

We will hereafter consider that frequency is in general a complex quantity. It can conveniently be represented on a plane such as that shown by Fig. 2.2. As the figure is drawn, the horizontal axis represents real values of p, and the vertical axis imaginary values of p or real values of frequency. Real frequencies are therefore obtained by reading up the vertical scale. This arrangement is normally the most convenient one in theoretical analysis, since p is a more convenient variable than f. If we prefer, however, the diagram can be given a quarter turn in a clockwise direction, so that real values of frequency are found on a scale reading from left to right in the normal fashion. In this event, complex frequencies are found above and below the real frequency axis. The other axis, corresponding to real values of p or pure imaginary values of frequency, represents the limiting case in which the driving voltage and responses are exponentially increasing or decreasing without oscillation.

It will be noticed that the diagram represents negative as well as positive values of frequency. The lower half of the plane, in which negative frequencies are found, is seldom of much actual concern in network analysis. In any physical circuit, the real component of the impedance is an even function of frequency, and the imaginary component is an odd function. In other words, the real component of the impedance at a negative frequency is equal to its value at the corresponding positive frequency, while the imaginary component at a negative frequency is the negative of the imaginary component at the corresponding positive frequency. Simple relations of symmetry, therefore, connect the upper and lower halves of the plane.

The distinction between the right and left halves of the p *plane, or the upper and lower halves of the frequency plane,* on the other hand, *is of primary importance.* This arises from the fact that on one of these halves, the driving voltage and response correspond to functions which decrease exponentially with time, while on the other half they represent exponentially increasing functions. As our later discussion will show, there is a close connection between the steady state response characteristics of the network, and its transient characteristics. Since a network whose transients increase as time goes on is unstable, or, in other words, non-physical, the characteristics of physical networks in the half of the plane corresponding to exponentially increasing functions are severely limited.

2.5. *Zeros and Poles of Impedance and Admittance*

The functions whose behavior on the complex plane will be of chief interest are the driving-point and transfer impedances Z and Z_T, and the corresponding admittances Y and Y_T. Each of these can be expressed in terms of determinants whose elements are relatively simple functions of frequency. In the mesh system, for example, the general impedance coefficient can be written as $Z_{ij} = (p^2L_{ij} + pR_{ij} + D_{ij})/p$. Since any of the determinants Δ, Δ_{11}, Δ_{12} used in the definitions of Z and Z_T can be expressed as the sum of products of quantities of this type, it is clear that they must all be polynomials in p divided by some power of p. The same result, of course, holds for determinants taken from the nodal system.

The individual functions, Z, Z_T, Y, and Y_T, are each expressible as the ratio of two determinants, from equations (1–8), (1–10), (1–23) and (1–24). Evidently, therefore, they must each appear, in general, as the ratio of two polynomials, as shown by

$$W_{(T)} = \frac{A_m p^m + A_{m-1} p^{m-1} + \cdots + A_1 p + A_0}{B_n p^n + B_{n-1} p^{n-1} + \cdots + B_1 p + B_0}. \tag{2–24}$$

Such an expression is called a *rational function* of p.

In studying the behavior of such a function as (2–24) on the complex frequency plane, it is convenient to give special attention to its *zeros* and *poles*, which are respectively the points at which the function becomes zero and infinite. This is easily expressed by rewriting both numerator and denominator of (2–24) as a product of factors, so that the equation becomes

$$W_{(T)} = \frac{A_m (p - p_1)(p - p_2) \cdots (p - p_m)}{B_n (p - p_1')(p - p_2') \cdots (p - p_n')}. \tag{2–25}$$

Evidently $p_1 \cdots p_m$ are the zeros, and $p_1' \cdots p_n'$ are the poles. Ordinarily the p's and p''s will all be different, so that the zeros and poles are all of the first order, or "simple." In special cases, however, two or more zeros or poles may coincide to give a multiple zero or pole. The zeros and poles are obviously the analogues, for general networks, of the resonances and anti-resonances which are familiar in purely reactive structures. The principal difference is the fact that the "resonances" and "anti-resonances" in a general network may occur at complex frequencies.

The consideration of the zeros and poles is important for two reasons. The first is the fact that except for the constant multiplier A_m/B_n they evidently specify (2–25) completely. Assuming, then, that W represents a driving-point impedance or admittance, we can conclude that *two driving-point impedances or admittances having the same zeros and poles can differ only by an ideal transformer.* Similarly, if W is a transfer impedance or admittance, we can say that *two transfer impedances or admittances having the same zeros and poles can differ only by a constant gain or loss.*

The other reason for paying particular attention to the zeros and poles will appear more clearly in later chapters. It depends broadly upon the fact that the location of the zeros and poles in the frequency plane furnishes our best index in classifying networks. Thus, unless the zeros and poles meet certain restrictions, the impedance functions which they specify cannot be furnished by a physical network. Assuming that these restrictions are met, further study of the zeros and poles permits the function to be assigned to one of several general categories.

2.6. *Zeros and Poles of a Resonant Circuit Impedance*

As an illustration of this discussion we may return to the resonant circuit which was analyzed earlier in the chapter. The impedance of this circuit, as given by (2–19), can be written as

$$Z = L\frac{(p - p_1)(p - p_2)}{p} \tag{2–26}$$

where

$$p_1 = -\frac{R}{2L} + \sqrt{\left(\frac{R}{2L}\right)^2 - \frac{D}{L}}; \quad p_2 = -\frac{R}{2L} - \sqrt{\left(\frac{R}{2L}\right)^2 - \frac{D}{L}}. \tag{2–27}$$

The quantities p_1 and p_2 are evidently the zeros of the impedance. Their location depends upon the two quantities, R/L and D/L. If we multiply R/L by any quantity, and D/L by the square of that quantity, however, p_1 and p_2 will merely be multiplied by the same quantity. It is, therefore, sufficient to study the possible locations of p_1 and p_2 when R/L is varied

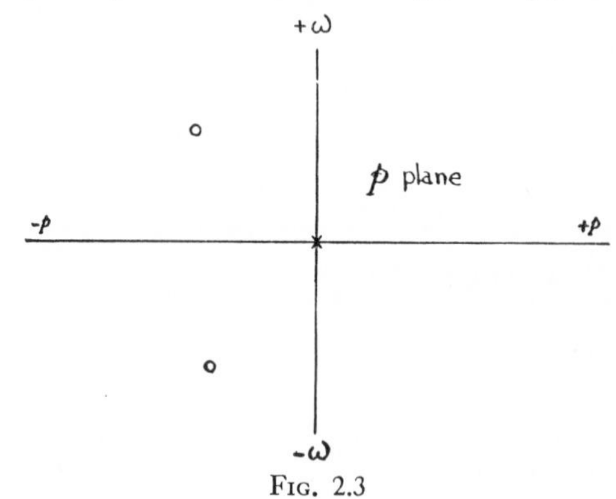

FIG. 2.3

while D/L is held fixed. If R/L is small compared to D/L, which corresponds to a resonant circuit with small damping, the quantities under the square root signs will be negative, and p_1 and p_2 will therefore be conjugate complex numbers with negative real parts. Typical locations for p_1 and p_2 are represented by the circles in Fig. 2.3. The cross at the origin represents the pole of impedance which is found when $p = 0$. It is customary to consider that there is another pole at $p = \infty$, since the impedance is also infinite there.

It is easily shown that, as R/L varies, p_1 and p_2 move along the circular paths indicated by Fig. 2.4. At the extreme points A and A', for which R vanishes, p_1 and p_2 lie on the real frequency axis. This corresponds to the ordinary resonance of a non-dissipative resonant circuit, in which the impedance vanishes at a real frequency. The points B and B' represent the zeros when the circuit contains a moderate amount of dissipation. This is similar to the case previously illustrated by Fig. 2.3. At C, on the other hand, $(R/2L)^2 = D/L$ and the two zeros are equal. In other words, the impedance has a double zero at this point. This is the critically damped case. Since C is found on the real p axis the corresponding physical voltage and current are non-oscillatory exponentially decreasing functions. If R/L is still larger, p_1 and p_2 are found respectively to the right and left of C on the real p axis as illustrated by D and D'. It will be noticed that, although the zeros can be assigned a great variety of positions by varying the relations among R, L, and D, they are always found in the left half of the p plane.

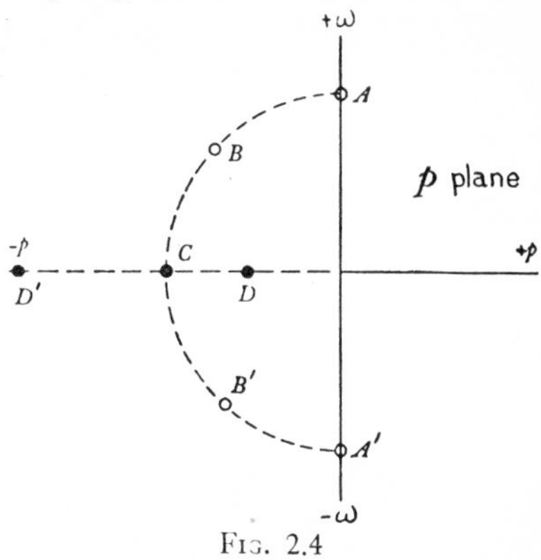

Fig. 2.4

2.7. *Analytic Functions*

The introduction of complex values of frequency is equivalent in mathematical terms to studying such quantities as the driving-point and transfer impedance by the methods of function theory. In this field, one of the most important tools available to the mathematician is the conception of an analytic function.

Definition: A function is said to be analytic at a given point in the plane of the independent variable provided it has a finite derivative, independent of direction, at that point.

The function is analytic over a given region provided it is analytic at every point in that region. Points for which it is not analytic are called *singular points* or *singularities*.

The restriction that the derivative be independent of direction is relatively unimportant for engineering purposes. It is effective only in eliminating such functions as the real component of Z, or the absolute value of Z. For example, $|Z|$ cannot be an analytic function of p at any point because $d|Z|$ must be a real quantity, and the phase angle of the derivative $d|Z|/dp$ must therefore change as we change the phase angle, or direction, in which dp is taken. As long as we restrict ourselves to functions which are in general complex, such as Z or $\log Z$, however, the fact that the derivative will be independent of direction can be taken for granted. The essential feature of the definition, then, is the fact that if the function is to be analytic the derivative must be *finite*.

The points at which the derivative of a rational function, such as (2–25), becomes infinite are readily determined. If, for example, we let N and D represent respectively the polynomials in the numerator and denominator of (2–25), the ordinary rules for differentiation give

$$\frac{dW_{(T)}}{dp} = \frac{D\dfrac{dN}{dp} - N\dfrac{dD}{dp}}{D^2}. \tag{2–28}$$

Since N and D are ordinary polynomials, neither they nor their derivatives can become infinite for any finite value of p. We can thus conclude that (2–28) will become infinite only at the points at which D vanishes, or in other words only at the poles of the original function. *The singular points of an impedance or admittance function are therefore its poles*, and the function will be analytic in any part of the p plane which contains no poles.

It will be seen that the analyticity of the impedance or admittance function W is not dependent upon the location of its zeros. If W is a transfer impedance or admittance, however, it is usually convenient to specify it in terms of attenuation and phase shift. This is equivalent to dealing with the function log W, rather than with W itself. The expression corresponding to (2–28) for the derivative of log W is

$$\frac{d \log W_{(T)}}{dp} = \frac{D\dfrac{dN}{dp} - N\dfrac{dD}{dp}}{ND}. \tag{2–29}$$

This is evidently infinite whenever either N or D vanishes. *The singular points* of the logarithm of an impedance or admittance are therefore the zeros and poles of the original function.* Log W will be analytic only in regions which contain no zeros or poles of W.

The properties of analytic functions furnish the most direct method of establishing Nyquist's criterion for stability. The first application of this material will be made in Chapter VIII, where Nyquist's criterion is discussed.

2.8. *Physical Validity of Complex Frequencies*

The conception of a complex frequency can be looked upon in several ways. If we like, we can think of complex frequencies as having real

* The singular points are " logarithmic singularities " and not poles. For the point p_0 to be a pole the function must approach infinity near p_0 as $1/(p - p_0)^n$, where n is an integer. Although log W approaches infinity at the zeros and poles of W, the approach is at a much slower rate. For example, it is shown in ordinary calculus that, although $\log x = -\log (1/x)$ approaches $-\infty$ as x vanishes, it increases so slowly that the limit of $x \log x$ is zero.

physical existence. The definitions of complex frequency and impedance have been so drawn that an analysis stated in terms of complex frequencies can be submitted to physical verification. There is no difficulty in supposing that a generator can be constructed to give a driving voltage varying as an exponentially increasing or decreasing sinusoid for a reasonable period of time. By energizing a network with such a generator, the response characteristics of the structure can be obtained by direct physical measurement. The conception of complex frequency can thus be checked in the laboratory by a direct comparison of measurement and computation.

Although this physical possibility is present, another point of view is more illuminating. We are finally interested in the response of the network only at real frequencies. It is only this characteristic which is specified in ordinary design problems. Moreover, the Fourier integral analysis tells us that if we know the responses of the network to driving voltages represented by pure sinusoids, we can find its response to any other driving voltage. The real frequency characteristic, therefore, tells the whole story. So far as the purely theoretical relations are concerned, we might start with the response at real frequencies and compute the response to the exponentially increasing and decreasing sinusoids corresponding to complex frequencies by Fourier integral methods.

Although the complex frequency conception is thus not essential, its introduction is of great value in facilitating the mathematical treatment of the theory. From a purely mathematical point of view, it is simpler to study the impedance function on the complex frequency plane than it is to consider only real frequencies. We have already noticed an analogous situation in the discussion of the response of the resonant circuit to a sinusoidal driving voltage. The addition of an imaginary component to the voltage, although it is later discarded, makes the mathematical expressions so much more symmetrical that the algebra is actually much simplified. Somewhat the same advantages are obtained when we generalize the conception of frequency to include complex as well as real values. In this book we will use the idea of a complex frequency chiefly as a tool to specify what kinds of network characteristics are physically realizable. The same conclusions theoretically should be obtainable by the use of Fourier methods on the real frequency characteristic, but the mathematics required with that treatment is much more difficult.

A curious and interesting qualification of this discussion of the relation between the complex and real frequency response arises when we consider the physical significance of a complex frequency in more detail. The characteristics we are examining are, of course, those which correspond to the steady state response of the network. Since we never have a network which has been acted upon by a given voltage for an infinite length of time, the steady state is never realized exactly in any experimental situation. We are accustomed to supposing, however, that a physical measurement of the steady state response can be obtained with sufficient exactness with a suddenly applied voltage if we delay the measurement until the transients have had time to decay sufficiently. There is evidently no difficulty about doing this when the driving voltage is a pure sinusoid. It is also possible if the driving voltage lies on the right side of the p plane, since then the steady state characteristic will emerge as an increasing exponential, while the transient terms are dying out. If the driving voltage is sufficiently far to the left of the p plane, on the other hand, the " steady state " response will diminish with time even more rapidly than do the transients. Evidently for frequencies in this part of the plane no physical measurement can be made which will lead to a response which is chiefly determined by the steady state characteristic of the network. Since the physical response can always be computed from the real frequency characteristic by the Fourier integral method, this suggests strongly that the connection between the steady state characteristics in the extreme left of the p plane and the characteristics at real frequencies is somewhat tenuous. It should be possible to manipulate the characteristics at the extreme left of the p plane with considerable freedom without affecting the characteristics at real frequencies appreciably, if at all. These possibilities have been exploited in some branches of network theory. A description of these methods, however, is beyond the scope of this book.

CHAPTER III

FEEDBACK

3.1. *Introduction*

THIS and the following three chapters are devoted to a general analysis of feedback circuits and a discussion of the meaning of feedback. The principal object of the analysis is the development of a general feedback theory in terms of the mesh or nodal equations of the amplifier as a whole without distinction between μ and β circuits. This is attempted partly because the mesh or nodal formulation is the most satisfactory one for analytical work, and partly because without such a general foundation it is difficult to provide a satisfactory theory for the multiple loop circuits which appear with increasing frequency in current design practice. As an introduction to this discussion, however, the present chapter gives a summary of the familiar theory of feedback amplifiers in terms of μ circuits and β circuits and also a description of some of the commonest feedback arrangements. This part of the discussion is given only in outline form since a general acquaintance with feedback circuits is assumed in this book.*

3.2. *Elementary Theory of Feedback Circuits*

In its simplest form, a feedback amplifier can be regarded as a combination of an ordinary amplifier, or μ circuit, and a passive network, or β circuit, by means of which a portion of the output of the μ circuit can be

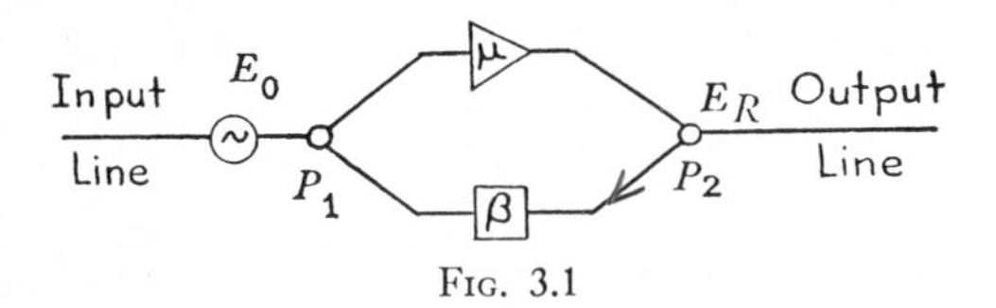

FIG. 3.1

returned to its input. Such a combination is shown by Fig. 3.1. Both the μ and β circuits are, of course, actually four-terminal structures. The circuits are represented by single lines in Fig. 3.1 for simplicity.

When a portion of the output voltage is returned to the input, the circuit

* See H. S. Black "Stabilized Feedback Amplifiers," B.S.T.J., or "Electrical Engineering" for Jan. 1934, also U. S. Patent No. 2,102,671. Good textbook references are Terman "Radio Engineer's Handbook," or "Applied Electronics" by the Electrical Engineering Staff of M.I.T.

may, in fact, break into spontaneous oscillation. In this event the circuit is normally inoperative as an amplifier. If we suppose for the moment that oscillations are avoided, however, the characteristics of the structure can be obtained without difficulty. It is merely necessary to recognize the fact that the operation of the μ and β circuits separately is fully defined by the voltages appearing across their terminals, without regard to the fact that they are parts of the feedback loop. For example, let E_0 and E_R represent, respectively, the signal voltage applied to the input and the final voltage delivered to the output, as is shown in Fig. 3.1, and let E_1 represent any additional voltage supplied at the input by the return of a part of the output voltage through the β circuit. Then the μ circuit, operating as an ordinary amplifier, must satisfy the equation

$$E_R = \mu(E_0 + E_1). \tag{3-1}$$

Similarly, if we let β represent the transmission characteristic of the β circuit, the voltage which it supplies at the input terminals must be given by

$$E_1 = \beta E_R. \tag{3-2}$$

Upon eliminating E_1 between these two equations, we find

$$E_R = \mu E_0 + \mu\beta E_R, \tag{3-3}$$

or in other words

$$E_R = \frac{\mu}{1 - \mu\beta} E_0. \tag{3-4}$$

Without the β circuit, the output voltage would be given by $E_R = \mu E_0$. We therefore have the

Theorem: Feedback reduces the gain of an amplifier by the factor $1 - \mu\beta$.*

The quantity $\mu\beta$ can be called the *feedback factor*.† It evidently repre-

* All the theorems in this chapter are to be taken as approximate, in the sense that they will be superseded by the more general propositions given in Chapters V and VI. We may also notice that in many statements of this theorem the factor by which the gain is reduced is written as $1 + \mu\beta$. The choice of the sign of $\mu\beta$ depends upon the way in which the phase shifts of the tubes are counted. Ordinary vacuum tubes give a phase reversal of the signal, in addition to any phase shifts contributed by the interstage impedances. In the standard μ circuit containing an odd number of tubes, therefore, there will be one net phase reversal. If this is included as part of μ the factor appears as $1 - \mu\beta$. If the phase reversal is counted separately, on the other hand, the proper expression is $1 + \mu\beta$.

† Cf. Terman, loc. cit. p. 395. The term " feedback " will be used in the following chapters for a quantity analogous to $1 - \mu\beta$.

sents the transmission around the complete loop from the input of the amplifier back to the input again. In ordinary practice, $\mu\beta$ is very much larger than unity. Under these circumstances, equation (3–4) is conveniently rewritten as

$$\frac{E_R}{E_0} = e^{\theta} = \frac{\mu\beta}{1-\mu\beta}\frac{1}{\beta} \tag{3–5}$$

and since the first factor on the right-hand side of (3–5) must be substantially unity in absolute value when $\mu\beta$ is large, we can conclude that the gain of the amplifier varies approximately inversely with the transmission through the β circuit or, in other words, is approximately proportional to the β circuit loss. The error in this conclusion due to the departure of $|\mu\beta/(1-\mu\beta)|$ from unity will be called the $\mu\beta$ *effect* or the $\mu\beta$ *error* in subsequent discussion.

Equation (3–5) evidently implies that the gain of the amplifier may be much affected by slight variations in the β circuit but that it is almost independent of variations in μ. In order to show this more clearly. we may differentiate (3–4), keeping β constant, to give

$$\frac{dE_R}{E_R} = \frac{1}{1-\mu\beta}\frac{d\mu}{\mu}. \tag{3–6}$$

In this equation, the quantities dE_R/E_R and $d\mu/\mu$ evidently represent corresponding changes in the amplifier gain and in the gain of the μ circuit when both gains are expressed in logarithmic units, such as nepers or decibels. We therefore have the

Theorem: The variation in the final gain characteristic in db, per db change in the gain of the μ circuit, is reduced by feedback in the ratio $(1-\mu\beta):1$.

The final property of feedback of fundamental engineering importance is the fact that it reduces the effects of extraneous noise or non-linear distortion in the μ circuit. In a broad physical sense, extraneous noise and non-linear distortion in any element can be regarded as " variations " in that element, and the sensitiveness of the circuit to such variations is always correlated with its sensitiveness to normal variations in the value of the element.* Fundamentally, therefore, this property is merely a reflection of the theorem just established. In order to demonstrate it independently, however, let it be supposed that a generator D_0 is inserted somewhere in the interior of the μ circuit as shown by Fig. 3.2. D_0 may represent either an extraneous noise voltage, such as would be produced, for

* This is shown generally in Chapter V.

example, by a bad contact or by hum in the power supply, or it may be taken to represent the voltages of the modulation products arising from non-linear distortion in the μ circuit. Let E_d represent the actual output

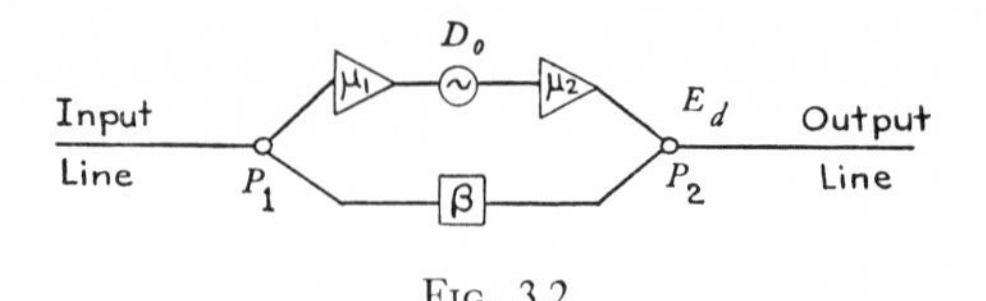

FIG. 3.2

voltage which appears on the line in consequence of this noise generator and let D_1 represent the additional voltage which appears between μ_1 and μ_2 by transmission around the $\mu\beta$ loop. Since the total voltage at this junction is $D_0 + D_1$ and the gain between this junction and the output line is μ_2, we must have

$$E_d = \mu_2(D_0 + D_1). \tag{3–7}$$

The voltage D_1 which is returned to the junction by transmission through the β circuit and through μ_1 is evidently given by

$$D_1 = \mu_1 \beta E_d. \tag{3–8}$$

Upon eliminating D_1 we therefore have

$$E_d = \frac{\mu_2 D_0}{1 - \mu\beta} \tag{3–9}$$

where μ has been written for the total gain $\mu_1\mu_2$. Since the noise which would appear in the output in the absence of feedback is $\mu_2 D_0$, this result is equivalent to the

Theorem: The noise level in the output of a feedback amplifier is reduced by feedback in the ratio $(1 - \mu\beta):1$.

We cannot conclude from this that the signal-to-noise *ratio* is reduced by this factor, because feedback may also change the effective signal level in the μ circuit. An accurate statement can, however, be easily obtained by comparing the structure with a non-feedback amplifier which has the same final gain $\mu/(1 - \mu\beta)$ and the same input and output voltages E_0 and E_R. The comparison is made most easily if we suppose that the complete μ circuit is broken up into μ_1 and μ_2 portions, as in Fig. 3.2, having respectively the gains $1 - \mu\beta$ and $\mu/(1 - \mu\beta)$. Then since both μ_2 and the comparison non-feedback amplifier have the same gain and deliver the same output voltage E_R, they will have the same signal levels throughout, and we can conclude that feedback is fully effective in improving the signal-to-noise ratio for any noises originating in this part of the circuit. In μ_1, on the other hand, the signal level is less than it is in any portion of the comparison amplifier and the improvement in the signal-to-noise ratio for noises originating in this portion of the μ circuit is consequently only partial. At the input terminals of the first tube, where the signal is also reduced by the factor $1/(1 - \mu\beta)$, feedback has no effect on the signal-to-noise ratio. Feedback is thus a useful tool in combating troubles due to modulation and perhaps power supply hum, in the case of tubes with directly heated cathodes, which are characteristic of output stages. It is of little value, however, in dealing with noises due to thermal agitation, shot effects, etc., which may be expected to be troublesome in the input stages.

The engineering importance of feedback circuits results from the possibilities they present of diminishing markedly the effects of noises or variations in gain in the μ circuit. The decrease in the external gain which follows from the use of feedback is unfortunate and makes it necessary in general to use a more complicated μ circuit to obtain adequate final gain. This, however, is an easy sacrifice to make to secure the improvements which are available in other directions. As an example, we may consider an amplifier having 40 db external gain and 40 db feedback. The μ circuit is then required to furnish 80 db gain, so that it represents an increase of 2 to 1 over the gain which would be required of a non-feedback amplifier. For this 2 to 1 increase in the complexity of the μ circuit, however, we secure an improvement of 100 to 1 in its effective linearity and gain stability.

3.3. *Types of Feedback Circuits*

The principal circuit configurations useful in feedback circuits can be classified most easily in terms of the way in which the μ and β circuits are connected to each other and to the line at the ends of the amplifier. The

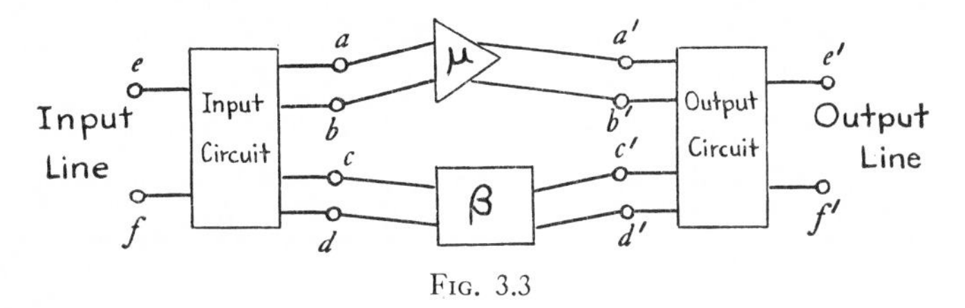

Fig. 3.3

varieties of connections which may be made do not appear very clearly from a single line drawing such as that of Fig. 3.1. Physically, however, the μ circuit, the β circuit, and the line must all be two-wire circuits. The actual situation is therefore that shown broadly by Fig. 3.3 in which the three circuits are connected together by means of a six-terminal network. The classification of feedback circuits thus depends upon the forms which these six-terminal connecting networks assume.

There may, of course, be an unlimited variety of six-terminal arrangements to select from. The simplest ones, and the ones which appear to be most useful are, however, shown by Figs. 3.4 to 3.8. In each structure, the terminals are labeled in accordance with the notation used in Fig. 3.3. Figure 3.4, for example, shows a series type of feedback circuit. The μ circuit is taken as a conventional three-stage amplifier, the interstage impedances being indicated by I_1 and I_2. The β circuit is represented for concreteness as the π of branches A, B, and C, but it may, of course, reduce to a single branch or it may assume a still more elaborate form. The effective line terminals e–f and e'–f' are indicated at the high sides of the transformers since the line and transformer characteristics evidently add directly.* The characteristic feature of this amplifier is the fact that the μ and β circuits, as seen from the line, are in series at each end of the amplifier.

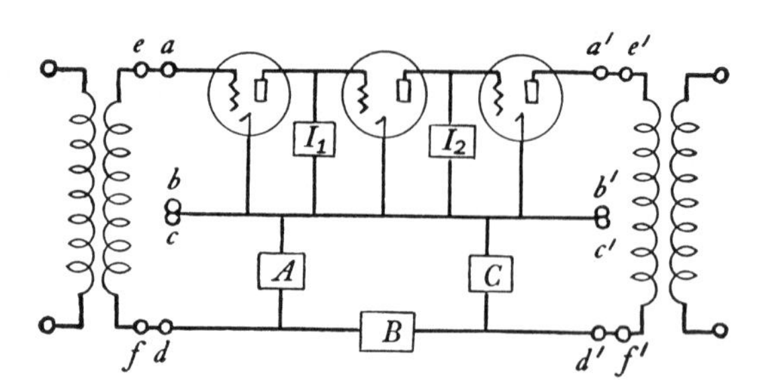

FIG. 3.4

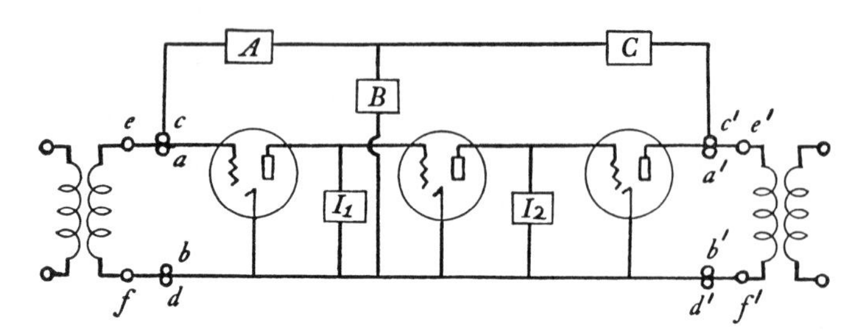

FIG. 3.5

Figure 3.5 shows a shunt type feedback system. The β circuit is here represented as a T, but, as in Fig. 3.4, it may in general be taken as any

* It is also possible to feed back on the low sides of the transformers. In this case the transformers become part of the μ circuit.

four-terminal structure.* The characteristic feature of this type of feedback is the fact that the μ circuit, β circuit, and line are all in parallel at each end of the amplifier.

Series and shunt feedback circuits are the simplest and probably the most convenient arrangements for most applications. In ordinary circumstances they are also the circuits which give a maximum amount of feedback. They suffer, however, from two major disadvantages. The first, which is

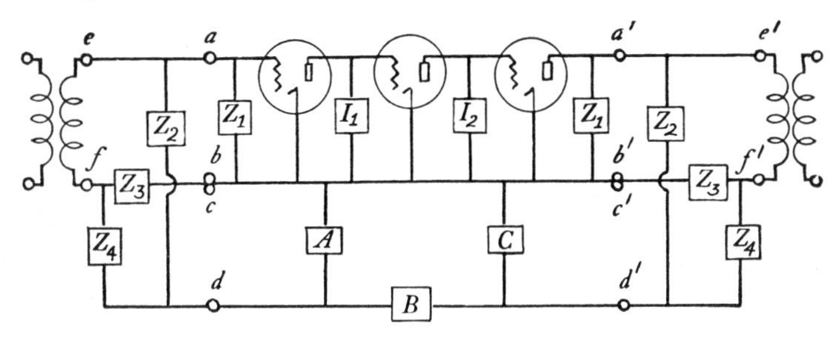

FIG. 3.6

discussed in more detail in Chapter V, is the fact that in these circuits feedback changes the impedance of the amplifier as seen from the line to either a very high or a very low value. They are thus not convenient arrangements to use with amplifiers which must have a good reflection coefficient against the line. The second is the fact that the line impedances form a part of the $\mu\beta$ loop. Variations in the line impedance may therefore affect the $\mu\beta$ characteristic and in some cases the effect may be great enough to cause instability.

These difficulties are overcome by the use of a bridge type feedback circuit, such as that shown by Fig. 3.6. This circuit includes three new branches, represented by Z_2, Z_3, and Z_4 in Fig. 3.6, at each end of the amplifier. A fourth branch, which is represented by Z_1, is also included to permit control of the input and output impedances of the μ circuit if necessary.† The three new branches, together with the impedances of the μ circuit, the β circuit, and the line, give a network having a total of six

* It should be noticed, however, that if the β circuit in Fig. 3.4 were chosen as a T, or that in Fig. 3.5 as a π, the extreme branches could in either case be assimilated as part of the line impedances. Since the insertion of unnecessary impedances in the line is likely to waste power, it is clear that these are unacceptable configurations unless the contributions of the extreme branches are so small as to be almost meaningless. The configurations actually shown in Figs. 3.4 and 3.5 are thus representative of those which would be appropriate in practical cases. These considerations are discussed in more detail in subsequent chapters.

† See the discussion of the effect of omitting Z_1 given later in Chapter V.

branches. If any one of the six is taken as a generator impedance, the remaining five can be arranged as the four arms of a bridge plus a galvanometer arm. For example, if the generator impedance is taken as the line, the galvanometer arm becomes the β circuit impedance. When the bridge is balanced in this arrangement the $\mu\beta$ loop is independent of the line impedance. The conjugacy between the line and the β circuit also destroys the effect of feedback on the amplifier impedance so that it becomes compara-

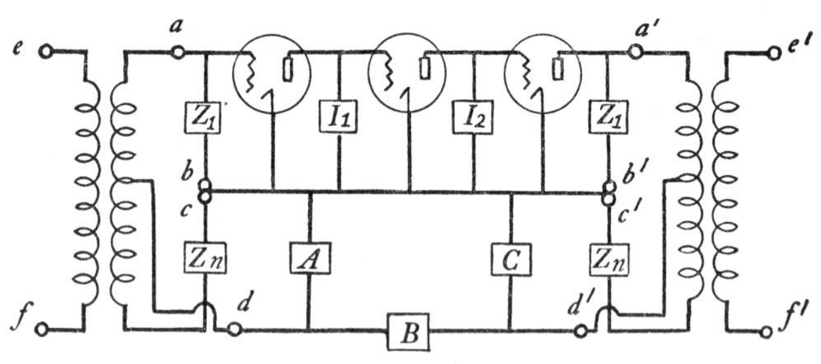

FIG. 3.7

tively easy to secure a moderate impedance which can be adjusted to match a given line by controlling the elements in the bridge.

The bridge type circuit suffers from the general disadvantages that it may require extreme impedance levels and that a portion of the output power may be consumed by the branches added to secure a bridge balance. These difficulties can be ameliorated by replacing the bridge by a three-

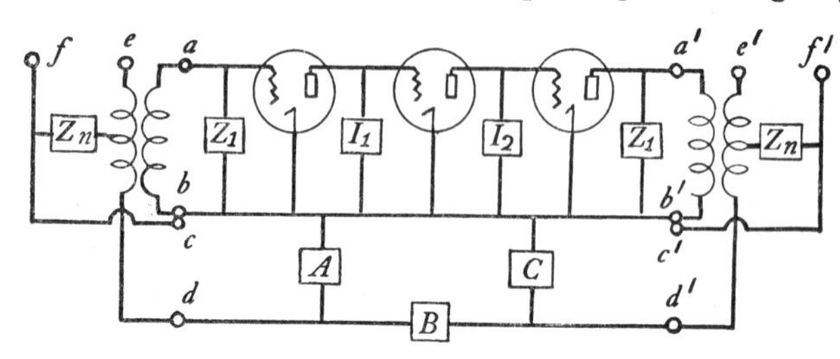

FIG. 3.8

winding transformer or hybrid coil. In view of the several known equivalences between a bridge and a three-winding transformer, there are several ways in which this substitution may be effected. Figure 3.7, for example, shows a " high-side " hybrid coil feedback. In this case Z_n represents the " balancing " impedance. Figure 3.8 shows a " low-side " feedback.

In the preceding figures, the same circuit connections have been shown at each end of the amplifier as a matter of simplicity. The number of available configurations, however, is much increased by the possibility of combining different connections at input and output. For example, Fig. 3.9 shows a series connection at the input terminals in combination

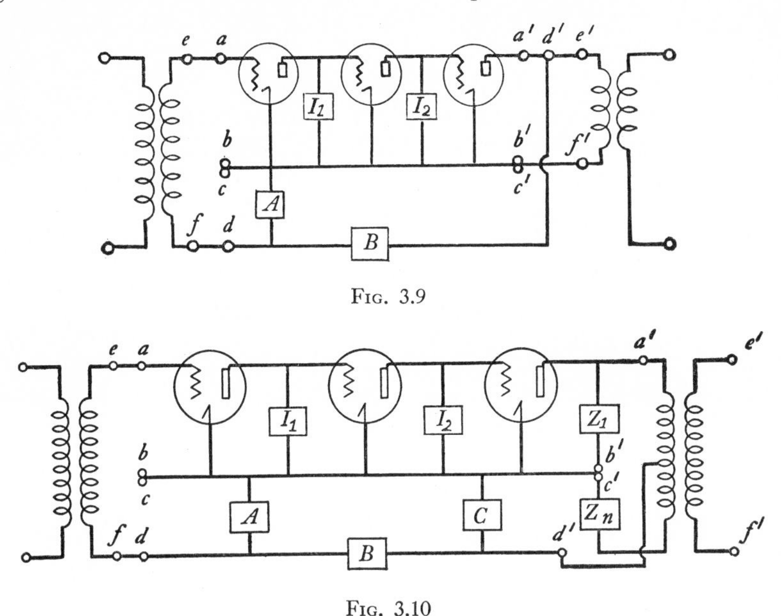

Fig. 3.9

Fig. 3.10

with a shunt connection at the output. Figure 3.10 shows a combination of series input and hybrid coil output.

3.4. *Cathode Feedback Circuits*

In addition to these general arrangements, a wide variety of other feedback circuits may be used in practice. A particularly important example, for practical purposes, is furnished by the so-called " cathode " feedbacks. These may exist in two forms, depending upon the number of stages in the μ circuit. In either case, the arrangement is essentially a modification of a series feedback amplifier. Figure 3.11*A*, for example, shows a series feedback for two stages in comparison with the corresponding cathode feedback shown by Fig. 3.11*B*. The β circuit is represented by the single branch Z_β. In this instance, the cathode connection is used to secure a phase reversal. As the discussion in Chapter I pointed out, the successive

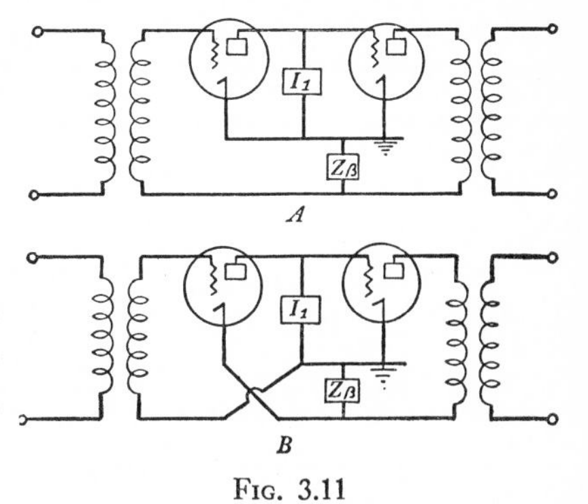

Fig. 3.11

tubes in the μ circuit produce successive phase reversals. With an odd number of tubes it turns out that the net resulting phase is of a sign suitable for feedback without instability. If there are an even number of stages as shown by Fig. 3.11*A*, however, the current delivered by the μ circuit has the wrong sign for direct return to the input. This is avoided in Fig. 3.11*B* by crossing the terminals in the β circuit to secure an additional phase reversal. The circuit is called a " cathode " feedback because the cathode of the first tube is off ground.*

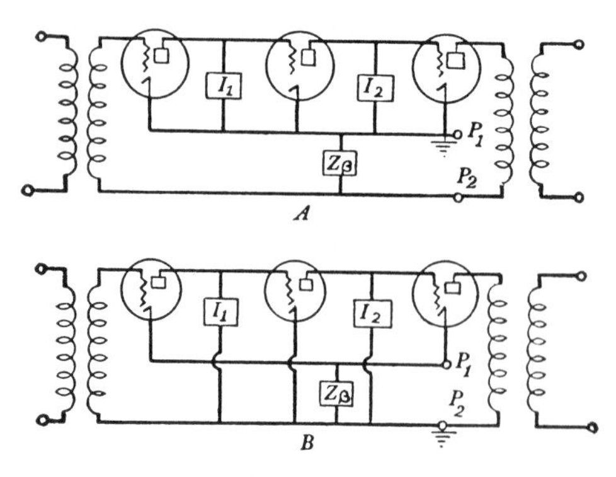

FIG. 3.12

The use of a cathode feedback circuit to replace a corresponding series feedback circuit when the μ circuit contains an odd number of stages is shown by Fig. 3.12. Here the cathode feedback is introduced principally to minimize distributed capacities to ground. As Fig. 3.12*A* shows, the conventional series feedback circuit is grounded at the cathode junction, P_1. The junction P_2, to which the transformers are connected, is off ground and their capacities to ground fall effectively across the β circuit. No improvement is obtained by transferring the ground terminal from P_1 to P_2 because this leaves the ground capacity of the μ circuit, which is at least equally large, to be accounted for. The total capacity can, however, be minimized by grounding most of the forward circuit in the manner shown by Fig. 3.12*B*. Since the cathodes of both input and output tubes are off ground there is no net phase reversal.

A special feature of the cathode circuits is the fact that some feedback may exist for the tubes whose cathodes are off ground even when the remaining tubes are dead. Thus in Fig. 3.11*B* the plate current for the

* We can evidently cross terminals without a change in ground by including a transformer in the loop. In ordinary situations, however, the inclusion of a transformer so restricts the available feedback, as determined by the methods described later, that Fig. 3.11 represents a preferable solution.

first tube can return to its cathode only by flowing through the β circuit impedance, so that some voltage would be returned to the first grid even if the second tube were removed. In Fig. 3.12*B* a similar situation holds for both the first and third tubes.

Speaking rather roughly, we can suppose that the β circuit impedance operates independently in producing this residual feedback and in producing the principal feedback. For example, Fig. 3.13 gives the approximate equivalent of Fig. 3.12*B* under this method of treatment. It is obtained

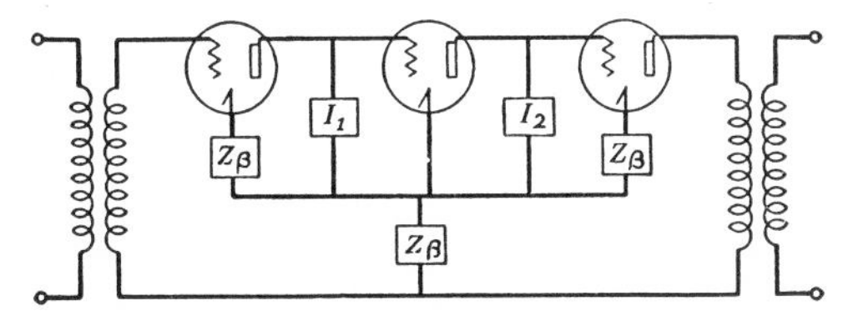

Fig. 3.13

from the original series feedback amplifier of Fig. 3.12*A* by inserting new impedances equal to the β circuit impedance in the cathode leads of the first and third tubes. The first and third tubes can evidently be regarded by themselves as miniature feedback amplifiers of the series type. These tubes thus have more total feedback than would appear if we considered only the transmission around the principal loop. On the other hand, since the local feedback reduces their gain, the transmission around the principal loop will be decreased unless some compensating change is made.

3.5. *Multiple Loop Feedback Amplifiers*

The circuits of Figs. 3.11*B* and 3.12*B* are examples of multiple loop amplifiers, or in other words of amplifiers in which voltage can be returned to some of the grids by more than one path, so that the effective feedbacks on the various tubes are different. In these particular structures the subsidiary paths are accidental results of the type of feedback connections adopted. In current amplifier development, however, there appears to be an increasing tendency to turn to multiple loop circuits deliberately in order to obtain results not available from single loop structures.

One simple type of multiple loop structure is shown by Fig. 3.14. The circuit is a series feedback amplifier with additional feedback on the last tube through the insertion of an impedance in its cathode lead. The structure is thus similar to the " equivalent " amplifier previously shown by Fig. 3.13, except that since the local feedback is now produced by the impedance $Z_{\beta 2}$, which is independent of the principal feedback impedance $Z_{\beta 1}$, it can be chosen arbitrarily. We can look upon the circuit as a device for securing more reduction in the non-linear distortion in the last tube than can be obtained, according to the principles laid down later, by feedback around the main loop alone.

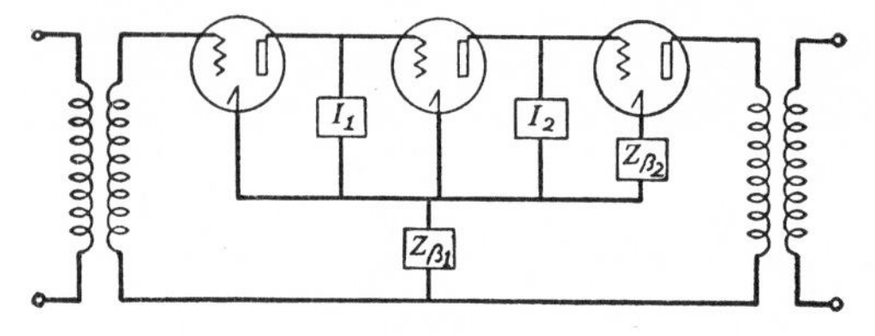

FIG. 3.14

Figure 3.15 shows a second type of multiple loop structure. It is similar to that shown by Fig. 3.14 except that the local path represents shunt rather than series feedback. The subsidiary path may be regarded either as a

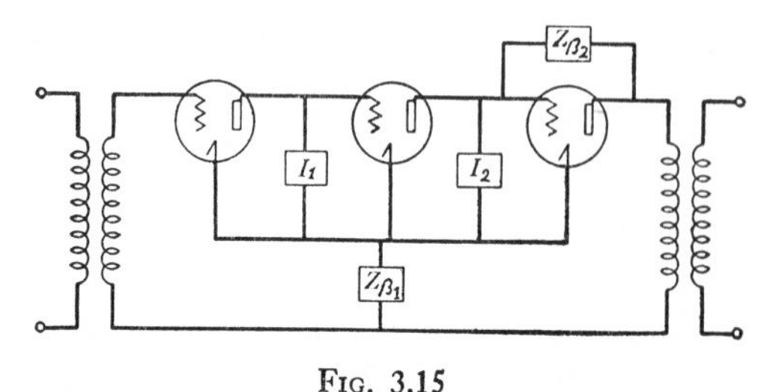

FIG. 3.15

branch deliberately added to improve the characteristics of the output tube, as in Fig. 3.14, or as a representation of a large parasitic grid-plate capacity, such as is found, for example, in the power triodes used for radio broadcasting.

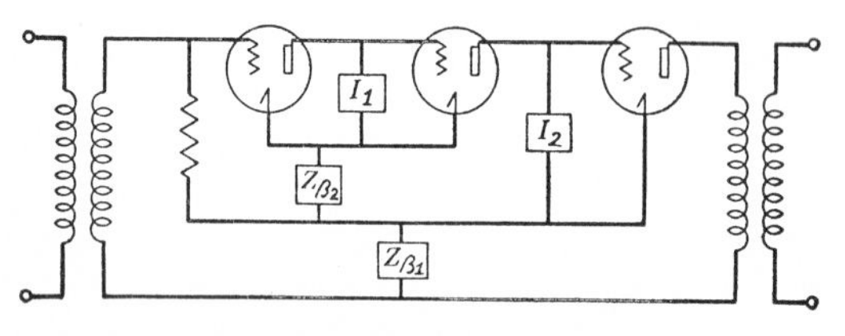

FIG. 3.16

Still a third example is shown by Fig. 3.16. Here local series feedback is applied around the first two stages of the complete μ circuit. We may imagine the local feedback to be regenerative, so that it provides a higher $\mu\beta$ gain around the complete loop than would otherwise be obtainable. In addition to the particular structures shown by Figs. 3.14 to 3.16, many other multiple loop amplifiers can evidently be secured either by combining two or three of the local feedback paths shown by these figures in a single amplifier or by providing still more paths.

3.6. *Other Feedback Circuits*

The preceding sections have been intended as a brief sketch of the types of physical configurations directly envisaged in this book. They are composed characteristically of linear vacuum tubes and passive elements. Feedback circuits may, however, also be designed to include non-linear or non-electrical elements. Many of these are sufficiently similar in fundamentals to a linear electrical circuit to be treated by the same methods, provided the proper precautions are taken.

The diversity of applications will be indicated by two illustrations. The first consists of a feedback circuit including frequency translating devices. Figure 3.17, for example, shows a radio transmitter in which a portion of the output is demodulated and returned to the signal input as voice frequency or "envelope" feedback. If the modulator and demodulator are nearly ideal and the carrier frequency is much higher than the voice band this can be analyzed essentially as a linear circuit. It is merely necessary to consider the transmission of an equivalent voice frequency around the complete loop. If the modulator outputs include a variety of products which can be transmitted around the loop, however, or if the carrier frequency is within a few octaves of the top of the voice band, the situation is more complicated and will not be considered here.

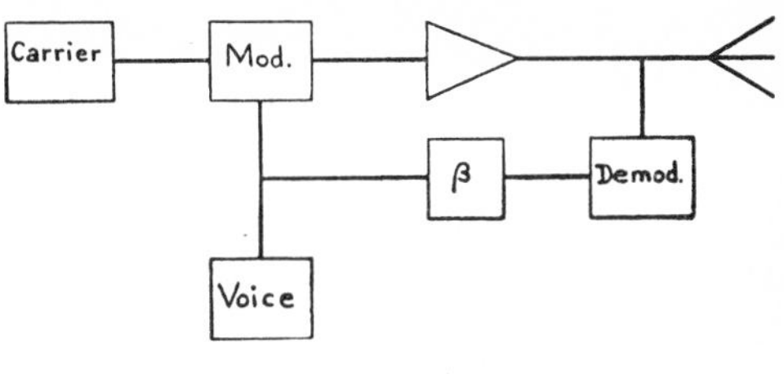

FIG. 3.17

The second general example is furnished by regulator circuits for such purposes as speed, voltage, or frequency control. Here the fact that the control circuit acts as a valve, producing a large change in output for the comparatively slight expenditure of energy required to change the control, gives an equivalent of vacuum tube amplification. The use of a portion of the output to adjust the control circuit is, of course, feedback. There is no definite useful band, in the sense in which this term is ordinarily understood in communication circuits, but an approximate effective band can ordinarily be assigned the circuit from a consideration of the rapidity with which the controls should operate. The essential problem, of course, is to avoid hunting, which is the equivalent of instability in a feedback amplifier.

CHAPTER IV

Mathematical Definition of Feedback

4.1. *Introduction*

The conception of a feedback amplifier developed in the preceding chapter can be summarized in the following words: The amplifier consists of a forward or μ circuit and a backward or β circuit. The feedback can then be determined from the product $\mu\beta$, which represents the transmission around the complete loop formed by the μ and β circuits together. The circuit has the fundamental physical property that the effects of variations in the μ circuit, whether they are taken as changes in the normal μ gain or as departures from strict linearity or from freedom from extraneous noise, are reduced by the factor $1 - \mu\beta$ in comparison with the effects which would be observed in a non-feedback amplifier.

This set of conceptions is almost indispensable in describing a feedback amplifier or in reasoning generally about the functions of the various parts. They will be retained here for this general purpose. For future analytical work, however, they are extended in this chapter to provide a purely mathematical definition of feedback. The mathematical definition is framed in terms of the general mesh or nodal equations introduced in the first chapter. The system of equations is taken with reference to the complete amplifier, without distinction between μ and β circuits, so that these conceptions disappear from the formal analysis.

This change is made for two reasons. The more obvious one is the fact that the mesh or nodal analysis furnishes a convenient foundation for further theoretical work. It is especially appropriate in discussing the relationship between feedback and stability.

The second reason for developing a general definition of feedback in terms of the equations of the circuit as a whole is that it allows us to avoid the ambiguities and uncertainties which appear if we rely exclusively upon an analysis in terms of separate μ and β circuits. The μ and β analysis supposes that these circuits are clearly distinguishable entities to which can be ascribed definite properties independently of one another. This was suggested, for example, in the generalized sketch shown by Fig. 3.1 of the preceding chapter. In fact, however, the actual physical configurations shown by the figures which appeared later in the chapter do not permit such a clear-cut separation between the two circuits so that what we are to call μ and what β remains somewhat vague. Since the properties of gain stabilization and distortion reduction hold only for the μ circuit, and the eventual gain is determined by the β circuit, this is a matter of considerable importance.

The simplest example of the difficulty of distinguishing sharply between μ and β is furnished by the computation of gain from the familiar equation

$$e^{\theta} = \frac{\mu}{1 - \mu\beta}.$$

The computation requires a knowledge of μ and $\mu\beta$. The product $\mu\beta$, representing the transmission around the loop, is itself well defined. The μ which must be used in order to make the equation an accurate expression for the amplifier gain is, however, not so apparent. It depends in part upon the way in which the current divides in the six-terminal connecting networks shown at the ends of the amplifier in Fig. 3.3 of the preceding chapter. In evaluating μ we must therefore make some allowance for the β circuit impedance, instead of removing β entirely, since otherwise the division of current in these networks will, in general, be changed. For particular cir-

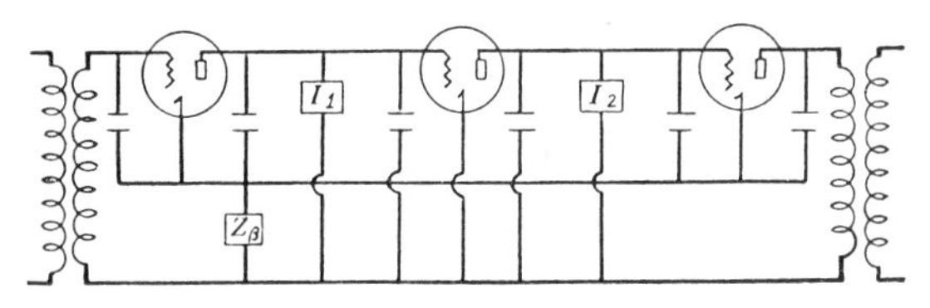

FIG. 4.1

cuits this can be examined by setting up detailed circuit equations, but without further theoretical study it is difficult to see, in general, just what branches of the β circuit should be included in making the allowance, and in any event it is clear that the problem of designing a β circuit to give a specified external gain characteristic may be confused by the fact that any elements we put in affect both μ and $\mu\beta$.

The difficulty of separating the amplifier into μ and β parts may become much greater in a multiple loop structure containing several feedback paths. A particularly extreme example is furnished by the cathode feedback circuit shown by Fig. 3.12*B* in the preceding chapter. As drawn there, the circuit includes only the elements which would be supplied in the design process. In a physical embodiment, however, it would be necessary to consider also the parasitic capacities between grid and cathode and between plate and cathode in each tube. When these are added the circuit appears in the form shown by Fig. 4.1. For design purposes it is possible to divide the elements of the circuit into a group which is most important in determining forward gain and another which is chiefly effective for feedback. It is clear, however, that no sharp division into μ and β circuits can be made. Every element in the structure enters to some extent into both forward and backward transmission.

4.2. *Return Voltage and Reduction in Effect of Tube Variations*

The consideration of multiple loop structures leads to another reason for developing a general mathematical definition of feedback, which may be less obvious than those previously discussed. In a single loop structure the fundamental quantity appears to be the loop transmission $\mu\beta$. This is the same as the return voltage which would appear by transmission around the complete loop if we applied a unit voltage to any grid and opened the circuit just behind it. In such a structure we know that the factor measuring the reduction in the effect of tube variations is $1 - \mu\beta$, so that it is always closely correlated with the return voltage.

In a multiple loop structure voltages may be returned to the grids of the tubes by various paths which differ from tube to tube. For any particular tube, however, the total return voltage can be obtained, at least on paper, by adding together the contributions from all available paths through the network. This is illustrated by Fig. 4.2. N represents the complete circuit exclusive of the tube in question and P_1 and P_2, connected together, the grid terminal for normal operation. The return voltage can then be defined as the voltage which would appear between P_1 and G in response to a unit voltage between P_2 and G when the connection between P_1 and P_2 is broken. The grid-plate and grid-cathode capacities C_1 and C_2 are shown as going to P_1 to indicate the fact that opening the loop should not disturb the admittances seen from the end point P_1.

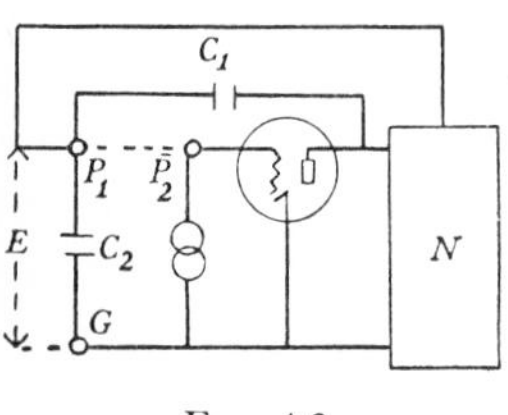

FIG. 4.2

Given any individual tube, it is also possible to determine the ratio between a prescribed small variation in its gain and the resulting change in the transmission characteristic of the complete circuit. It is natural to suppose that the correlation between this ratio and the return voltage on the tube will be the same for a general circuit as it is for a single loop structure. This is substantially true in the simplest and most common circuits. In exceptional circuits, however, the actual effect of individual tube variations on the final transmission characteristic may be much greater or much less than would be predicted from the return voltage. One of the objects in setting up a general mathematical definition of feedback is therefore to determine when the return voltage computation is a reliable index of the effect of tube variations and what corrections must be applied when it fails.

One other aspect of the general situation deserves attention. Since the vacuum tubes are ordinarily the most variable and non-linear constituents of a complete amplifier, feedback is of engineering importance chiefly in correcting for their characteristics. An incidental result of the application of feedback, however, is the fact that it also reduces the effect of variations in some of the bilateral elements of the circuit. The effects of variations in the elements of an interstage impedance, for example, are reduced by feedback to the same extent as are those of variations in the transconductances of the associated vacuum tubes. In any discussion of the relation between feedback and the effects of element variations, it is therefore legitimate to extend consideration to bilateral as well as unilateral elements. The analytical treatment of feedback developed in this chapter applies, in fact, equally well to elements of either type. In order to simplify exposition, however, each step in the development is introduced as though unilateral elements only were in question, the extension of the analysis to bilateral elements being described subsequently.

4.3. *Return Ratio, Return Difference, and Sensitivity*

The preceding section has indicated that the usual conception of feedback includes two distinct ideas. The first is that of a loop transmission or return of voltage, and the second that of a reduction in the effects of variations in the tube characteristics. In normal circuits these two are related by simple mathematical laws so that the term " feedback " can refer generically to both.

In exceptional circuits, when the correlation between the two breaks down, the first idea is evidently the one which most nearly agrees with the usual physical conception of feedback. It will therefore be taken as the basis for the definition of feedback in the general case. To prevent any possible confusion, this idea will also be described by the new name *return difference*. It is still worthwhile, however, to retain the general idea of a reduction in the effects of tube variations. This will be referred to by the name *sensitivity*.

The return difference, or feedback, and the sensitivity will be represented by the symbols F and S, respectively. They are to be regarded as the analogues, in general, of the quantity $1 - \mu\beta$ in a single loop structure. Thus, " return difference " is an abbreviation for " return voltage difference," meaning by this the voltage difference existing between P_1 and P_2 in Fig. 4.2 under the conditions of measurement indicated there. The quantity $1 - \mu\beta$, rather than $\mu\beta$ itself, is chosen as the fundamental unit, because it turns out to lead to simpler and more compact formulae in most situations. In order to have a symbol corresponding to the loop transmission $\mu\beta$ itself, however, we will also write $F = 1 + T$. Thus, $T = -\mu\beta$ in an ordinary amplifier.* T will be called the *return ratio*. To complete the nomenclature, we might similarly introduce a symbol for the quantity $S - 1$, but the number of occasions when such a symbol would be useful is too small to make this step worthwhile.

4.4. *Definitions of Return Ratio and Return Difference*

In order to secure more precise definitions of the quantities described in the preceding section, let the input of the general circuit be taken as the first mesh or node, and the output as the second mesh or node. We will also suppose that the grid and plate terminals of the tube under examination are labeled respectively 3 and 4, and that its transconductance or mutual impedance is represented by W. W is thus a constituent of Z_{43} or Y_{43} in the general system of mesh or nodal equations. In later sections the definitions of return ratio and return difference will be extended to bilateral elements. The form of these statements remains the same when W is a bilateral element, except that it is taken as a constituent of the self-impedance or admittance Z_{33} or Y_{33}, rather than of the coupling term Z_{43} or Y_{43}.

The loop transmission or return voltage in Fig. 4.2 can be obtained by multiplying the transimmittance, W, of the tube itself by the backward transmission from the plate to P_1. In making the latter calculation, the open circuit which appears between P_1 and P_2 can evidently be represented by supposing that P_1 and P_2 are connected together, as in normal operation, but that the tube is dead. If we let Δ^0 represent the circuit determinant when $W = 0$, therefore, equations (1–10) and (1–24) of Chapter I give the backward transmission as Δ_{43}/Δ^0. Since the negative sign introduced by the phase reversal in the tube is canceled by the fact that T is analogous to $-\mu\beta$, we therefore have

$$F = 1 + T = 1 + W\frac{\Delta_{43}}{\Delta^0}\cdot \tag{4–1}$$

But it follows from the discussion in connection with equations (1–11) to (1–14) that $\Delta^0 + W\Delta_{43}$ is the value which the circuit determinant assumes when the tube transimmittance has its normal value W. If we represent the normal circuit determinant by the usual symbol Δ, therefore, equa-

* The introduction of the minus sign may be explained by the fact that an ordinary feedback amplifier contains an odd number of tubes, which contribute an odd number of phase reversals to the loop. Thus T, as defined, is equal to the loop transmission without these phase reversals, and will ordinarily be a positive quantity except for the effects of possible phase shifts in the interstage or feedback networks. The sign chosen for T is also more convenient in dealing with bilateral elements.

tion (4–1) can also be written as

$$F = \frac{\Delta}{\Delta^0}. \tag{4–2}$$

In order to emphasize the importance of this last formula, and to pave the way for the treatment of bilateral elements in a subsequent section, the relation embodied in (4–2) will be restated as the

Definition: The return difference, or feedback, for any element in a complete circuit is equal to the ratio of the values assumed by the circuit determinant when the specified element has its normal value and when the specified element vanishes.

Equation (4–2) probably represents the most convenient working formula for the analytic treatment of feedback. A number of examples of its use in feedback circuit analysis will be given in the next chapter. The fact that the equation expresses F in terms of the determinant of the system is particularly convenient in studying the relation between feedback and stability since, as we shall see later, the roots of the determinant tell whether or not a system is stable. The formula is also especially useful in studying multiple loop systems, since if we once know the determinant we can readily evaluate the individual feedbacks without making a complete separate calculation for each tube.

4.5. *Return Difference for a General Reference*

It is convenient to introduce here a generalization of the conception of return difference whose meaning will probably not be fully apparent until a considerably later point. In developing equation (4–1), we based the calculation, in a sense, upon the reference condition of the circuit obtained by setting $W = 0$. Thus the backward transmission from plate to grid was obtained for this condition of the circuit, and the forward transmission W, by which the backward transmission was multiplied to produce the complete loop gain, may be thought of as $W - 0$, or the surplus of the actual tube transimmittance over this reference value.

We can evidently perform a similar computation for any reference condition $W = k$. The "loop gain," then, becomes the effective transimmittance, $W - k$, multiplied by the backward transmission from plate to grid evaluated for the condition $W = k$. Since the tube is no longer completely dead, this backward transmission must include the effects of a certain amount of physical feedback, but this is a practical rather than a theoretical complication. The reference k can be anything we like. For example, it might be the value of transimmittance at which the tube would be discarded in favor of a new one, or it might be the transimmittance which would lead to a certain specified gain through the over-all circuit. The latter condition is the one which will be used in future applications of this concept.

The return ratio and return difference resulting from this computation will be spoken of as the return ratio and return difference of W for the reference k. If F_k represents this return difference, we evidently have

$$F_k = 1 + (W - k)\frac{\Delta_{43}}{\Delta^k}, \tag{4–3}$$

where Δ^k is the value assumed by Δ when $W = k$. But since $\Delta^k = \Delta^0 + k\Delta_{43}$ and $\Delta = \Delta^0 + W\Delta_{43}$, where Δ^0 is, as before, the value of Δ when $W = 0$, equation (4–3) can be rewritten as

$$F_k = \frac{\Delta}{\Delta^k}. \tag{4–4}$$

This equation is obviously analogous to (4–2) and, like (4–2), will be regarded as a definition in future discussion.

Equation (4–4) leads to an easy method of computing the return difference for the reference k from the return difference for zero reference. Thus, if we multiply and divide the right side of (4–4) by Δ^0, we have

$$\begin{aligned} F_k(W) &= \frac{\Delta}{\Delta^0}\frac{\Delta^0}{\Delta^k} \\ &= \frac{F(W)}{F(k)}. \end{aligned} \tag{4–5}$$

Stated in words, this result is the

Theorem: The return difference of W for any reference is equal to the ratio of the return differences, with zero reference, which would be obtained if W assumed, first, its normal value, and, second, the chosen reference value.

The conception of a return difference for a reference other than zero will be utilized at the end of this chapter. Meanwhile, it can be assumed that the term " return difference " applies only to the zero reference case.

4.6. *Return Difference for a Bilateral Element*

In setting up equation (4–2) as a *definition* of return difference, we evidently extended the analysis formally to bilateral as well as unilateral elements, since Δ and Δ^0 are meaningful quantities for elements of either type. The physical significance of the return difference of a bilateral element, on the other hand, is most easily studied if we replace (4–2), for a bilateral element, by an equation more nearly in the form of (4–1). This is readily done. Thus, if W is a constituent of Y_{33} or Z_{33}, we evidently have $\Delta = \Delta^0 + W\Delta_{33}$ in the bilateral case. Substitution of this relation in (4–2) gives

$$F = 1 + T = 1 + W\frac{\Delta_{33}}{\Delta^0}, \tag{4–6}$$

which is like (4–1) except that Δ_{43} is replaced by Δ_{33}.

The meaning of the return difference for a bilateral element is easily understood from an examination of the terms in (4–6). Let it be supposed, for example, that W represents an impedance. Then Δ^0/Δ_{33} represents the impedance which would be seen by a generator in the mesh containing W if W were zero. In other words, it is the impedance which W faces. The return ratio $T = W\Delta_{33}/\Delta^0$ is therefore equal to the ratio of the impedance W to the impedance presented to W by the rest of the circuit. The return difference F is equal to the ratio of the complete impedance, including W, to the impedance of the external circuit. Similarly, if W represents an admittance, the return ratio T and the return difference F are, respectively, equal to the ratio of the admittance W to the admittance of the rest of the circuit, and the ratio of the admittance of the complete circuit, including W, to the admittance of the rest of the circuit.*

Viewed in this light, the conception of return difference for a bilateral element appears as an expression of the fact that a generator with internal impedance cannot be fully effective in driving an external circuit. The internal voltage drop is the " returned " voltage. It is " returned " to the source in the sense that it is unavailable to drive the external circuit. Thus, suppose that W is the impedance Z and that the impedance of the external circuit is represented by Z_0. In the absence of Z a unit generator would produce a current $1/Z_0$ in the circuit. The insertion of Z into a circuit carrying this current is equivalent to adding or " returning " the voltage $-Z/Z_0$ to the source. The current strength is not supposed to be changed when Z is added since this is the logical equivalent of opening the loop in the unilateral case to prevent the return voltage itself from producing a response. The return difference is then the difference between the

* These relations hold, of course, for both active and passive circuits. If the circuit does in fact contain vacuum tubes, however, it is important to notice that the impedance assigned to the external circuit must be the active impedance obtained when the tubes are lit. This may be quite different from the impedance which would be obtained from the passive elements alone. Methods of computing the active impedance from the passive impedance are described in the next chapter.

original and the returned voltage and measures the net voltage available to drive the external circuit.

4.7. *Definition of Sensitivity*

We turn now to the second leading conception of the present chapter, that of sensitivity. This conception can be illustrated by reference to equation (3–6) of the preceding chapter, which appeared as

$$\frac{dE_R}{E_R} = \frac{1}{1 - \mu\beta} \frac{d\mu}{\mu}. \tag{3–6}$$

Evidently, the equation states in effect that $1 - \mu\beta$ is the factor relating any given percentage variation in the μ circuit to the resulting percentage variation in the output voltage. In other words, $1 - \mu\beta$ is a measure of the sensitiveness of the over-all circuit to small variations in μ.

Equation (3–6) is, of course, limited to the μ elements in an ordinary feedback circuit. In order to generalize appropriately to any circuit, let the gain through the complete system be represented by θ. We then have the

Definition: The sensitivity, S, for an element W is given by

$$S = \frac{1}{\dfrac{\partial\theta}{\partial \log W}}. \tag{4–7}$$

The definition is intended to apply to both unilateral and bilateral elements.

The relation between (4–7) and (3–6) may be made more apparent if we express θ in terms of the logarithm of the output voltage E_R, and replace the partial derivative by ordinary differentiation, on the assumption that W is the only element in the circuit which varies. This allows (4–7) to be written as

$$\frac{dE_R}{E_R} = \frac{1}{S} \frac{dW}{W}. \tag{4–8}$$

Thus, S is the ratio between a given percentage change in W, in the general case, and the resulting percentage change in the delivered voltage E_R, just as $1 - \mu\beta$ expresses the corresponding ratio between changes in μ and E_R in the special case of the single loop amplifier.

In an average situation, we may expect S to be of the order of magnitude of unity. In an ordinary non-feedback amplifier, for example, the over-all gain varies by 1 db for each db change in the gain of any one of the tubes, and S for any tube is evidently 1 exactly. On the other hand, S may be much greater than unity. Thus, ignoring phase angles, if the final gain varies by 0.01 db for 1 db variation in W, the sensitivity S is 100. This is the result we would expect for the elements in the forward circuit of an amplifier with 40 db feedback. We might also secure such a result, however, even in a purely passive circuit, if W were an impedance element having comparatively little to do with the over-all transmission.

It is also possible for S to be much smaller than unity. This might occur, for example, in a regenerative amplifier at the point of singing or in an ordinary circuit which depends on a critical bridge balance or on sharply tuned reactance branches.

It is to be noticed that in the discussion of the return difference we labeled the input and output terminals of the system, but the input and output terminals did not actually enter into the analysis. Since the sensitivity, on the other hand, depends upon the transmission through the circuit, it must in general depend upon the nodes or meshes which we choose to regard as the terminals of the system, as well as upon the chosen element W itself.

4.8. *General Formula for Sensitivity*

The definition of sensitivity given by equation (4–7) can be made more concrete by an examination of the functional relationship between θ and W. If we retain the notation used in the preceding sections and represent the output impedance or admittance by W_R, the gain through the circuit can be written in the general form

$$e^{\theta} = \frac{\Delta_{12}}{\Delta} W_R. \tag{4–9}$$

The discussion of Chapter I shows, however, that both Δ_{12} and Δ must be linear functions of W. If we let Δ_{12}^0 and Δ^0 represent the values of these determinants when $W = 0$, we can therefore write equation (4–9) as

$$e^{\theta} = \frac{\Delta_{12}^0 + W\Delta_{1243}}{\Delta^0 + W\Delta_{43}} W_R. \tag{4–10}$$

This equation of course holds for any value of W. For purposes of future discussion, it will be convenient to pay particular attention to the case when W is zero. The gain under these conditions constitutes the so-called *direct transmission* gain.* If we let θ_0 represent this gain, we evidently have

$$e^{\theta_0} = \frac{\Delta_{12}^0}{\Delta^0} W_R. \tag{4–11}$$

* So-called because it represents a current transmitted directly to the output, without the intervention of the element W.

Returning to the general formula (4–10), if we apply the definition of S given by (4–7) to it directly, the result, after some manipulation, appears as

$$S = \frac{1}{W} \frac{(\Delta_{12}^0 + W\Delta_{1243})(\Delta^0 + W\Delta_{43})}{\Delta^0\Delta_{1243} - \Delta_{12}^0\Delta_{43}} \cdot \qquad (4\text{–}12)$$

This can be simplified by means of a general identity in determinant theory, which is of frequent application in network analysis. The identity is*

$$\Delta\Delta_{ab,cd} = \Delta_{ab}\Delta_{cd} - \Delta_{ad}\Delta_{cb}, \qquad (4\text{–}13)$$

where Δ is any determinant, a and c are any two rows of Δ, and b and d are any two columns of Δ. If we let Δ^0 of (4–12) be the general determinant Δ which appears in this equation and make the proper identifications of subscripts, this allows (4–12) to be written as

$$S = -\frac{1}{W} \frac{\Delta\Delta_{12}}{\Delta_{13}\Delta_{42}} \cdot \qquad (4\text{–}14)$$

If we assume that W is a bilateral element in Z_{33} or Y_{33}, rather than a unilateral element in Z_{43} or Y_{43}, all the steps from (4–9) to (4–14) can be repeated exactly, except that each subscript 4 is replaced by a subscript 3.

4.9. *Return Difference and Sensitivity in Simple Cases*

The general formula (4–14) in the preceding section was developed largely as a matter of completeness. In actual practice, it is ordinarily easier to evaluate the sensitivity indirectly from the return difference.

In general, the sensitivity and the return difference for a given element are not equal, so that if we are to calculate S from F it is first necessary to establish the relation between them. This will be the subject of the next several sections. For the moment, however, it is convenient to dispose of the especially simple case when the two are, in fact, equal. This occurs when the direct transmission term (4–11) vanishes. If we assume, then, that Δ_{12}^0 is zero, the analysis of the preceding section becomes very much simpler. Thus, if we substitute this condition directly in equation (4–12), we readily find

$$S = \frac{\Delta^0 + W\Delta_{43}}{\Delta^0} = \frac{\Delta}{\Delta^0} \cdot \qquad (4\text{–}15)$$

This, however, is exactly the same formula as the one which was developed for the return difference in equation (4–2). We therefore have the

Theorem: The sensitivity and return difference are equal for any element whose vanishing leads to zero transmission through the circuit as a whole.

* See, for example, Scott and Mathews *Theory of Determinants*, p. 64.

The most familiar examples of elements meeting this condition are probably the tubes in the forward circuit of an ordinary feedback amplifier. We can assume, for practical purposes, that the transmission through the structure will be zero if any one of the tubes fails. In strict accuracy, this is seldom exactly true. Some current will ordinarily* trickle through the β circuit into the load, even when $\mu = 0$. This trickle, however, is usually so much smaller than the normal output current that it can be neglected, so that the forward circuit can be regarded as falling within the scope of the theorem for practical purposes. In this case, of course, the theorem expresses nothing new. Since the theorem requires no assumption except that of negligible direct transmission, however, its application can evidently be extended to circuits which differ fairly substantially from the conventional single loop configuration.

In the field of bilateral elements, simple examples of the theorem are obtained from series-shunt or ladder networks. We can obtain zero transmission when $W = 0$ in circuits of this type by adopting an impedance analysis if W represents an element in shunt, or an admittance analysis if W is an element in series.

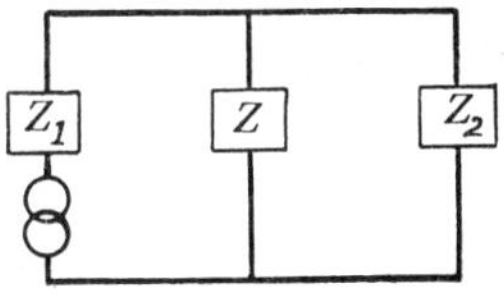

Z_1 Z Z_2

FIG. 4.3

A specific example is furnished by the circuit of Fig. 4.3. The transmission is supposed to take place from Z_1 to Z_2, while Z represents the variable W. The return difference is an impedance ratio which can be written down by inspection as

$$F = \frac{Z + \dfrac{Z_1Z_2}{Z_1 + Z_2}}{\dfrac{Z_1Z_2}{Z_1 + Z_2}} = \frac{Z_1Z_2 + Z(Z_1 + Z_2)}{Z_1Z_2} \cdot \tag{4-16}$$

On the other hand, the current flowing in Z_2 in response to a unit generator in Z_1 is given by

$$e^\theta = \frac{Z}{Z_1Z_2 + Z(Z_1 + Z_2)} \cdot \tag{4-17}$$

Hence,

$$d\theta = \frac{Z_1Z_2}{Z_1Z_2 + Z(Z_1 + Z_2)} \frac{dZ}{Z} \cdot \tag{4-18}$$

Since the coefficient on the right-hand side of (4–18) is $1/S$, by (4–8), the theorem is verified for this case.

* That is, in the absence of a balanced bridge at either input or output.

A second example, this time for a bridge circuit, is furnished by Fig. 4.4. The transmission is from Z_1 to Z_6 and the variable element is taken as Z, the remaining impedances being so chosen that the bridge is balanced when Z vanishes. For simplicity, let every impedance but Z be taken as 1. This makes Z and Z_4 conjugate so that Z_4 can be removed in determining the impedance which Z faces. With the help of this simplification, we readily find that Z faces the impedance 2. We therefore have

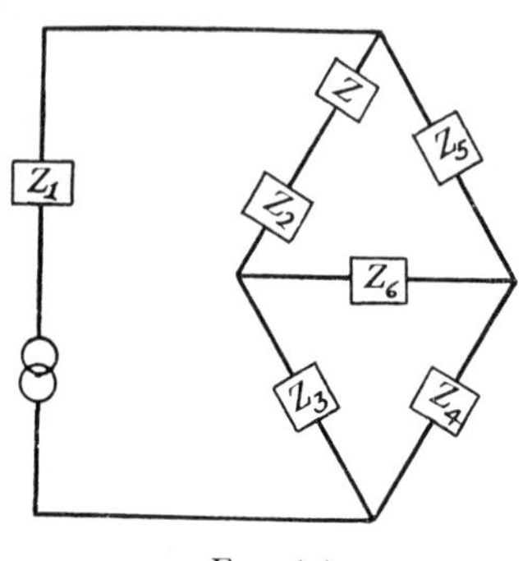

FIG. 4.4

$$d\theta = \frac{2}{2 + Z} \frac{dZ}{Z}. \tag{4–19}$$

This can be verified by direct consideration of the transmission equations for the bridge, but the algebra is too lengthy to be included here.

4.10. *Circuits with Appreciable Direct Transmission*

We turn now to situations in which the assumption of negligible direct transmission is no longer valid. Instances of elements giving a substantial direct transmission term are readily found even in conventional single loop amplifiers. For example, the β circuit elements belong generally to this class, as do many of the elements in customary input and output circuits. In the field of passive circuits, the elements of bridge type networks are usually of this type.*

More difficult situations involving a substantial amount of direct transmission may be found if W is the transimmittance of a tube in a multiple loop circuit. An example is shown by Fig. 4.5. The structure is drawn as a single stage feedback amplifier but it may also be taken as the last stage in the double loop feedback structure shown by Fig. 3.14 of the preceding chapter. The impedances Z_1 and Z_5 can be regarded as the terminating impedances in the single stage case. Z_3 represents the feedback branch and Z_2 and Z_4 are, of course, parasitic grid-cathode and plate-cathode impedances.

When the gain of the tube vanishes, the circuit reduces to the form shown by Fig. 4.6 and in the single stage case the transmission through this network evidently represents the quantity e^{θ_0} defined in equation (4–11). By proper adjustment of the elements Z_2, Z_3, and Z_4, the transmission through this path can be made anything we like in comparison with that through

* That is, in the absence of special situations like that of Fig. 4.4, where the bridge is supposed to balance when the variable element is zero.

the tube. For example, if Z_3 is very small while Z_2 and Z_4 are quite large, the direct transmission becomes insignificant. If we make Z_2 and Z_4 small enough, however, and Z_3 very large, it may be much more important than the transmission through the tube. By proper adjustment of the impedances, we can also secure an intermediate case in which the two paths exactly cancel, so that the net output under operating conditions is zero. In ordinary physical cases, Z_3 will, of course, be small, while Z_2 and Z_4 will be quite large so that we can regard the directly transmitted current as being much smaller than that flowing through the tube.

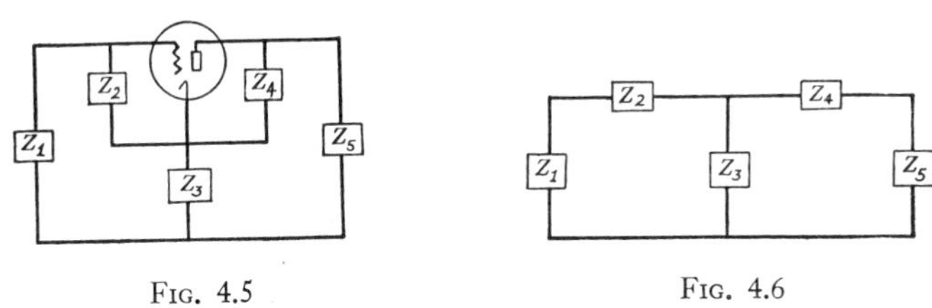

FIG. 4.5 FIG. 4.6

When the circuit represents a complete amplifier, this means that the directly transmitted current can be neglected in any ordinary situation. If the circuit is the last stage of a multiple loop structure, on the other hand, the rest of the structure must also be considered in determining the direct transmission to the final output impedance. In this case, even a slight trickle of current directly through the passive elements of Fig. 4.6 may be important in some circumstances. The reason for making this distinction will appear in a later section.

4.11. *General Relation between Sensitivity and Return Difference*

When the direct transmission is substantial, it is simplest to use it as a reference from which the remainder of the actual output voltage or current is calculated. We are then concerned explicitly only with the difference between the normal output and the directly transmitted term. Thus, from (4–10) and (4–11) we can write

$$e^{\theta} - e^{\theta_0} = \frac{\Delta_{12}^0 + W\Delta_{1243}}{\Delta^0 + W\Delta_{43}} W_R - \frac{\Delta_{12}^0}{\Delta^0} W_R$$

$$= \frac{W(\Delta^0\Delta_{1243} - \Delta_{12}^0\Delta_{43})}{\Delta^0(\Delta^0 + W\Delta_{43})} W_R. \tag{4–20}$$

This can be simplified with the help of the general relation (4–13). The result is

$$e^{\theta} - e^{\theta_0} = \frac{-W\Delta_{13}\Delta_{42}}{\Delta^0(\Delta^0 + W\Delta_{43})} W_R. \tag{4–21}$$

Let us now consider the "sensitivity" of the quantity $e^{\theta} - e^{\theta_0}$, using the term in our customary fashion to mean the ratio between a given percentage variation in W and the corresponding percentage variation in $e^{\theta} - e^{\theta_0}$. As a function of W, the right-hand side of (4–21) is very like (4–10) in the special case $\Delta_{12}^0 = 0$. The only difference is the fact that Δ_{1243} in (4–10) is replaced by $-\Delta_{13}\Delta_{42}/\Delta^0$ in (4–21). But when we calculated the sensitivity from (4–10) for the special case $\Delta_{12}^0 = 0$, we were led to (4–15), which does not depend upon Δ_{1234}. We may therefore draw the following conclusion:

Theorem: The sensitivity of the difference, $e^{\theta} - e^{\theta_0}$, between the normal output and the direct transmission for any element W is equal to the return difference for W.

This result, of course, includes our earlier theorem on circuits with zero direct transmission as a special case. If we begin with that earlier theorem, the present result is an obvious one for a circuit composed of two independent parallel paths, one of which contains W and has no direct transmission, and the other of which furnishes the over-all direct transmission and is independent of W. This is a situation which is very unlikely to occur physically, since there would almost always be interaction between the two paths at input and output terminals, if nowhere else, but the theorem states in effect that any circuit can be thought of in these terms even when the physical separation into two independent paths cannot be achieved.

The theorem just established can also be stated in an analytic form which is somewhat more convenient for purposes of calculation. It is obvious that if the output voltage of the system varies by a given amount, the percentage change which the given variation represents will be inversely proportional to the output we are considering. Thus, the percentage changes in e^{θ} and $e^{\theta} - e^{\theta_0}$, corresponding to a given variation in the element W, will be in the same ratio as the quantities $e^{\theta} - e^{\theta_0}$ and e^{θ}. Since sensitivity is an inverse measure of percentage change, from (4–8), the result expressed by the theorem can therefore be transformed immediately to the relation

$$\frac{F}{S} = \frac{e^{\theta} - e^{\theta_0}}{e^{\theta}} = 1 - \frac{e^{\theta_0}}{e^{\theta}}, \tag{4–22}$$

where S is, as before, the sensitivity for the complete output e^{θ}. This result can also be established by direct calculation from equations (4–2), (4–10), (4–11), and (4–14). It holds for any circuit and for either unilateral or bilateral elements.

Equation (4–22) is of particular interest as a means of estimating quickly whether the return difference is a reliable measure of sensitivity or whether a more elaborate calculation should be made. Since we are ordinarily interested in the sensitivity only to within several db, we can say, in general, that the return difference will be a conservative measure of sensitivity as long as the absolute value of e^{θ_0} is not greater than that of e^{θ}. It will, however, be a very pessimistic estimate if the two quantities happen to be nearly equal in phase angle as well as magnitude. On the other hand, the sensitivity is much poorer than the return difference in circuits for which the absolute value of e^{θ_0} is much greater than that of e^{θ}.

The use of equation (4–22) will be illustrated in more detail by a consideration of three different situations. As a first example, let it be supposed that W is the transconductance of one of the tubes in a normal feedback amplifier. We may suppose for concreteness that the normal gain e^{θ} is 40 db. The transmission e^{θ_0} which is obtained when W vanishes will depend somewhat upon the type of circuit which has been chosen. If either the input or the output is a balanced bridge, so that the β circuit and the line are conjugate, for example, this quantity is zero. In other circumstances it will not be precisely zero but we can estimate its value as -40 db from the general rule that the external gain is equal to the β circuit loss. Thus, the ratio e^{θ_0}/e^{θ} is of the order of magnitude of -80 db and the distinction between return difference and sensitivity is entirely negligible.

As a second example, let it be supposed that W is in the β circuit. It may be taken to represent a shunt impedance, a series admittance, or the transconductance of the final tube in the circuit shown later by Fig. 4.9. In any of these cases setting $W = 0$ opens the feedback so that e^{θ_0} is much greater than e^{θ}. Variations in W are thus much more important in affecting the final transmission characteristic than a calculation of the return voltage would indicate. This is, of course, to be expected for elements in the β circuit.

The third situation is represented by the circuit shown previously by Fig. 4.5. If this structure is taken as a complete feedback amplifier, the situation is essentially the same as that first described. The only difference results from the fact that, since the circuit contains only a single tube, θ_0 and θ would probably be numerically smaller than was assumed there. We might suppose, for example, that the ratio e^{θ_0}/e^{θ} is -30 db. This would still give a negligible distinction between return difference and sensitivity for most applications. An entirely different situation, on the other hand, may be obtained if the circuit is the last stage of a double loop amplifier. In these circumstances θ_0 and θ refer to the transmission characteristics of the complete amplifier and in virtue of the feedback around the principal loop this may not be much affected even by a considerable change in the transmission of the last tube. For example, if the normal feedback around the principal loop is 40 db, the assumed decrease of 30 db in the gain of the circuit of Fig. 4.5 when W vanishes will still leave a net feedback of 10 db around the principal loop. The difference between e^{θ_0} and e^{θ} is thus only that due to the change in the $\mu\beta$ effect in the principal loop caused by the reduction from 40 to 10 db. It is clear therefore that F will be much smaller than S in (4–20), so that the actual stabilization of the circuit against variations in the last tube is much greater than would be indicated by a computation of the return voltage on that tube.*

4.12. *Reference Value for W*

The method of computing sensitivity which we have thus far considered consists essentially in separating out the directly transmitted component

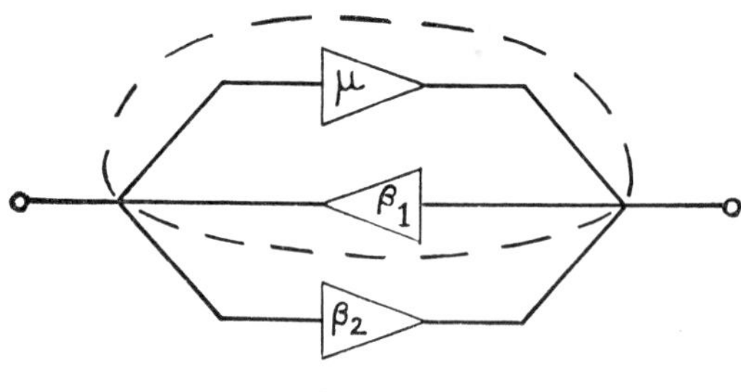

FIG. 4.7

of the total output current, so that in effect it becomes the origin from which the net output current is computed. This is illustrated for an ordinary single loop amplifier by Fig. 4.7. The actual bilateral β circuit in the amplifier is represented symbolically as the sum of the two unilateral

* A physical interpretation of this apparently surprising result can be obtained by noticing that in the multiple loop structure voltage can be returned from the plate of the last tube to its grid by two different paths. The first passes through the principal β circuit and the first stages of the forward circuit, while the second passes directly through the local feedback elements. These two paths together can be regarded as forming a feedback amplifier, the μ circuit of which is the first path, while the β circuit is represented by the second. Under the conditions which have been assumed, there is a net gain around the complete feedback loop of this amplifier and the insertion of the feedback path must therefore diminish its gain. The insertion of the local feedback elements in the final structure, in other words, reduces the return voltage on the last tube.

Speaking approximately, the difference between F and S is an indication that this effect should be neglected. The return voltage which most nearly represents the effective stabilization of the circuit against variations in W is that which would be obtained if the local feedback network were omitted. To a first approximation, the insertion of the local feedback circuit does not affect the feedback on the last tube, but it does of course affect the feedback on the remaining tubes by changing the transmission characteristic around the principal loop. This is discussed in more detail in a later chapter.

components β_1 and β_2. If we suppose that the variable element W is here identified with the whole μ circuit, the component β_2 will provide the directly transmitted term. The use of this term as a reference is equivalent to saying that the contribution of β_2 to the final output is to be considered separately from the contribution of the ideal feedback amplifier represented by the combination of μ and β_1 enclosed by the broken lines.

As an alternative to this procedure, we may also take account of the direct transmission term by changing the origin from which the variable element W is measured. In the circuit of Fig. 4.7, for example, we might

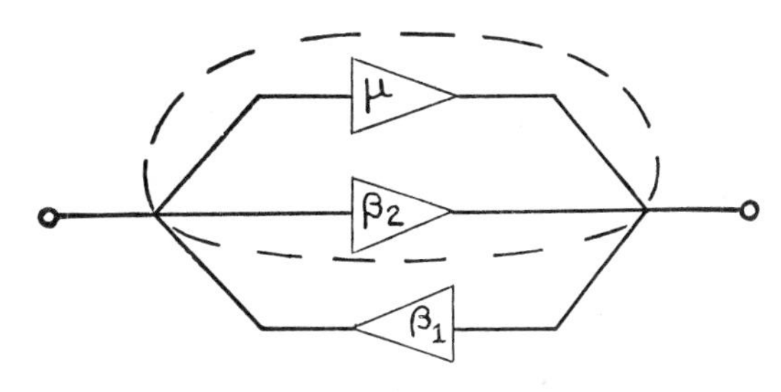

FIG. 4.8

begin by lumping μ and β_2 together, as shown by Fig. 4.8. The structure thus becomes an ideal single loop amplifier, without direct transmission, in which the effective forward gain is $\mu' = \mu + \beta_2$. This is equivalent to computing μ from the origin $-\beta_2$ rather than from zero. The use of an offset reference point for the variable element in this manner is merely an unnecessary complication in most elementary situations, where the methods we have already developed are adequate to deal with the problem. It is worth some attention, however, since in certain circuits it leads eventually to a simplified analysis. This will appear more clearly in Chapter VI.

For the general case the new origin for W will be called the *reference value* of W. It will be symbolized by W_0 and is specified by the

Definition: The reference value of any element is that value which gives zero transmission through the circuit as a whole when all other elements of the circuit have their normal values.

It was indicated earlier in the chapter that return difference computations could in general be based upon any arbitrary reference value for W. From this point of view, W_0 is only a special case which is called *the* reference in recognition of the unique output current to which it leads. The reference condition is evidently somewhat like a bridge balance and expressing W in terms of its departure from W_0 is similar to expressing the impedance of one arm of a bridge in terms of its departure from the impedance which would give an exact balance, rather than in terms of its actual value. It will be recalled that this is the device which was used to simplify the analysis of the circuit in Fig. 4.4.

It is apparent from such an expression as (4–10) that W_0 is given, for unilateral and bilateral elements respectively, by

$$W_0 = -\frac{\Delta_{12}^0}{\Delta_{1243}}, \tag{4–23}$$

and

$$W_0 = -\frac{\Delta_{12}^0}{\Delta_{1233}}. \tag{4–24}$$

If we let W' represent the departure, $W - W_0$, from the reference value, such an equation as (4–10) therefore becomes

$$e^\theta = \frac{W'\Delta_{1243}}{\Delta^0 - \dfrac{\Delta_{12}^0}{\Delta_{1243}}\Delta_{43} + W'\Delta_{43}} W_R. \tag{4–25}$$

This expression has the same form as a function of W' as the original equation (4–10) had as a function of W when we assumed $\Delta_{12}^0 = 0$. Thus we can apply to it the procedures we used previously to establish equation (4–15) for the sensitivity in the case of zero direct transmission. Since a given percentage change in W' will not be equal to the same percentage change in W, unless W and W' happen to be equal, however, the " sensitivity " computed from (4–25) will not in general be equal to the sensitivity defined in (4–7) or (4–8). To prevent confusion, therefore, the result of the present computation will be called the *relative sensitivity*, symbolized by S'. With this understanding, we can evidently write

$$S' = \frac{1}{\dfrac{\partial\theta}{\partial \log W'}} = 1 + W'\frac{\Delta_{43}}{\Delta'} = \frac{\Delta}{\Delta'}, \tag{4–26}$$

where the symbol Δ' is given by

$$\Delta' = \Delta^0 - \frac{\Delta_{12}^0}{\Delta_{1243}}\Delta_{43}, \tag{4–27}$$

and evidently represents the value assumed by Δ when $W' = 0$. If (4–27) is simplified by means of (4–13), the expression for S' can also be written as

$$S' = 1 - W'\frac{\Delta_{43}\Delta_{1243}}{\Delta_{13}\Delta_{42}} = -\frac{\Delta\Delta_{1243}}{\Delta_{13}\Delta_{42}}. \tag{4–28}$$

It is evident that there is a complete formal parallelism between this analysis and that of an ordinary circuit with zero direct transmission. For example, (4–26) is exactly like (4–15) except for the substitution of W' for W and Δ' for Δ^0. These, however, are exactly the modifications which are made in converting a return difference for zero reference into a return difference for the reference W_0. We therefore have the

Theorem: The relative sensitivity for any element W is equal to the return difference of W for the reference W_0.

There remain the problems of determining S' from more immediately measurable quantities and of relating S' to the actual sensitivity S. Of a variety of equations which can be used to determine S', perhaps the simplest is

$$S' = \frac{F(W)}{F(W_0)}, \tag{4–29}$$

where $F(W)$ is, as usual, the return difference for W when W has its normal value, and $F(W_0)$ is the return difference for W, calculated for $W = W_0$. This result follows immediately from (4–5). Another simple formula, useful in special circumstances, is

$$S' = \frac{e^{\theta_\infty}}{e^{\theta_\infty} - e^{\theta}}, \tag{4–30}$$

where e^{θ_∞} stands for $(\Delta_{1243}/\Delta_{43})W_R$ and is, from (4–10), the transmission through the system when the variable element W is infinite. If W represents a tube, this condition is, of course, an unrealizable one. It is also possible to determine S' from measurements made when $W = 0$, by modifying the circuit in certain special ways. The development of these methods, however, is postponed until Chapter VI.

The most straightforward relation between S' and S is probably

$$S = \frac{W'}{W} S' = \left(1 - \frac{W_0}{W}\right) S'. \tag{4–31}$$

This equation can be established immediately if we recall that the distinction between S and S' is due only to the fact that a given actual change in the physical network will produce different percentage changes in W and W' when these two quantities are unequal. Other useful formulae for the relation between S and S' are

$$S = \frac{F}{F - 1} (S' - 1), \tag{4–32}$$

and

$$S = S' + \frac{e^{\theta_0}}{e^{\theta} - e^{\theta_0}}. \tag{4–33}$$

They are both readily established from the preceding general equations for F, S, and S' and the identity (4–13). The various situations which may arise in these equations for different relations between e^{θ_0} and e^{θ} can be illustrated again by the examples used in the discussion of equation (4–22).

4.13. *Reference Value of W as an Index of Location in the $\mu\beta$ Loop*

If we exclude the special problems presented by multiple loop amplifiers, the introduction of the reference value W_0 into computations of sensitivity is, in a broad sense, the analytical counterpart of the physical fact that the properties of feedback circuits vary with the location of the element in the loop. It corresponds in other words to the fact that the stabilizing and distortion reducing properties of feedback hold only for elements in the μ circuit. Since we cannot, at best, decide what part of the complete loop is

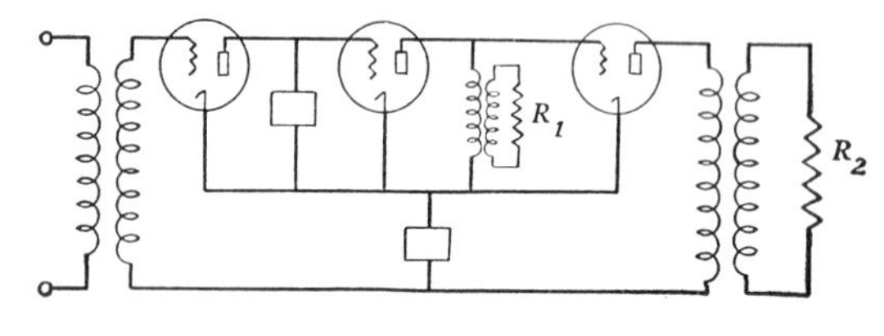

FIG. 4.9

μ and what part is β until we have chosen the input and output terminals, these properties thus depend not so much upon the fact that a feedback loop exists as they do upon the location of the element in question with respect to the transmission path which is eventually of interest. The reference value W_0, since it depends upon the particular choice of input and output terminals, takes this factor into account.

As the preceding examples have shown, the reference value for an element in the μ circuit is ordinarily quite small so that with a large return voltage the effective sensitivity is also large. When the element is in the β circuit, on the other hand, the value of W which will produce zero transmission in the complete system is in general large and variations in W when computed against this extreme reference correspond to relatively little stabilization of the final amplifier transmission characteristics.

The way in which the reference value appears as an index of location can be illustrated concretely by the circuit of Fig. 4.9. The structure is a normal single loop feedback amplifier with the output impedance taken as R_2, with the exception that the second interstage includes a transformer-resistance combination instead of some more conventional configuration. Letting W represent the transconductance of the output tube and assuming that the reference value for W is negligibly small, we readily find that

$$\frac{dE_R}{E_R} = \frac{\Delta^0}{\Delta}\frac{dW}{W} = \frac{1}{1+T}\frac{dW}{W}, \tag{4–34}$$

where $T = W(\Delta_{43}/\Delta^0)$ and can be identified with the negative of the transmission characteristic around the complete loop. This expresses the familiar result that feedback reduces the effect of variations in the tube gain by the factor $1 - \mu\beta$.

Let it be supposed now that the output impedance is taken as R_1, but that R_2 is retained as an ordinary circuit element. The feedback loop, regarded as a complete loop, is exactly the same as it was before. The change in the choice of output impedance has, however, transferred the last tube to the β circuit so that we may expect that the stabilizing properties of feedback have disappeared for variations in the gain of this tube. The situation can be analyzed by using the formula for relative sensitivity given by equation (4–26). If we set $\Delta' = \Delta - W'\Delta_{43}$, this formula can be written as

$$\frac{dE_R}{E_R} = \frac{\Delta - W'\Delta_{43}}{\Delta}\frac{dW}{W'}. \tag{4–35}$$

We now determine the W_0 which will lead to zero transmission through the complete amplifier. In the present instance W_0 must obviously be infinite since zero transmission can be obtained only with an infinite β circuit gain. If W_0 is infinite, however, W' must also be infinite and (4–35) therefore reduces to

$$\frac{dE_R}{E_R} = -\frac{\Delta_{43}}{\Delta}\,dW. \tag{4–36}$$

Upon multiplying and dividing the right-hand side of (4–36) by W and Δ^0 and comparing with (4–34), this becomes

$$\frac{dE_R}{E_R} = -\frac{\Delta^0}{\Delta}\frac{W\Delta_{43}}{\Delta^0}\frac{dW}{W} = \frac{-T}{1+T}\frac{dW}{W}, \tag{4–37}$$

where T still represents $-\mu\beta$ for normal operation. We can readily verify that this is the correct formula by direct differentiation of the ordinary equation for the gain of a feedback amplifier as a function of β.

CHAPTER V

General Theorems for Feedback Circuits — A

5.1. *Introduction*

This chapter and the one which follows will continue the general discussion of feedback circuits begun in the preceding chapter in terms of the definitions of return difference and sensitivity which were established there. They have for their principal object the development of general theorems on the relation between these quantities and impedance, gain, non-linear distortion, etc. The theorems of the present chapter are developed from simple mathematical identities which remain valid whatever the reference values for the elements may be. They are thus stated in terms of the return difference for a general reference, including the relative sensitivity and the return difference for zero reference as special cases.

5.2. *Impedance of an Active Circuit**

The first general theorem relates to the effect which feedback may have upon the impedance measured between any two points of the circuit. In addition to its general interest the theorem is of particular application with respect to the calculation of the return difference for bilateral elements, since it was shown in the preceding chapter that that depended upon the impedance of the circuit to which the element was connected. In developing the theorem it is supposed that the impedance which would be obtained in the absence of active elements is first determined by ordinary circuit methods. The theorem then is concerned with the modification produced in this impedance by the addition of the active elements. This is, of course, the heart of the problem.

The fact that the active elements must in general produce some effect is easily seen if we consider, for example, the input impedance of an ordinary feedback amplifier. By definition this impedance must be the ratio of the input voltage to the current which flows through the line into the amplifier. The net current which flows past the input terminals, however, is a composite of the current which would flow if we considered only the passive elements and of the current which is returned to the source through the feedback circuit. The presence of this feedback current may obviously

* The material of this section is a modified version of results originally due to R. B. Blackman (*B.S.T.J.*, October, 1943).

make the impedance of the amplifier quite different from the impedance which we would measure if the tubes were not operating.

Although the impedance of an active circuit may be quite different from that of the passive structure the relation between the two is easily built up. Let it be supposed, for example, that we are interested in the active impedance Z which would be measured from the terminals of a resistanceless generator inserted in the nth mesh of the circuit. This is obviously

$$Z = \frac{\Delta}{\Delta_{nn}}. \tag{5–1}$$

Now suppose that we choose any element, W, within the network. It is convenient to assume that W represents some mutual impedance Z_{ij}, although the final results are the same whether W is a unilateral or a bilateral element. We can rewrite (5–1) as

$$Z = \frac{\Delta}{\Delta_{nn}} = \frac{\Delta^0}{\Delta_{nn}^0}\frac{\Delta}{\Delta^0}\frac{\Delta_{nn}^0}{\Delta_{nn}}, \tag{5–2}$$

where, as in the preceding chapter, Δ^0 and Δ_{nn}^0 represent Δ and Δ_{nn} when $W = 0$.

In equation (5–2), Δ^0/Δ_{nn}^0 is evidently the impedance which would be measured if $W = 0$. Assuming that W or Z_{ij} is the mutual impedance of one of the vacuum tubes, then, we can call this the passive impedance Z_0, or the impedance which would be measured if this tube were dead. Moreover, Δ/Δ^0 is the return difference for W with the circuit in its normal condition, that is, with the terminals between which Z is measured shorted together. In addition, Δ_{nn} and Δ_{nn}^0 are the coefficients of Z_{nn} in Δ and Δ^0 respectively. The ratio $\Delta_{nn}/\Delta_{nn}^0$ is therefore the limit approached by Δ/Δ^0 as Z_{nn} becomes indefinitely great. It consequently follows that $\Delta_{nn}/\Delta_{nn}^0$ represents the return difference for W when the self-impedance of the nth mesh is made infinite, or in other words when the terminals between which Z is measured are left open. We can therefore write equation (5–2) as

$$Z = Z_0\frac{F(0)}{F(\infty)}, \tag{5–3}$$

where $F(0)$ and $F(\infty)$ are the return differences for W when the terminals between which Z is measured are respectively short-circuited and open-circuited.

If we base the analysis on admittances instead of impedances the result is the same and we can write

$$Y = Y_0\frac{F(0)}{F(\infty)}, \tag{5–4}$$

where $F(0)$ and $F(\infty)$ now represent the return differences with respect to W when zero and infinite admittance, respectively, are added across the terminals between which Y is determined.

Equations (5–3) and (5–4) describe the impedance or admittance at any part of a feedback circuit in terms of the impedance or admittance which would be obtained with any arbitrary element vanishing, and the return difference for that element. If the arbitrary element W is the mutual impedance or transconductance of a vacuum tube, therefore, we can discount the effect of this active element in the circuit. In ordinary feedback amplifiers zero gain in any one tube will interrupt the feedback circuit so that the actual impedance or admittance can be computed directly from (5–3) or (5–4) by choosing any one of the tubes as W. In more complicated cases a single dead tube may not reduce the calculation of impedances to the completely passive case. Evidently, however, by starting with all the tubes as dead and applying (5–3) and (5–4) repeatedly as each tube in turn is assigned its normal gain we can cover all circuits.

The analysis used in developing (5–3) and (5–4) has been based upon the assumption that the reference for W is zero. Since (5–2) is merely an identical form of (5–1), however, the zero value for W is a matter of indifference and we can choose any reference we like as long as we choose the same reference for both F's. The general result can therefore be stated in the following words.

Theorem: The ratio of the impedances seen at any point of a network when a given element W is assigned two different values is equal to the ratio of the return differences for W when the terminals between which the impedance is measured are first short-circuited and then open-circuited, if the return differences are computed by letting the first value of W be the operating value and the second the reference.

The relation between feedback and impedance can also be stated in another way. Let it be supposed that an arbitrary impedance Z_n is added in series with the nth mesh, and let Δ' and $\Delta^{0\prime}$ represent Δ and Δ^0, respectively, after the introduction of Z_n. The return difference for any W after Z_n is added can be written as

$$F = \frac{\Delta'}{\Delta^{0\prime}} = \frac{\Delta + Z_n\Delta_{nn}}{\Delta^0 + Z_n\Delta^0_{nn}}. \tag{5–5}$$

Now let Z_n be so chosen that $F = 0$. Upon comparing the result with (5–1) we readily establish the

Theorem: The impedance seen in any mesh is the negative of the impedance whose insertion in that mesh would give zero return difference for an arbitrarily chosen element in the circuit.

This is an obvious theorem in the light of the discussion of stability given in a later chapter since it will appear that either a zero return difference or zero impedance at any frequency corresponds to the possibility of a natural oscillation in the circuit at that frequency.

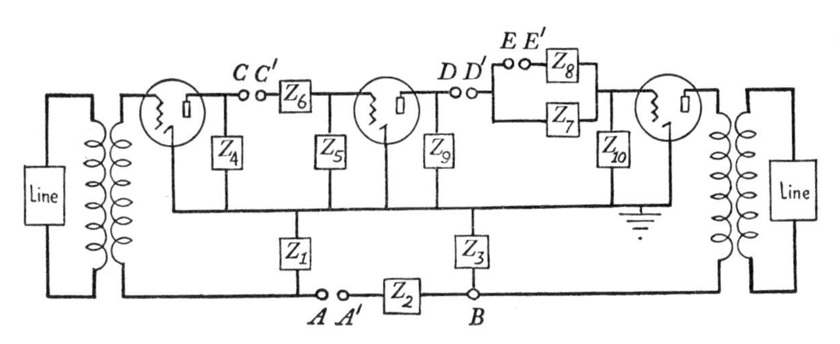

FIG. 5.1

5.3. *Examples of Active Impedances*

To exemplify these relations we will consider the series feedback amplifier shown by Fig. 5.1. Let the Z of equation (5–3) be the impedance which would be measured in series with any one of the series connected branches such as Z_2, Z_6 or either of the high side transformer windings. In other words it is the impedance which would be measured between any such pairs of terminals as AA', CC', or DD' in Fig. 5.1.

It will also be assumed that the W of equations (5–1) and (5–2) is the transconductance of any one of the tubes. With terminals AA', CC', or DD' shorted together the return difference with respect to W is $F(0) = 1 - \mu\beta$, where $\mu\beta$ is the transmission around the loop computed in the normal fashion. With the terminals opened, on the other hand, the return difference with respect to W is unity. Equation (5–3) consequently gives

$$Z = Z_0(1 - \mu\beta), \tag{5–6}$$

where Z_0 is the impedance which would be measured with one of the tubes dead and is evidently the ordinary passive impedance. The impedance measured in any series line is thus much larger than the passive impedance. For the impedance between A and A' for example we find

$$Z = (1 - \mu\beta)(Z_1 + Z_2 + Z_3), \tag{5–7}$$

upon the assumption that the input and output impedances of the tubes are very large in comparison with the impedances in the β circuit.

Next consider the apparent impedance which would be measured between any such points as A or C and ground. We now find that the normal return ratio will be obtained when the impedance connected between A or C and ground is infinite and that the return ratio vanishes when the terminals are short-circuited. In other words $F(0) = 1$ and $F(\infty) = 1 - \mu\beta$. Equation (5–3) thus gives

$$Z = \frac{Z_0}{1 - \mu\beta}. \tag{5–8}$$

The impedance measured across the path of the feedback loop is therefore reduced by feedback. For the impedance between A and ground, for example, we have

$$Z = \frac{1}{1 - \mu\beta} \frac{Z_1(Z_2 + Z_3)}{Z_1 + Z_2 + Z_3}. \tag{5–9}$$

As a more complicated example we may consider the impedance measured across the terminals E, E' in Fig. 5.1. Here we have

$$Z_0 = Z_8 + \frac{Z_7(Z_9 + Z_{10})}{Z_7 + Z_9 + Z_{10}}, \tag{5–10}$$

while

$$\begin{aligned} F(0) &= 1 - \mu\beta, \\ F(\infty) &= 1 - \mu\beta \frac{1}{Z_7 + Z_8}\left[Z_8 + \frac{Z_7(Z_9 + Z_{10})}{Z_7 + Z_9 + Z_{10}}\right], \end{aligned} \tag{5–11}$$

the factor multiplying $\mu\beta$ in the second equation being obtained by calculating the change produced in the transmission characteristic of the interstage when E, E' is open-circuited. The substitution of these values in equation (5–3) then gives the impedance sought for. If in particular we assume that $\mu\beta$ is very great the result becomes

$$Z = Z_7 + Z_8. \tag{5–12}$$

This result, of course, might have been foreseen from (5–6). If we consider that Z_7 and Z_8 together represent a series impedance it follows from this equation that the impedance of the circuit to which they are connected must be very high if the feedback is large. Only Z_7 and Z_8 therefore need be considered in determining the impedance at terminals E, E'.

These calculations have been based upon the first of the two theorems given in the preceding section. The same results follow from the second theorem. As an example, we may return to the discussion of the effect of feedback on a series impedance, as expressed by (5–6). Let the impedance whose insertion in the series arm would reduce the return difference to zero be represented by Z'. Its insertion in series with Z_0 will produce the loss $Z_0/(Z' + Z_0)$ in the transmission around the loop. For the return difference to vanish, however, the loop transmission, $\mu\beta$, must be reduced to unity. We therefore have

$$\frac{Z_0}{Z' + Z_0} = \frac{1}{\mu\beta}, \tag{5–13}$$

or

$$Z' = (\mu\beta - 1)Z_0, \tag{5–14}$$

which is the negative of the active impedance given by (5–6).

5.4. *Feedback for Bilateral Elements*

A knowledge of the active impedances of the circuit makes it a simple matter to compute the return differences and sensitivities of its bilateral elements in accordance with the methods of the preceding chapter. As an example we may choose the impedance Z_6 of Fig. 5.1. By the previous analysis, the return ratio for this element is equal to the ratio of its impedance or admittance to the impedance or admittance of the circuit which it faces, the return difference is equal to the return ratio increased by unity, and the sensitivity is equal to the return difference suitably modified to take account of direct transmission. If we exclude the slight trickle of current directly through the β circuit, zero output current is obtained when the branch Z_6 is an open circuit. It is obviously convenient, therefore, to use an admittance analysis, in which case the direct transmission term is zero and the sensitivity can be taken equal to the return difference.

It follows from (5–3) that the impedance seen at terminals C, C' of Fig. 5.1 is $(1 - \mu\beta)(Z_4 + Z_5 + Z_6)$ and the admittance which Z_6 faces is therefore the reciprocal of $(1 - \mu\beta)(Z_4 + Z_5 + Z_6) - Z_6$. Upon dividing the admittance of Z_6 by this admittance the return ratio and the return difference or sensitivity for the element Z_6 are obtained in the form

$$T = Y_6[(1 - \mu\beta)(Z_4 + Z_5 + Z_6) - Z_6],$$

and

$$F = S = (1 - \mu\beta)\frac{Z_4 + Z_5 + Z_6}{Z_6}. \tag{5–15}$$

The factor $(1 - \mu\beta)$ in this expression is self-explanatory. The remaining factor $(Z_4 + Z_5 + Z_6)/Z_6$ reflects the fact that the μ circuit gain does not vary in strict proportion to Z_6 because of the presence of the other impedances. If Z_6 were very small, for example, its impedance might vary considerably in per cent without greatly affecting μ and a corresponding term in the sensitivity expression must therefore be included in virtue of the fundamental definition given by equation (4–8) of the preceding chapter.

If we consider a shunt impedance such as Z_4 the procedure is essentially the same. In this case, the reference condition is a short circuit and it is convenient to use impedances rather than admittances in the analysis. Since the impedance which Z_4 faces, however, is now reduced by feedback the ratio between Z_4 and the impedance of the rest of the circuit is correspondingly increased. The essential result is of the same general type as equation (5–15).

As a third example we may consider the impedance Z_2 in the β circuit of Fig. 5.1. So far as the calculation of return ratio and return difference is concerned, the situation with respect to this element is exactly the same as it was for Z_6, and we can make use of (5–15) again, with appropriate substitution of Z_1, Z_2, and Z_3 for Z_4, Z_5, and Z_6. The presence of a large direct transmission term, however, complicates the computation of sensitivity. It is simplest to begin by determining the relative sensitivity S'. We can evidently secure zero transmission from the amplifier as a whole by assigning the β circuit a large gain equal to that of the μ circuit and a phase which will cancel the μ circuit output. The reference value for Z_2 must therefore be very nearly $-(Z_1 + Z_3)$ or, in other words, very nearly the negative of the passive impedance which it faces. The effective impedance, W', can therefore be taken as $Z_1 + Z_2 + Z_3$. The impedance which W' faces must be the difference, $\mu\beta(Z_1 + Z_2 + Z_3)$, between W' itself and the total impedance calculated in equation (5–7). The relative and absolute sensitivity are readily found from these facts, plus the relation $S'/S = W'/W$, to be

$$S' = \frac{1 - \mu\beta}{\mu\beta},$$

and

$$S = \frac{1 - \mu\beta}{\mu\beta} \frac{Z_1 + Z_2 + Z_3}{Z_2}, \tag{5–16}$$

and are obviously small in normal situations. The result is easily checked by direct differentiation of the gain equation for the amplifier in accordance with the fundamental definition of Chapter IV. It is interesting to notice that the difference between the very large sensitivity represented by equation (5–15) and the low value obtained in equation (5–16) is the result entirely of the difference in the two reference conditions. The situations otherwise are exactly the same.

5.5. *Effect of Feedback on Input and Output Impedances of Amplifiers*

The distinction between the active and passive impedances of a feedback circuit is particularly important in considering the effect of feedback on the impedance which an amplifier presents to the line. The principal results, for the basic connections described in Chapter III, can be listed as follows.

1. The active impedance of a series feedback amplifier is $(1 - \mu\beta)$ times its passive impedance. Since the input and output impedances of tubes are normally high anyway, the active impedance is, in general, almost infinite. A similar statement can be made for a cathode feedback circuit.
2. The active impedance of a shunt feedback amplifier is $1/(1 - \mu\beta)$ times its passive impedance. It is thus relatively low.
3. The active impedance of a balanced bridge amplifier is the same as its passive impedance. This connection is therefore intermediate between the series and shunt connections.
4. If the balance of the bridge in the circuit of the preceding paragraph is disturbed by a change in the final tube impedance, the reflection coefficient between the active impedance so obtained and the active impedance before the change is $1/(1 - \mu\beta)$ times the reflection coefficient which would be obtained if the circuit were passive, where $\mu\beta$ represents the loop transmission after the change is made.

The first three of these statements can be dismissed briefly. The line impedance in a series or shunt feedback amplifier is merely a special case of a general series or shunt impedance, the results for which have already been given by equations (5–6) and (5–8). In the balanced bridge circuit, the bridge balance produces conjugacy between the line and the β circuit. It follows from this that the loop transmission is independent of the line impedance.* We therefore have $F(0) = F(\infty)$ in (5–3), so that feedback does not affect the impedance.

The fourth statement may require amplification. In the theoretical balanced bridge connection the tube impedance is one of the arms through which the balance is obtained. Since tube impedances are ordinarily quite variable, the balance which can be relied upon in practice is imperfect. Moreover, it may be necessary to shunt the tube with a dissipative branch

* This follows readily from the principle of reciprocity. See, for example, the discussion in the next chapter under the heading "Reference Feedback as a Balanced Bridge."

in order to secure an impedance whose phase angle and magnitude are appropriate to produce a balance with permissible impedances in the other arms of the bridge. This is particularly unfortunate in an output bridge because of the wastage of output level to which it leads. The final statement says in effect that if the feedback is large the departures produced in the impedance which the amplifier presents to the line will be extremely small even when no effort is made to control the impedance of the tube. Naturally, however, the other property of a bridge circuit, that the loop transmission is independent of the line impedance, will no longer hold.

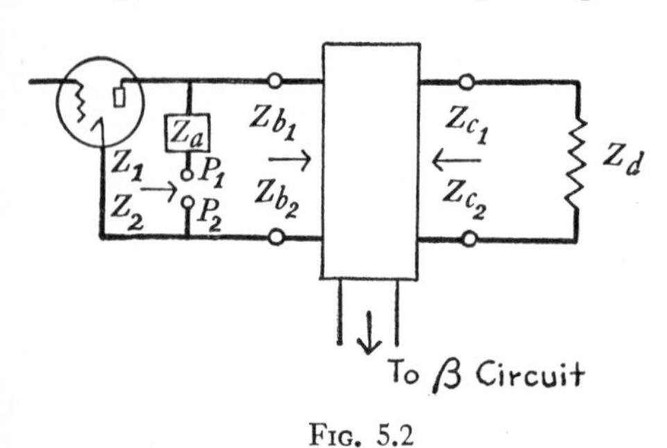

FIG. 5.2

This effect of feedback is easily demonstrated by using (5–3) in two different ways. Let Z_a in Fig. 5.2 represent the impedance whose removal produces the disturbance under consideration. It will be supposed that with Z_a present the bridge is perfectly balanced. Let Z_d represent the line impedance. Let Z_{b1} and Z_{b2} represent respectively the *passive* impedances of the circuit to the right of Z_a when Z_d has its normal value and when Z_d is replaced by a short circuit. Finally, let Z_{c1} and Z_{c2} represent respectively the *active* impedances looking into the amplifier when Z_a is present and when Z_a is removed by opening the terminals P_1, P_2.

The first step is the computation of the active impedance Z_1 looking into the terminals P_1, P_2 when the neighboring impedance is taken as Z_{b1}. Let this be the Z of (5–3) and let the F's of this equation refer to the last tube. Let the loop transmission with Z_a absent be represented by $\mu\beta$ so that $F(\infty) = 1 - \mu\beta$. From ordinary circuit considerations, the introduction of Z_a changes the loop transmission to $[Z_a/(Z_a + Z_{b1})]\mu\beta$. Moreover, the passive impedance Z_0 is $Z_a + Z_{b1}$. We therefore have

$$Z_1 = (Z_a + Z_{b1}) \frac{1 - \dfrac{Z_a}{Z_a + Z_{b1}} \mu\beta}{1 - \mu\beta}. \tag{5–17}$$

Now consider the impedance Z_2 corresponding to Z_{b2}. The passive impedance becomes $Z_a + Z_{b2}$. $F(0)$ is the same as it was in developing (5–17), since with Z_a present the bridge is balanced and a change in the line impedance does not affect the feedback loop. The ratio between the loop transmissions with Z_a present and Z_a absent is $Z_a/(Z_a + Z_{b2})$. We therefore have

$$Z_2 = (Z_a + Z_{b2}) \frac{1 - \dfrac{Z_a}{Z_a + Z_{b1}} \mu\beta}{1 - \dfrac{Z_a + Z_{b2}}{Z_a + Z_{b1}} \mu\beta}. \tag{5-18}$$

In this computation the F's of (5–3) have referred to the last tube. We now apply (5–3) again with the F's taken with respect to Z_d. It follows from (5–3) that the ratio of the return differences for Z_d with Z_a present and absent must be the same as the ratio of Z_1 to Z_2. We can therefore write

$$\frac{\dfrac{Z_{c1} + Z_d}{Z_{c1}}}{\dfrac{Z_{c2} + Z_d}{Z_{c2}}} = \frac{Z_1}{Z_2}, \tag{5-19}$$

or

$$\frac{Z_d(Z_{c2} - Z_{c1})}{Z_{c1}(Z_{c2} + Z_d)} = \frac{Z_1}{Z_2} - 1$$

$$= \frac{1}{1 - \mu\beta} \frac{Z_{b1} - Z_{b2}}{Z_a + Z_{b2}}. \tag{5-20}$$

If we set $Z_d = Z_{c1}$ the left-hand side of (5–20) is the reflection coefficient between the active impedances of the network before and after the removal of Z_a. On the right-hand side all the quantities except the factor $1 - \mu\beta$ represent the network in its passive state. The original statement is therefore proved.

5.6. *Use of Impedance Measurements to Determine Feedback*

The theorems in the first section were developed as a means of computing the active impedance of a circuit when the return differences are known. In practice, however, they are perhaps more frequently applied as a means of determining the return difference from impedance measurements. This is often a more convenient method of obtaining the return difference than a direct transmission measurement would be, since it does not require opening the feedback loop. The method can be applied even to unstable structures by including in the measurement a known impedance of a magnitude which will stabilize the circuit.

5.7. *Relation between Feedback for Two Elements*

The process used to develop the formula for active impedances can also be applied to obtain a theorem relating the return differences for two elements in the circuit under actual operating conditions to the return differences which would be found for each element if the other vanished. Let the two elements be represented by W_1 and W_2. To express the fact that the determinant of the system will depend upon both W_1 and W_2, we may write it, in general, as $\Delta(W_1,W_2)$. Then $\Delta(0,W_2)$ represents the determinant when W_1 is zero, $\Delta(W_1,0)$ the determinant when W_2 is zero, and $\Delta(0,0)$ the determinant when both W_1 and W_2 are zero.

The return difference for either element can be expressed as the ratio of the complete determinant to the determinant obtained when that element vanishes. Letting F_1 and F_2 be the return differences for W_1 and W_2, respectively, these relations, in our present notation, are

$$F_1 = \frac{\Delta(W_1,W_2)}{\Delta(0,W_2)},$$
$$F_2 = \frac{\Delta(W_1,W_2)}{\Delta(W_1,0)}, \qquad (5\text{–}21)$$

or

$$\frac{F_1}{F_2} = \frac{\Delta(W_1,0)}{\Delta(0,W_2)} = \frac{\Delta(W_1,0)}{\Delta(0,0)}\frac{\Delta(0,0)}{\Delta(0,W_2)}$$
$$= \frac{F_1(W_2=0)}{F_2(W_1=0)}. \qquad (5\text{–}22)$$

Equation (5–22) is evidently unaffected if the W's are assigned any reference values, as long as the reference values are taken as the same on both sides of the equation. We can therefore state the

Theorem: The ratio between the actual return differences for any two elements, for any reference conditions, is the same as the ratio which would be obtained if the return difference for each element were computed with the other element at its reference value.

As an example, we may take W_1 as Y_6 in Fig. 5.1 and W_2 as the transconductance of one of the tubes. We see by inspection that $F_2(W_1 = 0) = 1$ and $F_1(W_2 = 0) = (Z_4 + Z_5 + Z_6)/Z_6$. The theorem states that the ratio between these two F's will be preserved for any values of the W's. This is, of course, verified by equation (5–15).

5.8. *Thévenin's Theorem in Active Circuits*

The general formula for return difference also can be used to develop another type of identity which is even simpler than those described previously. Let it be supposed, for example, that W represents the transimmittance of the tube whose grid and plate are labeled respectively i and j. W must be a constituent of Z_{ji} or Y_{ji} in the general determinant. The return difference for W can be written, from (4–2), Chapter IV, as

$$F = \frac{\Delta}{\Delta^0} = \frac{\Delta}{\Delta_{ki}} \frac{\Delta_{ki}}{\Delta^0}, \tag{5–23}$$

where Δ^0 represents Δ when $W = 0$ and k is any other node or mesh in the circuit.

In equation (5–23) the determinant Δ_{ki} can equally well be written as Δ^0_{ki} since it contains no terms from the ith column of the original determinant and is therefore independent of W. The ratios Δ_{ki}/Δ and Δ_{ki}/Δ^0 are thus the transmissions* from k to i when W has its normal value and when W vanishes. Moreover, the identity evidently holds equally well if we use any arbitrary value instead of zero as a reference for W. We can therefore draw the following conclusion:

Theorem: The ratio between the transmissions from any point of the network to the grid of a given tube for an arbitrarily chosen reference condition and for the normal operating condition is equal to the return difference of the tube for the chosen reference.

A simple example is furnished by the transmission from the input line to the μ circuit of an ordinary amplifier. The effective signal level on the grid of any tube is $1/(1 - \mu\beta)$ times the level which would exist if that tube were dead.

We can also write the return difference equation as

$$F = \frac{\Delta}{\Delta^0} = \frac{\Delta}{\Delta_{jk}} \frac{\Delta_{jk}}{\Delta^0}. \tag{5–24}$$

The quantities Δ_{jk}/Δ and Δ_{jk}/Δ^0 evidently represent transmissions from the plate to k under normal and reference conditions. We therefore have the

Theorem: The ratio between the transmissions from the plate of a given tube to any point of the network for an arbitrarily chosen reference condition and for the normal operating condition is equal to the return difference of the tube for the chosen reference.

This is best exemplified by the discussion of the following sections.

* "Transmission" is used here as an abbreviation for transfer admittance in a mesh analysis or transfer impedance in a nodal analysis.

If W is a bilateral element the situation is essentially the same except that no distinction need be made between the " grid " and " plate " ends of W. We therefore have the

Theorem: The ratio between the transmissions from a given bilateral element to any point in the network, or vice versa, for an arbitrarily chosen reference condition and for the normal operating condition is equal to the return difference of the given element for the chosen reference.

The last theorem gives a clue to the characterization of the three theorems as a whole. If W is a bilateral element the return difference for W corresponding to any given reference is the ratio of the total immittances seen from W when W has its normal and reference values. But the statement that this is the same as the ratio of the transmissions from k to W under the two conditions is merely another way of expressing Thévenin's theorem.* On this account the group of three theorems on the relation between return difference and transmission will be described as *the generalized Thévenin's theorem*, applicable to unilateral as well as bilateral elements. In other words the return difference for a unilateral element plays the same role in determining the final response that the impedance relations at generator or receiver terminals would play in an ordinary transmission calculation.

5.9. *Computation of* W_0

As an example of these theorems we will consider the determination of the reference W_0 for one of the tubes in the circuit. It will be recalled that W_0 is the value which W must assume in order to provide zero transmission through the complete structure. An equation for W_0 has already been given by (4–23) of the previous chapter but the Δ's which appear in it are not easily recognized as quantities which could be determined by physical measurement. With the help of the generalized Thévenin's theorem of the preceding section it is possible to develop an alternative formula for W_0 involving quantities of more direct physical significance.

Let the input and output of the circuit as a whole and the grid and plate of the tube W be labeled respectively 1, 2, 3, and 4. The quantities $\gamma_1 = \Delta^0_{12}/\Delta^0$, $\gamma_2 = \Delta_{13}/\Delta^0$, $\gamma_3 = \Delta_{42}/\Delta^0$, and $\gamma_4 = \Delta_{43}/\Delta^0$ represent respectively the transmissions from input to output, from input to grid, from plate to output, and from plate to grid, all evaluated on the assump-

* Thévenin's theorem is discussed in most books on communication circuits. See, e.g., Shea, "Transmission Networks and Wave Filters," p. 55, or Terman, "Radio Engineer's Handbook," p. 198.

tion that the tube is dead. It will be supposed that all these transmissions are known.

If we begin with the tube dead, the excitation on the grid for a unit source in the input will be γ_2. The fact that the tube has the residual gain W_0 in the reference condition can therefore be represented by inserting an equivalent generator $-W_0\gamma_2$ in the plate circuit.* If this generator were actually an independent source of current or voltage it would evidently produce the response $-W_0\gamma_2\gamma_3$ in the output. The reference condition could then be established by finding what value of W_0 would lead to exact cancellation between this response and the direct transmission γ_1. But the introduction of the equivalent generator coincides with a change in tube gain from zero to W_0. In accordance with the theorems of the preceding section, this must reduce the transmission from plate to output by a factor equal to the return difference of the tube when $W = W_0$. This last quantity can be found from a knowledge of the transmission γ_4 from plate to grid. The correct relation is thus easily seen to be

$$\frac{W_0\gamma_2\gamma_3}{1 + W_0\gamma_4} = \gamma_1, \tag{5–25}$$

or

$$W_0 = \frac{\gamma_1}{\gamma_2\gamma_3 - \gamma_1\gamma_4}, \tag{5–26}$$

in which all the quantities can be measured directly. The fact that this is actually the same as the original formula for W_0 can be established by means of equation (4–13) of the preceding chapter.

5.10. *Reduction of Distortion by Feedback*

One of the principal practical advantages of feedback is the fact that its use reduces the flow of modulation currents in the load due to the non-linear distortion of the elements in the μ circuit. In order to investigate this, let it be assumed that the non-linear distortion is represented by the addition of a separate " distortion generator " in the plate circuit of the distorting tube, while the circuit itself remains linear. This supposes that the level of the fundamental components of the signal has been established in advance, so that the amount of non-linear distortion can be calculated, and also that the distortion is a small part of the signal, so that second order effects representing " distortion of the distortion " can be ignored. The distortion generator may also be used to represent a source of extraneous noise rather than a source of modulation products.

* The negative sign is due to the phase reversal in the tube.

An appropriate relation can be developed immediately from the generalization of Thévenin's theorem described previously. It is merely necessary to choose the point k to represent the output circuit. The second of the preceding three theorems can then be restated as the

Theorem: The noise or distortion current in the output produced by a prescribed distortion generator in one of the elements of the circuit is equal to the current which would be found with the element in an arbitrarily chosen reference condition divided by the return difference of the element for the chosen reference.

But, if we deal only with the portion of the output current which flows because the given element is activated, the return difference is also a measure of the sensitivity of the circuit to variations in the linear properties of the given element. It thus appears that the contributions of the given element to the distortion and to the fundamental frequency currents in the output are governed by the same laws. This is not surprising if it is recalled that a slight change in the linear properties of a circuit can be represented by the introduction of a small generator at the disturbed point.* The circuit must naturally have the same properties whether the generator represents distortion or a change in the linear characteristics of the circuit.

5.11. *Exact Formula for External Gain with Feedback*

The relation between feedback and external gain is customarily expressed by the statement that the gain is reduced by the amount of feedback. Equation (3–4) of Chapter III, for example, gives this result for the simple analysis in terms of independent μ and β circuits.

If we wish to make very precise gain calculations, this statement suffers from two objections. The first is that the meaning of gain in the absence of feedback is somewhat uncertain, on account of the interaction between the impedances of the μ and β circuits at the ends of the amplifier. It is not perfectly clear whether we should simply remove the feedback circuit entirely in making the calculation of gain before feedback, or whether we should make some allowance for the energy absorption of the β circuit elements at input and output, and if so, what that allowance should be. The second difficulty is the fact that the relation between gain and feedback was developed only for the conventional single loop amplifier. It is not clear how the relation should be applied to other situations, and in particular to situations in which there is an appreciable direct transmission term. As a final example of the methods established in Chapter IV, therefore, we

* See the "Compensation Theorem," in Shea, p. 56, or Terman, loc. cit., p. 198.

will develop an exact expression for the external gain in the presence of feedback.

It is convenient to begin with equation (4–21) of Chapter IV. If we multiply and divide by Δ^0, this equation can be written as

$$e^{\theta} - e^{\theta_0} = \frac{\Delta^0}{\Delta^0 + W\Delta_{43}} \frac{-W\Delta_{13}\Delta_{42}}{\Delta^0\Delta^0} W_R. \tag{5–27}$$

The quantity $\Delta^0/(\Delta^0 + W\Delta_{43})$ in this expression will be recognized as the reciprocal of the return difference F. If we replace the remaining terms by e^{θ_F}, the expression as a whole becomes

$$e^{\theta} - e^{\theta_0} = \frac{1}{F} e^{\theta_F}, \tag{5–28}$$

while if we make use of (4–22), Chapter IV, the equation can also be written as

$$e^{\theta} = \frac{S}{F^2} e^{\theta_F}. \tag{5–29}$$

The quantity e^{θ_F} will be called the *fractionated gain*. It may be regarded as an exact statement of what is meant by "gain before feedback." We notice that it is essentially the product of three factors. Two of them, Δ_{13}/Δ^0 and $(\Delta_{42}/\Delta^0)W_R$, represent, respectively, the transmission from the input to the grid and from the plate to the output with the tube dead. They thus include the input and output impedances of the β circuit just as it stands. The third is the gain W of the tube itself. In a single loop structure the fractionated gain is then the gain which would be realized if it were possible to open the β circuit without affecting its impedance at either end. An example is furnished by the circuit of Fig. 4.5 in the preceding chapter. If this structure is taken as a complete amplifier, the fractionated gain is readily computed to be

$$e^{\theta_F} = -\frac{Z_2}{Z_1 + Z_2 + \dfrac{Z_3(Z_4 + Z_5)}{Z_3 + Z_4 + Z_5}} \frac{Z_4}{\dfrac{(Z_1 + Z_2)Z_3}{Z_1 + Z_2 + Z_3} + Z_4 + Z_5} Z_5 W, \tag{5–30}$$

where Z_5 on the right-hand side is identified with W_R in the general expression (5–27) and the two preceding factors will be recognized as the input-grid and plate-output transmissions, Δ_{13}/Δ^0 and Δ_{42}/Δ^0, for this particular structure.

Equations (5–28) and (5–29) offer alternative ways of treating the gain reduction due to feedback in systems with appreciable direct transmission.

In equation (5–28), the gain reduction is applied only to the surplus of the total output over the direct transmission term. This is the most natural relation if we continue to think of the system as made up of two non-interacting paths in parallel, one of which is simply a fixed structure furnishing the over-all direct transmission, while the other contains the variable W and exhibits the essential phenomena of feedback. Equation (5–29) shows, however, that it is also permissible to apply the gain reduction due to feedback to the complete output provided we take " feedback " to be F^2/S.

Equation (5–27) can be regarded as a relation which is appropriate if we wish to give special attention to the reference condition $W = 0$. The quantities e^{θ_0} and Δ^0 evidently apply to this state. Just as with most of the other equations in this chapter, however, an analogous expression can be developed for any reference. The use of the reference W_0 is of particular interest, since it leads to an alternative " gain before feedback " expression based upon measurements made with an interrupted feedback path. This is discussed in the next chapter.

CHAPTER VI

General Theorems for Feedback Circuits — B

6.1. *Introduction*

This chapter will continue the development of general feedback theorems begun in the preceding chapter. The center of attention in the present chapter, however, is the relative sensitivity, S', and its use in expediting feedback and gain calculations. A large part of the discussion is concerned with multiple loop circuits, where the conception of relative sensitivity is most useful. The chapter can be omitted by readers interested only in simple feedback circuits.

6.2. *Reference Feedback as a Balanced Bridge*

In ordinary circuit calculations we frequently encounter a condition of bridge balance between two branches by means of which transmission calculations can be considerably simplified even when the transmission is not taken directly between the two branches in question. As an example we may consider the calculation of the current which would flow in branch F of Fig. 6.1 as a consequence of a generator in branch A under the assumption that branches B and F are conjugate. Such a problem might be encountered, for example, in connection with the design of a constant R equalizer structure. Since A and B are not conjugate and current must flow in B as a result of the generator in A, it might appear at first sight that the conjugacy condition allows no simplification in computing transmission from A to F. It follows from the principle of reciprocity,* however, that the current flowing in F as a result of the generator in A must be equal to the current which would flow in A when the generator is inserted in F. When the generator is inserted in F, however, no current can flow in B and we can consequently choose any value we like for this impedance without affecting the result. Obviously convenient values of B are zero and infinity, since with either one the circuit is reduced to a simple series-shunt

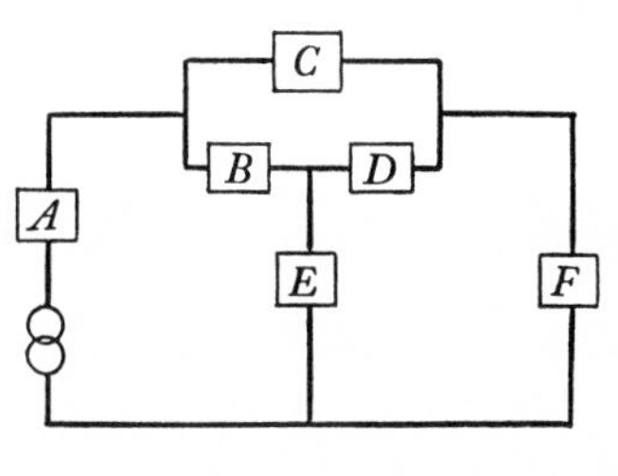

Fig. 6.1

* See Shea or Terman, loc. cit., pp. 52 and 198, respectively, or Guillemin "Communication Networks," Vol. I, p. 152.

configuration which is readily computed. A third convenient value for B is that one which balances the bridge composed of branches B, C, E, and F. This allows us to omit D, if we assume that the generator is in A, so that we can again reduce the structure to a simple series-shunt network.

In a broad sense computations on a feedback circuit in its reference condition present an analogous situation. Evidently, the reference, since it demands zero output current for any input generator, is somewhat similar to a bridge balance between input and output. Since the principle of reciprocity breaks down in circuits containing unilateral elements, we cannot use as simple a device as was suggested in connection with Fig. 6.1 in exploiting this possibility. This complicates the analysis without essentially affecting the results, however. We will find that in a number of subsequent theorems computations in the reference condition can be made with arbitrary choices of the impedances in the input and output circuits. The choice of an impedance which will simplify the calculation then becomes principally a matter of ingenuity.

6.3. *Return Difference and Relative Sensitivity*

The simplest illustrations of these possibilities are furnished by a set of relations between the return difference, the sensitivity, and the transmission from input to grid and output to plate terminals of the tube in question. As in Chapter IV, let 1, 2, 3, and 4 denote, respectively, the input, output, grid and plate. Then from (4–2) and (4–26) of Chapter IV we can write

$$\frac{F}{S'} = \frac{\dfrac{\Delta}{\Delta^0}}{\dfrac{\Delta}{\Delta'}} = \frac{\Delta'}{\Delta^0} = \frac{\Delta_{13}}{\Delta^0}\,\frac{\Delta'}{\Delta_{13}}, \tag{6–1}$$

where, as before, the superscripts ^{0} and $'$ indicate that the determinants to which they are attached are to be evaluated with $W = 0$ and $W' = 0$, respectively. We observe that the determinant Δ_{13} in (6–1) is independent of W and might equally well be written as Δ_{13}^0 or Δ_{13}'. Thus the factor Δ_{13}/Δ^0 in (6–1) is the transmission from input to grid with the tube dead, while the factor Δ'/Δ_{13} is the reciprocal of the transmission between the same points when the tube is in its reference condition. If we begin by multiplying and dividing F/S' by Δ_{42}, instead of Δ_{13}, we can also obtain an analogous expression involving the transmissions from plate to output for these two values of W.

The principal difficulty with these expressions as they stand is the fact that the input to grid or plate to output transmission in the reference state cannot be calculated without allowing for the residual feedback which exists because the residual transimmittance W_0 remains in the tube For most circuits, however, the idea of bridge balance between input and output in the reference condition allows the problem to be much simplified. Since the balance cannot depend upon the input and output impedances, we can study the input to grid transmission for an arbitrary value of the impedance connected to the output terminals, or the plate to output transmission for an arbitrary value of the input impedance. By choosing the proper values in each case it is generally* possible to interrupt the residual feedback path.

These possibilities are reasonably obvious physically, but it will simplify later analysis if we also verify them mathematically. To represent the effect of a change in the output line upon the input to grid transmission in the reference condition, then, we can rewrite (6–1) as

$$\frac{F}{S'} = \frac{\Delta_{13}}{\Delta^0} \frac{\Delta' + W_2 \Delta'_{22}}{\Delta'_{13} + W_2 \Delta'_{1322}}, \tag{6–2}$$

where W_2 is an arbitrary immittance added at the output terminals when the tube is in the reference condition. But we can also write

$$\Delta' \Delta'_{1322} = \Delta'_{13} \Delta'_{22}, \tag{6–3}$$

from the general identity (4–13), Chapter IV, if we recall that $\Delta'_{12} = 0$, since there is zero transmission from input to output in the reference state. It follows from (6–3) that (6–2) is independent of W_2, so that we can choose any value we like for this quantity without vitiating the original relationship between S' and F given by (6–1). In particular, then, we may give W_2 a value which will interrupt the return path from plate to grid, or in other words will make $\Delta_{43} = 0$. With this choice the second factor of (6–2) becomes independent of W_0, so that we are at liberty to suppose that the tube is dead rather than that it is in its reference condition. We can therefore state the following

Theorem: The ratio between the return difference and the relative sensitivity for any tube is equal to the ratio between the transmission from the input circuit to the grid of the tube when the output impedance has its normal value and the transmission between the same two points when the output impedance is assigned the value which interrupts the return path from the plate to the grid of the tube, if the tube itself is dead in both cases.

* That is, in the absence of some such special situation as that represented by the bridge-type feedback amplifiers described in Chapter III, in which the loop transmission is independent of the input and output line impedances.

If the transmission path is taken from plate to output the analysis is precisely similar and we have the

Theorem: The ratio between the return difference and the relative sensitivity for any tube is equal to the ratio between the transmission from its plate to the output circuit when the input circuit has its normal value and the transmission between the same points when the input circuit is assigned the value which interrupts the return path from the plate to the grid of the tube, if the tube itself is dead in both cases.

Simple illustrations of these theorems are furnished by ordinary single loop amplifiers. If we apply the first theorem to a series feedback amplifier, for example, the interruption of the return path is accomplished by open-circuiting the output line. This evidently produces a slight change in the input impedance of the β circuit, which would otherwise be terminated by the output line impedance in series with the output impedance of the μ circuit. Since the input line, the input of the μ circuit, and the input impedance of the β circuit are all in series at the input terminals, there is a corresponding slight change in the transmission from the input line to the μ circuit. In a shunt feedback structure the situation is similar except that the interruption in the return path is produced by short-circuiting the output terminals. In either instance, of course, the change in transmission is small in any ordinary application.

A more specific example can be obtained by returning to the structure shown by Fig. 4.5, in Chapter IV. If we use the first theorem, the interruption of the return path is accomplished by open-circuiting Z_5. For either the open-circuit or the normal value of Z_5, however, the transmission from a generator in series with Z_1 to the grid is inversely proportional to the impedance seen from the generator terminals. We can therefore write by inspection

$$\frac{F}{S'} = \frac{Z_1 + Z_2 + Z_3}{Z_1 + Z_2 + \dfrac{Z_3(Z_4 + Z_5)}{Z_3 + Z_4 + Z_5}}. \tag{6-4}$$

6.4. *External Gain with Feedback*

It was suggested at the end of the last chapter that gain expressions analogous to the ones given there could be developed by starting with any reference for the variable element W. If we begin, in particular, with the reference W_0, we are led to formulae involving considerations very similar to those we have just discussed.

The appropriate gain equation for calculations based on the reference W_0

is easily written from analogy with (5–27) of the preceding chapter. It is

$$e^{\theta} = \frac{1}{S'} \frac{-W'\Delta_{13}\Delta_{42}}{\Delta'\Delta'} W_R, \tag{6–5}$$

or

$$e^{\theta} = \frac{e^{\theta'_F}}{S'}, \tag{6–6}$$

if e^{θ} is written in place of the last group of factors in (6–5). The validity of (6–5) can be verified by direct calculation from equations (4–25) and (4–28) of Chapter IV, if we make use of the condition $\Delta'\Delta'_{1243} = -\Delta'_{13}\Delta'_{42}$, which follows from an argument similar to that used for (6–3) in the present chapter. In view of the various relations among S, S', and F which were developed in the last section and in Chapter IV it is also possible to write (6–5) and (6–6) in a variety of other obvious ways.

If we confine our attention to equations (6–5) and (6–6) as they stand, we are concerned principally with the quantity $e^{\theta'_F}$ This is evidently a fractionated gain expression very similar to the original fractionated gain e^{θ_F} which appeared in Chapter V, except that each of the three transmission factors of which it is composed is calculated with respect to the condition $W = W_0$ rather than with respect to the condition $W = 0$. As in the preceding section, the input and output transmission factors Δ_{13}/Δ' and Δ_{42}/Δ' can be calculated with an arbitrary value for the line impedance not directly involved in the transmission path. If we choose in particular the values which interrupt the return path, the calculations can be made with the tube dead. Thus the difference between these factors and those appearing in e^{θ_F} is that at each end they include the β circuit impedance as it would appear with the feedback loop interrupted at the other end, rather than as it would appear for the circuit connections as they stand.

A simple example is furnished by the series feedback amplifier shown by Fig. 4.5 of Chapter IV, which we used previously to illustrate the calculation of fractionated gain in the zero reference case. Evidently, the transmission from Z_1 to the grid in this structure is most easily evaluated if we suppose that Z_5 is infinite and the transmission from plate to Z_5 if we assume Z_1 to be infinite. The fractionated gain for the reference W_0 can, therefore, be written down as

$$e^{\theta'_F} = \frac{Z_2}{Z_1 + Z_2 + Z_3} \frac{Z_4}{Z_3 + Z_4 + Z_5} Z_5 W'. \tag{6–7}$$

This may be compared with equation (5–30) of the preceding chapter.

6.5. *Simplified Computation of* W_0

The material of the previous sections has been chosen principally to provide the simplest possible illustrations of the use of the bridge balance condition when the analysis, as a whole, is based upon the reference W_0. It is somewhat misleading, however, in the sense that we are, in fact, likely to choose W_0 rather than zero for the reference only if a relatively elaborate computation is to be attempted. The reason is apparent if we notice that the analysis in terms of W_0 depends essentially upon the variables W' and S', which are obviously more difficult to evaluate than are the corresponding variables W and F in the zero reference analysis. Thus, the use of the reference W_0 calls for an initial investment in labor not required with the other procedure. On the other hand, it leads in general to simpler relations. For example, (6–7) is simpler than its zero reference counterpart, and the simplification is enhanced if we include the fact that (6–7) can be applied directly to find the final output, while with the zero reference method it is still necessary to compute the direct transmission. We also need to know the direct transmission to find the absolute sensitivity in the zero reference case, whereas equation (4–31) of Chapter IV gives S directly if we begin with W' and S'. In general, it appears that these advantages should outweigh the extra difficulty of determining W' and S' initially if the circuit is complicated or if a long series of results is to be obtained, but the zero reference analysis is probably more advantageous in elementary situations.

Since the computation in terms of W_0 hinges primarily upon W' and S', it is of considerable interest to consider how these variables can best be evaluated. W', of course, depends directly upon W_0. S' can be determined indirectly from F by the methods described earlier in this chapter and in Chapter IV. This, however, involves the intermediate step of computing F. If we wish to determine S' directly, we are concerned, in general, with the backward transmission from plate to grid in the reference condition, since it was shown earlier that S' is equal to the return difference for the reference W_0.

Fortunately, the computation both of W_0 and of the backward transmission in the reference state can be simplified by means of the bridge balance condition we have already discussed. The situation is particularly favorable if the circuit belongs broadly to any one of the general types illustrated by Figs. 6.2, 6.3, 6.4, and 6.5. In each figure the networks N_1 and N_2 are arbitrary, but it will be seen that the relations between either the source and the grid or the plate and the load are particularly simple. For example, in Fig. 6.2, the plate and the load are " effectively in parallel " in the sense that if the plate-cathode impedance is a short circuit, there can be no transmission between either the input or the grid and the load. Similarly, Fig. 6.3 represents a series arrangement for the plate and load, while Figs. 6.4 and 6.5 give analogous relations between the input and the grid. The circuit need belong only " broadly " to one of these classes since minor departures will not seriously affect the results. For example, there may be other paths between input and output in addition to those shown by the figures, provided the transmission through these paths by themselves is relatively small, since Chapter IV shows that the distinction between S' and S or F depends only upon the ratio of e^{θ_0} to e^{θ}.

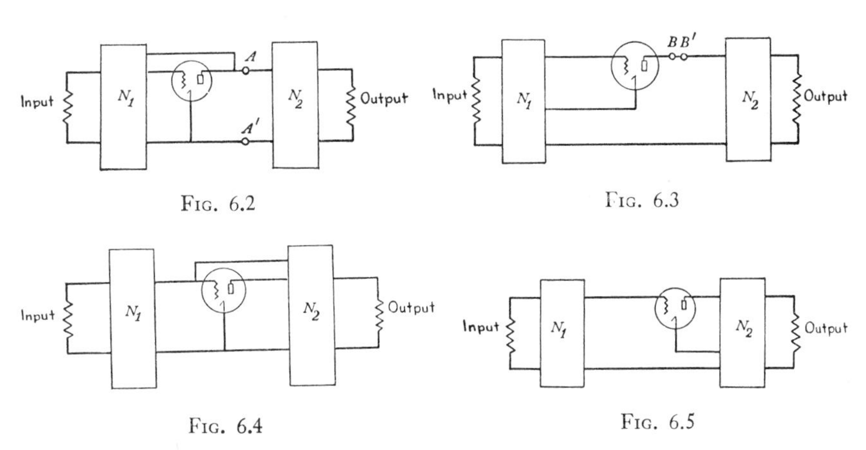

FIG. 6.2

FIG. 6.3

FIG. 6.4

FIG. 6.5

This section will deal only with the computation of W_0. If we consider in particular the circuit of Fig. 6.2, we notice that since no voltages can exist in the output in the reference condition, no voltage difference can exist across terminals AA' either. We can therefore determine the reference condition equally well if we begin by short-circuiting these terminals, provided we define the reference condition as that one which gives zero current through the short-circuit. This evidently demands cancellation between the current which would be supplied to the short-circuit by the rest of the network with the tube dead and the current supplied directly by the tube. In evaluating the latter, however, we need make no allowance for residual " feedback " since the short-circuit destroys the return path. The reference transconductance of the tube for the circuit of Fig. 6.2 is therefore equal to the ratio of the current flowing between A and A' to the voltage between grid and cathode, both quantities being evaluated with AA' short-circuited and the tube dead. It will be noticed that this requires a knowledge of only two transmissions, in comparison with the four appearing in (5–26) of the previous chapter.

A simple example is furnished by the structure of Fig. 6.6. Obviously a voltage E_g between grid and cathode will deliver a current Y_3E_g to a short-circuit between plate and cathode when the tube is inactive. We therefore have at once

$$W_0 = Y_3. \tag{6–8}$$

A structure belonging to the general class of Fig. 6.3 can be analyzed in a similar fashion if we replace the short-circuit between A and A' by an open-circuit between B and B'. The reference transimpedance is equal to

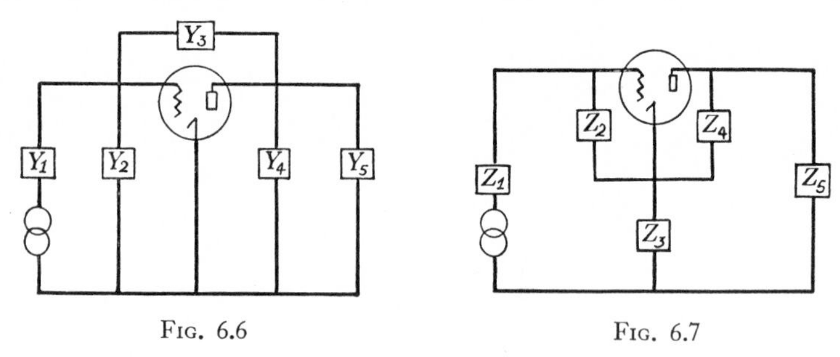

FIG. 6.6 FIG. 6.7

the ratio between the voltage across BB' and the current in the grid circuit, both quantities being evaluated with BB' open-circuited and the tube dead. For example, in the structure of Fig. 6.7 we have

$$W_0 = Z_3. \tag{6–9}$$

We may also continue to specify the reference condition in Fig. 6.7 in terms of admittances. Thus if we begin with any voltage between grid and cathode in that figure and compute directly the transconductance which will give a balance between the voltages across Z_3 and Z_4, with Z_5 open, we readily find that W_0, as a transconductance, is given by

$$W_0 = \frac{Z_3}{Z_2 Z_4}. \tag{6–10}$$

In a circuit belonging to the general class shown by Fig. 6.4 the interruption of the residual feedback path can be accomplished by supposing that a voltage generator, of zero internal impedance, is applied between grid and cathode, while in Fig. 6.5 we may assume that the circuit includes a current generator, of infinite impedance, in series with the grid lead. The reference transimmittance is equal to the ratio between a current or voltage source in the plate circuit and this voltage or current source in the grid circuit, when the plate and grid sources are adjusted to produce the same response in the output with the tube dead. These relations can be exemplified by using the structures of Figs. 6.6 and 6.7 again, and lead to the results we have already found in (6–8) and (6–9).

Although these results are physically obvious it will simplify the discussion in the next section to show how they can be demonstrated mathematically. We will consider in particular the structure of Fig. 6.2. It is convenient in this structure to use a nodal analysis, with the cathode of the tube on ground. In agreement with our earlier conventions, the input, output, grid, and plate will be taken as, respectively, the first, second, third, and fourth nodes. The short-circuit between A and A' will be represented by adding the arbitrarily large quantity Y_4 to the self-admittance of the fourth node.

In terms of this notation, the voltage on the grid and plate corresponding to a unit source applied to the input with the tube dead can be written as

$$E_3 = \frac{\Delta_{13}^0 + Y_4\Delta_{1344}}{\Delta^0 + Y_4\Delta_{44}}, \tag{6–11}$$

and

$$E_4 = \frac{\Delta_{14}}{\Delta^0 + Y_4\Delta_{44}}, \tag{6–12}$$

where Δ^0 represents the system with the tube dead and $Y_4 = 0$.

The current in Y_4 is E_4Y_4. The statement to be established is that the reference transconductance of the tube is equal to the ratio of this current to the grid voltage E_3 when Y_4 becomes infinite. A general formula for the reference is, however, given by (4–23) of Chapter IV. Upon inspecting (6–11) and (6–12) to find the current-voltage ratio when Y_4 becomes infinite we therefore obtain the required relation in the form

$$\frac{\Delta_{14}}{\Delta_{1344}} = -\frac{\Delta_{12}^0}{\Delta_{1243}}. \tag{6–13}$$

To prove this equation, let the voltage on the output node be written as

$$E_2 = \frac{\Delta_{12}^0 + Y_4\Delta_{1244}}{\Delta^0 + Y_4\Delta_{44}}. \tag{6–14}$$

When Y_4 becomes infinite, however, the configuration in Fig. 6.2 is such that E_2 vanishes. We must therefore have $\Delta_{1244} = 0$. Upon identifying Δ_{1244} with $\Delta_{ab,cd}$ in (4–13), Chapter IV, this gives

$$\Delta_{12}^0\Delta_{44} = \Delta_{14}\Delta_{42}. \tag{6–15}$$

The result (6–13) follows readily from (6–15) if we use (4–13) of Chapter IV again to replace Δ_{1344} and Δ_{1243} by their values in terms of first order minors.

6.6. *Simplified Computation of Transmission from Plate to Grid*

The fact that the input and output must be conjugate in the reference condition, which we have just used to simplify the computation of the reference W_0 itself, can also be applied to the computation of the plate-grid transmission when $W = W_0$. This can be illustrated by an examination of Fig. 6.2. For example, it follows from the conjugacy condition that the impedance looking to the left from terminals AA' in Fig. 6.2 must be independent of the input circuit when $W = W_0$. Otherwise, if we were to vary the input circuit, we would expect to find a varying impedance across AA' for a prescribed plate generator and consequently a varying current in the output circuit. Since a variation in the input impedance can be represented by keeping the input impedance constant and adding a suitable generator in series with it, this is impossible by the conjugacy condition. Similarly, once the current gets over to the input impedance and the associated elements in N_1, the way in which it divides in the various meshes of N_1 must be independent of the output impedance. We can therefore divide the total transmission between plate and grid in the reference condition into two factors, one of which depends broadly upon the load impedance and upon the elements of N_2, but is independent of the input impedance, and another which depends upon the input impedance and the elements of N_1, but is independent of the output.

These relations may be expressed by the following

Theorem: If the structure is in any one of the forms shown by Figs. 6.2, 6.3, 6.4, or 6.5 the actual circuit used in computing the transmission between plate and grid in the reference condition can be replaced by an equivalent circuit in which the output impedance is assigned an arbitrary value, provided the strength of the energizing source in the equivalent circuit is so chosen with respect to the source in the original circuit that they give the same voltages on the input side of the tube for any one arbitrarily chosen value for the impedance of the amplifier input circuit.

The equivalent source may be associated either with the plate circuit or with the load and the comparison of voltages may be made either at the grid itself or at the input circuit terminals. In the application of the theorem, of course, one would attempt to choose the output impedance in a way to facilitate the final computation of feedback, while the input impedance would be chosen to facilitate the intermediate step of comparing the voltages.

The notation of the preceding section will be retained in the proof of the theorem. The fact that the output circuit is arbitrary in the equivalent structure will be represented by adding the arbitrary quantity Y_2 to the self-admittance Y_{22}, while the arbitrary input mesh assumed in the voltage comparison will similarly be represented by the addition of Y_1 to Y_{11}.* Let I_4 represent the actual plate source and I_2 the equivalent source, while E_1 is the voltage which each produces across the input. When the voltage comparison is made, we have

$$E_1 = I_4 \frac{\Delta_{41}}{\Delta' + Y_1\Delta'_{11}}, \tag{6–16}$$

and

$$E_1 = I_2 \frac{\Delta'_{21}}{\Delta' + Y_1\Delta'_{11} + Y_2\Delta'_{22} + Y_1Y_2\Delta'_{1122}}, \tag{6–17}$$

where Δ' is the determinant of the actual circuit when $Y_1 = Y_2 = 0$ and $W = W_0$. In accordance with the conditions of the theorem I_2 must be so chosen with respect to I_4 that the E_1's determined by the two equations are equal.

On the other hand, when the input circuit is assigned its actual admittance value, the equivalent source I_2 will produce a voltage between grid and cathode given by

$$E_3 = I_2 \frac{\Delta_{23}}{\Delta' + Y_2\Delta'_{22}}. \tag{6–18}$$

If we replace I_2 by its value in terms of I_4 as determined from equations (6–16) and (6–17) this can also be written as

$$E_3 = I_4 \frac{\Delta_{41}\Delta_{23}}{\Delta'\Delta'_{21}} \frac{\Delta'(\Delta' + Y_1\Delta'_{11} + Y_2\Delta'_{22} + Y_1Y_2\Delta'_{1122})}{(\Delta' + Y_1\Delta'_{11})(\Delta' + Y_2\Delta'_{22})}. \tag{6–19}$$

It follows from (4–13), Chapter IV, however, that

$$\Delta'\Delta'_{1122} = \Delta'_{11}\Delta'_{22}, \tag{6–20}$$

if we recall that, since there can be no transmission from input to output in the reference condition, we can set $\Delta'_{12} = 0$.

With the help of (6–20), it is readily seen that the second factor of (6–19) must be equal to unity. This equation therefore reduces to

$$E_3 = I_4 \frac{\Delta_{41}\Delta_{23}}{\Delta'\Delta'_{21}}. \tag{6–21}$$

* With corresponding changes in wording, if we use an impedance rather than an admittance analysis. As in the preceding section, it is assumed as a matter of simplicity that the input, output, and cathode are all grounded, so that changes, for example, in the input and output affect only a self-admittance term.

But the transmission from plate to grid for the actual circuit is given by

$$E_3 = I_4 \frac{\Delta_{43}}{\Delta'}. \tag{6–22}$$

The theorem is therefore demonstrated provided we can assume that

$$\frac{\Delta_{41}\Delta_{23}}{\Delta_{43}\Delta'_{21}} = 1. \tag{6–23}$$

The final step is to establish the fact that (6–23) holds for any structure of the general type illustrated by Figs. 6.2 to 6.5. It is sufficient to examine Fig. 6.2. From an argument similar to that used to establish equation (6–15) it is clear that $\Delta_{2144} = \Delta_{2344} = 0$ for this structure. Corresponding to (6–15) itself we must therefore have

$$\Delta'_{21}\Delta_{44} = \Delta'_{24}\Delta_{41}, \tag{6–24}$$

and

$$\Delta_{23}\Delta_{44} = \Delta'_{24}\Delta_{43}, \tag{6–25}$$

from which (6–23) follows by direct division.

The proof of (6–23) for the other configurations can be made by the same methods. We may also notice that although (6–23) was established on the assumption that the equivalent source was associated with the output and that the voltage comparison was made at the input, it would also have been obtained if we had introduced the equivalent source in the plate and compared the two voltages at the grid, so that the theorem holds for this condition also.

As a simple example of the theorem, we may consider the structure previously shown by Fig. 6.7. Z_1 in this figure will be taken to represent the input circuit and Z_5 to represent the load. For the equivalent source, it is convenient to suppose that $Z_5 = \infty$, since this removes all the plate side elements from the computation. In making the voltage comparison, on the other hand, it will be supposed that $Z_1 = \infty$ since this allows us to ignore the grid elements. If the original plate current source is I_4, the voltage across Z_3 (or across Z_1) for the comparison condition is given by $I_4[Z_3Z_4/(Z_3 + Z_4 + Z_5)]$. The equivalent source must of course be adjusted to give this same voltage across Z_3. The equivalent source, however, corresponds to an open plate circuit. When we restore the input impedance to make the actual measurement, therefore, we find that a fraction $Z_2/(Z_1 + Z_2 + Z_3)$ of the voltage which it would produce across Z_3 in the comparison condition must appear between grid and cathode. If we include also the factor W' to give complete loop transmission, therefore, the return ratio for the reference W_0 can be written as

$$T' = \frac{Z_2}{Z_1 + Z_2 + Z_3} \frac{Z_4}{Z_3 + Z_4 + Z_5} Z_3 W'. \tag{6–26}$$

Equation (6–26) is evidently the expression for the return voltage which would be deduced by inspection upon the assumption that Z_3 is so small compared to the other impedances that there is no interaction between the two ends of the network. The choice of the reference value W_0 is equiva-

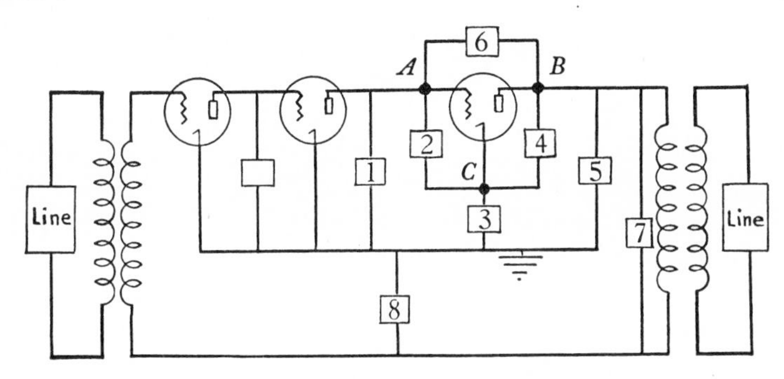

Fig. 6.8

lent in effect to destroying the interaction between input and output, so that in terms of this reference value the equation becomes an exact expression for T' even when Z_3 is not small. In other words, in the reference condition the two forward couplings represented by Z_3 and the transconductance of the tube cancel one another. The transmission backward from plate to grid is therefore unilateral and the two ends of the network are independent of one another in exactly the same way that the plate circuit and grid circuit of an ideal vacuum tube are independent.

6.7. *Amplifier with Local Feedback — Computation of W_0*

These various theorems will be exemplified by means of the structure shown in Fig. 6.8. The circuit is a multiple loop amplifier of the general type illustrated by Figs. 3.14 and 3.15 of Chapter III. The main feedback is provided by the branch Y_8. The last tube is provided with additional local feedback by means of branches Y_3 and Y_6. This stage is evidently similar to the structures which we have already analyzed, as complete amplifiers rather than as constituents of a multiple loop circuit, in connection with Figs. 6.6 and 6.7 of the present chapter.

Although the analysis does not depend upon any particular assumption concerning the elements, we may conveniently suppose that Y_6 is a parasitic grid plate capacity and that Y_3 is a physical element deliberately added to enhance the total feedback on the tube. Y_2 and Y_4 are introduced to represent the fact that in a physical tube a portion of the total grid and plate admittances must be considered as going directly to the cathode and this portion must be distinguished from the portion which goes to ground when the cathode is off ground, as it is in this case. Y_1 and Y_5 represent normal parasitic capacities and design elements connected to ground while Y_7 is used to represent the total output admittance.

The presence of both Y_3 and Y_6 does not appreciably complicate the structure in theory, but it leads to considerably more complicated circuit equations, principally because the circuit with both elements present is essentially a bridge rather than a series-shunt configuration. In order to simplify the discussion, therefore, each stage of the analysis will be begun on the assumption that only one of these two elements is present and the complete equation will be supplied only as a final step.

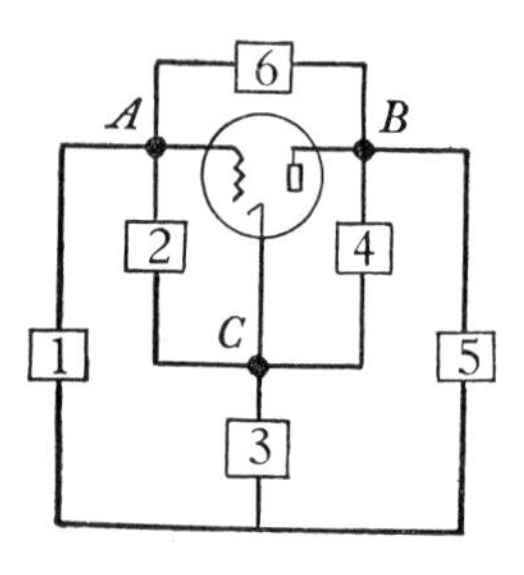

FIG. 6.9

Since the properties of the circuit for the first and second tubes are similar to those which would be found in a single loop amplifier, we can turn immediately to the output stage. The first step is to determine the reference value W_0 for the transconductance. Since no current can flow in the output circuit for the reference condition, we can suppose that Y_7 is removed and the fundamental condition then becomes that the sum of the voltages across Y_8 and Y_5 must vanish. The voltage across Y_8, however, is obviously very small and will be neglected also. The circuit is thus reduced to the form shown by Fig. 6.9 and the problem becomes that of determining a transconductance W_0 such that there is zero transmission from A to B.

It follows from the discussion early in this chapter that W_0 must be independent of Y_1 and Y_5, so that any convenient values for these admittances can be assumed in making the computation. If one of the branches 3 or 6 is missing the structure reduces to one of the types shown by Figs. 6.6 and 6.7, for which the reference transconductance has already been calculated by equations (6–8) and (6–10). With suitable changes in notation to agree with Fig. 6.9 the results may be reproduced here as

$$W_0 = \frac{Y_2 Y_4}{Y_3}, \tag{6–27}$$

if Y_6 vanishes, and

$$W_0 = Y_6, \tag{6–28}$$

if Y_3 is infinite.

In the general case, when neither Y_3 nor Y_6 can be ignored, we can continue to determine W_0 from a transmission computation, using arbitrary values of Y_1 and Y_5. A convenient choice is now $Y_5 = 0$ and $Y_1 = -Y_3$. This choice interrupts the return path from plate to grid, so that the net output voltage, which must be set equal to zero, can be calculated by simple superposition of the voltage due to the original source and the voltage due to the flow of plate current. With the tube dead, and these values for Y_1 and Y_5, it is easy to calculate that a current source I_A applied to node A in Fig. 6.9 will produce the voltage

$$E_{B_1} = -\frac{I_A}{Y_3^2(Y_4 + Y_6)}(Y_4Y_6 + Y_2Y_6 + Y_2Y_4 + Y_3Y_6) \qquad (6\text{–}29)$$

from node B to ground, that is, across Y_5. The grid-cathode voltage produced by the same energizing current is $-I_A/Y_3$. Allowing for the phase reversal in the tube, the corresponding plate current in the reference condition is I_AW_0/Y_3. When this current source is applied to the network, again with the tube dead and the chosen values inserted for Y_1 and Y_5, the resulting voltage drop across Y_5 is

$$E_{B_1} = \frac{I_AW_0}{Y_3}\frac{1}{Y_4 + Y_6}\left(1 - \frac{Y_6}{Y_3}\right). \qquad (6\text{–}30)$$

But the sum of the two voltages in (6–29) and (6–30) must be zero. The correct value of W_0 is consequently

$$W_0 = \frac{Y_4Y_6 + Y_2Y_6 + Y_2Y_4 + Y_3Y_6}{Y_3 - Y_6}, \qquad (6\text{–}31)$$

from which (6–27) and (6–28) follow as special cases.

It is also possible, on the other hand, to determine W_0 directly from the nodal equations without using any special devices. Since this procedure is perfectly general, it is worth illustration. For the circuit of Fig. 6.9, the nodal equations appear as

$$\begin{aligned} E_A(Y_1 + Y_2 + Y_6) - E_BY_6 - E_CY_2 &= I_A, \\ -E_A(Y_6 - W) + E_B(Y_4 + Y_5 + Y_6) - E_C(Y_4 + W) &= 0, \qquad (6\text{–}32) \\ -E_A(Y_2 + W) - E_BY_4 + E_C(Y_2 + Y_3 + Y_4 + W) &= 0, \end{aligned}$$

if we assume that the circuit is energized by the current I_A flowing into node A. When $W = W_0$ we must have zero transmission from A to B. This corresponds to $\Delta_{AB} = 0$ so that W_0 is the solution of

$$\begin{vmatrix} -(Y_6 - W_0) & -(Y_4 + W_0) \\ -(Y_2 + W_0) & (Y_2 + Y_3 + Y_4 + W_0) \end{vmatrix} = 0. \qquad (6\text{–}33)$$

When the determinant is expanded, we obtain again the formula for W_0 already found in (6–31).

6.8. *Amplifier with Local Feedback — Computation of Local Feedback*

We will assume that the final object of the analysis of the circuit of Fig. 6.8 is the determination of the relative sensitivity for the last tube. The absolute sensitivity for this tube can, of course, be determined immediately from the relative sensitivity and the ratio W/W', which is fixed by the known value of W_0. It is convenient to base the computation of S' for the last tube upon the theorem following equation (5–22) of Chapter V. We will take W_1 to represent the transconductance of the output tube and W_2 that of one of the preceding tubes. The reference values which appear in the statement of the theorem will be chosen as W_0 and zero, respectively. The return difference of the output tube for the reference W_0 is, of course, the same as S'. Moreover, when W_1 assumes its reference value the return difference for W_2 is unity, since the main loop is opened. Similarly, with W_2 at reference the return difference of W_1 for the reference W_0 is merely that which would be obtained from a consideration of the " local " structure of Fig. 6.9, including the associated line and β circuit impedances. It follows from the theorem, therefore, that the actual relative sensitivity for W_1 is the product of the return difference for W_2 and the "local" relative sensitivity for W_1.

This section will be concerned only with the computation of the local sensitivity. If $Y_6 = 0$, the local circuit is identical with that previously shown by Fig. 6.7 except that $Z_7 + Z_8$ has been added in parallel with Z_5. The local sensitivity can, therefore, be immediately written down from equation (6–26) in the form

$$S_l' = 1 + \frac{Z_2}{Z_1 + Z_2 + Z_3} \frac{Z_4}{Z_3 + Z_4 + Z_9} Z_3 W', \tag{6–34}$$

where Z_9 has been written for brevity to represent the complete impedance composed of Z_7 and Z_8 in parallel with Z_5.

If Z_3 vanishes, on the other hand, the circuit is of the type represented by Fig. 6.2. The theorem on the computation of the feedback by the use of an equivalent source is, therefore, still valid. In this instance it is convenient to suppose that the equivalent source is defined by $Y_9 = \infty$ and that the comparison of grid responses is made for the condition $Y_1 = \infty$. With $Y_1 = \infty$, a current I_j in the plate circuit will evidently produce a voltage $I_j/(Y_4 + Y_6 + Y_9)$ between B and C. With Y_1 normal, on the other hand, a generator of unit voltage and zero internal impedance applied across B and C will produce a voltage $Y_6/(Y_1 + Y_2 + Y_6)$ between A and C. The local sensitivity is, therefore,

$$S_l' = 1 + \frac{Y_6}{Y_1 + Y_2 + Y_6} \frac{W'}{Y_4 + Y_6 + Y_9}. \tag{6–35}$$

If neither of the branches 3 or 6 can be ignored the analysis becomes considerably more complicated. Since the circuit no longer falls in any one of the classes represented by Figs. 6.2 to 6.5, it is not possible to use the theorem on equivalent sources to compute the feedback. We can, however, develop a suitable expression directly from the expansion of the system determinant. As an alternative which requires substantially the same algebraic work, although it may seem simpler, it is also possible to derive the sensitivity from the return difference. By ordinary circuit analysis the return difference for the local circuit can be found as

$$F = 1 + \frac{Y_1Y_9 + Y_6(Y_1 + Y_9) + Y_3Y_6}{a + bY_3 + cY_6 + dY_3Y_6} W, \tag{6-36}$$

where

$$\begin{aligned} a &= Y_1Y_2Y_4Y_9\left(\frac{1}{Y_1} + \frac{1}{Y_2} + \frac{1}{Y_4} + \frac{1}{Y_9}\right), \\ b &= (Y_1 + Y_2)(Y_4 + Y_9), \\ c &= (Y_1 + Y_9)(Y_2 + Y_4), \\ d &= Y_1 + Y_2 + Y_4 + Y_9. \end{aligned} \tag{6-37}$$

We know, however, that S_l' is equal to the F of (6–36) divided by the value which F would assume if we set $W = W_0$. From the known value of W_0 this gives

$$S_l' = 1 + \frac{[Y_1Y_9 + Y_6(Y_1 + Y_9) + Y_3Y_6](Y_3 - Y_6)W'}{(Y_1Y_2 + Y_3Y_6)(Y_4Y_5 + Y_3Y_6) + Y_3(a + bY_3 + dY_3Y_6)}. \tag{6-38}$$

6.9. *Amplifier with Local Feedback — Final Properties*

In accordance with our preceding discussion the actual S' for the third tube in Fig. 6.8 can be obtained by multiplying (6–38) by the return difference for one of the other tubes. The return ratio for either the first or second tube, however, is simply the transmission around the main loop. This in turn can be broken up into two components, one representing the transmission from A in Fig. 6.9 to some point such as B, say, and the second representing the transmission around the rest of the loop. The second will be symbolized by K and will be assumed to be known since it presents no special problem.

Since we already know S_l' for the last tube, equations (6–5) and (6–6) allow us to compute the transmission from A to B as soon as the fractionated gain of this tube for the reference condition is determined. It will be recalled that the grid transmission term in this gain can be calculated for an arbitrary choice of the load impedance and the plate transmission term for an arbitrary choice of the input impedance.

Let it be supposed, first, that $Y_6 = 0$. It is then convenient to choose the arbitrary impedance as an open circuit in each computation. This has already been examined in connection with (6–7). For the present circuit the resulting transmission from A to B can be written as*

$$e^{\theta_{AB}} = \frac{1}{S_l'} \frac{Z_1 Z_2}{Z_1 + Z_2 + Z_3} \frac{Z_4 Z_9}{Z_3 + Z_4 + Z_9} W', \tag{6–39}$$

where, corresponding to the fact that we have assumed $Y_6 = 0$, S_l' must be determined from (6–34).

If we assume $Z_3 = 0$, on the other hand, it is most convenient to determine the grid transmission for the condition $Z_9 = 0$ and the plate transmission for the condition $Z_1 = 0$. With these two assumptions the two transmissions are readily seen to be $1/(Y_1 + Y_2 + Y_6)$ and $1/(Y_4 + Y_6 + Y_9)$. The gain from A to B consequently becomes

$$e^{\theta_{AB}} = \frac{1}{S_l'} \frac{1}{Y_1 + Y_2 + Y_6} \frac{1}{Y_4 + Y_6 + Y_9} W', \tag{6–40}$$

where S_l' is determined from (6–35).

If neither of the branches 3 or 6 can be neglected the analysis is naturally somewhat more complicated but it can be made by the same general methods. For example, in computing the transmission to the grid, we can conveniently assume that $Y_9 = -Y_6[(Y_1 + Y_3)/(Y_1 + Y_6)]$. This is the value of Y_9 which gives zero transmission from Y_4 to Y_2 so that the flow of current in Y_4 due either to transmission in the passive parts of the network or to transmission through the residual transconductance W_0 will not affect the voltage across Y_2. The computation can thus be made for any assumed value, such as a short circuit, for Y_4. Similarly in computing the transmission from plate to load we can assume $Y_1 = -Y_6[(Y_3 + Y_4)/(Y_6 + Y_9)]$ which allows us to short-circuit Y_2.

* The numerator of (6–39) includes the factors Z_1 and Z_9, for which no corresponding terms exist in (6–7). These factors are introduced to express the result in nodal rather than mesh terms. Thus in (6–7), where an impedance analysis was used, the driving force was taken as a unit generator in series with Z_1 and the response was stated in terms of the current through the load. The introduction of the factor Z_1 in effect expresses the driving force as a unit current applied to Z_1, while the introduction of Z_9 is equivalent to expressing the response as the voltage across the load. A nodal analysis is chosen here for consistency with the other equations of this section.

The expression for the transmission from A to B is accordingly

$$e^{\theta AB} = \frac{1}{S_l'} \frac{Y_3 - Y_6}{Y_1Y_2 + Y_1Y_3 + Y_2Y_3 + Y_3Y_6} \times \frac{Y_3 - Y_6}{Y_3Y_4 + Y_3Y_6 + Y_3Y_9 + Y_4Y_9} W', \tag{6–41}$$

where the first and second expressions involving the Y's are, respectively, the transmission from the source to the grid and from the plate to the load.

Upon multiplying the appropriate one of these expressions by K, which represents the transmission from B around the rest of the loop, including the transconductance of the second tube, we secure the complete $\mu\beta$ characteristic. This then is $-T$ for either the first or the second tube. In accordance with the theorem on the relation between two return differences, the actual relative sensitivity for the third tube can be obtained by multiplying the corresponding F for the first or second tube by the S_l' for the third tube, as expressed by equations (6–34), (6–35), or (6–38). For example, if we assume $Y_3 = \infty$ and write S' for the total relative sensitivity of the third tube, the result from (6–35) and (6–40) is

$$\begin{aligned} S' &= S_l'\left(1 + \frac{1}{S_l'} \frac{1}{Y_1 + Y_2 + Y_6} \frac{1}{Y_4 + Y_6 + Y_9} W'K\right) \\ &= 1 + \frac{1}{Y_1 + Y_2 + Y_6} \frac{1}{Y_4 + Y_6 + Y_9} (Y_6 + K)W'. \end{aligned} \tag{6–42}$$

As the final step in the analysis we may compute the distortion which would appear in the load as the result of a prescribed distortion generator in the plate circuit of the third tube. The theorems of Chapter V show that this is equal to the distortion which would flow in the load when the third tube is in the reference condition divided by S' for that tube. We have, however, already computed the ratio between a given plate current and the voltage between B and ground for the reference condition. If we let k represent the ratio between the voltage at B and the resulting voltage across the final load impedance with the amplifier input circuit open, therefore, the results can be immediately written down as

$$\begin{aligned} E_L &= \frac{k}{S'} \frac{Z_4Z_9}{Z_3 + Z_4 + Z_9} I_j, \quad \text{for} \quad Y_6 = 0 \\ &= \frac{k}{S'} \frac{1}{Y_4 + Y_6 + Y_9} I_j, \quad \text{for} \quad Z_3 = 0 \\ &= \frac{k}{S'} \frac{Y_3 - Y_6}{Y_3Y_4 + Y_3Y_6 + Y_3Y_9 + Y_4Y_9} I_j, \quad \text{in general,} \end{aligned} \tag{6–43}$$

where I_j is the prescribed distortion generator and S' in each case is the appropriate relative sensitivity for the third tube.

It will be recalled that a double loop feedback circuit essentially similar to the one under discussion here was used in Chapter IV to illustrate the fact that the sensitivity of a tube in the μ circuit of a multiple loop structure was not necessarily equal to its return difference. The illustration can be made somewhat more specific with the help of the present equations. For example, suppose we set $W' = -W_0$ in (6–42). This is equivalent to setting $W = 0$, so that the corresponding return difference will be unity. It is clear, however, that the ratio of relative sensitivity to return difference is independent of W, so that it will be the same for actual operating conditions as it is for this special choice. Upon introducing $W_0 = Y_6$, from (6–28), for the case represented by (6–42) we therefore have

$$\frac{S'}{F} = 1 - \frac{Y_6(Y_6 + K)}{(Y_1 + Y_2 + Y_6)(Y_4 + Y_6 + Y_9)}. \tag{6–44}$$

It is evident from (6–44) that if we can make K large enough the sensitivity* can be made much greater than the return difference. On the other hand, by choosing special values for K and the various Y's we can also secure a sensitivity which is much smaller than the return difference. The values of these quantities which would appear naturally in normal design practice are probably not such as to make either extreme very likely. The fact that the sensitivity and return difference are not necessarily identical is of considerable theoretical interest, however, since the limitations on available "feedback" developed in the following chapters are actually limitations only on the return difference.

* No distinction between S and S' need be made here, since we can readily choose a W_0 small enough to make the two approximately equal, without affecting the rest of the argument.

CHAPTER VII

Stability and Physical Realizability

7.1. *Introduction*

The preceding chapters have been devoted largely to the problem of active network analysis. It has been assumed, in other words, that the structure under consideration was given, and that we were interested in finding out what it would do. To this end, the mesh and nodal equations were first introduced. The succeeding chapters consist principally of applications of these equations to various situations, with particular attention to what they could tell us about the relation between a single given element and the characteristics of the complete network within which it appears.

Beginning with the present chapter, attention will be turned broadly from problems of analysis to those of synthesis or design. It will be assumed in other words that our primary interest is in working backward from a prescribed type of response characteristic to a network which might exhibit it. This chapter will serve only to introduce the subject. It is devoted principally to a consideration of the requirements which a network must meet if it is to be stable and of the limitations which this imposes on the network characteristics which are available for design.

7.2. *Design Methods and the Problem of Physical Realizability*

The development of final design methods for feedback amplifiers is approached here by way of a lengthy and perhaps indirect introduction. Before beginning the discussion it may consequently be desirable to say a few words concerning the point of view which motivates this approach. It must be recognized to begin with that the processes of synthesis or design are in some respects essentially different from those of analysis. If a network is given, only one response to any prescribed force is possible, and that response can, in theory, be obtained by a mechanical computation, so that the whole operation is reduced to a routine level. The design process cannot be described so exactly. In a broad sense it consists in the construction of a larger unit by the establishment of a pattern of relationships among a number of smaller and more easily controlled units. In a feedback amplifier, for example, we are concerned in the first instance with the provision of suitable characteristics for the amplifier as a whole by the establishment of an appropriate pattern of relationships among the separate units, such as tubes, input and output circuits, feedback and interstage networks, etc., of which it is composed. Beyond this point we may be concerned with the relation between any one of these circuits individually and the various elements from which it is built.

In almost all design situations several or many patterns of relationships may yield a satisfactory result. For example, we may obtain a given forward gain for a feedback amplifier from various combinations of input and output circuits, tubes, and interstage networks. On a smaller scale, a given interstage characteristic can usually be represented, within tolerable limits, by structures of several different physical configurations. The choice between the possible solutions may depend upon ulterior considerations, such as economy, reliability, power consumption, the speed with which parts can be secured, etc., which are not readily taken into account, at least in detail, in a theoretical discussion. Or it may be purely arbitrary. In any event the establishment of any one pattern involves essentially an effort of imagination on the part of the designer. As such it is a creative operation, on a more or less difficult plane, and defies exact analysis. In a group of structures which are very much alike, such as a set of amplifiers meeting similar requirements in about the same frequency range, a general type of pattern may become so well established that much of the work is reduced to a routine level. As the diversity of application increases, however, the essentially creative nature of the design process becomes more apparent.

It follows from this discussion that design methods suitable for a variety of applications can never be reduced entirely to a set of rules. They are best when they leave the final synthesis in the hands of the designer but stress the development of conceptions and processes which make the establishment of any particular set of relationships as simple and easy a matter as possible. This can be done in part by pointing out types of relationships which are plausible but either cannot be carried out or lead to unsatisfactory results. It is futile, for example, to plan a feedback amplifier about an assumed input transformer whose gain is greater than can be obtained with the existing parasitic capacities. On the positive side, design can be expedited by the construction of general patterns of relations which can be extended to a variety of situations by the choice of numerical values for a few parameters, and by the discovery of simple methods of specifying the subsidiary units which make up a complete structure. An excellent example here is furnished by conventional filter theory. The general pattern is the composite filter with matched image impedances. The subsidiary units are the discrete sections. They are particularly easy to deal with since an individual section is specified, in essentials, by a single parameter, and in their significant properties the sections are directly additive. The choice of any particular combination of sections to meet a particular set of requirements, however, is left in the hands of the designer.

It is evident from this background that what we need most of all in developing design methods for feedback structures is a characterization of the available units which may enter the complete structure in terms which are as easy as possible to handle in planning the over-all design. This is, of course, necessary if we are to avoid blind alleys of the type described previously. It is also required in planning any general design patterns which are likely to be of practical value and it is necessary again in fixing the proportions of any specific pattern. As a matter of actual experience, it appears that if the characteristics of the units of the amplifier can be properly specified in broad terms the road to a final detailed design is relatively straight.

In network synthesis, a characteristic is " available " in the broadest sense if it can be furnished from some combination of physically obtainable elements. The restriction to physical elements is one which does not appear in network analysis. It makes no difference in the routine of determining the response of a given structure whether the elements are positive or negative, to say nothing of whether or not they are accompanied by parasitic effects of the types which might occur in practice. In network design, however, the restriction is fundamental and will be the next object of investigation. It is unfortunately a difficult topic and will require several chapters.

The quantities which appeared most conspicuously in the preceding analysis were the driving point and transfer immittances, the return difference, and the sensitivity. They may be lumped together under the general name, *network functions*. They are all defined as ratios of determinants so that they are all rational functions of p. It will be recalled from Chapter I that any rational function can be specified, except for a constant multiplier, by its zeros and poles. In the next few chapters the condition of physical realizability will be discussed in terms of the restrictions it imposes upon the location of the zeros and poles of the various network functions on the complex p plane. Following this discussion, the restrictions on the zeros and poles will be converted into equivalent restrictions on the behavior of the functions on the real frequency axis. This background is necessary in order to provide a specification in useful form of what is available in designing a feedback structure. With it as a foundation we will at length be able to approach the actual design problem directly.

7.3. *Criteria of Physical Realizability*

Before we can study the restrictions which the condition of physical realizability places upon available network functions, it is evidently necessary to find some formulation of what we mean by physical realizability which can be used as a basis for deduction. Perhaps the most obvious formulation is expressed by the statement that a physically realizable network is a combination of vacuum tubes and positive inductances, capacities, and resistances. This, however, is both awkward and misleading. Except in the very simplest configurations a study of the relationship between the signs of the elements and the resulting network characteristic entails intolerable algebraic complexities. Moreover, it can readily be shown* that any negative element can be simulated, at least in the ideal case, by a suitable combination of tubes and positive elements. The distinction between positive and negative elements thus cannot be the heart of the problem.

Although the sign of the elements cannot be used as a basis for analysis, some importance can be attached to the fact that the elements must at least be *real.* It follows immediately from this that if the frequency variable is taken as p, the coefficients in the mesh and nodal equations, and therefore the coefficients in the network functions, must also be real. If we replace p by its conjugate in any term of a network function, consequently, that term must assume the conjugate of its original value. Since conjugate values everywhere in the function must lead to a conjugate result, this establishes the

Theorem: A physically realizable network function assumes conjugate complex values at conjugate complex points on the p plane.

For most applications this theorem can be expressed more conveniently by means of the following two corollaries:

1. Any zeros and poles of a physical network function which are not real must occur in conjugate complex pairs.
2. The real and imaginary components of a physical network function on the real frequency axis have respectively even and odd symmetry about the origin.

The first of these evidently follows from the fact that zero and infinite values of a network function are their own conjugates, while the second is established if it is noticed that symmetrical positive and negative real frequencies are a special case of conjugate p's. We may also observe that since the zeros and poles specify the network completely except for a constant

* See, for example, the circuits described near the end of Chapter IX.

multiplier, and the multiplier must be real if the second corollary is to hold, the two corollaries together are equivalent to the original theorem.

The theorem on real element values is sufficient to restrict the range of available characteristics only very generally. The field can be narrowed much further from a consideration of the stability of the network. It is a familiar fact that many hopefully designed feedback structures " sing," or break into spontaneous oscillation, when the circuit is closed. This is customarily explained by regarding the free oscillation as a manifestation of one of the natural transients of the system. It is assumed, in other words, that the system has been exposed to some small shock which produces a normal transient response. In most systems transients are exponentially decreasing functions of time and quickly die out. If the system sings, however, it is supposed that one of the transients is negatively damped, and so increases with time. In this case it will eventually become very large, no matter how small the initial shock may have been. Since random small shocks, on the level of thermal vibrations at least, are unavoidable, the phenomenon must occur if the system has any possible transient response which increases with time.

In a physical situation the amplitude of the oscillation may become large enough to burn out part of the system. Otherwise, it is limited by the inability of the system to maintain a linear response characteristic for amplitudes beyond a certain range. This is true, for example, in an ordinary oscillator, where the amplitude is limited normally by the physical possibilities of the output tube. Since the analysis in this book is confined to linear circuits either eventuality removes the structure from our purview.*

It may seem at first sight that although the possibility that the network may break into free oscillation may be important, it should be considered separately from our immediate problem, which is the investigation of the steady state characteristics of the network. A connection between the two problems, however, appears from the well-known fact that the transient response of a network can be predicted from its steady state characteristics. The analysis given in later chapters shows that this connection is so close that the steady state characteristics which may be obtained from stable structures are radically limited in comparison with the characteristics obtainable from mathematical functions chosen at random. Since there is no point in discussing the hypothetical " steady-state " character-

* In some modern oscillator circuits the amplitude of the oscillation is limited by a thermally controlled element. These are essentially linear circuits, since the change in the thermistor over one cycle is negligible, and it is not intended to exclude them here. After the thermistor reaches its steady value they can be regarded as stable structures, but with a root on the real frequency axis, as described later.

istic of a structure which will in fact sing when it is constructed, there is economy of thought in combining the two ideas to begin with. The essential statement of what we will mean by physical realizability can therefore be expressed by the following

Definition: A network function will be said to be physically realizable if it corresponds to a network of real elements having no modes of free vibration whose amplitudes increase indefinitely with time.

This will also be regarded as a definition of what is meant by a *stable** circuit. The relationship between the modes of free vibration and the steady state network functions is described in the following sections and, more generally, in later chapters.

The definition just given is the foundation upon which the analysis of general circuits, including both vacuum tubes and passive elements, will be based. A structure composed exclusively of passive elements, on the other hand, cannot give as wide a variety of characteristics as would be admissible from this definition alone. Since many of the units of which a typical feedback amplifier is composed, such as the interstage networks and the feedback circuit itself, are purely passive, it is of interest to determine what these additional restrictions on passive circuits may be. An analysis of this problem is given at the end of this chapter. Pending this analysis, the following results will be assumed:

1. A passive circuit is always stable.
2. The real component of a passive immittance is never negative at real frequencies.
3. If a passive network is driven by a single real frequency generator the power delivered to the network as a whole is always at least as great as the power consumed by any one resistance in the structure.

The second and third of these conditions are evidently merely consequences of the principle of conservation of energy, in combination with the fact that a passive network cannot contain a source of power. The justification for the first may not be quite so obvious, but the proof given later establishes it on the same general grounds, using the methods of classical dynamics.

* It is to be noticed that stability as defined here includes, as a limiting case, the possibility of purely sinusoidal transients which neither increase nor decrease with time, such as characterize purely reactive structures. This limiting case is discussed in more detail in a later section.

7.4. *Stability and the Roots of* Δ

Our first object will be the development of some analytic tool for investigating the relation between the steady state characteristics of the network and its stability. The stability of the circuit depends upon its possible transient responses and is therefore best determined from a study of the differential equations representing it. This is facilitated by the fact that the general mesh and nodal equations of Chapter I were first developed in differential form. Equations (1–2) of that chapter, for example, give the differential mesh equations and can be rewritten here as

$$
\begin{aligned}
&L_{11}\frac{di_1}{dt} + R_{11}i_1 + D_{11}\int i_1 dt + \cdots \\
&\qquad\qquad + L_{1n}\frac{di_n}{dt} + R_{1n}i_n + D_{1n}\int i_n dt = 0 \\
&L_{21}\frac{di_1}{dt} + R_{21}i_1 + D_{21}\int i_1 dt + \cdots \\
&\qquad\qquad + L_{2n}\frac{di_n}{dt} + R_{2n}i_n + D_{2n}\int i_n dt = 0 \\
&\cdots\cdots\cdots\cdots\cdots\cdots\cdots\cdots\cdots\cdots\cdots\cdots \qquad (7\text{–}1) \\
&\cdots\cdots\cdots\cdots\cdots\cdots\cdots\cdots\cdots\cdots\cdots\cdots \\
&L_{n1}\frac{di_1}{dt} + R_{n1}i_1 + D_{n1}\int i_1 dt + \cdots \\
&\qquad\qquad + L_{nn}\frac{di_n}{dt} + R_{nn}i_n + D_{nn}\int i_n dt = 0.
\end{aligned}
$$

These are essentially the same as the original expressions, but the instantaneous currents have been represented by small rather than capital letters and differentiation and integration with respect to time have been written out explicitly in order to avoid confusion with later notation. The driving voltages on the right-hand side of the equations have also been omitted, since we are interested only in the free response of the system.

Let it be supposed that the possible transients are exponentials of the general form e^{pt}. The individual currents $i_1, i_2, \cdots, i_n$ can be written as $I_1e^{pt}, I_2e^{pt}, \cdots, I_ne^{pt}$, where the I's are constants whose magnitudes will depend upon the original disturbance. In general, the p's representing possible transients may exist either as real quantities or as conjugate complex pairs. If p is complex the "currents" I_1e^{pt}, I_2e^{pt}, etc., must also be complex. As in Chapter II, however, the real components of these "currents" satisfy the differential equations by themselves and may be taken to represent the actual physical transients.

Upon substituting I_1e^{pt}, I_2e^{pt}, etc., in (7–1) and dividing out the common time factor, e^{pt}, the result appears as

$$\left(pL_{11} + R_{11} + \frac{D_{11}}{p}\right) I_1 + \left(pL_{12} + R_{12} + \frac{D_{12}}{p}\right) I_2 + \cdots + \left(pL_{1n} + R_{1n} + \frac{D_{1n}}{p}\right) I_n = 0$$

$$\left(pL_{21} + R_{21} + \frac{D_{21}}{p}\right) I_1 + \left(pL_{22} + R_{22} + \frac{D_{22}}{p}\right) I_2 + \cdots + \left(pL_{2n} + R_{2n} + \frac{D_{2n}}{p}\right) I_n = 0$$

$$\cdots\cdots\cdots\cdots\cdots\cdots\cdots\cdots \qquad (7\text{–}2)$$

$$\left(pL_{n1} + R_{n1} + \frac{D_{n1}}{p}\right) I_1 + \left(pL_{n2} + R_{n2} + \frac{D_{n2}}{p}\right) I_2 + \cdots + \left(pL_{nn} + R_{nn} + \frac{D_{nn}}{p}\right) I_n = 0.$$

It is evident that $I_1 = I_2 = \cdots = I_n = 0$ is always a solution of equations (7–2). Since there are n equations and n I's we may expect, in general, that the I's will be uniquely determined, so that this is the only solution. If the transient is to exist physically, however, some, at least, of the I's must be different from zero. This will be possible provided p is so chosen that the n equations represent fewer than n independent conditions on the I's. We might find, for example, that with a special choice of p one of the equations was equal to the sum of two others. It can be shown* that the general condition for the n equations to represent fewer than n independent relations is that the determinant of the coefficients in the equations should vanish. The expression which fixes the values of p which may represent transients is therefore

$$\Delta = 0 \qquad (7\text{–}3)$$

where Δ is, of course, identical with the Δ we have previously used and is a polynomial in p divided by some power of p.

If one of the p's which satisfies (7–3) lies in the left half-plane, it follows from the discussion in connection with Fig. 2.2 that the corresponding physical transient will be a damped sinusoid of the general form $e^{-\alpha t} \cos \beta t$. If p lies in the right half-plane, on the other hand, the transient will be of the form $e^{\alpha t} \cos \beta t$, where α is positive in either case. A sinusoid with exponentially increasing amplitude, such as $e^{\alpha t} \cos \beta t$, is, however, a

* See, for example, Dickson's *Modern Algebraic Theories*, p. 55, or Bôcher's *Introduction to Higher Algebra*, p. 47.

runaway transient of the type barred out by our preceding definition of physical realizability. We can therefore state the following

Theorem: None of the zeros of the principal determinant of a physical network can lie in the right half of the p plane.

An example of a permissible distribution of zeros is given by Fig. 7.1. As the figure shows, some of the zeros are taken as real and others as conjugate complex pairs. Most of the zeros are found in the interior of the left half-plane, but there is in addition one zero at the origin and a pair of conjugate zeros on the real frequency axis. Zeros of this type correspond to transients whose amplitudes are maintained with time but do not increase. There is thus no physical reason for barring them out on grounds of instability, but they represent the extreme limit which can be attained in a stable structure.

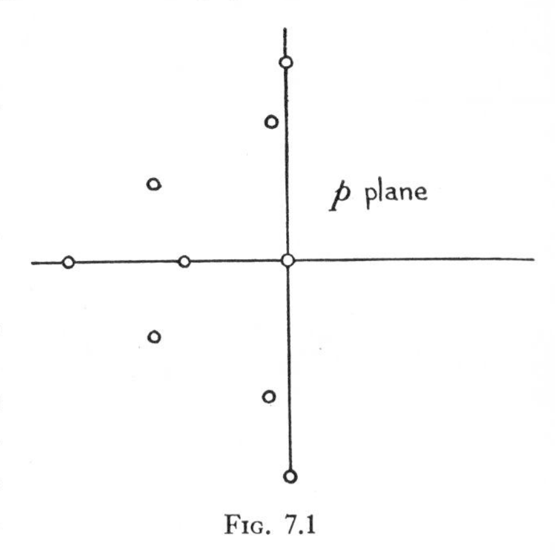

FIG. 7.1

A more detailed example of permissible zeros can be obtained by returning to the damped resonant circuit which was used as an illustration in Chapter II. The zeros were given by equation (2–27) of that chapter as

$$p_1 = -\frac{R}{2L} + \sqrt{\left(\frac{R}{2L}\right)^2 - \frac{D}{L}}; \quad p_2 = -\frac{R}{2L} - \sqrt{\left(\frac{R}{2L}\right)^2 - \frac{D}{L}}. \tag{7–4}$$

They were described there as the zeros of impedance but since $Z = \Delta/\Delta_{11}$ they are evidently the same as the zeros of Δ. When $R = 0$ the two p's lie on the real frequency axis. With moderate damping they occupy conjugate points in the left side of the p plane, while when the damping is extreme they are found on the negative real axis. This is illustrated by Fig. 2.4 of Chapter II. It is interesting to notice that in this simple case the stability requirement corresponds almost exactly to the requirement that all the elements be positive. If we change the sign of any one or any two of the elements at least one of the zeros will be found in the right half-plane. The only possibility is the obviously symmetrical situation obtained by making all three elements negative.

7.5. *Zeros of Δ on the Real Frequency Axis*

The possibility of securing zeros of Δ at real frequencies, which was exemplified by Fig. 7.1, merits further discussion. In passive structures zeros must be found at real frequencies if the network is composed only of pure reactances.* In the resonant circuit just described, for example, real frequency zeros were obtained by setting $R = 0$. They may also be obtained, even with dissipation, in active circuits containing sources of power which just balance the dissipative losses. As an example of this condition we may imagine a feedback amplifier which is normally stable but can be made unstable by an appropriate change in some continuously variable control. Zeros would be found on the real frequency axis in this circuit if we could set the controlling element on the exact point dividing the regions of stability and instability.

The probability of securing such exact balances or such ideally dissipationless elements in a physical structure is evidently infinitesimal. We are thus entitled to assume, if we wish, that all the zeros in physical circuits are somewhat to the left of the real frequency axis. This possibility will not be utilized in dealing with ordinary reactive resonances in passive circuits. The assumption of zero dissipation is frequently a convenient idealization, especially in dealing with driving-point immittances. On paper, it may also arise in transfer immittance problems, as it would, for example, if we were computing the transmission through a dissipationless filter which is either open- or short-circuited at both ends. For practical purposes, however, the consideration of four-terminal problems will be restricted to circuits in which the terminations, at least, are dissipative.

The other possibilities of securing real frequency zeros arise in circuits containing active elements. Here it will be convenient to suppose that the zeros lie, in fact, slightly to the left of the real frequency axis. Aside from the question of convenience, there are special physical reasons for making this assumption. At a real frequency zero a driving force of corresponding frequency inserted in any part of the circuit will produce an infinite response everywhere else in the circuit. For example, if the input and output of an amplifier are represented respectively by 1 and 2 the output current in response to a unit input voltage is Δ_{12}/Δ, so that there should be infinite gain to a driving force whose frequency coincided with one of the zeros of Δ. In a physical situation, of course, we would expect the active elements to become overloaded and excessively non-linear as soon as this frequency was approached. Since the exact location of the zero would be immaterial in any case if we were interested only in driving forces at more remote frequencies, there is thus a special justification for the assumption on grounds of linearity.

A convenient example is furnished by the thermistor controlled oscillator described in a previous footnote. If the amplitude of the oscillation is

* See, for example, the discussion given near the end of the chapter.

small and there is reasonable selectivity in the thermistor circuit this should be a linear network for signal voltages at frequencies remote from that of the natural oscillation. In these ranges, however, the steady state characteristics are negligibly affected if we move the zero of Δ slightly away from the real frequency axis. If driving forces in the neighborhood of the zero are applied the circuit must become non-linear, since we can no longer assume high discrimination against signal currents in the thermistor circuit, and the thermistor temperature will be affected by the heat generated due to the passage of signal currents through it.

If zeros of Δ *are* assumed to occur at real frequencies they are subject to one restriction which has not appeared heretofore. It was tacitly assumed in discussing (7–3) that all the zeros were separate. In special cases, however, multiple zeros may occur. It is known that in such circumstances the form of the transient solution may be changed. Instead of consisting solely of exponentials it may also include exponentials multiplied by powers of t. For example, if p is a double zero of (7–3) the corresponding transient appears in the general form $Ae^{pt} + Bte^{pt}$. If p is in the interior of either the right or left half-plane the extra factor t in the second term is of no significance in determining whether the transient will increase or diminish with time, since it is overwhelmed by the exponential. In the special case when p is on the real frequency axis, however, it makes an increasing transient of one which would otherwise be merely persistent. Since transients which increase with time are inadmissible we can therefore state the

Theorem: Zeros of Δ on the real frequency axis must be simple.*

7.6. *Zeros of Other Determinants*

In addition to Δ itself, the network formulae which have been developed involve other determinants derivable from Δ in various ways. One group of these includes Δ^0 and what may be called the "symmetrical" minors Δ_{ii}, Δ_{jj}, Δ_{iijj}, etc. Each of these quantities can be regarded as the form to which Δ reduces when some prescribed change is made in the network

* This theorem is not rigorously true in degenerate circuits. Suppose, for example, that the system consists of two identical but entirely independent units. A single set of mesh equations may be used to describe both units. The determinant of the system will be the product of the determinants for the two units separately, and must have a double zero at any real frequency at which the determinants of the separate units have simple zeros. The slightest coupling between the units, however, will destroy this relation. In any event, such an exception does not destroy the physical consequences of the theorem, since we are eventually interested in the zeros, not of Δ itself, but of the ratio of Δ to one of its principal minors. If Δ has a multiple zero because of such a degeneracy, the minor will have a zero one order lower, so that the zero of the ratio is still simple.

and their zeros can consequently be limited in the same way as those of Δ itself if the network is known to be stable after the change is made. Thus Δ^0 is the form to which Δ reduces when some given element W vanishes and can have no zeros in the right half-plane, and only simple zeros at real frequencies, if the circuit is stable with W absent. This would certainly be true, for example, if W represents one of the tubes in an ordinary single loop amplifier, since when W vanishes the loop is opened.

Similarly, such quantities as Δ_{ii} or Δ_{jj} are the cofactors of W_{ii} or W_{jj} in Δ. They are thus the forms to which Δ reduces* when W_{ii} or W_{jj} becomes infinite. This is equivalent to open-circuiting the ith or jth mesh, if we are using a mesh analysis, or short-circuiting the ith or jth node to ground, if we are using a nodal analysis. In the same way, Δ_{iijj} gives the result when the open or short circuit is applied both at i and at j. The zeros of any of these quantities are restricted in the same way as those of Δ itself if the network is stable after the open or short circuit is applied. This is true, for example, if we are dealing with a series impedance or shunt admittance in a single loop amplifier, since an open-circuited series branch or a short-circuited shunt branch will break the feedback loop.

All these relations become particularly simple in passive networks. Obviously, a passive network is still passive after any of these various operations is performed upon it. The proposition stated previously, that a passive network is always stable, therefore allows us to establish the

Theorem: In a passive circuit none of the zeros either of Δ^0 or of any of the symmetrical minors of Δ can lie in the right half of the p plane, and any zeros on the real frequency axis must be simple.

The remaining determinants which appear in the network formulae are "unsymmetrical" minors of the general types Δ_{ij}, Δ_{ijkk}, Δ_{ijkl}, etc. These can evidently be regarded as the forms to which Δ reduces when indefinitely large unilateral couplings are added to the circuit. For example, since Δ_{ij} is the cofactor of W_{ij}, it is the limit which would be approached by Δ if we introduced into the circuit an ideal vacuum tube of extremely high gain with grid terminals at j and plate at i. Unfortunately, there is ordinarily no simple method of determining whether the circuit will be stable after this modification is made, so that such a physical interpretation is of no great value. For circuits of general physical configuration it appears that the zeros of these unsymmetrical cofactors may appear in any part of the plane, even when the structure is made up entirely of passive

* Obviously, the limits approached by Δ in the two cases are actually $W_{ii}\Delta_{ii}$ and $W_{jj}\Delta_{jj}$. Since we are concerned only with the location of the zeros of Δ, however, the multipliers W_{ii} and W_{jj} can be disregarded.

elements. They are restricted only by the conjugacy condition. Restrictions on these zeros can sometimes be imposed when the network is known to have one of certain special physical configurations, but this is more conveniently discussed in a later chapter.

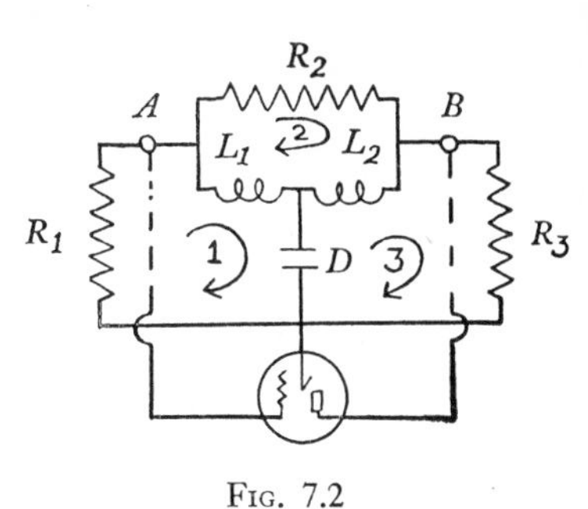

Fig. 7.2

7.7. *Zeros in an Illustrative Circuit*

These principles will be exemplified by means of the circuit shown by Fig. 7.2. The structure will be taken initially as the Bridged-T of purely passive elements. The broken lines shown going to *A* and *B* are connections made to the vacuum tube at a later stage to show how an active element affects the stability of the circuit.

It will be assumed for concreteness that all the passive elements are of unit magnitude. If the meshes are chosen as shown in the figure, with the tube deleted, the mesh equations in the absence of any driving force are

$$\begin{aligned} \left(p + 1 + \frac{1}{p}\right) I_1 - pI_2 - \frac{1}{p} I_3 &= 0 \\ -pI_1 + (2p + 1)\, I_2 - pI_3 &= 0 \\ -\frac{1}{p} I_1 - pI_2 + \left(p + 1 + \frac{1}{p}\right) I_3 &= 0. \end{aligned} \tag{7-5}$$

The equation corresponding to (7–3) is consequently

$$\Delta = \begin{vmatrix} p + 1 + \frac{1}{p} & -p & -\frac{1}{p} \\ -p & 2p + 1 & -p \\ -\frac{1}{p} & -p & p + 1 + \frac{1}{p} \end{vmatrix} = 0 \tag{7-6}$$

or

$$\Delta = \frac{1}{p}(3p^3 + 4p^2 + 7p + 2) = 0. \tag{7-7}$$

The roots of (7–7) are $p = -\frac{1}{3}$ and $p = -\frac{1}{2}(1 \pm i\sqrt{7})$. They are indicated by the circles in Fig. 7.3. They are all on the left half of the p plane, as of course they should be, since the network, being passive, is necessarily stable.

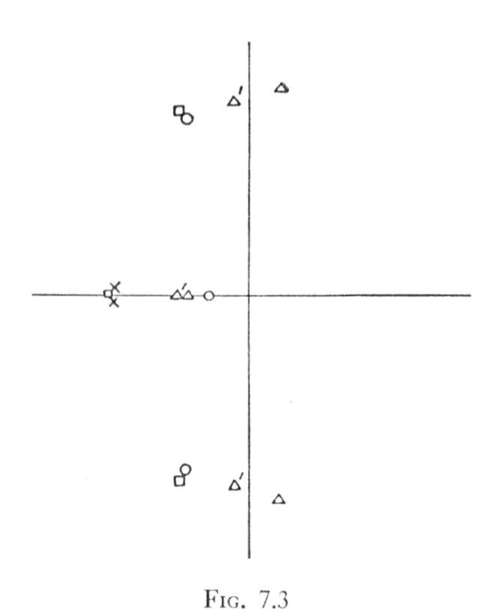

FIG. 7.3

We may next proceed to verify that the zeros of Δ^0 and of the symmetrical minors of Δ are also confined to the left half-plane, for the passive structure. Let it be supposed that Δ^0 represents the system when $L_2 = 0$. The disappearance of L_2 is equivalent to replacing the Z_{22}, Z_{23}, Z_{32}, and Z_{33} terms in (7–6) respectively by $(p + 1)$, 0, 0, and $(1 + 1/p)$. We readily find that the equation corresponding to (7–7) appears as

$$\Delta^0 = \frac{2}{p}(1 + p)^2. \tag{7–8}$$

This has a double root at $p = -1$, which is, of course, in the left half-plane. The double root is represented by the crosses in Fig. 7.3. Similar results hold if Δ^0 represents the system after any other element has vanished.

As an example of a symmetrical minor we will take Δ_{22}. This quantity is given from (7–6) as

$$\Delta_{22} = \begin{vmatrix} p + 1 + \frac{1}{p} & -\frac{1}{p} \\ -\frac{1}{p} & p + 1 + \frac{1}{p} \end{vmatrix}$$

$$= \frac{1}{p}(p^3 + 2p^2 + 3p + 2). \tag{7–9}$$

The roots are in the left half-plane at the points -1 and $-\frac{1}{2}(1 \pm i\sqrt{7})$. They are indicated by the squares in Fig. 7.3.* The second order symmetrical minors are still simpler since they are the same as the self-impedances

* The fact that many of the roots of these various expressions happen to coincide is due to the specially simple and symmetrical form of the network, and would not be true in general. For example, R_1, R_3, L_1, and L_2 constitute a balanced bridge as seen from R_2. A generator in series with R_2 can therefore produce no current in D, so that the driving point impedance measured in the second mesh must be much simpler than the structural complexity of the circuit would indicate. This is reflected by the fact that Δ and Δ_{22} have common roots, which cancel out in the ratio Δ/Δ_{22}, representing this impedance.

of the several meshes. For example, we have $\Delta_{1133} = 2p + 1$, with a root at $p = -\frac{1}{2}$.

The properties of the unsymmetrical minors will be illustrated by means of Δ_{31}. We find from (7–6) that

$$\Delta_{31} = \begin{vmatrix} -p & -\dfrac{1}{p} \\ 2p+1 & -p \end{vmatrix}$$

$$= \frac{1}{p}(p^3 + 2p + 1). \tag{7–10}$$

The roots occur at $p = -0.453$ and at $p = +0.227 \pm i1.47$, as shown by the triangles in Fig. 7.3. They are thus found in both halves of the plane. This must be anticipated, in general, whenever we are dealing with unrestricted circuits. By choosing special configurations or special element values, on the other hand, the roots of an unsymmetrical minor may be confined to the left half-plane, just as are those of the determinants previously considered. As an example, suppose that a resistance R is added in series with L_1 of Fig. 7.2. We may suppose that R is simultaneously subtracted from R_1 and R_2, so that the change affects Z_{12} and Z_{21} but not the self-impedances Z_{11} and Z_{22}. It is readily shown that (7–10) becomes

$$\Delta'_{31} = \frac{1}{p}(p^3 + Rp^2 + 2p + 1). \tag{7–11}$$

All the roots lie in the left half-plane when $R > \frac{1}{2}$. For example, if $R = \frac{2}{3}$ they are found at $p = -0.52$ and at $p = -0.074 \pm i1.38$. These locations are shown by the primed triangles in Fig. 7.3. The reason for paying particular attention to networks for which the roots of at least certain specified unsymmetrical minors can be confined to the left half-plane is that this leads to the "minimum phase" condition, which is of considerable importance in amplifier theory. "Minimum phase" networks are mentioned again in one of the following sections, but a detailed discussion of their properties is reserved for a later chapter.

In order to exemplify the changes which may be produced in these results by the presence of an active element, we may suppose that the vacuum tube is added to the network by closing the connections indicated by the broken lines in Fig. 7.2. We can take R_1 and R_3 to represent the grid and plate impedances of the tube. Since $R_1 = 1$, the transimpedance of the tube, which is equal in general to μ times its grid impedance, becomes simply μ, and the incorporation of the tube is equivalent to adding μ to Z_{31} in the mesh equations. The new determinant of the system is readily found from this as

$$\Delta = \begin{vmatrix} p + 1 + \frac{1}{p} & -p & -\frac{1}{p} \\ -p & 2p + 1 & -p \\ \mu - \frac{1}{p} & -p & p + 1 + \frac{1}{p} \end{vmatrix}$$

$$= \frac{1}{p}[3p^3 + 4p^2 + 7p + 2 + \mu(p^3 + 2p + 1)]. \qquad (7\text{–}12)$$

When μ is very small the zeros of (7–12) will evidently be very close to those originally determined from (7–7). As μ is made larger and larger, however, some of them will eventually appear in the right half-plane, so that the network will become unstable. This can be studied most easily by observing that since the zeros must vary continuously with μ they can go from one half-plane to the other only by crossing the real frequency axis. If we assign a pure imaginary value to p in (7–12), however, the real and imaginary components of the expression can be separated and equated to zero individually. This gives

$$(3 + \mu)p^3 + (7 + 2\mu)p = 0 \qquad (7\text{–}13)$$

and

$$4p^2 + (2 + \mu) = 0. \qquad (7\text{–}14)$$

If we eliminate μ between (7–13) and (7–14) the result is

$$4p^5 + 7p^3 - 3p = 0, \qquad (7\text{–}15)$$

which is satisfied by $p = 0$, $p^2 = -2.1$, and $p^2 = +0.35$. The last of these can be disregarded, since it evidently does not correspond to a point on the real frequency axis. It represents an accidental solution of (7–13) and (7–14) in another part of the plane. The first two, however, are valid solutions and correspond respectively to $\mu = -2$ and $\mu = +6.4$. We can therefore conclude that the network will be stable for $6.4 > \mu > -2$, and will sing when μ is taken beyond these limits. For example when $\mu = 9$ the zeros are $p = -0.43$ and $p = +0.05 \pm i1.45$, while when $\mu = -2.5$ they are $p = +0.18$, $p = -0.74$ and $p = -7.5$.*

These relations are illustrated by Fig. 7.4. As the gain of the tube is changed from $\mu = 0$ to $\mu = +\infty$ the zeros move along the approximate

* The negative μ assumed here could not, of course, be obtained from an ordinary tube, but it might be secured by using one of the " negative transconductance " tubes which have been developed experimentally.

paths shown by the solid lines in the drawing, following the directions indicated by the arrows. The paths for the range $\mu = 0$ to $\mu = -\infty$ are shown by the broken lines. The crosses and squares correspond to the roots just determined for the special values $\mu = 9$ and $\mu = -2.5$. The circles give the original positions of the zeros when $\mu = 0$ and the triangles their final positions when $\mu = \pm\infty$. As a comparison of (7–10) and (7–12) indicates, the final positions are the same as those of the roots of

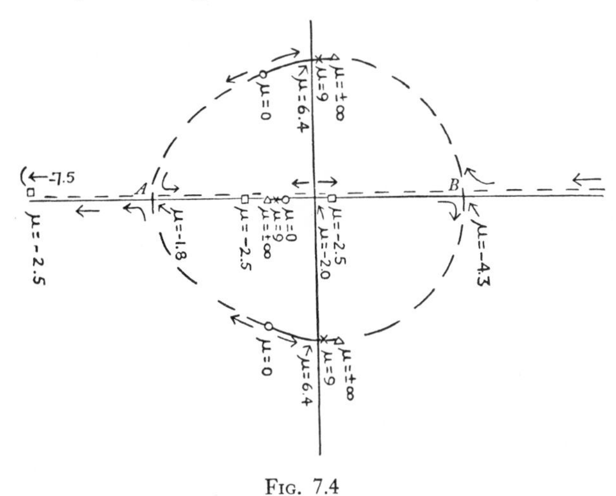

Fig. 7.4

Δ_{31}. Since some of the roots of Δ_{31} are found in the right half-plane in this illustration, it is evident without further analysis that the circuit must sing if μ is made sufficiently large in either direction. This may serve to explain to some extent the reason why so much stress was laid in our previous discussion on the possibility of confining the roots of this determinant to the left half-plane.

The modifications produced in the other determinants of the network by the addition of the active element are of a similar type. The chief point to notice is that the zeros of Δ^0 and of the symmetrical minors necessarily occur in the left side of the plane only when the circuit is passive. After the addition of the tube they will, in general, appear in the right side for μ's beyond a certain range. As a final example we may consider the effect of the tube on Δ_{22}. When μ is included this determinant becomes

$$\Delta_{22} = \frac{1}{p}(p^3 + 2p^2 + 3p + 2 + \mu). \tag{7–16}$$

We readily find with the help of methods similar to those used in connection with (7–12) that all the zeros of this expression lie in the left half-plane for $4 > \mu > -2$, but that some of them occur in the right half-plane for μ's outside this range.

It is to be observed that the range of stability for Δ_{22} is not identical with that for Δ. For example, if we were to choose $\mu = 5$ the network as it stands would be stable, since all the zeros of Δ are still in the left half-plane, but the structure would sing if R_2 were open-circuited, since with this value of μ some of the zeros of Δ_{22} have crossed the real frequency axis.

7.8. *Summary of Requirements on Network Functions*

It is convenient to pause here to summarize the implications of the preceding discussion for the various network functions. The network functions can be listed as the driving point immittance $W = \Delta/\Delta_{jj}$, the transfer immittance $W_T = \Delta/\Delta_{ij}$, the return difference $F = \Delta/\Delta^0$, the absolute sensitivity $S = -\Delta\Delta_{12}/W\Delta_{13}\Delta_{42}$, and the relative sensitivity $S' = -\Delta\Delta_{1243}/\Delta_{13}\Delta_{42}$. The two sensitivities and the return difference are included here largely for the sake of completeness. Design methods to give direct control of sensitivity, in cases where it departs materially from the return difference, have not yet been developed. The return difference is under better design control, but in ordinary circumstances it is most easily treated in terms of the return ratio, which, since it is a loop transmission characteristic, has properties essentially similar to those of the transfer immittance.

We will begin by listing the requirements which must be met by network functions corresponding to any stable physical circuit, and continue with additional requirements which are satisfied by special classes of structures of particular interest, though not by all structures. The most obvious requirements arise from the fact that the driving point and transfer immittances, the return difference, and the two sensitivities are all rational functions of p with real coefficients. They must therefore meet the following conditions:

1. Zeros and poles are either real or occur in conjugate complex pairs.
2. The real and imaginary components are respectively even and odd functions of frequency on the real frequency axis.

These are the only requirements which can be placed upon the sensitivities, in general. We cannot even restrict the location of their zeros, since the numerators of the two expressions include, respectively, the unsymmetrical minors Δ_{12} and Δ_{1243}, whose roots may lie anywhere. These functions will therefore not be considered further here. The numerators of the remaining three functions consist of Δ alone. For these functions, consequently, we can state the following additional requirements:

3. None of the zeros can be found in the right half-plane.
4. Zeros on the real frequency axis must be simple.*

These four requirements are the only ones which can be stated for the driving point and transfer immittances and the return difference in the general case. For example, in terms of the notation adopted earlier in this section the poles of these several functions are respectively the roots of the determinants Δ_{jj}, Δ_{ij}, and Δ^0. It will be recalled from our earlier discussion that nothing in general could be said about the roots of Δ_{ij}. The roots of Δ_{jj} and Δ^0 were interpreted as the natural modes of vibration of the network after it was modified in certain special ways, and therefore could not appear in the right half-plane if the modifications did not make the circuit unstable. In general, however, there is no necessary connection between the stability of the modified and unmodified structures. For example the illustrative circuit described in the preceding section was stable in its normal condition when the gain of the tube lay in an intermediate range near $\mu = 5$, but became unstable in this range for the condition represented by making Δ_{22} the criterion.

We must therefore conclude that in the most general case the poles of the return difference and of the driving point and transfer immittance functions may lie anywhere in the plane. Nevertheless, the special conditions for which they are confined to the left half-plane are of particular interest. They may be listed as follows:

5a. None of the poles of the return difference can lie in the right half-plane, and poles on the real frequency axis must be simple, if the circuit remains stable when the specified element W vanishes. This requirement is always met by a passive network.

5b. None of the poles of a driving point immittance can lie in the right half-plane, and poles on the real frequency axis must be simple, if the circuit remains stable when an infinite immittance is added between the driving terminals. This requirement is always met by a passive network.

5c. Poles of the transfer immittance may occasionally be found in the right half-plane, even for passive networks. Transfer immittances having no poles in the right half-plane, however, have the special property of being " minimum phase shift " functions. The reason for adopting this name, and the significance of the minimum phase relation, will be discussed in later chapters. It makes no difference for the minimum phase property whether poles on the real frequency axis are simple or multiple.

These five requirements complete the list of conditions of special interest

* With the restriction that zeros exactly on this axis may sometimes be regarded as inadmissible from the considerations discussed previously.

for the return difference, but it is desirable to carry the consideration of driving point and transfer immittances one or two steps further. The principal remaining point is the fact that either of these immittance functions can satisfy all the preceding requirements and still not correspond to a passive network. The additional requirements which must be satisfied by passive structures are, however, readily derived from the conditions described earlier and can be written as follows:

6a. The real component of the driving point immittance of a passive circuit cannot be negative at real frequencies.

6b. If a transfer immittance function corresponds to a passive network, the response which it specifies in the final branch, representing the load, must not be so great that the power consumed in the load at any real frequency would exceed the power which would be delivered by the generator if it were separated from the network and connected to a load equal to the conjugate of its own internal immittance.

Condition *6a* is evidently only a restatement of the second of the three conditions given previously for passive structures. The fact that it is not a consequence of the first five conditions is easily seen if we notice that they would be satisfied equally well by the negative of a passive immittance. It is also possible to satisfy them with an immittance function whose real component is positive in some frequency ranges and negative in others, as is shown by the examples given in the next section. Condition *6b* can be understood if it is recalled that the maximum power obtainable from a generator with a prescribed internal immittance is secured when the load is equal to the conjugate of the internal immittance.* This maximum must evidently be at least as great as the power which would flow from the generator into the actual network, and therefore, from the last of the three power conditions, at least as great as the power consumed by the actual load.

It is important to notice that *6a* and *6b*, although they both refer to passive circuits, are in other respects quite dissimilar and cannot be interchanged. For example, another way of expressing *6a* is to say that the phase angle of a driving point immittance cannot exceed $\pm 90°$. This would be an entirely irrational limitation in most transfer immittance problems, where the phase shifts may, in general, be made as large as we please. Similarly, in dealing with *6b* we may notice that the transfer immittance, since it is a rational function of frequency, is completely determined by its zeros and poles together with a multiplying constant. The

* See, for example, K. S. Johnson, *Transmission Circuits for Telephonic Communication*, p. 14.

response in the final branch varies inversely with the transfer immittance and, with given zeros and poles, can be made as small as we please* everywhere on the real frequency axis, by choosing the constant multiplier large enough. Condition *6b* is thus, in effect, a limitation on the constant multiplier and would have no meaning in a driving point immittance problem.

One final requirement, which specifies a particular class of driving point immittances analogous to the minimum phase shift class of transfer immittances, may also be mentioned. As in the minimum phase shift case, the properties to which the restriction leads will be discussed in a later chapter. It is introduced here merely to secure a complete list for future reference. We have:

7. A driving point impedance which meets the foregoing requirements on driving point immittances and in addition has no zeros on the real frequency axis is of "minimum susceptance" type, and it is of "minimum reactance" type if it has no poles on the real frequency axis. If the function represents a driving point admittance the terms "minimum susceptance" and "minimum reactance" are interchanged. It is evidently possible for an immittance to be both "minimum susceptance" and "minimum reactance."

7.9. *Examples of Admissible Network Functions*

These various requirements may be exemplified by the set of expressions given in the following list.

$$
\begin{aligned}
Z_1 &= \frac{p^2 + p + 2}{5p^2 + 3p + 4} & R_1 &= \frac{5\omega^4 - 11\omega^2 + 8}{(4 - 5\omega^2)^2 + 9\omega^2} \\
Z_2 &= \frac{p^2 + p + 2}{4p^2 + 2p + 2} & R_2 &= \frac{4(1 - \omega^2)^2}{(2 - 4\omega^2)^2 + 4\omega^2} \\
Z_3 &= \frac{p^2 + p + 2}{3p^2 + p} & R_3 &= \frac{3\omega^2 - 5}{9\omega^2 + 1} \\
Z_4 &= \frac{p^2 + p + 2}{2p^2 - 2} & R_4 &= \frac{\omega^2 - 2}{2(\omega^2 + 1)}.
\end{aligned}
\tag{7-17}
$$

The expressions have been written as impedances, since driving point immittance functions, in general, may satisfy the most elaborate set of requirements. The R's represent the real components of the corresponding

* Since the analysis implies that the circuit is dissipative, zeros of transfer immittance at real frequencies, which would invalidate this argument, are ruled out for the reasons given previously.

Z's at real frequencies, and are determined by substituting $p = i\omega$ and rationalizing in the ordinary manner. Each impedance is obtained from the preceding one by combining it in parallel with a resistance of value -1.* This is illustrated by Fig. 7.5, where the internal impedance of the generator is assumed to be zero. The short-circuit generator impedance is important, since the impedance zeros which determine stability are those of the complete network, including the generator. If the generator impedance is not zero the addition of the successive negative resistances may evidently affect the zeros of the complete impedance, and therefore the stability.

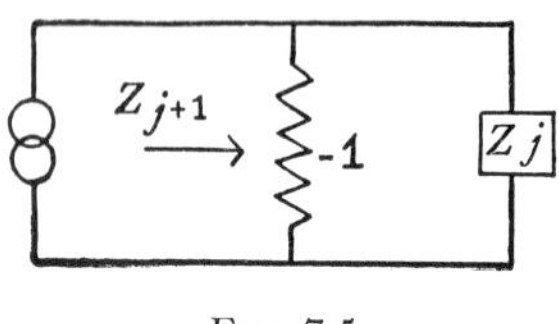

FIG. 7.5

Turning first to Z_1 in (7–17), we notice that it is a rational function of p with real coefficients whose zeros and poles are all in the left half-plane. It thus meets requirements 1, 2, 3, 4, and *5b* of the preceding list. In the corresponding R_1, the denominator, being a sum of squares, is always positive at real frequencies. The numerator is also always positive, since it can change sign only by passing through zero, and it is readily seen that it has no zeros for real values of ω. Z_1 therefore meets requirement *6a* also and represents a passive impedance. Since it has no zeros or poles on the real frequency axis, it also meets, incidentally, the " minimum reactance " and " minimum susceptance " conditions as given by requirement 7.

As we add negative conductance gradually in parallel with Z_1, there is at first no change in the character of the function.† The resistance component however diminishes and may at length become negative. The boundary condition is represented by Z_2. R_2 is still positive everywhere, but touches zero at $\omega = \pm 1$. With further increments of negative conductance, condition *6a* is no longer satisfied, although the remaining conditions, including *5b*, may still be valid. For example, in Z_3 the resistance component changes sign at $\omega = \pm\sqrt{5/3}$. The poles are still in the left half-plane, although one of them is on the boundary at $p = 0$. Finally, Z_4 represents an impedance satisfying only the first four conditions.

The addition of more and more negative conductance in the circuit of Fig. 7.5 will evidently not make the circuit unstable, so that beyond Z_4 the first four conditions are always satisfied. An example of an unstable

* The introduction of the negative resistance is adopted merely to provide a systematic way of going from one impedance expression to the next, and is not intended to raise any questions concerning the physical construction or characteristics of such a device. The purposes of the present section are served if we take the impedance expressions one at a time without regard to any physical relation between them.

† That is, it still meets the passive requirements and could be represented by *some* network including only positive passive elements.

circuit can, however, be obtained by adding an appropriate negative resistance in series with the early Z's, or either a negative or a positive resistance in series with Z_4. Thus if we add $+2$ to Z_4 the result is

$$Z_5 = \frac{5p^2 + p - 2}{2p^2 - 2}. \tag{7-18}$$

This has zeros at $p = -0.74$ and $p = +0.54$ and therefore represents an unstable structure.

The same set of rational expressions can also be used to exemplify the other network functions. For example, if we regard the various Z's as representing transfer rather than driving point impedances, we can immediately classify Z_1, Z_2, and Z_3 as physically realizable expressions of the minimum phase type. Z_4 is physically realizable but non-minimum phase, since it includes a pole in the right half-plane, while Z_5 is non-physical. The chief differences occur in the application of the passive network conditions. For the transfer impedance case, the vanishing of the real component on the real frequency axis, as exemplified by Z_2, is no longer a matter of particular significance. We are interested, on the contrary, in the minimum absolute values of the various functions on the real frequency axis. For example, it is readily shown that the minimum absolute value of Z_2 at real frequencies is 0.19. This means that the maximum current flowing in the load in response to a unit generator in the source will be $1/0.19 = 5.29$, so that if we represent the load resistance by R_j the corresponding power is $28.0R_j$. The maximum power obtainable from a unit generator is however $1/4R_i$, where R_i is the internal resistance of the generator. The passive network condition therefore demands that

$$28.0R_j \leq \frac{1}{4R_i}. \tag{7-19}$$

Z_2 as it stands will therefore represent a passive function if R_i and R_j are sufficiently small. In other cases it can be made into a passive function by multiplying it by a suitable constant.

If the rational functions are taken as return differences, the first four Z's represent physically realizable expressions, although Z_4 corresponds to a network which would be unstable if the prescribed W vanished. If the expressions represent sensitivities the situation is still simpler, since there is no limitation even on the zeros of this function, and all five expressions can be regarded as physically realizable.

7.10. *Energy Relations in a Passive Network*

As the final step in this discussion, we will turn to the consideration of the three special conditions on passive networks which were postulated, without proof, near the beginning of the chapter. Since the distinctive feature of a passive network is the fact that it does not contain a source of power, an obvious point of departure in establishing these conditions is found in a study of the power and energy relations in the circuit.*

The instantaneous power dissipated in any one resistance R in the structure is i^2R, where i is the instantaneous current flowing through the element. Similarly, the instantaneous energy stored in the magnetic field of an inductance is $\frac{1}{2}i^2L$, while the instantaneous energy storage in a condenser is $\frac{1}{2}q^2D$, where $q = \int i\,dt$ is the charge on the condenser. Each of these quantities must be positive if the corresponding R, L, or D is positive and in a network containing only positive elements the total stored energy or dissipated power must therefore be positive for any choices of the instantaneous i's and q's. This is the fundamental condition upon which the analysis is based.

The expression of the total stored energy or dissipated power directly in terms of the individual elements of the network is not very useful, principally because none of our other formulae are stated in these terms. It is a comparatively simple matter, however, to construct alternative power and energy formulae in terms of the coefficients in the mesh or nodal equations. We may begin, for example, with a set of differential mesh equations similar to (7–1), except that the equations will be referred to the steady state condition by introducing the instantaneous voltages $e_1, \cdots, e_n$ on their right-hand sides. Let it be supposed that the first equation is multiplied by i_1, the second by i_2, etc., and that the equations are then added. The result is

$$\sum_{r,s=1}^{r,s=n}\sum R_{rs}i_ri_s + \sum_{r,s=1}^{r,s=n}\sum L_{rs}i_r\frac{di_s}{dt} + \sum_{r,s=1}^{r,s=n}\sum D_{rs}i_rq_s = \sum_{r=1}^{r=n} e_ri_r \tag{7–20}$$

where the first summation, for example, represents a series of terms of the form

$$R_{11}i_1^2 + R_{12}i_1i_2 + \cdots + R_{1n}i_1i_n + R_{21}i_2i_1 + R_{22}i_2^2 + \cdots + R_{nn}i_n^2,$$

and q_s in the third summation has been written, for brevity, in place of $\int i_s\,dt$.

On the right-hand side, each term of the form e_ri_r is evidently equal to the instantaneous power fed into the circuit by the rth generator, so that the summation gives the total instantaneous power supplied to the circuit

* The method given here is a paraphrase of the standard dynamical treatment of small oscillations. See, for example, Webster's *Dynamics*, Chapter V, or Whittaker *Analytical Dynamics*, Chapters II and VII.

from the outside. The first summation on the left-hand side must represent the instantaneous power dissipated by the resistances, since it is the only term which would be present in a purely resistive network. It can be written as twice* the " dissipation function " F, where F is defined by

$$F = \frac{1}{2} \sum_{r=1}^{r=n} \sum_{s=1}^{s=n} R_{rs} i_r i_s. \tag{7-21}$$

The remaining terms on the left-hand side represent the rates of change of the stored energies associated with the coils and condensers of the network. For example, if $r = s$ in the second summation we can write the corresponding term as $L_{rr} i_r (di_r/dt) = (d/dt) \frac{1}{2} L_{rr} i_r^2$. If $r \neq s$ we may make use of the fact that since this is a passive circuit we must have $L_{rs} = L_{sr}$.† The sum of the corresponding rs and sr terms can therefore be written as

$$L_{rs}\left(i_r \frac{di_s}{dt} + i_s \frac{di_r}{dt}\right) = L_{rs} \frac{d}{dt}(i_r i_s) = \frac{d}{dt}\frac{1}{2}(L_{rs} i_r i_s + L_{sr} i_s i_r).$$

Evidently, the complete second summation becomes dT/dt, where T is the stored magnetic energy and can be written as

$$T = \frac{1}{2} \sum_{r=1}^{r=n} \sum_{s=1}^{s=n} L_{rs} i_r i_s. \tag{7-22}$$

In the third summation it is convenient to set $i_j = dq_j/dt$. Following the procedure just used, this allows us to write the summation as dV/dt, where V represents the stored energy in the condensers and is given by

$$V = \frac{1}{2} \sum_{r=1}^{r=n} \sum_{s=1}^{s=n} D_{rs} q_r q_s. \tag{7-23}$$

The essential result of this discussion has been the development of the expressions for the quadratic forms F, T, and V, as given by (7-21), (7-22), and (7-23). It follows from our previous discussion that in a network composed only of positive elements, F, T, and V must all be positive. Moreover, we can regard the individual i's and q's as assuming arbitrary values in making this statement, since we began with arbitrary generators in each mesh. F, T, and V must therefore remain positive if we assign the

* The factor two is introduced arbitrarily to secure symmetry with the functions considered later. The use of the symbols F, T, and V for the energy functions follows standard dynamical usage. There should be no confusion with the other meanings, of return difference, return ratio, etc., assigned to the same symbols, since the energy function discussion is not continued beyond the present chapter.

† The use of the reciprocity condition here and in later sections should be noticed particularly, since it explains why this type of analysis is restricted to passive networks.

i's and q's any other values whatever, positive or negative, and can vanish only if all the i's and q's vanish.* In mathematical language the three functions are *positive definite.*

The positive definite conditions can best be understood as a set of restrictions on the values which the mesh coefficients R_{rs}, L_{rs}, and D_{rs} can assume if the system of mesh equations as a whole is to correspond to a passive network. Suppose, for example, that all the i's except i_1 were chosen equal to zero. F would reduce to $\frac{1}{2}R_{11}i_1^2$. The positive definite condition evidently requires that $R_{11} > 0$. Similarly, all the other coefficients of the type R_{jj}, L_{jj}, or D_{jj} must be positive. If the energy functions included only " self " coefficients of this type, as they would if they represented sums of powers and energies for the individual physical elements, this would be the whole story. Account must, however, also be taken of coupling terms such as $R_{rs}i_ri_s$, where $r \neq s$. Whatever the sign of R_{rs} may be, this term may evidently be made negative by proper choice of the signs of i_r and i_s. The positive definite condition therefore requires that the absolute values of such mutual coefficients as R_{rs} be not too great in comparison with the self coefficients. An example is furnished by the function

$$F = i_1^2 + ki_1i_2 + i_2^2. \tag{7–24}$$

If $|k| < 2$, this expression is positive for all real values of i_1 and i_2, as we can see most easily by setting the expression equal to zero and noticing that the roots, in terms of i_1/i_2, must be complex. For other values of k, however, the expression may be made to cross zero and become negative by varying i_1/i_2 appropriately. For $|k| > 2$, therefore, the expression is no longer positive definite. With more than two i's the situation is more complicated but the essential pattern of relationships is preserved. In general, the self and mutual coefficients obey the same laws as the self and mutual inductances in a set of coils with physically realizable coefficients of coupling, as we might expect, since both conditions reflect a positive energy requirement.

7.11. *Impedance and Energy Relations at Real Frequencies*

With the development of expressions for the functions F, T, and V we are prepared to prove the three special conditions on passive networks postulated near the beginning of the chapter. The present section will consider only the second and third of these conditions.

* The last part of this statement is intended as a characterization of networks in general, and may have exceptions in special cases. For example, if the first mesh includes no inductance the stored magnetic energy will evidently be zero for any choice of i_1, as long as the other i's vanish.

Since the second and third conditions are stated in terms of steady state characteristics, it is natural to begin with the ordinary steady state mesh equations for the circuit. The analysis will be based upon a set of energy expressions built up by multiplying each mesh equation by a corresponding current and then summing all the equations, much as was done in obtaining (7–20). One modification, however, must be made to take account of the fact that since (7–20) was developed from the differential equations of the circuit, its energy functions were expressed in terms of the true instantaneous currents and voltages in the structure. The I's and E's which appear in a set of ordinary steady state mesh equations, on the other hand, are merely complex quantities which are brought into the analysis when the true currents and voltages are replaced by fictitious expressions of the type $I_j e^{pt}$ and $E_j e^{pt}$, in accordance with the conventions described in Chapter II. This, however, still allows us to secure a meaningful result if, instead of multiplying each mesh equation by the corresponding I, we multiply it by the *conjugate* of that I. If the equations are then added, the result appears as

$$i\omega \sum_{r,s=1}^{r,s=n}\sum L_{rs}\bar{I}_r I_s + \sum_{r,s=1}^{r,s=n}\sum R_{rs}\bar{I}_r I_s + \frac{1}{i\omega}\sum_{r,s=1}^{r,s=n}\sum D_{rs}\bar{I}_r I_s = E_1\bar{I}_1 \qquad (7\text{–}25)$$

where p has been replaced by $i\omega$ since we are interested only in real frequency characteristics, and $\bar{I}_j$ represents the conjugate of I_j. Only the single generator E_1 is included, in order to state the eventual result in terms of the impedance seen in the first mesh.

Since the I's in (7–25) are not functions of time the three summations cannot represent the actual instantaneous physical energy functions. The summations can, however, be identified term-by-term with multiples of the *time averages* of the corresponding terms in the true energy expressions. To show this, we may begin by considering a " self "-inductance term such as $L_{11}I_1\bar{I}_1$. Upon replacing I_1 and $\bar{I}_1$ by $I_{1a} + iI_{1b}$ and $I_{1a} - iI_{1b}$, respectively, this term becomes $L_{11}(I_{1a}^2 + I_{1b}^2)$. The corresponding term in the expression for the true electromagnetic energy of the circuit is $\frac{1}{2}L_{11}I_1^{*2}$, where I_1^* represents the instantaneous physical value of the first mesh current. It follows from the definition of I_1, however, that

$$\begin{aligned} I_1^* &= \text{Real component of } (I_{1a} + iI_{1b})(\cos\omega t + i\sin\omega t) \\ &= I_{1a}\cos\omega t - I_{1b}\sin\omega t. \end{aligned} \qquad (7\text{–}26)$$

This term in the true electromagnetic energy can therefore be written as

$$\tfrac{1}{2}L_{11}I_1^{*2} = \tfrac{1}{2}L_{11}(I_{1a}^2\cos^2\omega t - 2I_{1a}I_{1b}\sin\omega t\cos\omega t + I_{1b}^2\sin^2\omega t). \qquad (7\text{–}27)$$

If we average this expression over a long period of time, the $\sin\omega t\cos\omega t$

term disappears while the $\cos^2 \omega t$ term and the $\sin^2 \omega t$ term each becomes $\frac{1}{2}$. The average value of the electromagnetic energy due to the flow of I_1^* in L_{11} is therefore

$$(\tfrac{1}{2}L_{11}I_1^{*2})_{\text{av}} = \tfrac{1}{4}L_{11}(I_{1a}^2 + I_{1b}^2) \tag{7–28}$$

which is just $\frac{1}{4}$ of the value found for the term $L_{11}I_1\bar{I}_1$ in the first summation of (7–25).

Similarly, when we examine a pair of " mutual " inductance terms of (7–25), such as $L_{12}I_2\bar{I}_1 + L_{21}I_1\bar{I}_2$, we readily find, with the help of the relation $L_{12} = L_{21}$, that they may be written as $2L_{12}(I_{1a}I_{2a} + I_{1b}I_{2b})$. The corresponding term in the expression for the true electromagnetic energy is

$$\tfrac{1}{2}(L_{12}I_1^*I_2^* + L_{21}I_1^*I_2^*) = L_{12}[I_{1a}I_{2a}\cos^2 \omega t - (I_{1a}I_{2b} + I_{2a}I_{1b}) \sin \omega t \cos \omega t + I_{1b}I_{2b}\sin^2 \omega t] \tag{7–29}$$

whose average value is $\frac{1}{2}L_{12}(I_{1a}I_{2a} + I_{1b}I_{2b})$. This is again just $\frac{1}{4}$ of the amount given by the summation of (7–25). We conclude, therefore, that when all the terms of this summation are evaluated they will represent four times the average value of the total electromagnetic energy T, taken over a long period of time.

Obviously the second summation of (7–25) is in a precisely similar fashion equal to four times the average value of the dissipation function F. The third summation of (7–25) cannot be identified directly with a multiple of the average value of the final energy function V since it depends upon products of currents, and if it were to represent V, the quantities should, on the contrary, be charges. We may notice, however, that since a current is the derivative of a charge, the effect of introducing a current in place of a corresponding sinusoidally varying charge is to produce a shift in phase, which is of no importance for averages taken over a long period of time, and to multiply the expression by ω. Since there are two I's in the third summation, the introduction of currents for charges therefore increases its value by a factor of ω^2, and we can conclude that the summation is equal to $4\omega^2$ times the average value of the stored energy of the condensers.

Using the values just found for the three summations replaces (7–25) by

$$4i\omega T_{\text{av}} + 4F_{\text{av}} - 4i\omega V_{\text{av}} = E_1\bar{I}_1. \tag{7–30}$$

If we assume that the driving voltage E_1 is of unit amplitude, the current I_1 will be equal to the admittance of the network. $\bar{I}_1$ is, of course, the same as I_1 except for a change in the sign of the imaginary part. Equation (7-30) can therefore be used to furnish a relation between the energy functions of the network and its input admittance. We find

$$Y = 4[F_{\text{av}} + i\omega(V_{\text{av}} - T_{\text{av}})] \tag{7–31}$$

where F_{av}, V_{av}, and T_{av}, are to be evaluated under the assumption that the network is energized by a voltage of unit amplitude.*

The second of the three conditions on passive networks postulated at the beginning of this chapter is to the effect that the real component of a driving point immittance is never negative at real frequencies. Since F must be positive this is established immediately by (7–31). The third condition states that the total power fed into the network by an outside generator at real frequencies must be at least as great as the power consumed by any one resistance. This can be shown by investigating the way in which any individual element enters the expression for F. A simpler method, however, is to suppose the given resistance removed and replaced by a generator having a voltage equal to the drop across the resistance produced by the prescribed external generator. This will leave the distribution of currents in the rest of the network unaltered. If we repeat the analysis which led to (7–31) for the modified network driven by both generators, however, the real component of the right-hand side of the result-

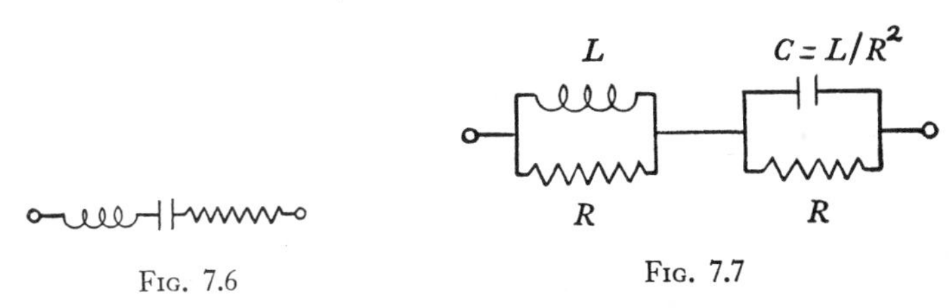

FIG. 7.6 FIG. 7.7

ing expression will still represent the average F for the modified structure and must be positive or zero. Evidently, therefore, the power consumed by the rest of the network cannot be negative, so that the total power consumed by the complete structure must be at least as great as that consumed by the prescribed resistance.

As examples of (7–31) we may take the networks of Figs. 7.6 and 7.7. The impedance of the network of Fig. 7.6 is a pure resistance when the inductance and capacity resonate. The average values of the energies stored in the inductance and capacity must therefore be equal at this frequency. The network of Fig. 7.7 is equivalent to a pure resistance at all frequencies. By the same reasoning, therefore, the average values of its T and V must be the same at all frequencies. Both of these conclusions can, of course, be readily checked by calculation.

* " Unit amplitude " here means that the maximum value of the sinusoidal wave representing the voltage is unity. Since we are dealing with energy, it is perhaps more natural to use the rms or " effective " emf, which is $1/\sqrt{2}$ times the maximum value. If we use a unit effective voltage, therefore, the constant 4 in the right-hand side of (7–31) should be replaced by 2.

7.12. *Stability of Passive Networks*

The first of the three special conditions on passive circuits mentioned near the beginning of the chapter states that a passive circuit is always stable. As the final step in this analysis we will prove that this is a consequence of the fact that the three energy functions F, T, and V, of a passive network are positive definite. The relation between stability and energy arises, of course, from the fact that it takes energy to set a circuit into motion and that, generally speaking, the greater the disturbance the greater the energy. It might appear at first sight from this argument that stability will be assured from the positiveness of F alone, since if F is positive the circuit as a whole will lose energy continuously, whatever the sign of T and V may be. In fact, however, the positiveness of T and V is equally important. If one of these functions may be negative the circuit may lose energy through I^2R losses continuously and still remain very far from its position of equilibrium provided more and more negative energy* is stored. Insolvency is no bar to a spendthrift life as long as one's credit at the bank is good.

The relation between stability and the energy functions can be developed most easily if we return to the set of equations given by (7–2) of the present chapter. These were identical with the ordinary mesh equations except that the driving voltages were set equal to zero and p was supposed to assume one of the special values corresponding to a transient oscillation in the network. Upon treating the equations by the processes used in developing (7–25) the result is readily seen to be

$$p \sum_{r,s=1}^{r,s=n}\sum L_{rs}\bar{I}_r I_s + \sum_{r,s=1}^{r,s=n}\sum R_{rs}\bar{I}_r I_s + \frac{1}{p}\sum_{r,s=1}^{r,s=n}\sum D_{rs}\bar{I}_r I_s = 0 \qquad (7\text{–}32)$$

which is the same as (7–25) except that the right-hand side has been set equal to zero and $i\omega$ has been replaced by p since transient oscillations are not necessarily restricted to real frequencies.

In the previous discussion we identified each of the summations of (7–32) with the average value of one of the energy functions of the network. We cannot make the same identification here, since if the frequency is

* If a "negative energy" is difficult to visualize, we may suppose that the circuit under consideration is a passive structure except for the inclusion of the equivalent of a negative inductance, provided by means of one of the vacuum tube circuits described later. As long as the negative inductance is taken as an entity the complete circuit can still be analyzed by the methods used for passive structures, since the principle of reciprocity is maintained. The "negative energy" stored in the inductance, however, can be regarded physically as positive energy drawn from the vacuum tubes and transmitted to the rest of the circuit.

complex the physical currents in the network will be increasing or decreasing and there is no good way of taking a time average. Fortunately, however, no such precise physical interpretation is necessary. It will be recalled that when I_1 in (7–25) was replaced by its value in terms of I_{1a} and I_{1b} the L_{11} term of the first summation became $L_{11}(I_{1a}^2 + I_{1b}^2)$. Similarly, the sum of the L_{12} and L_{21} terms became $(L_{12} + L_{21})(I_{1a}I_{2a} + I_{1b}I_{2b})$. Both the " self " and " mutual " inductance terms therefore broke up into the sum of two terms, one involving products of the I_a's and the other, products of the I_b's. Corresponding results, of course, held for the R and D terms. Even without the help of a physical interpretation of the summations, therefore, we can rewrite (7–32) in the same way as

$$p \sum_{r,s=1}^{r,s=n}\sum L_{rs}(I_{ra}I_{sa} + I_{rb}I_{sb}) + \sum_{r,s=1}^{r,s=n}\sum R_{rs}(I_{ra}I_{sa} + I_{rb}I_{sb}) + \frac{1}{p}\sum_{r,s=1}^{r,s=n}\sum D_{rs}(I_{ra}I_{sa} + I_{rb}I_{sb}) = 0. \quad (7\text{–}33)$$

The summation $\sum_{r,s=1}^{r,s=n}\sum L_{rs}I_{ra}I_{sa}$ is obviously twice the energy function T when for each instantaneous physical current we use the corresponding quantity I_{ra}. We can, therefore, represent this portion of equation (7–33) by $2T(a)$. Similarly, the summation $\sum_{r,s=1}^{r,s=n}\sum L_{rs}I_{rb}I_{sb}$ represents twice the T function when each physical current is replaced by the corresponding I_b. It can therefore be written as $2T(b)$. The other parts of equation (7–33) represent in the same fashion twice the F and V functions when we substitute the I_a's and I_b's for the corresponding physical currents and charges. The complete expression can therefore be written as

$$p[T(a) + T(b)] + F(a) + F(b) + \frac{1}{p}[V(a) + V(b)] = 0. \quad (7\text{–}34)$$

The T's, F's, and V's which appear in (7–34) do not necessarily correspond to any physical energies actually present in the circuit. They are merely certain mathematical expressions secured by replacing the instantaneous currents in the true energy expressions by the I_{ja}'s and I_{jb}'s. In general, they may be expected to have different values as we go from one possible transient to another, since the distribution of currents in the network, and therefore the I_{ja}'s and I_{jb}'s, will depend upon the transient frequency. However, we at least know that the original energy expressions were positive for all possible values of the instantaneous currents. It follows that the new T's, F's, and V's must be positive in all cases. Any p corresponding to a possible transient must therefore satisfy a quadratic equation like (7–34) in which all the coefficients are positive. From the usual formula for the roots of a quadratic we can readily deduce that permissible p's, or zeros of Δ, must satisfy the following conditions:

1. The zeros will be found at negative real values of p if either T or V is identically zero. In other words, impedances corresponding to networks containing only capacities and resistances, or only inductances and resistances, must have zeros on the negative real axis of p.
2. The zeros will be found on the negative real axis even if both T and V are present provided F is sufficiently great. This means that very highly dissipative networks will have negative real zeros even when both kinds of reactive elements are present.
3. If F is identically zero, the zeros will occur on the imaginary axis. In other words, the impedance of a non-dissipative network vanishes only at real frequencies.
4. If none of these conditions is met, the zeros ordinarily occur in conjugate complex pairs. The real parts of the zeros are always negative.

These propositions are best exemplified by the discussion given in a later chapter. They evidently contain much more detailed information than is provided by the bare statement that a passive network must be stable. It is clear, however, that among them they at least confirm that statement.

7.13. *Comparison of Criteria of Physical Realizability*

The preceding discussion has developed the properties of physically realizable structures from a variety of criteria. In dealing with passive structures, for example, we began with the statement that the circuit could contain only positive elements and later replaced it by the statement that its energy functions must be positive definite. In dealing with active structures, on the other hand, we relied chiefly upon the postulate that a physical circuit must be stable. As they stand, these criteria are not readily compared directly, chiefly because the formulae for the energy functions were developed on the assumption that the circuit met the reciprocity condition $Z_{ij} = Z_{ji}$, so that they are not easily extended to the general case. To put the criteria on the same footing, it will be assumed that the active elements appear only as parts of negative impedance devices, so that if these devices are taken as entities the circuit can be regarded as made up exclusively of bilateral elements.* It is then readily seen that the various criteria are not logically equivalent. As the list was

* Cf. the discussion in an earlier footnote. In accordance with the assumption made here, the word " element " in the present section will be taken to mean a bilateral element.

given, the criteria appear in the order of diminishing severity. In other words, a network all of whose elements are positive always has positive definite energy functions and a network with positive definite energy functions is always stable. The converses of these propositions are, however, not true. A network which is stable does not necessarily possess positive definite energy functions, and a network with positive definite energy functions is not necessarily composed exclusively of positive elements.

The fact that the positive energy condition is not equivalent to the positive element condition is easily seen in trivial cases. For example, the energy condition will evidently be maintained if we add a negative resistance either in series with an actual network containing an equal or larger positive series resistance, or in series with an equivalent of such a network. A more elaborate example is suggested by the equivalent T of a two-winding transformer. It will be recalled that the central branch of the T contains a negative inductance representing the mutual coupling. The energy stored in the inductances as a whole, however, is always positive. Evidently the energy would still be positive if we replaced the transformer by a corresponding arrangement of three separate positive and negative inductances. The energy conditions will also be fulfilled if, instead of using inductances, we insert positive and negative impedances of any description in the same ratio. On the other hand we will be able to show that any impedance function meeting the requirements derived from the energy conditions can always be represented by some network containing only positive elements together with systems of ordinary mutual inductances. In this sense, therefore, the energy conditions and the positive element conditions are equivalent.

The relation between the conditions that the network be stable and that its energy functions be positive definite is less easy to understand. If the network includes only two kinds of elements, it can be shown that it will be stable only when both associated energy functions are positive definite. When all three kinds of elements are present, however, the positive definite condition is not necessary. This may be exemplified by means of the illustrative impedance formulae given by (7–17). For example, the last two of these represented impedances which met the stability requirement but had real components which were negative in some portions of the real frequency spectrum. Evidently in such impedances the positive definite condition does not apply to the dissipation function F. We may also recall that, in order to restrict the location of the poles of impedance, it was necessary to suppose that the structure would be stable when its driving point terminals were open-circuited. Since positive definite energy functions remain positive definite when the current in the driving mesh is set equal to zero, open circuit stability is assured when the energy conditions are met. As such examples as Z_4 of (7–17) show, however, open circuit stability is not a property of all structures which are stable under their nominal operating conditions, so that this represents another way in which a stable structure which does not meet the energy conditions can be obtained.

CHAPTER VIII

Contour Integration and Nyquist's Criterion for Stability

8.1. *Introduction*

The analysis of the preceding chapter consists, in essentials, of an investigation of the restrictions which must be placed upon the zeros and poles of the several network functions if the structure is to be stable under various conditions. This is obviously a necessary first step in attacking the general problem of determining the characteristics obtainable from physically realizable structures. Of itself, however, it is of limited utility. Its chief limitation is the fact that the restrictions are stated in terms of the behavior of the function at complex frequencies, while for practical design purposes only the real frequency characteristics are ultimately of interest. As the situation stands, the relations between the two are too indirect to be of much value. For example, it is not very clear from the restrictions on the zeros and poles just what sorts of real frequency characteristics are physically possible. Moreover, if we have a known structure, whose computed real frequency characteristics are satisfactory, it is a long and tedious process, in general, to determine whether the roots of Δ meet the stability requirement. If some of the roots turn out to be in the wrong side of the plane we are still at a loss to know whether we have merely made an unfortunate choice in some unimportant feature of the design or whether the result is inevitable in any circuit having the desired type of behavior.

What we evidently need in order to bring the analysis to a useful conclusion is some mathematical tool by means of which the restrictions on the behavior of network functions at complex frequencies can be transformed directly into equivalent restrictions on their behavior at real frequencies. The real frequency axis can be looked upon as the boundary of the right half-plane, which is the region in which special restrictions on the network functions occur, so that the broad mathematical problem is that of relating the behavior of a function inside a given region to its behavior on the boundary of the region. The most useful tool for this purpose is found in Cauchy's theory of analytic functions in terms of integrals around closed contours. This chapter is intended primarily as a sketch of some of the elementary aspects of this theory.* The most extensive applications of

* For supplementary reading, reference may be made to any book on the theory of functions of a complex variable. Particularly good accounts are found in Goursat, Townsend, or Pierpont.

the material are made several chapters later, after an intermediate discussion of the general properties of driving point and transfer immittances. The theory is exemplified in the present chapter by a discussion of the Nyquist diagram method of determining stability. The chapter also includes two specific theorems which are useful in the discussion of driving point and transfer immittances given in the next few chapters. The analysis relies upon the general framework of ideas given by Chapter II, and this material should be reread if necessary before the present chapter is undertaken.

8.2. *Integration in the Complex Plane*

In ordinary calculus we are familiar with the conception of an integral as the area under a curve. Figure 8.1, for example, shows the approximation to the area under a given curve by means of a number of thin vertical strips. We say that the integral of the function from x_1 to x_2 is equal to the limit

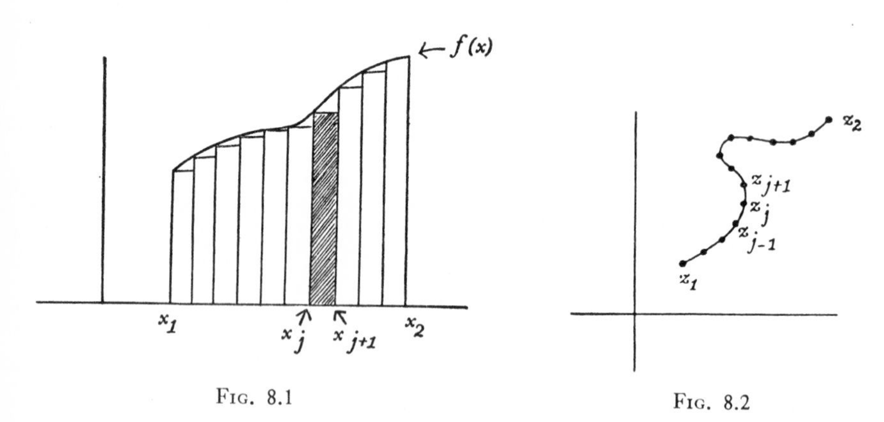

FIG. 8.1 FIG. 8.2

approached by the area of the strips when the number of strips becomes indefinitely great and each one is made indefinitely thin. The area of any strip, such as the shaded one in the figure, however, is evidently equal to its height times its breadth or, in other words, to $f(x_j)(x_{j+1} - x_j)$. This definition of an integral can therefore be expressed by the equation

$$\int_{x_1}^{x_2} f(x)dx = \lim \sum f(x_j)(x_{j+1} - x_j). \tag{8-1}$$

Integrals of functions of a complex variable are defined in a precisely similar way. If we suppose, for example, that the function $f(z)$ is to be integrated along a prescribed curve running from z_1 to z_2 in the complex z plane, as shown by Fig. 8.2, we may begin by choosing a number of intermediate points, z_j. For any given choice of the intermediate points we can set up the corresponding sum $\sum f(z_j)(z_{j+1} - z_j)$. The integral, then, is defined as the limit* approached by this sum when the number of points of division is made indefinitely great and the successive points are brought indefinitely close together. In other words, the integral may be expressed by

$$\int_{z_1}^{z_2} f(z)dz = \lim \sum f(z_j)(z_{j+1} - z_j). \tag{8-2}$$

It will be seen that this is formally similar to equation (8-1). The only difference lies in the fact that since $f(z_j)$ and $(z_{j+1} - z_j)$ will in general be complex quantities, the final result will ordinarily be complex.

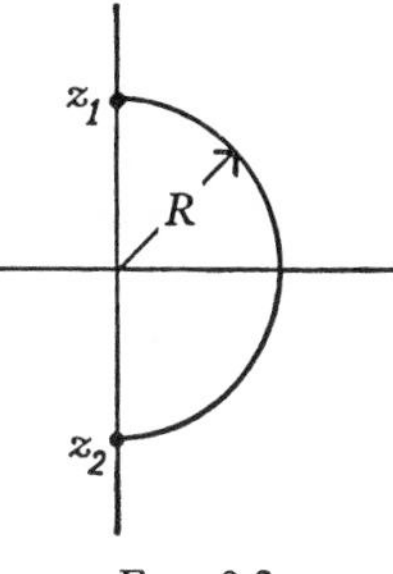

FIG. 8.3

8.3. *Integrals in Limiting Cases*

The definition of an integral given by equation (8-2) leads immediately to a simple consequence which we will use repeatedly in later discussion. We observe from (8-2) that the absolute value of the integral cannot be greater than the sum of the absolute values of all the component terms, $f(z_j)(z_{j+1} - z_j)$. Now suppose that M represents the largest absolute value of $f(z)$ over the path considered. The absolute value of each of the component terms can be no greater than the absolute value which would be obtained if $f(z_j)$ were replaced by M. We therefore have

$$\left| \int_{z_1}^{z_2} f(z)dz \right| \leq \int_{z_1}^{z_2} M\,|\,dz\,| = M \times \text{path length}. \tag{8-3}$$

As an example of this relation, let it be supposed that the path of integration is the semicircle with radius R shown by Fig. 8.3, where it is supposed that R can be made indefinitely large. The path length is πR. If $f(z)$ varies as some positive power of z for very large values of z, we can evidently say nothing about the integral on the basis of equation (8-3) since both M and the path length will become very large as R becomes large. Equation (8-3) also fails to provide a limit if $f(z)$ approaches a constant value other than zero as z approaches infinity. On the other hand, if $f(z)$ varies as some negative power of z, such as z^{-2}, M must vary as R^{-2}. We see from equation (8-3) that the integral must therefore vanish for a sufficiently large value of R in spite of the fact that the path length is

* This discussion, of course, ignores such questions as the demonstration that the limit exists, for an appropriate $f(z)$, and that it is independent of the precise choice of the z_j's, which would require consideration in a formal analysis.

indefinitely great. The same result, of course, holds if $f(z)$ varies as any larger negative power of z.

If the semicircle of Fig. 8.3 is supposed to be very small, rather than very large, essentially similar results are secured. The path length now vanishes in the limit, so that it is clear from (8–3) that the integral also vanishes if $f(z)$ either approaches a constant value or behaves as any positive power of z near the origin. If $f(z)$ behaves as z^{-2}, or as any larger negative power of z, on the other hand, M increases so rapidly as R diminishes that we can say nothing about the integral on the basis of (8–3).

In both situations, an intermediate case occurs if $f(z)$ varies as z^{-1}. When the semicircle is very large this gives an M which diminishes as the path length increases, while when the semicircle is small M increases as the path length decreases, the relative rates of increase and decrease being such that in either case the product of the two is a constant. Equation (8–3) thus gives a finite upper limit to the integral, but we are not sure just what its exact value may be.

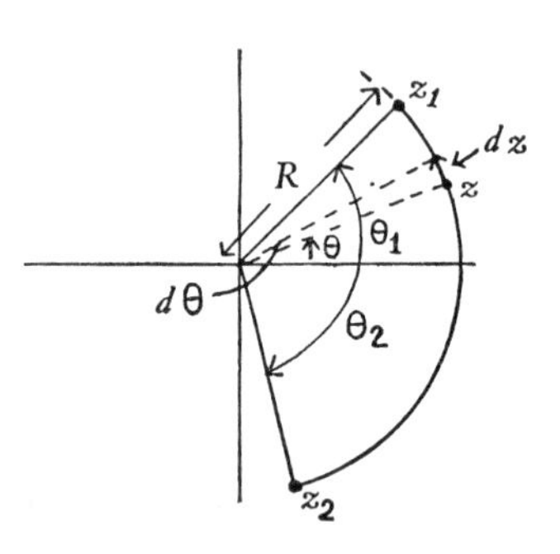

FIG. 8.4

This situation can be treated by specifying z in terms of a polar angle θ, as shown by Fig. 8.4. For the sake of generality the path is shown as an arbitrary arc of a circle, with end-points at $\theta = \theta_1$ and $\theta = \theta_2$, rather than as a complete semicircle. If we write $z = Re^{i\theta}$ we evidently have $dz = iRe^{i\theta}d\theta$, so that the integral from θ_1 to θ_2 becomes

$$\int_C \frac{dz}{z} = \int_{\theta_1}^{\theta_2} \frac{iRe^{i\theta}d\theta}{Re^{i\theta}} = \int_{\theta_1}^{\theta_2} i d\theta = -i(\theta_1 - \theta_2), \tag{8–4}$$

while if the integral is taken in the other direction the result is evidently the same except for a reversal in sign. We thus have the

Theorem: The integral of z^{-1} over an arc of a circle centered at the origin is $+i$ or $-i$ times the central angle of the arc, in radians, accordingly as the integration is taken in a counterclockwise or in a clockwise direction.

The importance of these results lies in their utility in evaluating integrals in many limiting cases. For example, in future discussion we will have frequent occasion to consider the integrals, over a very large semicircle, of functions which behave near infinity like $(A_{-1}/z) + (A_{-2}/z^2) + (A_{-3}/z^3) + \cdots$. Evidently if the semicircle is sufficiently large we can discard all the terms in this series except the first and evaluate that one by means of the theorem just given.

For purposes of future analysis this discussion requires amplification in one particular. We have thus far merely rejected cases, for either the very large or very small semicircle, in which $f(z)$ varies as such a power of z that the product $M \times$ path length becomes indefinitely large as the limiting case is approached. We can draw no conclusions about such situations from (8–3) alone, and nothing significant can be said, in fact, as long as the path of integration is an arbitrary arc of a circle. In the following sections, however, there will be occasion to consider paths of integration extending around a complete circle and back to the starting point. This gives a particularly symmetrical situation for which the integral can be much simplified. To show this, we may repeat the analysis of (8–4), replacing z^{-1} by z^n and the upper and lower bounds of integration by $-\pi$ and π. This gives

$$\int_{\bigcirc} z^n dz = \int_{\pi}^{-\pi} [R^n e^{in\theta}] iRe^{i\theta} d\theta$$

$$= iR^{n+1} \int_{\pi}^{-\pi} [\cos (n + 1)\theta + i \sin (n + 1)\theta] d\theta. \quad (8\text{–}5)$$

If n is any positive or negative integer except -1 these expressions must vanish since the integral of either a sine or a cosine over a complete cycle is zero. If $n = -1$ the result is $-2\pi i$, for the clockwise direction of integration indicated, as we can see either from (8–5) or by the preceding theorem. We therefore have the

Theorem: The integral of z^n around a complete circle centered at the origin is zero unless $n = -1$. If $n = -1$ it is $-2\pi i$ for integration in a clockwise direction and $+2\pi i$ for integration in a counterclockwise direction.

8.4. *Relation between the Integral and the Path of Integration*

In spite of the parallelism which exists between the definitions of real and complex integration as indicated by equations (8–1) and (8–2), one difference exists which has not been previously emphasized. In defining the real integral in equation (8–1) it was sufficient to give the integration limits x_1 and x_2, since it was clear that the points x_j were necessarily taken on the x axis between these limits. For the complex variable z, on the other hand, it was necessary to specify not only the limits z_1 and z_2 but also the particular curve between those limits on which the points of subdivision z_j were supposed to be chosen. The question naturally arises whether the choice of the path between z_1 and z_2 is significant or whether the same result would be secured if we connected z_1 and z_2 by some different path, as shown by Fig. 8.5.

This question is answered by an important theorem, due to Cauchy, which is sometimes called the "Principal Theorem of Analysis." Cauchy's theorem states that the integral between z_1 and z_2 will be the same for either of the two paths provided the function to be integrated is analytic on both paths and in the intermediate region bounded by the paths. In most circumstances it is convenient to replace the conception of an integration from z_1 to z_2 along two different paths by the conception of an integration around a complete closed loop and back to the starting point. In Fig. 8.5, for example, we might regard the loop integration as composed of a forward integration from z_1 to z_2 along path A and a backward integration from z_2 to z_1 along path B. Clearly, however, the integral from z_2 to z_1 along B must be the negative of the integral from z_1 to z_2 along B. It must therefore also be the negative of the integral from z_1 to z_2 along A, if the integrals from z_1 to z_2 along the two paths are equal. Cauchy's theorem can consequently be stated in the following words:

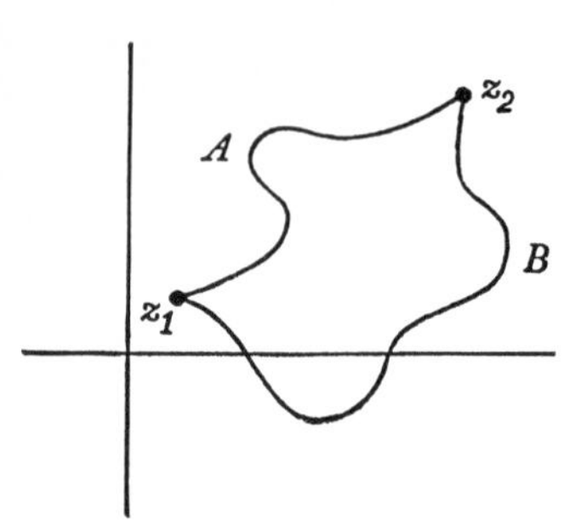

FIG. 8.5

Theorem: If a function $f(z)$ is analytic within a closed curve and also on the curve itself, the integral of $f(z)$ taken around that curve is equal to zero.

This theorem will be assumed here without proof.

Cauchy's theorem is readily illustrated by our preceding discussion of the integration of powers of z on circular paths. Let it be supposed, for example, that the closed loop is taken as a circle about the origin and that $f(z)$ is chosen as the polynomial $A_0 + A_1z + \cdots + A_nz^n$. Then $f(z)$ is analytic on and within the circle so that according to Cauchy's theorem the integral around the complete circle must vanish. This is, of course, verified by the preceding discussion, which showed that the integral of each term in the polynomial vanishes.

We may next suppose that the term k/z is added to the polynomial. This additional term produces a pole at the origin so that the function is no longer analytic at all points within the circle and the conditions of Cauchy's theorem are not met. Correspondingly, we find from our preceding discussion that the integral no longer vanishes, but becomes $2\pi ik$, if the integration is supposed to take place in a counterclockwise direction. On the other hand, if we were to add k/z^2, rather than k/z, to the polynomial the loop integral would remain zero, although the new function would still not be analytic at the origin. It thus appears that the converse of Cauchy's theorem is not true. In special cases the loop integral may be zero even though the function is not analytic at all points within the contour.

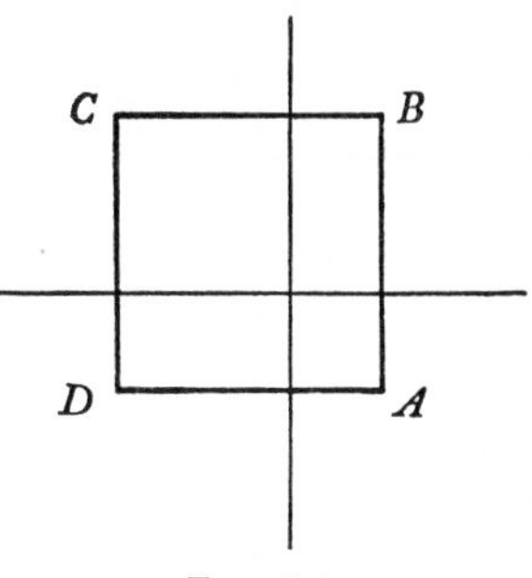

Fig. 8.6

In these examples the closed contour has been taken as a circle. This, of course, is a particularly easy path for purposes of computation. It is important to notice, however, that Cauchy's theorem shows that the same results would be secured if the circle were distorted into a path of any other shape. To illustrate this, we will consider the integral of z^2 around the square path shown in Fig. 8.6. The side of the square is taken as 3 units and the corners A, B, C, and D as $1 - i$, $1 + i2$, $-2 + i2$, and $-2 - i$, respectively. If we write $z = x + iy$, z^2 becomes $x^2 - y^2 + 2ixy$. On the side AB we have $x = 1$ and $dz = idy$. This portion of the complete loop integration can therefore be written as

$$\int_A^B z^2dz = \int_{-1}^{2} [(1 - y^2) + 2iy]idy. \tag{8-6}$$

This can be evaluated by the methods of ordinary calculus and is equal to -3. Similarly, over the side BC we have $y = 2$, $dz = dx$, and the integral becomes

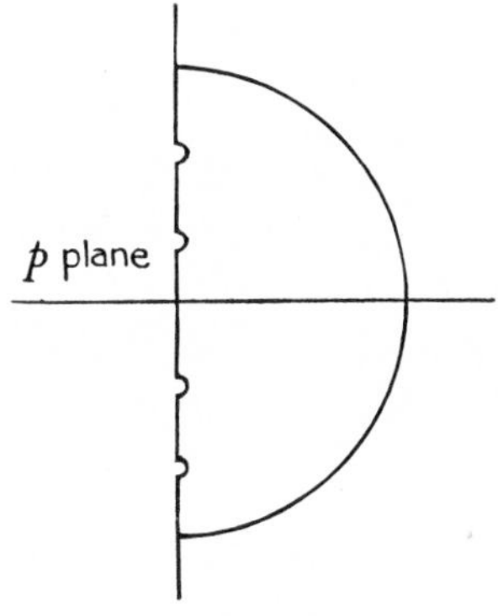

Fig. 8.7

$$\int_B^C z^2dz = \int_1^{-2} [(x^2 - 4) + 4ix]dx$$
$$= 9 + 6i. \tag{8-7}$$

The integrals over the remaining two sides can be treated in the same way and are equal respectively to $-6 - 9i$ and $3i$. The sum around the complete loop is easily seen to vanish, thus confirming Cauchy's theorem for this case.

In future discussion, Cauchy's theorem will be applied chiefly to closed loops in the p plane of the type shown by Fig. 8.7. The loop consists broadly of a large semicircle in the right half of the p plane closed by a diameter lying on the real frequency axis. The small indentations away from the real frequency axis are supposed to be very small semicircles introduced to avoid any singularities which may be found there. The integral around the complete path will be represented by the symbol $\oint$ and the integral around the large semicircle by the symbol $\int\!\!\!\!\supset$.

This path is chosen because our previous discussion on the location of the zeros and poles of physically realizable network functions can readily be converted into a specification of the analyticity either of the network functions themselves or of certain derived functions in the right half of the p plane. Cauchy's theorem can thus be used in studying the integrals of these expressions around the complete loop. If we suppose that the path is very large, however, the integrals around both the large semicircle and the small indentations can be dismissed easily by means of the methods described in a preceding section. What is left, then, is an integral along the real frequency axis from some very large negative frequency to a correspondingly large positive frequency so that Cauchy's theorem allows us to relate the real frequency characteristics of the structure directly to the conditions of physical realizability.

8.5. *The Calculus of Residues*

Before studying these possibilities in detail, it is desirable to consider briefly what happens to the integral of a given function around a closed path when the function is not analytic inside the path. The results have already been suggested by the examples given previously. To study the general case, suppose that the function is analytic except for a simple pole at z_a so that near z_a it can be expanded in the form*

$$f(z) = \frac{A_{-1}}{z - z_a} + A_0 + A_1(z - z_a) + A_2(z - z_a)^2 + \cdots. \qquad (8\text{–}8)$$

Now choose the path of integration shown by Fig. 8.8. The function is analytic within this closed path so that the integral around the complete path

* The series in (8–8) is introduced here as a convenient way of characterizing the behavior of the function in the neighborhood of z_a. From the point of view of pure mathematics its use is somewhat illogical, since the justification for such an expansion depends upon an analysis of the type under consideration at present. We may notice, however, that all we really need to know is that $f(z)$ can be represented as the sum of the first term in (8–8) and a remaining portion which is bounded in the neighborhood of z_a. This is readily established from the definition of a pole. It follows from (8–5), however, that the integral of the bounded portion around a very small circle near z_a can be ignored, so that the correct result is secured without using the complete expansion.

must be zero. The contributions of the integrations along the path between P_1 and P_2 in each direction, however, evidently cancel out. The integral around the outside loop from P_1 back to P_1 again must therefore be the negative of the integral around the small inside circle enclosing the point z_a. If we integrate $f(z)$, as given by (8–8), around this small circle, however, all the terms except the first must drop out, while if we transfer the origin to z_a the first can be evaluated by the methods of equation (8–4). We therefore find that the integral around the outside loop is given by*

$$\oint f(z)dz = -2\pi i A_{-1}. \quad (8\text{–}9)$$

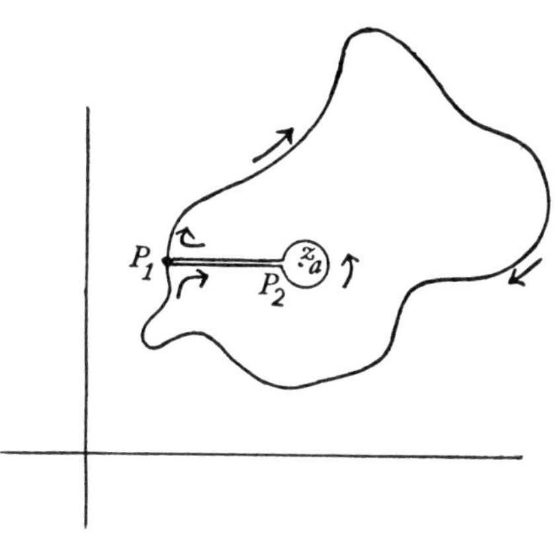

Fig. 8.8

The coefficient A_{-1} is called the *residue* of the function at the pole z_a. If there are a number of poles in the interior of the loop, then by a continuation of the same process we can include them one by one, thus securing in general, an expression of the form

$$\oint f(z)dz = -2\pi i[A_{-1} + B_{-1} + C_{-1} + \cdots + N_{-1}]. \quad (8\text{–}10)$$

Since equation (8–5) shows that only simple poles have integrals different from zero around small circular paths enclosing them, only the coefficients of the first order poles at any point should be considered in building up an expression such as (8–10).

Illustrations of the calculus of residues can be obtained by using the same material as was previously employed to illustrate the general Cauchy theorem. Since the fact that the integral of $1/z$ over a small circle about the origin is equal to $2\pi i$ was used in establishing (8–9) and (8–10), we are perhaps not justified in regarding this result as an illustration. We can,

* It is important to notice that the negative sign in the right-hand side of (8–9) appears because of the direction of integration (clockwise around the outer loop) which is chosen in Fig. 8.8. It is convenient to choose this direction here because it leads to a positive direction of integration along the real frequency axis when we eventually apply the result to contours of the type shown by Fig. 8.7. In most treatments of the Cauchy integral, however, the loop integration is conventionally taken in the opposite direction, so that the equation corresponding to (8–9) appears without the minus sign.

however, at least exemplify the fact that the result is independent of the shape of the path by considering the integral of the same function around the square contour of Fig. 8.6. Setting $z = x + iy$, as before, we have $1/z = [x/(x^2 + y^2)] - [iy/(x^2 + y^2)]$. The integral from A to B is readily written from this as

$$\int_A^B \frac{dz}{z} = \int_{-1}^{2} \left[\frac{1}{1 + y^2} - \frac{iy}{1 + y^2}\right] i\,dy. \tag{8-11}$$

This can be evaluated by ordinary calculus and gives the result $\frac{1}{2} \log 5 - \frac{1}{2} \log 2 + i \tan^{-1}(2) - i \tan^{-1}(-1)$. In the same way we find that the integral from B to C can be written as

$$\int_B^C \frac{dz}{z} = \int_1^{-2} \left[\frac{x}{x^2 + 4} - \frac{2i}{x^2 + 4}\right] dx$$
$$= \frac{1}{2} \log 8 - \frac{1}{2} \log 5 - i \tan^{-1}(-1) + i \tan^{-1}(\tfrac{1}{2}). \tag{8-12}$$

Using similar methods, the results for the other two sides are found to be, respectively, $\frac{1}{2} \log 5 - \frac{1}{2} \log 8 - i \tan^{-1}(-1) + i \tan^{-1}(\frac{1}{2})$ and $\frac{1}{2} \log 2 - \frac{1}{2} \log 5 + i \tan^{-1}(1) - i \tan^{-1}(-2)$.

If the integrals for all four sides are added together it is readily seen that the sum of the real components vanishes. The sum of the imaginary components can be studied most readily by observing that each component separately is equal to the central angle subtended at the origin by the corresponding side. For example, the imaginary component $i \tan^{-1} 2 - i \tan^{-1}(-1)$ obtained from the integration along AB is equal to the angle, in radians, between straight lines drawn from the origin to the corners A and B. Evidently, the total central angle subtended by all four sides is one revolution, or 2π radians. The complete loop integral is therefore $2\pi i$. This agrees with (8–9) if account is taken of the fact that the direction of integration in the present instance is counterclockwise.

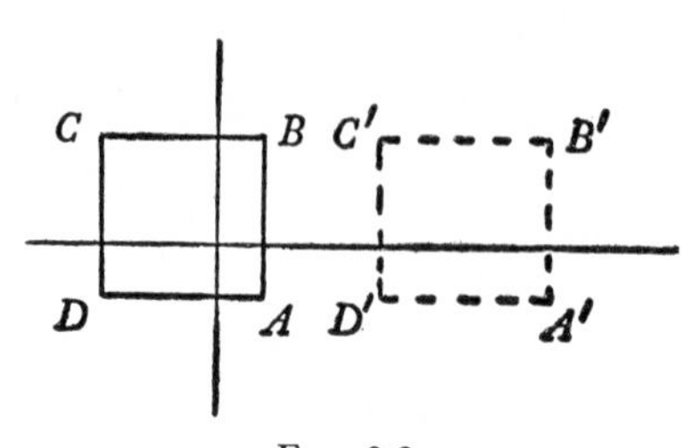

FIG. 8.9

The fact that the imaginary component produced by integration along each side is equal to the central angle subtended by that side is important, since it indicates why the significant feature of the situation is not the exact shape of the path, but the fact that the pole at the origin is inside the path. Evidently, any slight distortion of the path would still leave the total central angle subtended equal to one revolution, or 2π radians. On the other hand, suppose that the path were translated without distortion to some position such as $A'B'C'D'$ in Fig. 8.9 for which it no longer included the pole at the origin. Then evidently the total central angle subtended by all four sides would be zero, so that the loop integral would vanish.

An example of a different sort is furnished by one of the classical theorems in the calculus of residues. Let $g(z)$ be a function which is analytic on and within a given closed contour and let q be any point within the contour. Then $g(z)/(z - q)$ is a function which is analytic in the same region except for a simple pole at $z = q$. The residue at this pole must be $g(q)$, the value assumed by g when $z = q$, as we can easily see by expanding $g(z)$ near this point in the Taylor's series $g(q) + g'(q)(z - q) + (1/2!)g''(q)(z - q)^2 + \cdots$, and noticing that after division by $z - q$ the series takes the same form as that given for $f(z)$ in (8–8). If we identify $g(z)/(z - q)$ with $f(z)$, therefore, (8–9) allows us to write

$$\oint \frac{g(z)}{z - q}\,dz = -2\pi i g(q) \tag{8–13}$$

where, as before, the integration is taken in a clockwise direction.

This theorem is of interest here because of its bearing on the general problem of relating the values assumed by an analytic function within a given region to its values on the boundary of the region, which was discussed earlier in the chapter. Evidently, if we know $g(z)$ we can perform the integration on the left-hand side of (8–13) and calculate the special value $g(q)$ directly. In order to make this possible, however, we need know $g(z)$ only on the path of integration, that is, only on the boundary. Equation (8–13) thus provides a method of determining an analytic function anywhere inside a given region from a knowledge of its behavior only on the boundary of the region. The problem with which we are actually concerned is that of determining what properties a function must have on the boundary of the region when it is known to have certain properties in the interior. This problem is evidently in many respects the converse of that solved by (8–13), although it is much more general, since we begin with a specification only of the general properties of the function rather than with a knowledge of its behavior in detail. On this account it is not possible to present an adequate answer in terms of a single compact formula such as (8–13). The range of questions of practical interest requires the development of a considerable variety of formulae, only a few of which are given in the present chapter. Except for these qualifications, however, the solution of the converse problem will be found to imply relations between the values of a function on the boundary of a region and in its interior as tightly knit as that given by (8–13).

8.6. *Integral of the Logarithmic Derivative*

For the immediate purposes of the present chapter, the preceding discussion is valuable chiefly because it permits the development of a theorem which is of direct interest for amplifier design. Let it be supposed that $f(z)$ is some given function which may, in general, have both zeros and poles, but no singularities aside from poles, within some prescribed contour. The object of the theorem is to determine, as far as possible, how many zeros and poles lie within the contour from an inspection of the values assumed by $f(z)$ on the contour itself.

The theorem is developed from a study of the integral of the derivative of the logarithm of the function. In other words, we let $\theta = A + iB = \log f(z)$, and write

$$\oint \frac{d\theta}{dz} dz = \oint \left[\frac{dA}{dz} + i\frac{dB}{dz}\right] dz = \oint \frac{f'(z)}{f(z)} dz. \tag{8–14}$$

The integrand in the last expression of (8–14) will evidently be analytic within the contour except possibly for points at which $f(z)$ is either zero or infinite. If we suppose that z_0 represents one such point and that the function has an nth order zero or pole at z_0, we can write

$$\begin{aligned} f(z) &= (z - z_0)^n g(z), \\ f'(z) &= n(z - z_0)^{n-1} g(z) + (z - z_0)^n g'(z), \\ \frac{f'(z)}{f(z)} &= \frac{n}{z - z_0} + \frac{g'(z)}{g(z)} \end{aligned} \tag{8–15}$$

where n will be positive if z_0 is a zero and negative if z_0 is a pole and $g(z)$ is analytic and not zero in the neighborhood of z_0. We thus see that $f'(z)/f(z)$ has a simple pole of residue n at $z = z_0$.

The integral around the complete contour, as expressed by (8–14), must be $-2\pi i$ times the sum of all these residues, if the integration is taken in a clockwise direction. At the points for which $f(z)$ is zero, however, n will be positive and the sum of such residues is therefore equal to the total number of zeros within the contour when each zero is counted in proportion to its multiplicity. Similarly, at a pole n will be negative, and the sum of all such residues will therefore be equal to minus the number of poles when multiple poles are weighted according to their multiplicity. The complete equation (8–14) must therefore be

$$\oint \frac{f'(z)}{f(z)} dz = 2\pi i(P - N) \tag{8–16}$$

where N and P are respectively the number of zeros and the number of poles, and the integration is supposed to take place in the clockwise direction.

On the other hand, the first and second expressions in (8–14) are merely the integrals of the derivative of θ, or $A + iB$, and can therefore be integrated directly. The result must be the difference between the initial and final values of θ, or $A + iB$, as we go around the complete loop. Since the right-hand side of (8–16) is pure imaginary, we have only to consider the imaginary term iB. If we let 1 and 2 symbolize the initial and final points, this equation consequently becomes

$$\frac{1}{2\pi} \left| B \right|_1^2 = P - N. \tag{8–17}$$

The relation expressed by (8–17) can be given a simple graphical interpretation. If we represent $f(z)$ on a complex plane of its own, the values which $f(z)$ assumes as z traverses the prescribed contour can be represented as a moving point in that plane. But the left-hand side of (8–17) is $1/2\pi$ times the total change in the phase angle of $f(z)$ as z itself travels around the complete contour. Since 2π radians is one revolution, this is the same as saying that the left-hand side of (8–17) is equal to the number of times the moving point representing $f(z)$ revolves around the origin in the $f(z)$ plane while z itself moves once around the path of integration. In order to evaluate the left-hand side, therefore, we need merely plot the values of $f(z)$ which correspond to z's on the prescribed contour and count the number of loops of the plot which encircle the origin. The result given by (8–17) can consequently be expressed as the following

Theorem: If a function $f(z)$ is analytic, except for possible poles, within and on a given contour the number of times the plot of $f(z)$ encircles the origin of the $f(z)$ plane in the positive direction,* while z itself moves around the prescribed contour once in a clockwise direction, is equal to the number of poles of $f(z)$ lying within the contour diminished by the number of zeros of $f(z)$ within the contour, when each zero and pole is counted in accordance with its multiplicity.

As an elementary example of this theorem, let it be supposed that $f(z) = z$ and that the contour of integration in the z plane is chosen either as the unit circle or the square of Fig. 8.6. Evidently in this case the paths traced out by the moving point in the $f(z)$ plane are the same as these contours in the z plane. They are shown by I and II in Fig. 8.10. Corresponding to the fact that each contour in the z plane includes one zero and no poles, each of these paths is traversed once in the clockwise direction as z moves clockwise once around the associated integration contour.

* The positive direction is, of course, that one for which the phase angle of $f(z)$ is increasing. In other words, it represents a counterclockwise encirclement of the origin in the $f(z)$ plane by the moving point.

On the other hand, if $f(z) = 1/z$, the paths in the $f(z)$ plane corresponding to the circle and the square in the z plane are respectively the circle and the curvilinear quadrilateral shown by I and II in Fig. 8.11. Each of these paths is traversed once in the counterclockwise direction as z moves clockwise once around the associated z contour, corresponding to the fact that

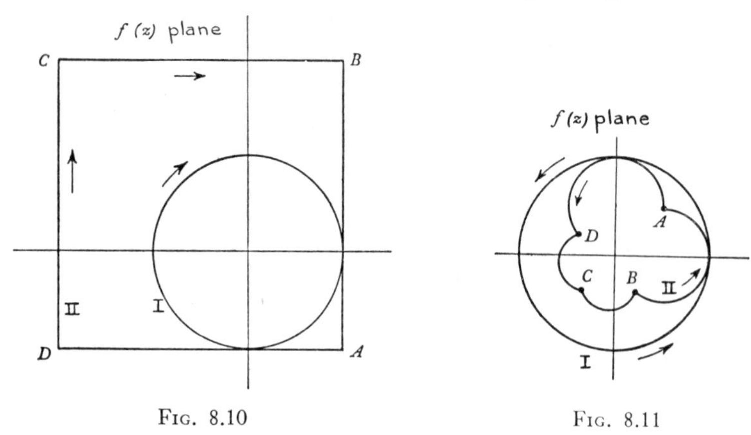

FIG. 8.10

FIG. 8.11

each contour now includes one pole and no zeros of $f(z)$. If we choose more complicated expressions for $f(z)$ the paths will, of course, ordinarily become more complicated and may encircle the origin more than once. Such situations, however, can best be illustrated by the examples given in later sections.

As the preceding examples may suggest, the theorem on the logarithmic derivative amounts, in simple cases, to a statement of a certain correspondence between specified areas in the z and $f(z)$ planes. Thus suppose

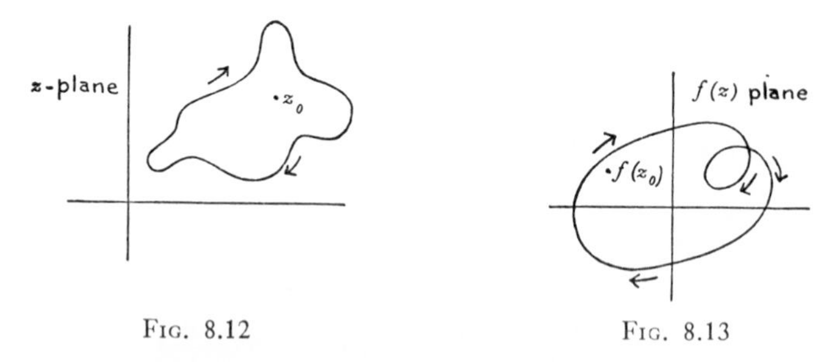

FIG. 8.12

FIG. 8.13

that the z contour is that shown by Fig. 8.12, and that it encloses one zero and no poles of $f(z)$, although zeros and poles may be found outside the contour. The associated $f(z)$ path must encircle the origin in the $f(z)$ plane once, as shown by Fig. 8.13. Then the theorem says, in effect, that in a certain sense the interiors of the two contours correspond to one another. For example, there is, by assumption, one point in the interior of the z contour of Fig. 8.12 at which $f(z) = 0$. Correspondingly, the point $f(z) = 0$, or the origin in the $f(z)$ plane, is found in the interior of the contour in that plane, as shown by Fig. 8.13. Suppose, however, that we were to choose any other point z_0 inside the z contour. Then the new function $f(z) - f(z_0)$ would still have a zero but no pole inside this contour, so that its plot must enclose the origin in its own plane. The plot of $f(z) - f(z_0)$ can be obtained from that of $f(z)$ in Fig. 8.13, however, merely by a translation of amount $f(z_0)$, so that this result is only possible if $f(z_0)$ lies inside the contour in Fig. 8.13.* Thus every point in the interior of the contour of Fig. 8.12 corresponds to some point in the interior of the contour of Fig. 8.13.

If, on the other hand, the contour of Fig. 8.12 includes a pole but no zeros we can show by an argument of the same type that any point in the interior of the z contour must correspond to a point which is outside the contour for $f(z)$. Thus the interior of one contour corresponds to the exterior of the other. This is manifested by the fact that the $f(z)$ contour is traversed in the reverse direction. As the number of zeros and poles in the interior of the z contour is increased, these relations, of course, grow more complicated. We must, in general, think of the interior of the z contour as being broken up into several subregions, some of which correspond to the interior and others to the exterior of the $f(z)$ plot, or to the interior and exterior of specified loops in the $f(z)$ plot if the plot crosses itself several times.

8.7. *Nyquist's Criterion for Stability — Single Loop Case*

The importance of the theorem just established arises from the fact that it leads immediately to the familiar criterion for stability due to Nyquist.† To show this, let the independent variable, which has hitherto been taken as z, be represented by p. Let the integration contour be the path in the p plane shown previously by Fig. 8.7. It will be supposed that this path is made indefinitely large. We will let the function whose logarithmic derivative is integrated around this path be the return difference $F = \Delta/\Delta^0$ for one of the tubes in the circuit. It will be assumed that F has no

* The interior loop in Fig. 8.13 has been drawn to illustrate the fact that for special values of $f(z_0)$ the plot of the new function $f(z) - f(z_0)$ may encircle the origin more than once. Thus there may be more than one point inside the z contour corresponding to a prescribed $f(z_0)$. This is evidently only possible when the $f(z)$ contour crosses itself. In other circumstances there is a one-to-one correspondence between the points in the two interiors.

† *Regeneration Theory*, B.S.T.J., Jan. 1932. See also Peterson, Kreer, and Ware, *Regeneration Theory and Experiment*, Proc. I.R.E., Oct. 1934.

singularities on the real frequency axis so that the small indentations shown by Fig. 8.7 can be ignored.

The Nyquist diagram for determining the stability of a circuit is in essentials a plot of the values of F corresponding to p's lying on this contour, prepared in the manner described in the preceding section. In drawing the diagram, however, advantage may be taken of a number of simplifying possibilities. In the first place, any physical tube must contain parasitic plate-cathode and grid-cathode capacities which will short-circuit the transmission path from plate to grid at extremely high frequencies. This is equivalent to saying that the return ratio of the tube will vanish, or its return difference will approximate unity, if p is made indefinitely great. As we make the contour in Fig. 8.7 larger and larger, consequently, the moving point which traces the path of F in the F plane will become more and more nearly stationary as p moves around the semicircular part of the complete contour. In the limit, this part of the contour can be disregarded entirely so that the complete diagram becomes a plot of only the real frequency values of F for the complete real frequency axis from $-\infty$ to $+\infty$.

The second simplification arises from the even and odd symmetry, respectively, of the real and imaginary components of F on the real frequency axis, which was discussed in the preceding chapter. This makes it necessary to compute the path in the F plane only for positive frequencies. The half of the path which corresponds to negative frequencies can be inserted as the mirror image of this part with respect to the real axis of the plane.

The third simplification is perhaps more important than either of the first two. The zeros and poles of F are respectively the roots of Δ and of Δ^0. If we make the path of integration in Fig. 8.7 sufficiently large we can suppose that all the roots in these two quantities which lie in the right half-plane will fall within the contour. We can therefore determine the difference between the number of roots of Δ and Δ^0 which lie within the right half-plane by counting the number of loops of the plot of F which encircle the origin. But the stability of the structure depends upon the location of the roots of Δ only, so that counting the loops gives only ambiguous information concerning the stability of the circuit unless we know how many roots of Δ^0 are included in the total. For the time being this difficulty will be avoided by assuming that the circuit is known to be stable when the prescribed W vanishes. This is true, for example, for an ordinary single loop amplifier, which was the case actually considered by Nyquist in his original treatment of the problem, since the failure of any one of the tubes will open the feedback loop. In these circumstances Δ^0 can have no roots in the right half-plane so that the stability or instability of the circuit can be determined unambiguously from the Nyquist plot. Evidently the condition for stability is that the plot shall not encircle the origin, while any encirclements which do occur must be in the clockwise direction.

A number of illustrative plots are shown by Figs. 8.14, 8.15, and 8.16. In each case the region of maximum F is taken as a band centered about some point ω_0. As we go from ω_0 to infinite frequency the return difference must, of course, reduce to unity for the reasons mentioned previously. In each drawing F is shown as reducing to unity at zero frequency also, since plate supply coils and blocking condensers will normally interrupt the d-c

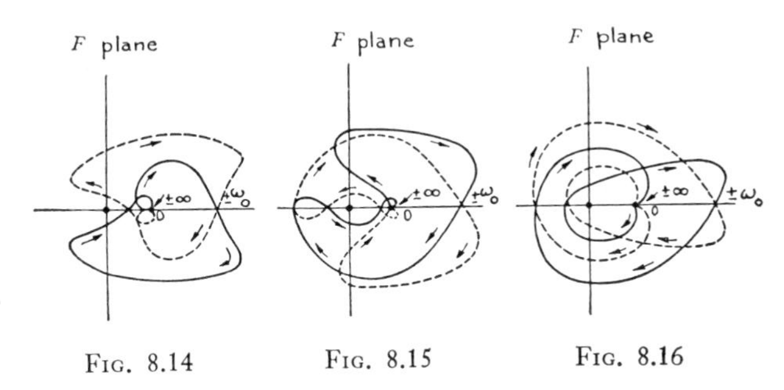

FIG. 8.14 FIG. 8.15 FIG. 8.16

feedback path.* The portions of each plot corresponding to positive and to negative frequencies are shown respectively by the solid and the broken lines. The directions in which the plots are traced as ω varies from $-\infty$ to $+\infty$ are indicated by the arrows. Evidently, Fig. 8.14 represents a stable structure. Figure 8.16, on the other hand, represents a structure which is unstable, with four roots in the right half-plane, since the plot encircles the origin four times. At first glance, it may appear that the structure of Fig. 8.15 is also unstable. It is easy to see, however, that the net phase rotation of a vector connecting the origin to a moving point on the path, over the complete contour, is zero, so that this structure is stable.

The foregoing description of the Nyquist diagram has been based upon the return difference F as a matter of theoretical simplicity. In practice, however, the diagram is usually plotted in terms of the return ratio T, or the loop

* By using special circuits, however, it is possible to provide a d-c return path, so that maximum feedback can be assumed to occur over a band centered about zero frequency. It is also often convenient to assume such a case, ignoring the power supply elements, in analytic work in order to make use of the transformation from symmetrical band-pass to low-pass characteristics described in one of the following chapters. The two examples given later in this section are of this type. Approximate illustrative characteristics can be obtained from Figs. 8.14 to 8.16 by omitting the portions of each plot between $-\omega_0$ and $+\omega_0$ and identifying $\pm\omega_0$ with zero frequency.

transmission characteristic $\mu\beta$. Since $F = 1 + T = 1 - \mu\beta$ the relations among the three plots are easily ascertained. For example, Fig. 8.17 shows the diagram of Fig. 8.14 plotted in terms of T. It is the same as Fig. 8.14 except for a translation one unit to the left. Figure 8.18 shows the same plot in terms of $\mu\beta$, and is the same as Fig. 8.17 rotated through 180°. In each figure the negative frequency characteristic has been omitted for simplicity. Evidently a loop around the origin in the F

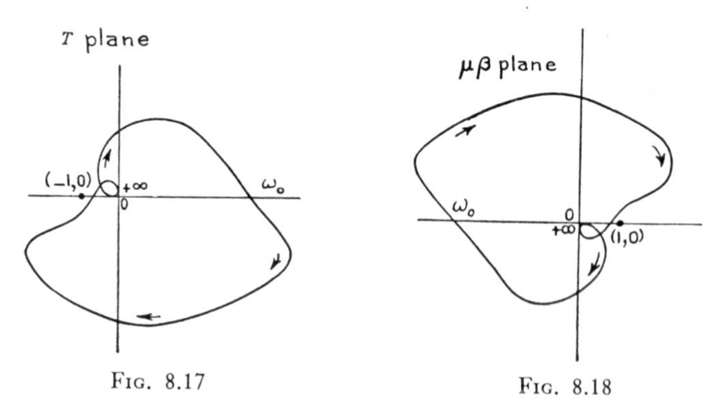

FIG. 8.17 FIG. 8.18

diagram is the same as a loop around $-1,0$ in the T diagram, or a loop around 1,0 in the $\mu\beta$ diagram. Calling these three the *critical points*, therefore, the general result of this discussion can be summed up in the

Theorem: If a structure is stable when a given element vanishes, the necessary and sufficient condition for it to remain stable when the element assumes its normal value is that the Nyquist diagram for the return difference, return ratio, or loop transmission of the element should not encircle the appropriate critical point.

The choice between the T and $\mu\beta$ diagrams can conveniently be related to the well-known fact that under normal circumstances a feedback amplifier must contain an odd number of stages in its forward circuit. In an ordinary design, for example, the purely passive parts of the feedback loop will give a very small phase shift in the neighborhood of the band center ω_0, while on each side of ω_0 they will vary in a manner somewhat similar to that shown by the diagram of Fig. 8.17. It is clear that if the passive circuits furnish the complete $\mu\beta$ characteristic such a diagram will encircle the point 1,0 and produce instability unless the loop transmission is very small. There is, however, a phase reversal associated with each tube. By using an odd number of tubes we secure one net phase reversal. This rotates the $\mu\beta$ diagram into the position shown by Fig. 8.18, and permits the use of a substantial amount of feedback near ω_0 without instability. The $\mu\beta$ diagram is thus appropriate when we consider the complete phase shift around the feedback loop, including the tubes, while the use of the T diagram, in an amplifier containing an odd number of stages, is equivalent to considering the phase shifts of only the passive parts of the structure. The amplifier can, of course, be built with an even number of stages by using one of the devices described in Chapter III.

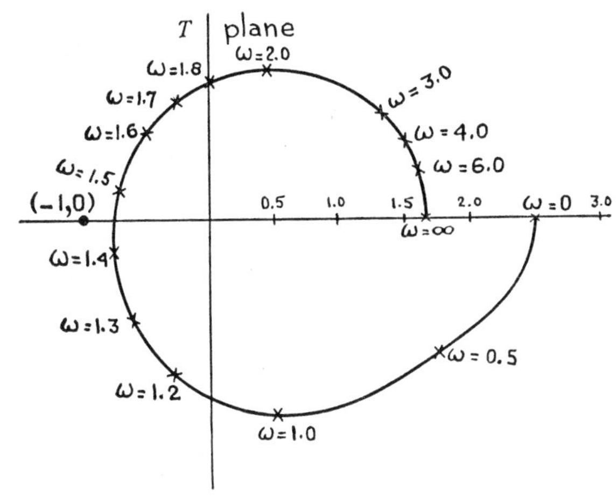

Fig. 8.19

As a quantitative example of a Nyquist diagram we may consider the circuit shown by Fig. 7.2 in the preceding chapter. It is apparent from equation (7–12) of that chapter that the return ratio T for the tube can be written as

$$T = \mu \frac{p^3 + 2p + 1}{3p^3 + 4p^2 + 7p + 2}. \tag{8–18}$$

If we assume, for definiteness, that $\mu = 5$, this yields the values of T given in the following table.

ω	T	ω	T
0	$2.5 - i0$	1.7	$-0.26 + i0.87$
0.5	$1.73 - i1.05$	1.8	$0 + i1.02$
1.0	$0.5 - i1.5$	2.0	$0.44 + i1.12$
1.2	$-0.33 - i1.17$	3.0	$1.29 + i0.81$
1.4	$-0.79 - i0.26$	4.0	$1.48 + i0.59$
1.5	$-0.73 + i0.23$	6.0	$1.59 + i0.38$
1.6	$-0.53 + i0.61$	10.0	$1.64 + i0.22$

The Nyquist diagram obtained by plotting these points is shown by Fig. 8.19. The plot does not enclose the point $-1,0$ so that the system is stable. We may notice, however, that the whole diagram is proportional to μ and would enclose $-1,0$ if μ were multiplied by perhaps 1.25 or 1.3. This agrees with the calculations made in the preceding chapter, where it appeared that some of the zeros of Δ would be found in the right half-plane for $\mu > 6.4$. The stability of the circuit for negative μ's can be examined conveniently by using the same diagram with the critical point taken as 1,0. We observe that to make the system stable under these conditions we must multiply μ by a factor of about 0.4, which agrees with the limit $\mu = -2$ determined in the preceding chapter. We may also notice that the values of ω at which the Nyquist plot crosses the real axis, which, of course, mark the places at which the plot encounters the two critical points when μ is assigned its limiting values, are respectively ± 1.45 and 0. These agree with the values given in Chapter VII for the points at which the various zeros of Δ cross from the left to the right side of the plane.

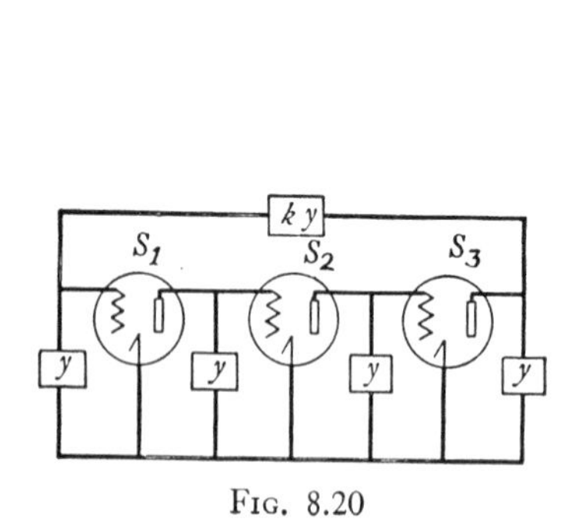

FIG. 8.20

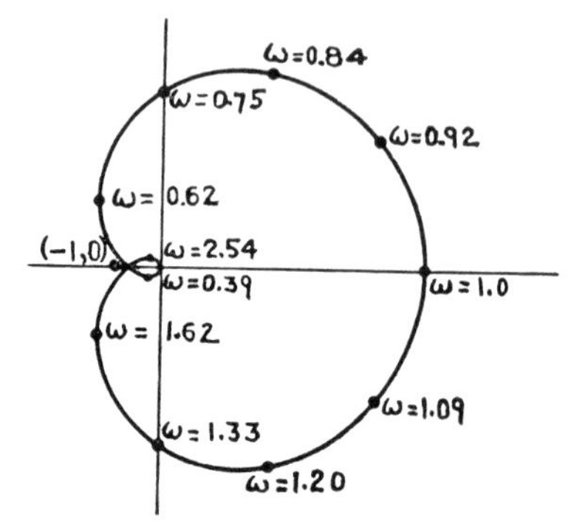

FIG. 8.21

A second example is furnished by the circuit of Fig. 8.20. The structure represents a normal three stage amplifier with shunt feedback except that to simplify the computations all the branches have been taken as proportional to a given admittance y. Let the transconductances of the three tubes be represented by S_1, S_2, and S_3. If we ignore the phase reversals due to the tubes, the voltage gains from the first grid to the second and from the second to the third are respectively S_1/y and S_2/y, while that from the third grid back to the first is $kS_3/(1 + 2k)y$. The product of these three is the return ratio T for any one of the tubes. We therefore have

$$T = \frac{k}{1 + 2k} S_1 S_2 S_3 \frac{1}{y^3} \cdot \tag{8-19}$$

To plot the Nyquist diagram, we will suppose that $y = 1 + p + (1/p)$. This corresponds to a resistance, capacity, and inductance all in parallel.

Such a structure might represent a simple form of amplifier transmitting a band of frequencies in the neighborhood of the resonance of the coil and condenser. If we choose $kS_1S_2S_3/(1 + 2k) = 6$, this gives the Nyquist diagram shown by Fig. 8.21. Only the positive half of the diagram is shown, since with the symmetrical characteristics chosen the negative half is an exact duplicate. It will be seen that the circuit is stable and gives a return difference in the center of the band of 17 db. The circuit becomes unstable, however, if the tubes are assumed to have slightly more gain.

8.8. *Nyquist's Criterion for Stability — Multiple Loop Case*

The discussion in the foregoing section has been based upon the assumption that none of the roots of Δ^0 can be found in the right half-plane, or in other words, that the circuit is stable when the prescribed W vanishes. This assumption is, of course, valid if W represents a tube in any single loop amplifier, and it can also be expected to hold for the majority of multiple loop cases. On the other hand, certain multiple loop circuits may be stable under operating conditions but become unstable when specified tubes fail. This section will consider the application of the Nyquist diagram to such situations.

If some of the roots of Δ^0 are found in the right half-plane, it is evident that the circuit will *not* be stable if the Nyquist diagram fails to encircle the critical point. In accordance with (8–17) such a situation implies that there are as many roots of Δ as there are of Δ^0 in the right half-plane. To assure stability the Nyquist plot should encircle the critical point in a counterclockwise direction as many times as there are roots of Δ^0 to consider. It is therefore necessary to know the number of these roots. This can be determined from the Nyquist diagrams for the other tubes of the circuit with the original tube dead. To analyze the situation generally, let it be supposed that the tubes are originally all dead and are assigned their normal gains one by one in some chosen order. As each tube is restored to its operating condition we may compute its return difference for the condition of the other tubes existing at that stage of the process and plot the corresponding Nyquist diagram. It follows from (8–17) that the diagram for the jth tube will encircle the critical point $P_j - N_j$ times in a counterclockwise direction, if P_j and N_j represent respectively the numbers of poles and zeros of the jth return difference which appear in the right half-plane. The total number of encirclements for all plots is $(P_1 - N_1) + (P_2 - N_2) + \cdots + (P_n - N_n)$. But the Δ which appears in the numerator of any return difference is the same as the Δ^0 in the denominator of the succeeding return difference. We therefore have $N_j = P_{j+1}$. Moreover, $P_1 = 0$, since the circuit with all tubes dead must be stable. The final circuit will be stable if $N_n = 0$. We therefore have the

Theorem: If a circuit is stable when all its tubes have their normal gains, the total number of clockwise and counterclockwise encirclements of the critical point must be equal to each other in the series of Nyquist diagrams for the individual tubes obtained by beginning with all tubes dead and restoring the tubes successively in any order to their normal gains.

In applying this theorem, it is important to notice that the gains of the tubes may be restored in a variety of orders. If the amplifier contains n tubes there are, in the general case, $n!$ possible arrangements. Although the final index of stability or instability must be independent of the order in which the tubes are chosen, the diagram for any individual tube may be vastly affected by the point in the series at which its gain is supposed to be restored.

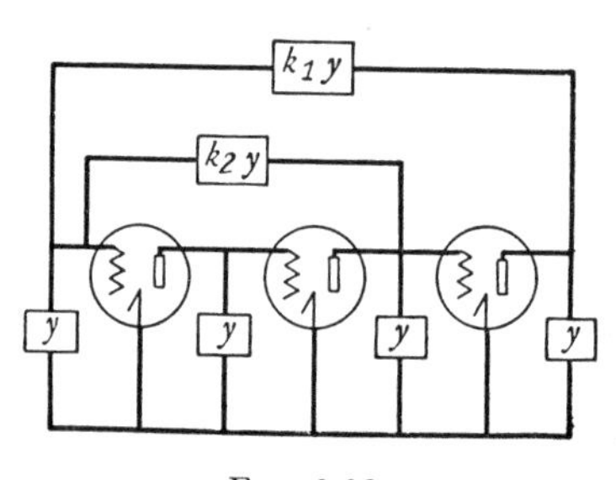

FIG. 8.22

An example of this theorem is furnished by the circuit of Fig. 8.22. The structure is the same as that shown previously by Fig. 8.20 except for the addition of a subsidiary feedback around the first two stages of the forward circuit.* A two-stage subsidiary loop is a convenient choice here, where we are interested in illustrating a circuit which may become unstable when one of the tubes fails, since, as shown previously, an even number of stages leads to a returned voltage which is broadly of the wrong sign for stability. In the present instance we may therefore expect the circuit to sing when the output tube fails, if the gain of the first two stages is sufficiently great.

It will be assumed, for definiteness, that $k_1 = 0.001$ and $k_2 = 0.01$. We may expect from these numbers that questions of stability will arise as soon as the voltage gain per stage is greater than about 10. The several Nyquist diagrams which are required to determine whether the structure will be stable can, of course, be obtained from loop transmission computations, as was done in connection with Fig. 8.20. For the variety of cases to be considered here, however, it is simpler to base the analysis upon the determinant of the system. Using nodal methods, we readily find that

* This general type of circuit was described by F. B. Llewellyn, (U.S. Pat. No. 2,245,598), who called the subsidiary feedback the α circuit, in distinction to the principal, or β, feedback. The present example is, of course, not intended to illustrate the contemplated engineering applications of such a circuit.

$$\Delta = \begin{vmatrix} (1+k_1+k_2)y & 0 & -k_2y & -k_1y \\ S_1 & y & 0 & 0 \\ -k_2y & S_2 & (1+k_2)y & 0 \\ -k_1y & 0 & S_3 & (1+k_1)y \end{vmatrix}$$

$$= y^4 + k_1k_2y^3S_3 - k_2y^2S_1S_2 + k_1yS_1S_2S_3 \tag{8-20}$$

where S_1, S_2, and S_3 are, as before, the transconductances of the three tubes, and the second expression has been simplified by ignoring the small quantities k_1 and k_2 in comparison with unity.

Since the circuit contains three tubes there are $3! = 6$ orders in which the gains of the tubes can be restored. The first two tubes, however, can be regarded for analytic purposes as a single tube, since they are directly in tandem and cannot affect the stability of the circuit unless both are operative. This is evidenced by the fact that S_1 and S_2 appear only as the product S_1S_2 in (8–20). We need consider, consequently, only two possibilities, one in which the gains are restored in the order $S_3;S_1S_2$, and the other in which they are restored in the order $S_1S_2;S_3$.

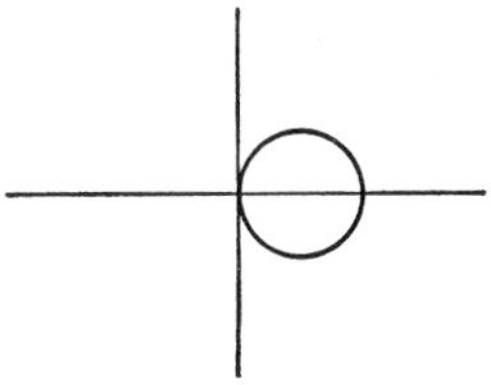

FIG. 8.23

The simpler Nyquist diagrams are found if we begin by restoring the gain of S_3. After S_3 is restored, its return ratio is readily found from (8–20) by means of the formula $T = (\Delta/\Delta^0) - 1$, where, of course, Δ represents the determinant when S_3 has its normal value, Δ^0 the determinant when S_3 vanishes, and both quantities are to be evaluated under the assumption that $S_1S_2 = 0$, since the gains of these tubes have not yet been restored. This gives

$$T = \frac{k_1k_2S_3}{y}. \tag{8-21}$$

Upon choosing $y = 1 + p + (1/p)$, as before, this leads to a Nyquist diagram whose positive frequency half is shown by Fig. 8.23. For practical values of S_3 the path would be very small because of the very small value of k_1k_2, but in any event it is clear that it does not encircle the critical point $-1,0$.

We next restore the gains of the tubes S_1 and S_2 to their normal values. The resulting return ratio for these tubes can be found by the same general method as was used in obtaining (8–21) and appears as

$$T = \frac{k_1S_3 - k_2y}{k_1k_2y^2S_3 + y^3}\,S_1S_2. \tag{8-22}$$

A series of curves for the positive frequency half of T for $\omega > 1$ is shown by Fig. 8.24.* In each case it has been assumed that $S_1 S_2 = 200$. The results for other values of $S_1 S_2$ can, of course, be obtained merely by expanding or shrinking the curves actually given. Assuming that $S_1 S_2 = 200$, Curve I gives the Nyquist plot when $S_3 = 40$. It will be seen that the plot encircles the critical point $-1,0$. In the preceding diagram of Fig. 8.23, on the other hand, the critical point was not encircled. The net number of encirclements in the two plots together is therefore not zero and in accordance with the preceding theorem the structure is consequently unstable.

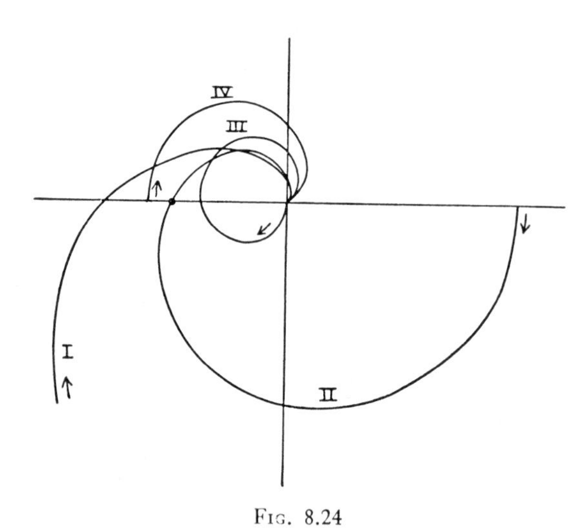

FIG. 8.24

Curve II gives the result when S_3 is assumed to be 20. The circuit is now on the edge of instability, since the plot passes directly through the critical point. As S_3 is diminished below 20 the circuit becomes definitely stable. Curve III, for example, shows the result when $S_3 = 10$. Very low values of S_3, on the other hand, lead once more to instability. For example, when $S_3 = 4$ the plot is that shown by Curve IV and once more encircles the critical point.

Instead of following this arrangement we can also restore the gains in the order $S_1 S_2; S_3$. The return ratio for S_1 and S_2 with $S_3 = 0$ can be obtained from (8–20) as

$$T = \frac{-k_2 S_1 S_2}{y^2}. \tag{8–23}$$

* The images of these curves about the real axis correspond to values of $\omega < 1$.

The corresponding Nyquist diagram where $S_1S_2 = 200$ is shown by Fig. 8.25.

It will be seen that the curve in Fig. 8.25 encircles the critical point once in a clockwise direction.* In accordance with the preceding theorem the final plot of the return ratio for S_3 must consequently encircle the critical point once in a counterclockwise direction if the complete circuit is to be stable. This can be examined by setting up the return ratio for S_3 as

$$T = k_1 \frac{k_2y^2 + S_1S_2}{y(y^2 - k_2S_1S_2)} S_3. \quad (8\text{–}24)$$

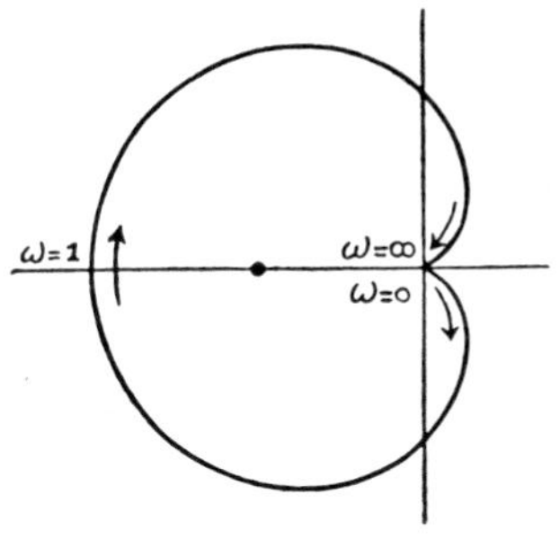

Fig. 8.25

The Nyquist diagram corresponding to this equation when $S_3 = 10$ and $S_1S_2 = 200$ is shown by the solid curve of Fig. 8.26, while the diagrams obtained for the same value of S_3, but with S_1S_2 chosen as 100 and 400, are shown respectively by the broken line Curves I and II. Considering in particular the solid curve, it will be seen that the plot does in fact loop around $-1,0$ once in a counterclockwise direction, so that the final structure is stable. This is, of course, in agreement with the conclusion previously reached in connection with Fig. 8.24, since the assumed S's are the same as those which apply to Curve III of that figure.

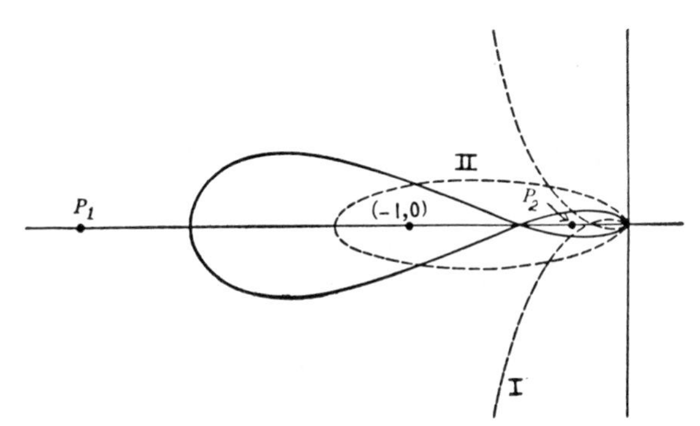

Fig. 8.26

By varying S_3 it is also possible to confirm the conclusions reached previously for the conditions represented by the other curves of Fig. 8.24. The changes in S_3 can be represented in Fig. 8.26 by expanding or contracting

* Figure 8.25 gives only the positive frequency half of the complete plot. A second loop around the critical point is, of course, provided by the negative half.

the diagram or, more conveniently, by keeping the plot fixed and moving the critical point. If we retain the choice $S_1S_2 = 200$, it will be observed that the circuit remains stable if S_3 is varied by a small amount in either direction from the original value 10, but that it becomes unstable for larger changes. As an example we may select $S_3 = 4$ which corresponds to Curve IV in Fig. 8.24. This is equivalent to moving the critical point to the position P_1 in Fig. 8.26. The critical point is thus placed outside the solid curve, which corresponds to instability in this situation. On the other hand, the choice $S_3 = 40$, which corresponds to Curve I in Fig. 8.24, moves the critical point to the position P_2. With this change, the point is still encircled by the curve, but the encirclement takes place in the wrong direction.

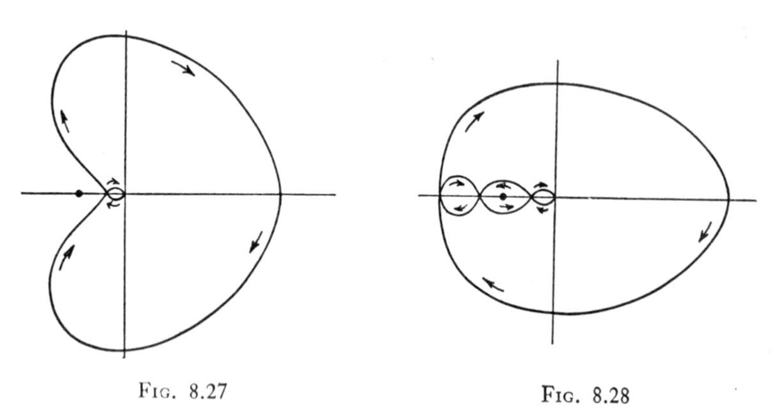

FIG. 8.27 FIG. 8.28

8.9. *Conditional and Unconditional Stability*

In a formal mathematical sense, the above criteria of stability, based entirely upon the encirclement of the critical point in the Nyquist diagram, require no qualifications. Any structure that meets them is stable. For practical engineering purposes, however, it is desirable to pay some attention to the general shape of the Nyquist plot in addition to counting the number of times it loops around the critical point. This gives rise to two general classes of stable structures, as illustrated by the return ratio diagrams for single loop structures shown by Figs. 8.27 and 8.28. Both diagrams represent stable circuits. The first, however, is *absolutely* or *unconditionally* stable, while the second is merely *Nyquist** or *conditionally* stable.

The reason for making this distinction appears if it is recalled that for practical purposes we are really interested in the stability of an amplifier

* So-called because it was generally assumed before Nyquist's work that it was not possible to obtain a positive real $\mu\beta$ greater than unity without instability.

over a period of time. Most of the elements of the amplifier can be expected to remain fairly constant. The gains of the tubes, however, are likely to diminish with age and since one of the usual objectives in applying feedback to a circuit is to allow a large variation in the tubes without much effect on the external gain, it must be supposed that this diminution will be substantial. Since the return ratio diagram in a single loop feedback structure swells or shrinks in direct proportion to the gain of the tubes, the effect of aging therefore will be to contract the loop. If a diagram such as that shown in Fig. 8.28, in which the return ratio path goes beyond 180° for an interval in which there is a net gain around the loop, is sufficiently decreased the plot will take the form shown by Fig. 8.29 and evidently represents an unstable circuit. If the diagram is of the unconditionally stable type shown by Fig. 8.27, on the other hand, it can be decreased indefinitely without producing instability.

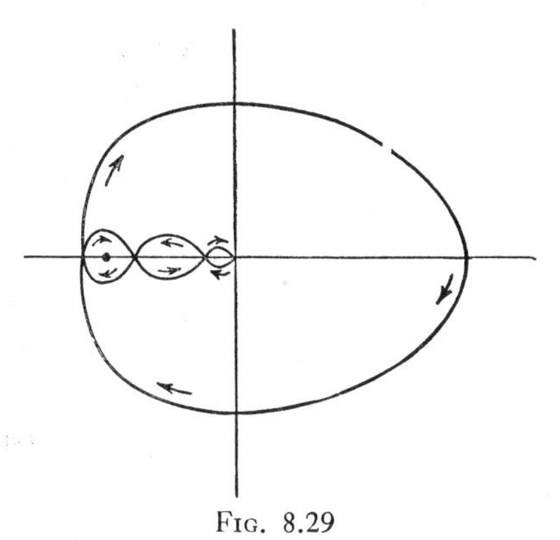

FIG. 8.29

Another possibility of securing a change in tube gains with time occurs when the power is first applied to the tubes. Until the cathodes are warm the gain of the tubes will be very small. As power is applied to the circuit, therefore, we must imagine that the return ratio diagram begins by being very small and expands continuously to its final position as the cathode temperatures increase. If the final diagram is of the type shown by Fig. 8.28, there will be an intermediate point in the course of this expansion for which the system is unstable. When this intermediate point is reached natural oscillations begin and build up exponentially. At the same time, of course, the gains of the tubes increase as the cathodes approach their operating temperatures so that there is a tendency for the amplifier to pull itself out of the unstable condition. In most circumstances, however, the sing develops so rapidly that the tubes are overloaded before the gain is sufficient to bring the Nyquist diagram out of the unstable condition. Since overloading usually reduces the effective gains of the tubes, the system is very likely to persist in an unstable condition permanently.

These difficulties are not necessarily unanswerable. For example, we may close the feedback loop after the gains of the tubes have reached their normal values, or we may apply " B " battery to the tubes after the cathode temperatures are sufficiently high. For practical purposes, however, these devices represent undesirable complications. Moreover, even if they are used the amplifier is somewhat unreliable, since it may still sing if the tubes age sufficiently or if the power supply is momentarily interrupted. For these reasons, most of the analysis which follows will assume that the amplifier is to be unconditionally stable. On the other hand, it turns out that under equivalent circumstances a conditionally stable amplifier may exhibit much more feedback than would be obtainable from an unconditionally stable structure. Conditional stability thus represents an important possibility when adequate feedback is hard to secure.

A second qualification on this discussion is also pertinent. In describing the characteristics of a conditionally stable circuit it was tacitly assumed that the structure contained only a single feedback loop. Evidently, the same physical considerations affect multiple loop structures also. In the single loop case, however, we can distinguish between conditionally and unconditionally stable situations merely by inspecting the shape of the Nyquist diagram, since changes in tube gains affect only the size of the diagram. In a multiple loop circuit, on the other hand, both the shape and the size of the Nyquist diagram for any one tube may be affected by changes in the gains of the other tubes. Examples are furnished by the preceding Figs. 8.24 and 8.26. This evidently produces a much more complicated situation. The analysis of the problem is too lengthy to be given here and will be presented at a later point.

8.10. *Extensions of Nyquist's Criterion*

Thus far we have applied the Nyquist diagram method of determining stability only to the return difference Δ/Δ^0. Since Δ will appear in almost any transmission or impedance expression we care to set up, however, it is clear that the application of the criterion is not necessarily restricted to this one function. Some of the possible extensions are considered here. The discussion is given only in outline, since the essential situation is the same as it is for the return difference function. The chief point to notice is that any transmission or impedance expression will contain Δ in combination with some other determinant, just as the return difference includes both Δ and Δ^0. In general, the Nyquist diagram will give only the difference between the zeros and poles of the impedance or transmission function or, in other words, only the difference between the number of zeros of Δ and of the determinant with which it is associated. In extending Nyquist's criterion, therefore, it is necessary to assume that we have some means of determining the number of zeros in the right-hand half-plane furnished by the other determinant. This is usually equivalent to saying that we must know that the structure is stable for some particular reference condition or if it is not stable what modes of instability it has.

1. *Nyquist's Criterion for a Driving Point Immittance.* The immittance which will be seen at the terminals of a generator applied to the nth mesh or node of a general network can be written as

$$W = \frac{\Delta}{\Delta_{nn}}. \tag{8–25}$$

If we make a Nyquist plot of this expression, it follows from (8–17) that the number of loops encircling the origin will be the difference between the number of zeros of Δ and of Δ_{nn} in the right-hand half-plane. The quantity Δ_{nn}, however, is the form to which the determinant of the system reduces when an infinite immittance is across the driving terminals or, in other words, when the driving terminals are open-circuited in an impedance analysis or short-circuited in an admittance analysis. If the system is known to be stable under these conditions (8–25) can have no poles in the right half-plane. If it also has no zeros in this region, so that the system is stable under normal conditions, it follows that the Nyquist plot cannot encircle the origin.

This result can be generalized. Suppose that instead of adding an infinite immittance between the driving terminals we add only the finite amount W_n. Since Δ_{nn} must be independent of W_n (8–25) becomes

$$W' = W + W_n = \frac{\Delta'}{\Delta_{nn}} \tag{8–26}$$

where Δ' represents the new value of Δ. Division of (8–25) by (8–26) gives

$$\frac{W}{W'} = \frac{W}{W + W_n} = \frac{\Delta}{\Delta'}. \tag{8–27}$$

If the system is known to be stable after the addition of W_n, (8–27) can have no poles in the right half-plane and the previous argument applies. We therefore have the

Theorem: If a system is stable when a prescribed immittance is added between a pair of terminals it will be stable without the given immittance provided the Nyquist plot of the ratio between the total immittances at the terminals in the two cases does not encircle the origin. In particular, it is necessary to plot only the normal immittance itself if the system is stable when an infinite immittance is added between the driving terminals.

In applying this theorem, it must be borne in mind that the complete Nyquist contour of Fig. 8.7 includes the large semicircle in the right half-plane as well as the real frequency axis. This part of the path was dismissed in the consideration of F on the assumption that a physical return difference always approached unity at infinite frequency. The same simplification obtains here if the quantity which is plotted approaches a constant value at infinity. If it behaves as either a positive or a negative power of frequency near infinity, however, the Nyquist diagram must include an arc of a very large or very small circle to represent the values assumed by the function over this part of the path.

2. *Nyquist's Criterion for a Transfer Immittance.* The transfer immittance from point i to point j in a general network can be written as

$$W_T = \frac{\Delta}{\Delta_{ij}}. \tag{8–28}$$

The Nyquist diagram corresponding to (8–28) will encircle the origin as many times as there are roots of Δ in the right half-plane provided there are no roots of Δ_{ij} in this region. From the discussion under 5*c* in the list of general network conditions given in the preceding chapter, the restriction on the roots of Δ_{ij} is equivalent to specifying that the transfer immittance must be a minimum phase shift function. We can therefore conclude that if the transfer immittance is known to be of minimum phase type the network will be stable provided the Nyquist diagram of the transfer immittance does not encircle the origin. As an example we may consider the familiar expression $\mu/(1 - \mu\beta)$ for the gain of an ordinary feedback amplifier. Since a transfer immittance has the physical significance of a loss, this expression can be regarded as the reciprocal of the transfer immittance from input to output. The poles of transfer immittance are consequently either points at which μ vanishes or points at which β becomes infinite. None of the latter group of points can be found in the right half-plane, since the β circuit, being passive, is necessarily stable. None of the former group of points will appear in the right half-plane if the gain μ by itself represents a minimum phase shift expression. This will be true for any of the μ circuits encountered in ordinary design practice. In any ordinary situation, therefore, the stability of the amplifier can be determined by observing whether or not the Nyquist plot of its external gain encircles the origin.*

This analysis can be generalized by methods similar to those used for the

* In making such a plot, however, allowance must again be made for the fact that the complete Nyquist path includes the large semicircle in the right half-plane. In practical situations, the gain of the amplifier must eventually drop off as some negative power of frequency. The final part of the diagram must include an arc of a very small circle to represent the behavior of such a function over the large semicircular portion of the path.

driving point immittance. We observe that Δ_{ij} in (8–28) must be independent of the self-immittances at i and j. If we make an arbitrary change in either or both self-immittances, therefore, we can write the new transfer immittance as

$$W'_T = \frac{\Delta'}{\Delta_{ij}} \tag{8–29}$$

where Δ' represents the new value of Δ. The ratio of (8–28) and (8–29) is

$$\frac{W_T}{W'_T} = \frac{\Delta}{\Delta'} \tag{8–30}$$

and the Nyquist diagram of this function will encircle the origin as many times as there are roots of Δ in the right half-plane if there are no roots of Δ' in this region. We therefore have the

Theorem: If a system is stable when prescribed immittances are added at two points in a circuit, it will also be stable without the added immittances if the Nyquist plot of the ratio of the transfer immittances between the two points in the two cases does not encircle the origin. In particular, it is necessary to plot only the transfer immittance in the second case if the function is known to be of minimum phase type.

8.11. *Two Theorems from Function Theory*

The discussion of this chapter will be concluded by the demonstration of two standard theorems from function theory. The theorems are developed here for use in the next few chapters. They can conveniently be regarded as by-products of the Nyquist diagram method of treating stability, although they are usually established independently.

To develop the first theorem, let $f_1(z)$ and $f_2(z)$ be two functions which are analytic within and on the boundary of a given region. Both $f_1(z)$ and $f_2(z)$ may, however, have zeros within the region. It will be assumed that $|f_1(z)| > |f_2(z)|$ at all points on the boundary. Consider the function $F(z)$ defined by

$$F(z) = \frac{f_1(z) + f_2(z)}{f_1(z)} = 1 + \frac{f_2(z)}{f_1(z)}. \tag{8–31}$$

In accordance with (8–17), the number of times the origin is encircled by the Nyquist plot of $F(z)$ is equal to the difference between the number of zeros of $F(z)$ and the number of poles of $F(z)$ lying within the region. But the zeros and poles are respectively the roots of $f_1(z) + f_2(z)$ and $f_1(z)$. Furthermore, since we have assumed $|f_1(z)| > |f_2(z)|$ on the boundary, it is clear from the right-hand side of (8–31) that the Nyquist plot must be inside the unit circle in Fig. 8.30. Evidently the plot cannot encircle the origin at all. We therefore have the

Theorem: If $f_1(z)$ and $f_2(z)$ are analytic on and within a given closed contour and $|f_1(z)| > |f_2(z)|$ on the contour, the functions $f_1(z)$ and $f_1(z) + f_2(z)$ have the same number of roots within the contour.

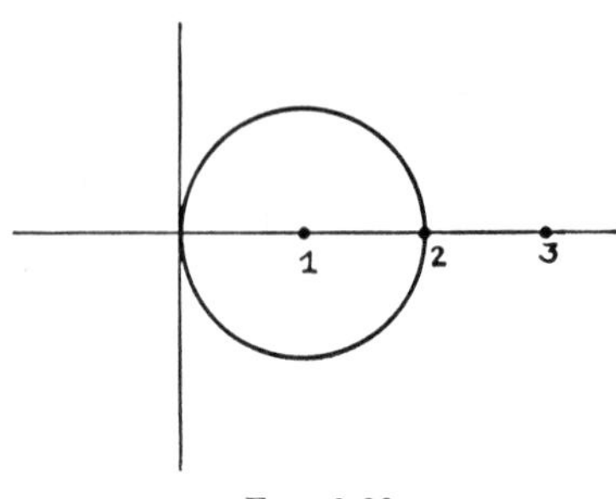

FIG. 8.30

The general field of application of this theorem is obviously that of determining rough limits within which changes in a structure can be expected not to affect its stability. As an example, suppose $f_1(z)$ represents an impedance looking into some pair of terminals in an amplifier. It will be supposed that $f_1(z)$ is "open-circuit stable" — so that it has no poles in the right half-plane. Let $f_2(z)$ be an ordinary passive impedance added between these terminals. If $|f_1(z)| > |f_2(z)|$ at all points on the real frequency axis the addition of the passive impedance cannot affect the stability or instability of the structure.

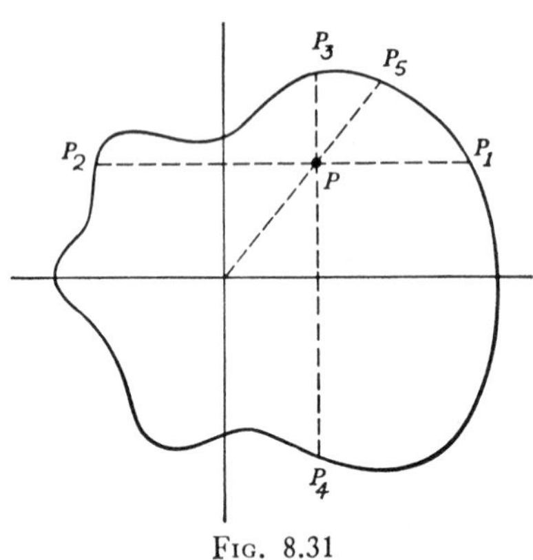

FIG. 8.31

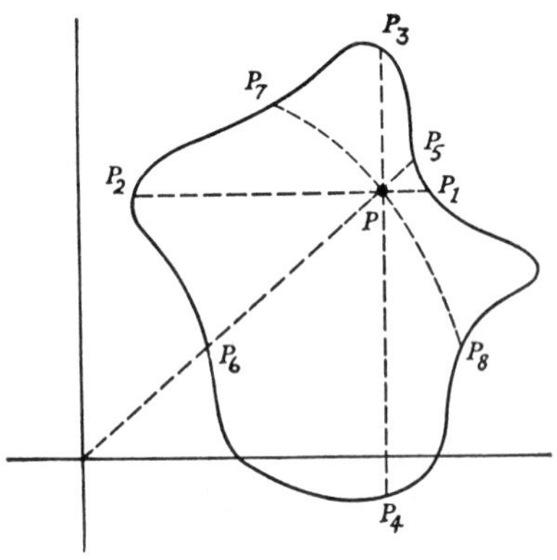

FIG. 8.32

To establish the second theorem, let $f(z)$ be analytic within and on the boundary of some given region. The Nyquist plot of $f(z)$ will take one of the forms indicated by Figs. 8.31 and 8.32, depending upon whether or not there is a root of $f(z)$ in the region. Let z_0 be any point in the region. In accordance with the argument advanced in connection with Fig. 8.13, $f(z_0)$ can be represented by some point P lying within the Nyquist plot in Fig. 8.31 or 8.32. Evidently the real component of $f(z_0)$ cannot be as great as the real component exhibited by $f(z)$ in some parts of the boundary because in either figure we can find some point P_1 on the plot itself which lies to the right of P. Similarly, the existence of points such as P_2 indicate that there must be parts of the boundary for which the real component of $f(z)$ is less than that of $f(z_0)$. The points P_3 and P_4 illustrate similar relations for the imaginary component. In both plots, also, there is a point P_5 corresponding to an absolute value of $f(z)$ greater than that of $f(z_0)$. In Fig. 8.32 we can, in addition, pick out a point P_6 corresponding to a smaller absolute value than that of $f(z_0)$, as well as points P_7 and P_8 at which the phase angle is greater than and less than that of $f(z_0)$. But the z_0 with which we started was *any* point in the interior of the region. We have therefore established the

> *Theorem:* If $f(z)$ is analytic within and on a given closed contour the maxima and minima of the real and imaginary components of $f(z)$ and the maximum absolute value of $f(z)$, for the region composed of the contour itself and the points interior to it, are all found on the contour. If $f(z)$ has in addition no zeros within the contour the minimum absolute value of $f(z)$ and the maximum and minimum phase angles of $f(z)$ are also found on the contour.

An example of this theorem is furnished by the common engineering problem of maximizing or minimizing some aspect of the performance of a complete passive network at a prescribed frequency by making the most suitable choice of some branch impedance which is under our control. It will be supposed that the branch impedance may be a reactance, a resistance, or some combination of the two. In general, any ordinary passive network characteristic, such as a driving point or transfer impedance, will have neither zeros nor poles considered as a function of one of the branch impedances, as long as the branch impedance has a positive resistance component.* In other words, both the driving point or transfer impedance and its logarithm will be analytic functions in the right half of the plane representing the branch impedance. It follows that the real and imaginary components of the driving point and transfer impedances, their absolute values, and their phase angles will all assume both larger and smaller values on the imaginary axis than they do anywhere in the right half-plane. Since we cannot assign a negative resistance component to the branch impedance, *the maximum and minimum values which are physically obtainable for any of these quantities must therefore be found when the branch impedance is a pure imaginary.* It is not necessary to examine dissipative impedances.

* An exception to this statement must be made for the transfer impedances for certain types of bridge circuits, in which zero delivered current can be secured by bridge balance. These are the non-minimum phase shift networks described in a later chapter.

CHAPTER IX

Physical Representation of Driving Point Impedance Functions

9.1. *Introduction*

This and the succeeding chapter are devoted to a general discussion of the properties of driving point impedance and admittance functions on the basis of the requirements laid down in Chapters VII and VIII. The material is not intended to constitute a complete theory. It is presented principally to illustrate the general requirements deduced in preceding chapters by showing some of the more elementary physical consequences to which they lead. For the sake of logical coherence, however, the present chapter will be centered about the general problem of showing that the conditions on driving point impedances laid down in Chapter VII are sufficient as well as necessary or, in other words, that any impedance functions meeting these conditions can be realized in a physical structure. Miscellaneous additional topics will then be treated in Chapter X.

The list of requirements on driving point impedance functions given in Chapter VII includes both general conditions applicable to all networks, active or passive, and additional special conditions applicable only to passive structures. Purely passive impedances, however, are both those for which the greatest experience is available and those of greatest present importance in design. The discussion will consequently be directed principally at impedances of this type. Active impedances are treated by indicating the points at which they require formal extensions in the passive analysis. In particular, the present chapter will begin by showing how any impedance function meeting the passive requirements can be realized. The problem of realizing an active impedance expression is then treated by showing that any active impedance can be obtained from a combination of a passive impedance and a negative resistance.

9.2. *Resistance Reduction of Passive Impedances*

The conditions which must be met by any passive impedance function were given as 1, 2, 3, 4, 5*b*, and 6*a* in the list of Chapter VII. Our first object is to show that an actual physical structure can be found which will represent any impedance function meeting these requirements. Methods of solving this problem have been invented by Brune* and Darlington.† Darlington's structure consists of a four-terminal reactance network terminated in a resistance. He is able to show that by properly proportioning the network the input impedance of the structure can be assigned any functional form which meets these requirements.

For the purposes of this book the method developed by Brune is the more useful. Brune's method depends upon two principles. In order to explain the first, let it be supposed for simplicity that the impedance function has no zeros or poles on the imaginary axis. The fact that this assumption is immaterial is shown in the next section. Both the impedance and admittance will then be analytic in the right-hand half of the p plane, including the imaginary axis. This is a situation which can be examined by the second of the two theorems developed at the end of the preceding chapter if we regard the right half of the p plane as the region of analyticity and the imaginary axis as the boundary. For our present purposes, we will be particularly interested in the conclusion that the minimum value of the resistance or conductance along the imaginary axis is less than any value of resistance or conductance in the right-hand half-plane. Since the real component of the impedance is positive at all points on the real frequency axis, from 6*a* of Chapter VII, it consequently follows that it must also be positive throughout the right half of the p plane. Brune described this situation by the statement that a passive impedance is a *positive real* function, by which he meant that the real component of Z is always positive when the real component of p is positive.

The same result can also be established by the energy function argument of Chapter VII if we write the right-hand side of equation (7–32) of that chapter as $E_1\bar{I}_1$, as in the preceding equation (7–25), instead of zero, so that the equation refers to the steady-state rather than to the transient condition of the network. The term $E_1\bar{I}_1$ will, of course, be retained in the final expression (7–34) and can be interpreted as the conjugate of the driving point admittance in the same way as was done in connection with (7–30). If we represent the phase angle of the impedance by θ, set $p = p_1 + ip_2$, and write T, F, and V for brevity to represent the sums $T_a + T_b$, etc., this allows us to write

$$\theta = \tan^{-1} \frac{p_2\left(T - \dfrac{V}{p_1^2 + p_2^2}\right)}{F + p_1\left(T + \dfrac{V}{p_1^2 + p_2^2}\right)}. \tag{9–1}$$

* *Journal of Mathematics and Physics*, M.I.T., Vol. X, Oct. 1931, pp. 191–235.

† *Journal of Mathematics and Physics*, M.I.T., Vol. XVIII, No. 4, Sept. 1939, pp. 257–353.

The quantities T, F, and V are, of course, always positive. In the right half-plane, where p_1 is also positive, it is easily seen that the absolute value of θ is less than, or at most equal to, the absolute value of $\tan^{-1} p_2/p_1$. In other words, when p lies in the right half-plane, Z must have a phase angle less than or in the limit equal to that of p itself. Evidently, therefore, the phase angle of Z cannot reach $\pm 90°$, so that the real component of Z must be positive.

The fact that the minimum resistance occurs on the real frequency axis may also be used to deduce a second result. Evidently, if we subtract any resistance not greater than this minimum from the impedance function we will still have a positive resistance throughout the right half-plane. The new function can therefore have no zeros in this region. The poles of the function and the various conditions of conjugacy are, moreover, not affected by the subtraction of a finite real constant. Since an exactly symmetrical situation is obtained if the analysis is expressed in terms of admittances rather than impedances, this allows us to state the

Theorem: A passive immittance will continue to meet the conditions of physical realizability in passive networks if it is diminished by any real constant as long as the real component of the resulting expression does not become negative at any real frequency.

An immittance function will be called a *minimum resistance* or *minimum conductance* expression if its real component vanishes at some point on the real frequency axis, so that no further diminution is possible without violating the passive conditions.

As an example of these relations we may consider the impedance Z_1 given by the first of equations (7–17) of Chapter VII. The corresponding R_1, also given by these equations, has a minimum at $\omega^2 = 1.63$, at which point it is equal to 0.105. The impedance will consequently continue to satisfy the passive conditions if we subtract from it any resistance not greater than 0.105. The limiting, or minimum resistance, expression is given by

$$Z_1' = Z_1 - 0.105 = \frac{0.48p^2 + 0.69p + 1.58}{5p^2 + 3p + 4}. \tag{9–2}$$

As an alternative to this procedure we may also examine the reciprocal of Z_1, using an admittance analysis. The real component of $1/Z_1$ reaches a minimum value of unity at $\omega^2 = 1$. The corresponding minimum conductance expression is

$$Y_1' = \frac{1}{Z_1} - 1 = \frac{4p^2 + 2p + 2}{p^2 + p + 2}. \tag{9–3}$$

This is the same as $1/Z_2$ in (7–17) in Chapter VII, as we might expect from the relation between Z_1 and Z_2 indicated by Fig. 7.5 in that chapter.

The principle of resistance or conductance reduction has been introduced here primarily as a step in the development of Brune's method of synthesizing networks. It is, however, of occasional value also in actual design problems. As an example, let it be supposed that an interstage network has been designed without regard to plate or grid-leak conductance and that we wish to take account of these quantities. If the interstage design includes a parallel resistance of sufficiently low value there is, of course, no difficulty in making the appropriate changes. The preceding theorem shows, however, that if the minimum conductance of the network is sufficiently large the impedance can always be represented with such a branch, even if the original structure of the network is quite different. In this example, of course, the equivalent circuit, while it may be physically realizable in a theoretical sense, may not be found in a configuration which lends itself readily to actual construction.

9.3. *Reactance Reduction of Passive Impedances*

The preceding section has shown that the real component of a passive immittance can be varied by a constant amount, within certain limits, without affecting the passive character of the complete expression. Similar possibilities may also exist for the imaginary component except that the change, instead of being a constant, is a prescribed function of frequency.

These possibilities are associated with the presence of zeros and poles of impedance on the real frequency axis. It will be recalled that zeros and poles of impedance at real frequencies are always simple and occur in plus and minus pairs. Let $\pm p_0$ represent such a pair of zeros or poles. If p_0 represents a pole we can write $Z = Z'/(p - p_0)$, where Z' has no pole at p_0 and can consequently be expanded in a Taylor's series about this point. We can therefore write

$$Z = \frac{1}{p - p_0}[A_0 + A_1(p - p_0) + A_2(p - p_0)^2 + \cdots]$$

$$= \frac{A_0}{p - p_0} + A_1 + A_2(p - p_0) + \cdots \qquad (9\text{–}4)$$

If p_0 represents a zero, we have, similarly,

$$Z = (p - p_0)[B_0 + B_1(p - p_0) + B_2(p - p_0)^2 + \cdots]. \qquad (9\text{–}5)$$

When p is very close to p_0, the terms $A_0/(p - p_0)$ and $B_0(p - p_0)$ in these expressions are much more important than any others. Since $p - p_0$ is a positive imaginary for values of p on the imaginary axis on one side of p_0 and a negative imaginary for values on the other side, both A_0

and B_0 must be real quantities if the impedance is not to have a negative resistance component for frequencies sufficiently close to p_0 on one side or the other.

Both A_0 and B_0 must also be positive. This is immediately apparent if we make use of (9–1). Unless A_0 and B_0 are positive the impedance will be approximately a negative resistance, with a phase angle certainly greater than $\pm 90°$, for values of p sufficiently close to p_0 in the right-hand half-plane. The fact that A_0 and B_0 must be positive can also be shown directly from a Nyquist stability diagram. In applying this method it must be recalled that the integration contour assumed in preparing the diagram may include small indentations away from the real frequency axis, as shown by Fig. 8.7 of Chapter VIII, to avoid singularities of the integrand on that axis. Since the integrand in the Nyquist method is the logarithmic derivative of the impedance function such an indentation must be made for each zero and pole of impedance on the real axis. If we consider in particular a pole, the resulting Nyquist diagram may be studied by means of Fig. 9.1. The solid line shows the behavior of the function on the small indentation and adjacent parts of the real frequency path when A_0 is supposed to be positive, while the broken line gives a similar plot when A_0 is negative. The dotted line indicates the plot corresponding to other parts of the real frequency axis. The exact shape here is unimportant, but this part of the complete plot must of course link up with either the solid or the broken line portions without leaving the right half-plane. It is clear that if we choose the broken line path the complete plot will encircle the origin, so that the stability condition will be violated.

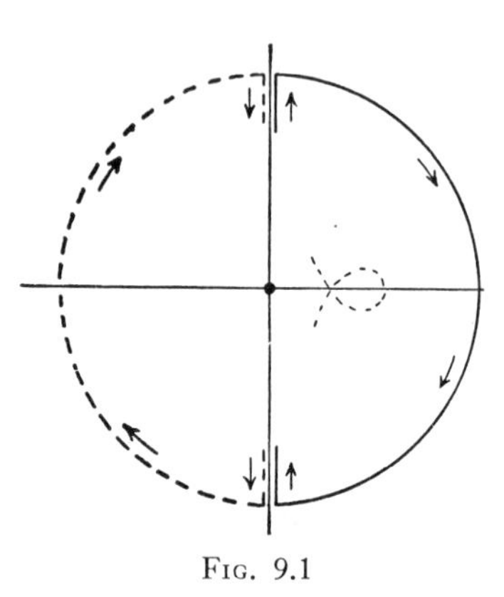

FIG. 9.1

From these facts, it is easy to show that a zero or pole at real frequencies can always be represented as an ordinary resonant or anti-resonant network. Corresponding to (9–4), for example, there must be a similar expansion about the conjugate pole at $-p_0$. While the two expansions will not, in general, be identical, it is easy to see that the constant A_0, at least, will be the same in both. The sum of the two terms representing the poles is, however, $2A_0p/(p^2 - p_0^2)$. This can be identified with $pD/(p^2 + D/L)$, which represents the impedance of an anti-resonant network, provided we have

$$D = 2A_0; \quad L = -\frac{2A_0}{p_0^2}. \tag{9–6}$$

Since A_0 is positive and p_0^2 is negative, both elements must be positive. In the special case when the pole occurs at zero or infinity the anti-resonant network reduces to a condenser or an inductance. In an exactly similar way, of course, we can represent zeros of impedance, or poles of admittance, by series resonant circuits in parallel with the rest of the network.

An impedance all of whose real frequency poles have been deleted in this manner will be called a *minimum reactance* network, while if the zeros have been removed it will be called a *minimum susceptance* structure. In either case the removed branch is, of course, a pure imaginary on the real frequency axis.* The resistance of the remainder at real frequencies is therefore still positive and we need merely repeat the argument of the preceding section to show that the remainder must consequently meet all the passive conditions. This establishes the

Theorem: A passive impedance or admittance will continue to meet the conditions of physical realizability in passive networks if it is diminished by the reactance or susceptance corresponding to its real frequency poles.

As an example of this process we may consider the impedance function

$$Z = \frac{2p^2 + p + 1}{p^3 + p^2 + p + 1}. \qquad (9\text{–}7)$$

The expression meets all the requirements of physical realizability in a passive network. There are three poles, one at $p = -1$ and the remaining two at $p = \pm i$. The latter pair, since they occur on the real frequency axis, indicate that Z is not a minimum reactance function. In order to extract these poles, it is convenient to begin by noticing that A_0 in (9–4) and (9–6) must satisfy the relation

$$A_0 = \lim_{p \to p_0} [(p - p_0)Z]$$

$$= \lim_{p \to p_0} \left[\frac{p^2 - p_0^2}{2p_0} Z \right]. \qquad (9\text{–}8)$$

* In the right half-plane, however, it has a positive real component, as we can see by inspection of the branch immittance expression. This is of interest in connection with the analysis of the preceding section, which was based upon the assumption that the immittance had no singularities on the real frequency axis and the consequent fact that its real component attains smaller values on the axis than it does anywhere in the interior of the right half-plane. It is clear that the argument holds *a fortiori* if we begin with a non-minimum reactance or susceptance expression.

In the present instance, where $p_0^2 = -1$, this gives

$$A_0 = \lim_{p \to i} \left[\frac{p^2 + 1}{2i} \, \frac{2p^2 + p + 1}{(p + 1)(p^2 + 1)} \right]$$
$$= \tfrac{1}{2}. \qquad (9\text{–}9)$$

Using this in (9–6), we find that the elements of the corresponding anti-resonant circuit are given by $L = D = 1$. If the impedance of these components is written separately the complete expression corresponding to (9–7) appears as

$$Z = \frac{p}{1 + p^2} + \frac{1}{1 + p}. \qquad (9\text{–}10)$$

The first term on the right-hand side represents the anti-resonant network, while the second is the minimum reactance part of the complete expression. The second is readily identified with the impedance of a resistance in parallel with a condenser so that the complete structure is that shown by Fig. 9.2.

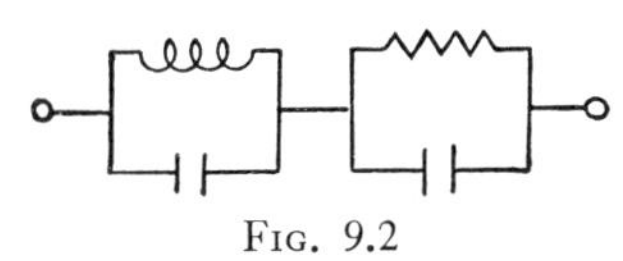

FIG. 9.2

In amplifier design, the principle of reactance or susceptance reduction is chiefly useful as a guide to available interstage configurations. An example is shown by Figs. 9.3 and 9.4. In Fig. 9.3 we observe that, aside

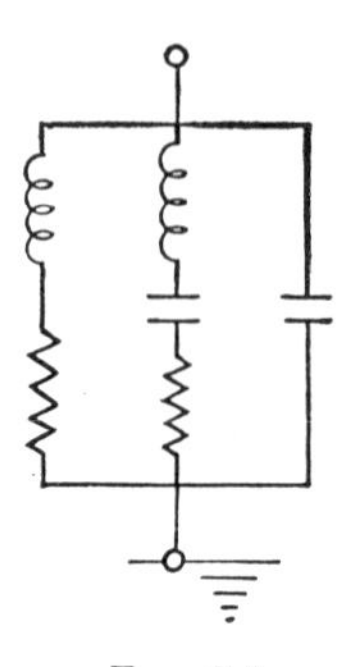

FIG. 9.3

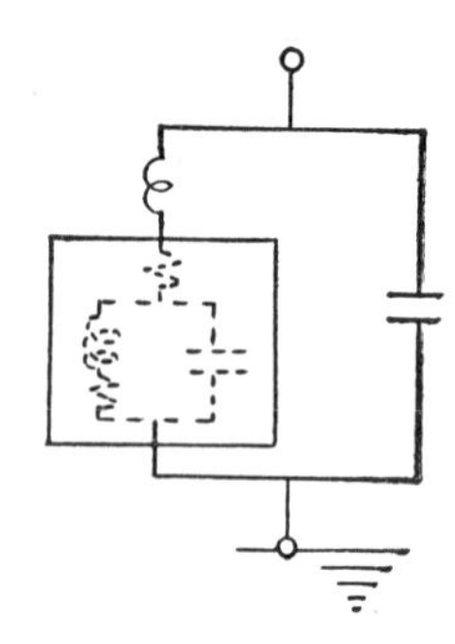

FIG. 9.4

from the parasitic capacity, the interstage impedance must have a pole at infinity, since both branches contain series inductances. It is consequently possible to represent this portion of the network as a single inductance in series with some other physical impedance. This is illustrated by Fig. 9.4, the residual network after the pole at infinity is extracted being represented by the box. The exact configuration of the residual portion will depend somewhat upon the numerical values of the elements in the original structure, but one possibility is indicated by the broken lines.

Although the two structures are theoretically equivalent the structure of Fig. 9.4 has the practical advantage that it tends to minimize the effects of element capacities to ground. At high frequencies, in Fig. 9.4, we have, in effect, to reckon with the ground capacity of only the single series coil, so that the introduction of interstage elements produces only a slight increase in the total interstage capacity.

As a second example, let it be supposed that the structure of Fig. 9.2, in association with the usual parasitic capacity, represents an interstage impedance. This particular configuration is a convenient one for many design purposes. From a theoretical point of view, however, it is obviously inefficient, since it includes a capacity path through the network at high frequencies. This corresponds analytically to a pole of admittance at infinity. As the previous discussion shows, the pole can be split out as a separate shunt capacity which can be absorbed as part of the normal parasitic capacity of the interstage, thus allowing the same impedance characteristics to be duplicated at a higher level. The decomposition is effected by writing the admittance corresponding to (9–7) as

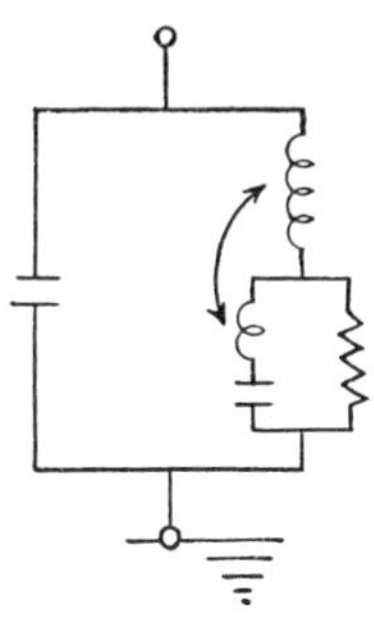

FIG. 9.5

$$Y = \frac{p}{2} + \frac{1}{2}\frac{p^2 + p + 2}{2p^2 + p + 1}. \qquad (9\text{–}11)$$

The network corresponding to this expression is shown by Fig. 9.5. The first term in (9–11) is, of course, represented by the parallel capacity. The method by which a representation of the second term is secured may be less obvious, but it will be explained in a later section. The fact that this part of the network requires mutual inductance for an exact representation is unfortunate, but for most purposes a sufficiently good approximation can be obtained with a network of the same configuration without the mutual coupling.

9.4. *Properties of Networks of Pure Reactances**

In later chapters it will be shown that minimum resistance and minimum reactance networks have the special property that in each case one of the components of the impedance is fully determined as soon as the other is known. Thus, for example, if a network is of minimum reactance type its reactance characteristic can be computed from its resistance characteristic. The only possibilities of changing the reactance without affecting the

* The material of this section is based upon the classic paper by R. M. Foster, "A Reactance Theorem," *B.S.T.J.* April 1924, pp. 259–267.

resistance lie in the addition of a pure reactance network. Particular interest thus attaches to the properties of purely reactive impedances.

As we have already seen, any zeros or poles of impedance on the real frequency axis can be represented by resonant or anti-resonant networks. Conversely, if the network is composed exclusively of pure reactances, this is the only possible location for the zeros and poles. The proof depends merely on the fact that the reactive component of any physical network must always be an odd function of frequency. If the network is composed of pure reactances, therefore, the impedance as a whole must be an odd function. It follows that if the reactive network has a zero or pole at any point p_0 in the complex plane, there must be a corresponding zero or pole at $-p_0$. Since we can never have zeros or poles in the interior of the right half-plane, however, this means that no zeros or poles can be found in the interior of the left half-plane either. The zeros and poles must consequently be confined to the imaginary axis. They must, of course, then be simple and occur in positive and negative pairs.

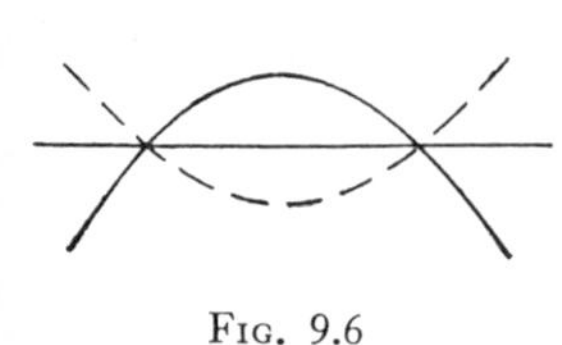

FIG. 9.6

One more fact will complete the mathematical specification of the impedance of a network of pure reactances. In a general network there is no particular restriction on the relative number or arrangement of the real frequency zeros and poles. In a purely reactive network, on the other hand, the number of zeros must be the same as the number of poles if we include the extreme zeros and poles at zero and infinite frequency, and zeros and poles occur alternately along the real frequency axis. To show why this must be so, let it be supposed, on the contrary, that two zeros were to occur consecutively. The reactance characteristic in their neighborhood would evidently take some such shape as that indicated by the broken or solid lines of Fig. 9.6. In either case, the derivative of the reactance characteristic is positive at one zero and negative at the other. In equation (9–5), however, B_0 can evidently be identified with the derivative at the corresponding zero. If all the B_0's are to be positive, therefore, the situation shown in Fig. 9.6 is not possible. A similar argument can be used to show that two poles cannot occur in succession.

With this background, we can write a general formula for the impedance of any reactive network in the following form

$$Z = kp \frac{(p^2 - p_2^2)(p^2 - p_4^2) \cdots (p^2 - p_m^2)}{(p^2 - p_1^2)(p^2 - p_3^2) \cdots (p^2 - p_{m-1}^2)}. \tag{9–12}$$

In this expression, the quantity k is a positive real constant, while p_1^2, p_2^2, etc., are negative real quantities. Each of the factors $(p^2 - p_q^2)$ thus represents a pair of zeros or poles at positive and negative real frequencies.

We can take care of the fact that zeros and poles must alternate by imposing the condition that

$$-p_m^2 \geq -p_{m-1}^2 \geq \cdots \geq -p_2^2 \geq -p_1^2 \geq 0.$$

As equation (9–12) is written, the impedance is zero at zero frequency and infinite at infinite frequency, which means that there is an inductive path but no capacitative path through the network. Evidently either a zero or pole must be found at both zero and infinite frequency, but there is no particular reason in general why either point should be one thing rather than the other. We can therefore classify reactive networks into *L–L*, *L–C*, *C–L*, and *C–C* forms, depending upon the types of elements which their impedances approximate at these frequencies. For example, equation (9–12) as it stands represents an *L–L* network. In order to take care of the other cases, we shall suppose that p_1 may assume the special value zero

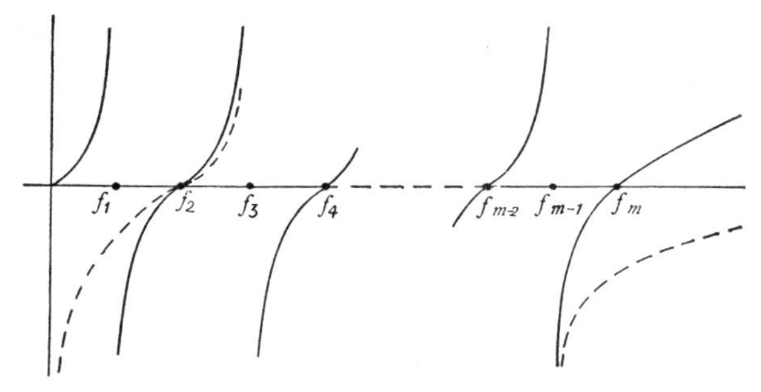

FIG. 9.7

if we wish to represent a network whose reactance is similar to that of a capacity at zero frequency, and that the last factor $p^2 - p_m^2$ may be omitted in order to represent networks which behave like a capacity at infinite frequency. A sketch of a typical characteristic corresponding to (9–12) is shown by Fig. 9.7, the modifications necessary to represent other types of networks being indicated roughly by the broken lines.

Granted any such general formula as (9–12), a corresponding physical network can be obtained either by representing the poles by anti-resonant networks in series or by representing the zeros by resonant networks in parallel, following the methods already described. The only change arises from the fact that if the structure is composed of pure reactances the representation of the real frequency zeros or poles gives the complete network. There is no residual " minimum reactance " or " minimum susceptance " network requiring some other form of representation. Thus if we expand in terms of impedance poles the resulting structure takes the general form shown by Fig. 9.8, while if the expansion is taken with respect to the impedance zeros the result is of the form shown by Fig. 9.9. In Fig. 9.8 the final series inductance and capacity represent poles at infinite and zero frequency,

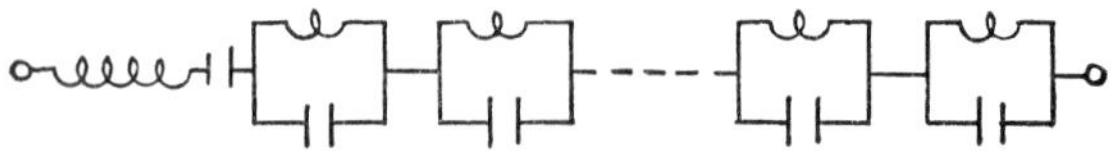

FIG. 9.8

respectively, so that the structure is of the C–L type, in the notation of the previous paragraph. In Fig. 9.9, on the other hand, the parallel inductance and capacity indicate a structure of the L–C type. In both cases, however, the networks can be modified to suit other conditions by omitting either or both of the odd elements.

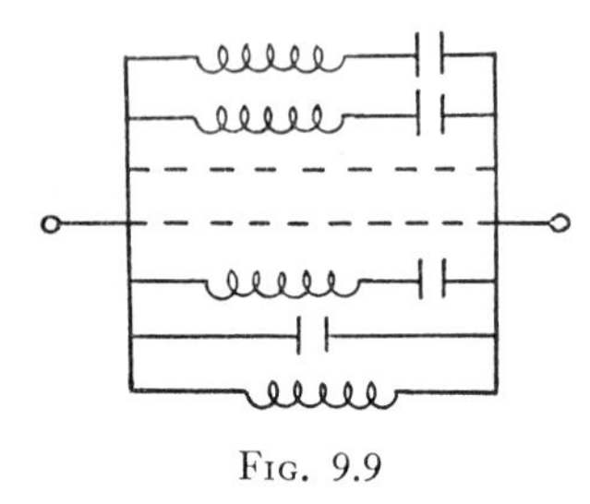

FIG. 9.9

With either configuration, the element values can be computed by the methods already discussed in connection with (9–4) and (9–6). In the structure of Fig. 9.8, if L_j and C_j represent the elements of the anti-resonant network corresponding to the poles at $\pm p_j$, these equations can conveniently be combined to give

$$\frac{1}{C_j} = -p_j^2 L_j = \left[\frac{p^2 - p_j^2}{p_j} Z\right]_{p=p_j}. \tag{9–13}$$

The corresponding formula for the elements in Fig. 9.9 is

$$L_j = -\frac{1}{p_j^2 C_j} = \left[\frac{p_j Z}{p^2 - p_j^2}\right]_{p=p_j}. \tag{9–14}$$

In most circumstances, the choice between the two configurations depends upon which one leads to more convenient element values. In general, we find that the configuration of Fig. 9.9 is the one which requires the larger inductances and smaller capacities.

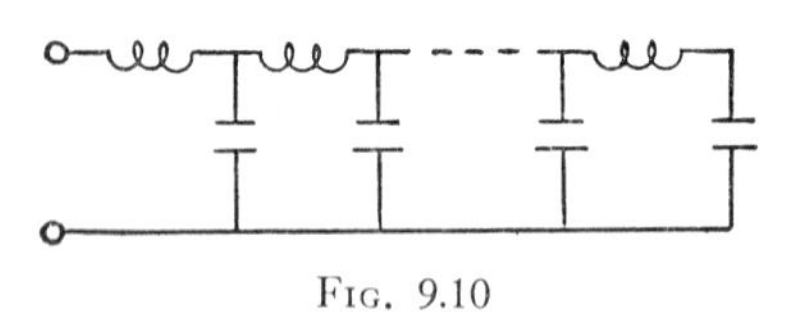

FIG. 9.10

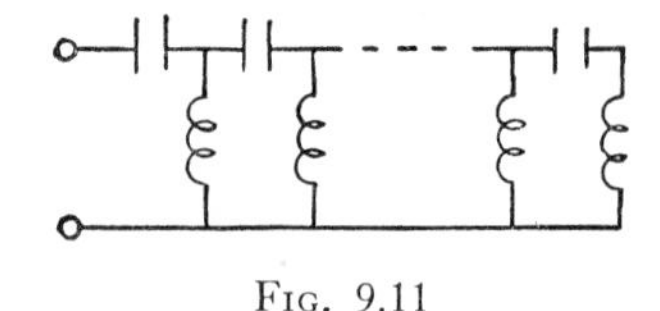

FIG. 9.11

Reactive networks can, of course, be built also in a variety of other configurations. Two fairly obvious possibilities are given by Figs. 9.10 and 9.11. In order to represent any reactance network in the form shown by Fig. 9.10, for example, we may begin by representing the network in the form shown by Fig. 9.8, and identifying the first series coil in that structure with the first series coil in Fig. 9.10. The remainder of the reactive network can then be converted to the form shown by Fig. 9.9, and the shunt condenser identified with the first shunt condenser of Fig. 9.10. By repeating the process the complete circuit is built up.

For general engineering purposes, the most significant aspect of networks of pure reactances is perhaps the fact that the characteristics which they may exhibit exist in such limited variety. Over the complete positive and negative real frequency axis a simple inductance or capacity sweeps once with positive slope through all values between $-\infty$ and $+\infty$. The most general reactive network characteristic, as illustrated by Fig. 9.7, is merely the same characteristic repeated several times on a distorted frequency scale.

The distortion of the frequency scale always leads to a reactance characteristic whose slope is greater than that of a simple inductance or capacity. This can be shown most easily by returning to the energy analysis given in Chapter VII. Thus in the special case of a purely reactive structure equation (7–31) of that chapter reduces to

$$\frac{1}{X} = 4\omega(T - V). \tag{9–15}$$

For a purely reactive network, however, it is also possible to establish the relation

$$\frac{dX}{d\omega} = 4X^2(T + V), \tag{9–16}$$

where, as in (9–15), T and V are evaluated on the assumption that the network is energized by a voltage of unit maximum amplitude. If the second of these relations is divided by the first the result is

$$\frac{dX}{d\omega} = \frac{X}{\omega}\frac{T + V}{T - V} \geq \frac{|X|}{\omega}, \tag{9–17}$$

where the equality sign holds, of course, only if the network consists exclusively of inductances or exclusively of capacities. This establishes the

Theorem: The slope of the reactance characteristic of a general reactive network at any frequency is always greater than that of a simple inductance or capacity having the same reactance at the given frequency.

These relations are illustrated by Fig. 9.12.

It is to be noticed that (9–15) and (9–16) together determine T and V from X and $dX/d\omega$. This is of some interest in connection with high power circuits, such as radio transmitters, where the cost of the elements is largely determined by their kva ratings. It is clear that the total kva rating of the complete network, for any single frequency signal, depends only upon its external characteristics and is independent of its configuration.

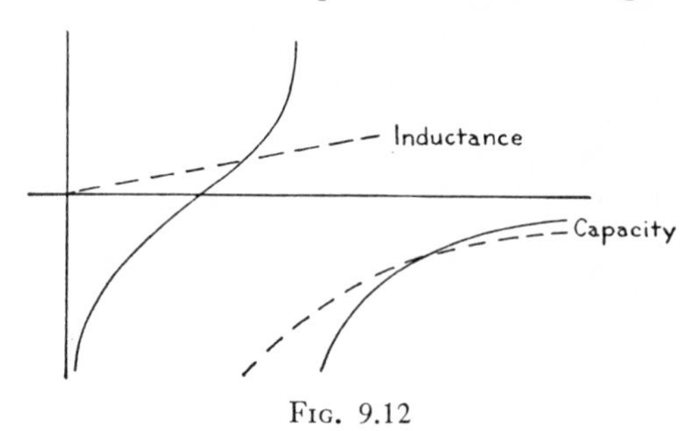

FIG. 9.12

9.5. Brune's Method of Developing a General Passive Impedance

The two processes of resistance reduction and reactance reduction were used by Brune to show that any impedance expression meeting the general passive conditions could actually be represented by a physical network. Brune's method of finding the network is a step-by-step one. The successive branches are found one at a time until the last branch is a pure resistance.

The process begins by the representation of the impedance poles at real frequencies as a number of anti-resonant networks in series, in the manner just described. After all the poles of impedance have been removed, the zeros of impedance, or poles of admittance, of the reduced impedance are similarly treated. There will result then as the next few elements of the network a number of resonant circuits in parallel. After the zeros of impedance have been removed we may find new poles which must be taken out, and then again new zeros, and so on. We will thus secure as the first part of the expansion a ladder network of the general type shown by Fig. 9.13.

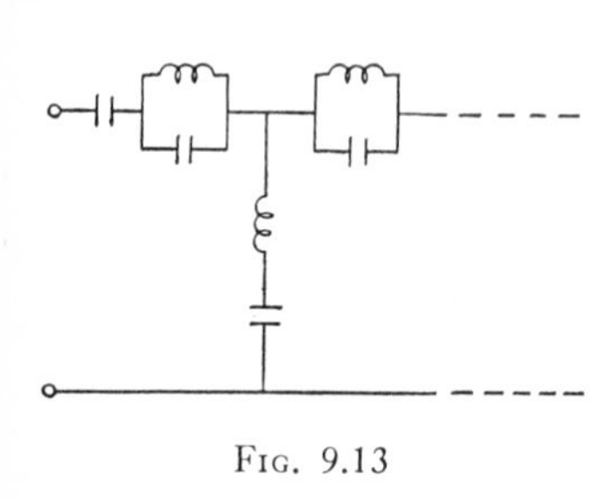

FIG. 9.13

Since each stage in the representation of the zeros and poles decreases the degree of the rational function representing the impedance, it is obvious that the process will either succeed in giving us the complete impedance or else that we must eventually reach a stage at which there are neither zeros nor poles on the real frequency axis. Suppose that Z_1 of Fig. 9.14 represents the impedance after it is no longer possible to subtract purely reactive elements from the circuit either in series or in parallel. In order to continue the analysis we artificially introduce a zero along the real frequency axis so that reactive elements in shunt can again be subtracted. The first step in this process is to subtract from the impedance a series resistance (R of Fig. 9.14) equal to the minimum value of the resistance along the axis. This leaves the new impedance Z_2, which at some point along the axis is a pure reactance. The reactance at this point is eliminated by subtracting a suitable element. An inductance rather than a capacity is chosen for this purpose since we will later require a negative mutual impedance, which can be obtained physically with inductances but not with capacities, to construct the network.

Suppose first that the required inductance is negative, as shown by $-L_1$ on Fig. 9.14. Subtracting it leaves the impedance Z_3, which must be zero at the frequency at which the resistance component of Z_1 was a minimum.

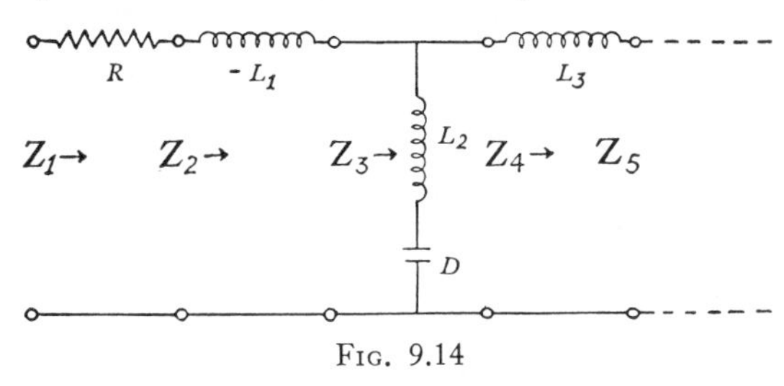

FIG. 9.14

We can therefore introduce a corresponding resonant circuit L_2-D in shunt. This leaves Z_4. Now the impedance Z_2 had no pole at infinity, but the introduction of $-L_1$ gave us a pole at infinity in Z_3 and obviously Z_4 must still have such a pole. Let this be removed by the introduction of the element L_3, leaving the impedance Z_5, which again has neither poles nor zeros along the imaginary axis. It is easily shown that if neither Z_2 nor Z_5 is to have a pole at infinity, the inductances $-L_1$, L_2, and L_3 must represent the equivalent T of a transformer having finite inductance and perfect coupling. By using such a transformer, therefore, we can provide the negative inductance $-L_1$ which is required. If L_1 is positive the process is exactly the same except that now L_3 turns out to be negative.

It is easily seen that if the original impedance met the requirements of physical realizability, each of the successive new impedances will also meet these requirements.* Z_5 therefore meets the same conditions as Z_1, except that as a rational function it is of somewhat lower degree. By repeating the process, therefore, we will eventually construct the complete network.

As an example of this process we may consider the representation of twice

* There is a temporary departure from the strict requirements if L_1 is positive. This is amended, however, as soon as L_3 is added.

the residual admittance $(p^2 + p + 2)/2(2p^2 + p + 1)$ which appears in (9–11). This expression is already of minimum susceptance and minimum reactance type, so that we can begin immediately with the stage in the expansion represented by Fig. 9.14. Upon identifying the reciprocal of the admittance with the Z_1 of Fig. 9.14, we readily find that the corresponding resistance is

$$R_1 = 2\,\frac{(1 - \omega^2)^2}{\omega^4 - 3\omega^2 + 4}. \tag{9–18}$$

This reaches its minimum value, zero, at $\omega^2 = 1$. In the present instance, therefore, it is not necessary to consider the resistance reduction sym-

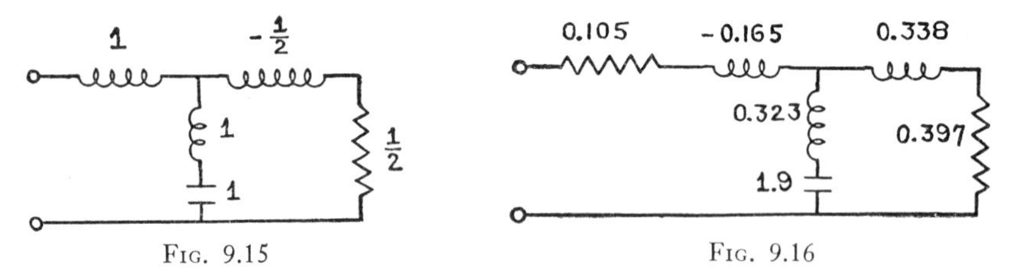

FIG. 9.15

FIG. 9.16

bolized by R in Fig. 9.14. At $\omega = 1$ we find that $Z_1 = i$. The inductance represented by $-L_1$ in Fig. 9.14 is therefore $+1$. After the subtraction of this inductance, Z_3 is given by

$$Z_3 = \frac{2p^2 + p + 1}{p^2 + p + 2} - p = \frac{(1 - p)(1 + p^2)}{p^2 + p + 2}. \tag{9–19}$$

The factor $(1 + p^2)$ in (9–19) represents the zero corresponding to the resonance of L_2 and D in Fig. 9.14. With the help of (9–14) these elements can be evaluated as $L_2 = D = 1$. When their contribution is subtracted from Z we obtain, finally,

$$Z_4 = -\frac{p}{2} + \frac{1}{2}. \tag{9–20}$$

The term $-p/2$ evidently represents the inductance L_3 in Fig. 9.14. It is, of course, negative, since the first inductance was positive. The term $\frac{1}{2}$ represents the terminating impedance Z_5. In this example it is necessary to carry the process illustrated by Fig. 9.14 through only one stage in order to reach a terminating impedance which is a constant resistance because the original impedance expression was of only the second degree. The complete structure is shown by Fig. 9.15.

Since Z_1 in (7–17) of Chapter VII has been used frequently for illustrative purposes it is convenient to adopt this expression as a second example of Brune's expansion. The situation is essentially the same as that just examined except for the fact that the present impedance is not initially in minimum resistance form. We have already found in connection with (9–2), however, that the minimum resistance of Z_1 is 0.105. This gives the R of Fig. 9.14 and the remainder of the network follows readily. The complete structure is shown by Fig. 9.16.

As an alternative, we may begin with a conductance reduction of the impedance, following the analysis given in connection with (9–3). Since a minimum conductance network is also minimum resistance, this is an equally legitimate method of going from the initial expression to the stage represented by Z_2 in Fig. 9.14. In the present instance it yields the structure shown by Fig. 9.17.

For practical purposes the chief objections to Brune's method are the facts that it uses mutual inductance and that a very considerable amount of labor is required to compute the elements one by one. On the other hand, the technique demands a knowledge of the impedance only at real frequencies, so that it has some advantage in the simulation of impedances which are specified only by curves.

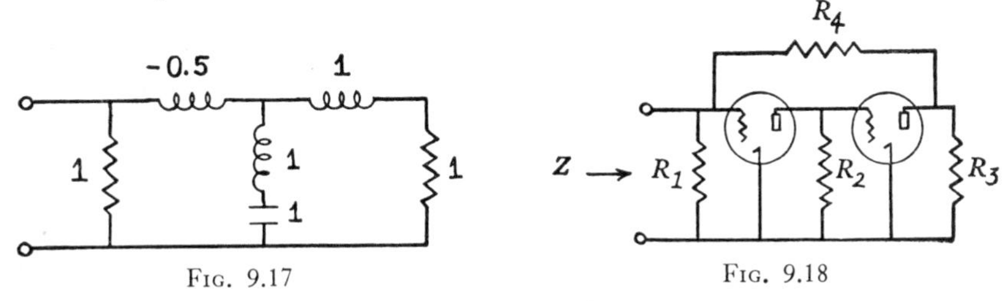

Fig. 9.17

Fig. 9.18

9.6. *Negative Resistances*

The discussion thus far has considered only impedance functions meeting the passive requirements. The corresponding physical structures, of course, then consist of combinations of the three passive elements, resistance, inductance, and capacity. To consider more general cases we need one additional building block. The additional unit can conveniently be taken as a negative resistance, since such an element expresses most distinctively the difference between a passive network and a general circuit, containing a source of power.

A negative resistance can be obtained in a variety of rather familiar ways. No attempt will be made to consider this field in any detail here. Broadly, one possibility rests upon the difference between the active and passive impedances of feedback circuits as expressed, for example, by (5–3) or (5–4) of Chapter V. Evidently, a negative resistance can be obtained from any feedback circuit of pure resistances if the circuit is so arranged that the two return differences $F(0)$ and $F(\infty)$ in these equations are of opposite sign. An example is shown by Fig. 9.18. If we assume that the vacuum tubes are ideal the passive impedance at the input terminals is $R_1(R_3 + R_4)/(R_1 + R_3 + R_4)$. The return difference $F(0)$ reduces to unity, since the return ratio vanishes when the input terminals are short-circuited. The return ratio with the input terminals opened is negative, corresponding to the fact that with the two stages indicated in Fig. 9.18 there is no net phase reversal in the tubes, and is readily evaluated as $-G_{m_1}G_{m_2}R_1R_2R_3/(R_1 + R_3 + R_4)$, where G_{m_1} and G_{m_2} are the transconductances of the tubes. Substitution in (5–3) of Chapter V therefore gives

$$Z = \frac{R_1(R_3 + R_4)}{R_1 + R_3 + R_4} \frac{1}{1 - \dfrac{G_{m_1}G_{m_2}R_1R_2R_3}{R_1 + R_3 + R_4}}$$

$$= \frac{R_1(R_3 + R_4)}{R_1 + R_3 + R_4 - G_{m_1}G_{m_2}R_1R_2R_3}. \qquad (9\text{–}21)$$

Z will evidently be a negative resistance if the R's are chosen appropriately. For example, if R_1 and R_3, which are introduced only to make the idealization of the circuit appear somewhat less forbidding, are made infinite, Z will always be negative, as evidenced by the expression

$$Z = \frac{-1}{G_{m_1}G_{m_2}R_2}. \qquad (9\text{–}22)$$

Negative resistances can also be secured through a variety of other devices, such as the dynatron or an arc-discharge. An illustrative characteristic for the dynatron is shown by the solid line in Fig. 9.19. The ratio e/i, representing the resistance to any steady voltage e, is always positive. Near the point C, however, the slope of the characteristic is negative. If the impressed e is taken as the sum of a d-c component and a small superimposed a-c component, as in the analysis of the characteristics of a vacuum tube, the effective resistance to the a-c component, therefore, will be negative when the operating point is near C.

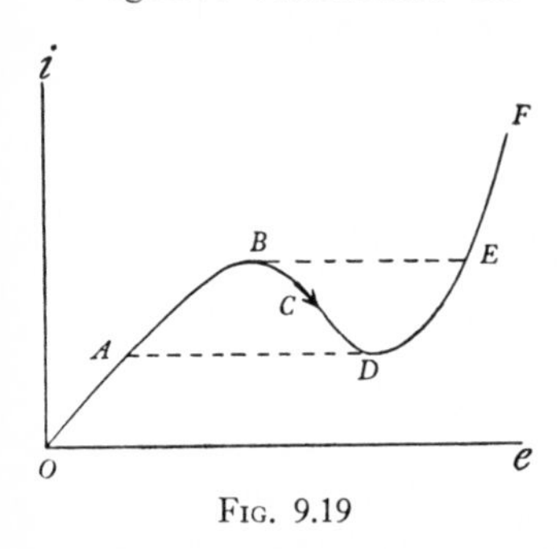

FIG. 9.19

Negative resistances are introduced here merely as convenient devices to explore the purely mathematical implications of the general set of requirements on driving point immittance functions laid down in Chapter VII. For this purpose they will be regarded as idealized elements of exactly the same type as positive resistances. Too much emphasis, however, cannot be laid upon the fact that an actual negative resistance is a much more complicated device, subject to many restrictions which are ignored in such an idealization. Depending upon the circuit to which the negative resistance is connected, and perhaps even upon the past history of the circuit, this may lead on occasion to marked departures from the behavior which would be computed from an idealized analysis. For example, Fig. 9.19 represents a characteristic which we might expect to trace physically if the circuit were energized by a battery of controllable voltage and zero internal impedance. Suppose, on the other hand, that the device is supplied by means of a much higher voltage operating through a high external impedance. Then, in effect, we are controlling the current, rather than the voltage, at the negative resistance terminals. It is evidently possible that the actual characteristic may skip from one branch to

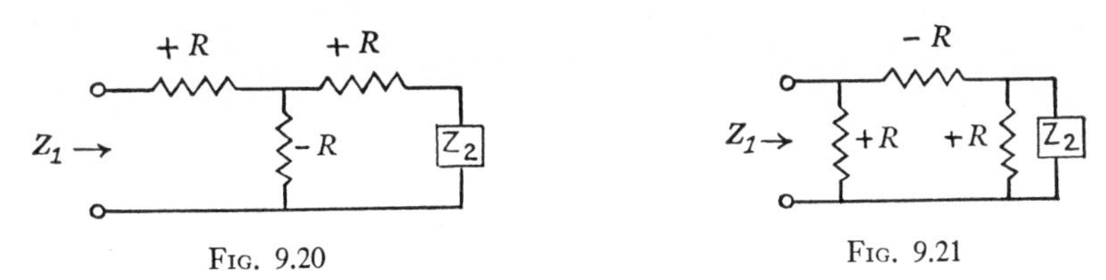

FIG. 9.20 FIG. 9.21

the other, as suggested by the broken lines *AD* and *BE*, in such a way as to avoid the negative slope part of the nominal characteristic entirely. If the external impedance includes reactive elements the skip may depend upon transient effects or, in other words, upon the past history of the circuit and the rate at which the energizing source is varied. Since some external impedance is required in order to segregate the a-c and d-c components these considerations cannot be avoided entirely in any application.

In a negative resistance device which relies upon vacuum tubes complicating factors are introduced principally by the unavoidable parasitic capacities of the tubes. These will evidently convert the negative resistance into an ordinary passive impedance at sufficiently high frequencies. The change may be unimportant in some applications, but in others it may produce singing. Which type of behavior is actually followed will depend, in general, upon both the external circuit and the type of feedback used to produce the negative resistance.

If we do postulate ideal negative resistance elements it follows immediately that negative elements of other types are also available. This can be shown most easily by reference to the well-known circuits shown in Figs. 9.20 and 9.21. A simple computation shows that the input impedance Z_1 is given in either case by

$$Z_1 = \frac{-R^2}{Z_2}. \tag{9–23}$$

Thus any negative impedance, including as special cases a negative capacity and a negative inductance, can be produced by terminating the T in the positive inverse of the required impedance.

9.7. *Representation of General Driving Point Immittance Functions*

The requirements of the general list in Chapter VII which are relevant to driving point immittance functions are 1, 2, 3, 4, *5b*, and *6a*. Of these, the first four must be satisfied by any immittance function. This suggests that possible functions may be divided into three general classes, depending upon whether they meet the first four requirements alone, the first four and *5b*, or all six requirements.* With the addition of two rather obvious subclasses the scheme is

I*a*. Functions which have no poles in the right half-plane and whose real components are positive (or zero) at all points of the real frequency axis.

I*b*. Functions which have no poles in the right half-plane and whose real components are negative (or zero) at all points of the real frequency axis.

II. Functions which have no poles in the right half-plane and whose real components are positive on some parts of the real frequency axis and negative on others.

III*a*. Impedance functions in which some poles occur in the right half-plane.

III*b*. Admittance functions in which some poles occur in the right half-plane.

The Class I*a* is, of course, the class of ordinary passive immittances. The functions in I*b* are exactly the negatives of ordinary passive functions. They will be called *negative* immittances. The more general functions described in the later classes will be called *general* or *active* immittances. The conception of a negative immittance is introduced here as a convenient theoretical abstraction. Such a function can evidently be obtained, under idealized circumstances, by the methods suggested by Figs. 9.20 and 9.21. In view of the limitations of physical negative resistance devices, however, it is probable that any actual function would belong to one of the more general Classes II or III.

Impedance functions and admittance functions have been written separately in Class III to emphasize the fact that the driving source for an

* The apparent fourth class, consisting of functions which meet the first four requirements and *6a* but fail to satisfy *5b*, cannot exist. If *5b* is not satisfied, so that there are poles in the right half-plane, the Nyquist plot of the function must encircle the origin, which is inconsistent with *6a*. The specification of both the sign of the real component and the location of the poles in some of the items of the subsequent list is introduced merely for clarity.

impedance function is a voltage generator of zero internal impedance, while for an admittance function it is a current generator of infinite internal impedance. Networks corresponding to functions of the two types may then be described as *short-circuit stable* and *open-circuit stable* respectively. If the functions belong to Class III the corresponding networks will not, of course, remain stable if the energizing sources are interchanged. In the other classes, which have zeros and poles confined to the same half-plane, these distinctions are unnecessary. If the active immittance is obtained from a feedback circuit we can frequently determine whether it is open-circuit stable or short-circuit stable by inspection. For example, any immittance measured in series with the feedback loop, as at AA' or BB' in Fig. 9.22, must be open-circuit stable, while any immittance measured across the loop, as at CC' or DD', must be short-circuit stable, since in either case the introduction of the appropriate generator impedance will interrupt the feedback.

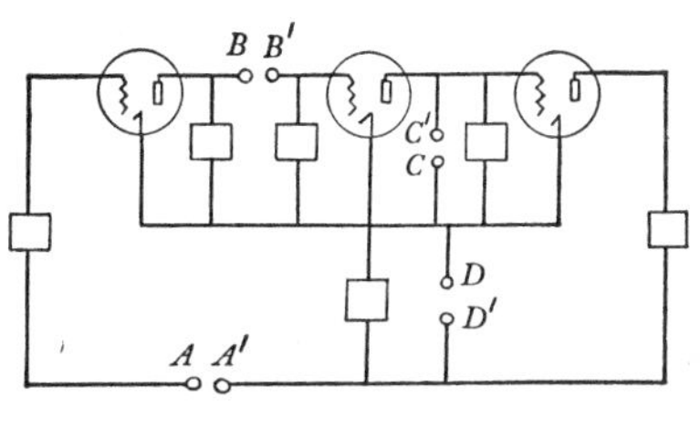

FIG. 9.22

For purposes of analytic description, the construction of active impedances is most easily treated by an extension of the processes of resistance and conductance reduction described earlier in the chapter. In discussing passive immittances these processes were limited by the fact that the real component of a passive immittance could not become negative. With the addition of a negative resistance to the normal passive elements this limitation is unnecessary and we are led at once to a representation of active immittances by a simple extension of the methods used for passive circuits.

To exemplify this process, let it be assumed that the function to be represented is an impedance of Class III*a*. It will also be supposed that none of the zeros of the impedance occur exactly on the real frequency axis.*

* If zeros on the real axis do occur, the corresponding residues of $1/Z$ must be positive real, negative real, or complex. Zeros corresponding to positive real residues can be represented separately by resonant circuits in the manner already described for passive networks. The other possibilities pose a more difficult problem. They may exist theoretically in, for example, a feedback amplifier which is on the point of singing. Consideration of these possibilities will, however, be avoided here on the ground, mentioned in Chapter VII, that a physical circuit exhibiting such zeros would be excessively non-linear. Negative real residues can, of course, be represented theoretically by negative reactance elements but the consideration of this possibility is especially unrealistic because, in addition to the question of non-linearity, a structure exhibiting such zeros must necessarily become unstable if it is fed through a generator circuit including the slightest trace of dissipation.

The reciprocal, Y, of the specified impedance will consequently be analytic in the right half-plane including its boundary, the real frequency axis. Let G_1 and $-G_2$ represent the maximum and minimum values of the real component of Y on the axis. In accordance with the preceding theorems these will also be the maximum and minimum values of the real component with respect to the complete right half-plane. If we rewrite the admittance as $-G_2 + (Y + G_2)$, therefore, the term $Y + G_2$ will have a positive real component throughout the right half-plane. In Brune's language it is a " positive real " function and can be represented by an ordinary passive impedance. The first term $-G_2$ represents, of course, a parallel negative

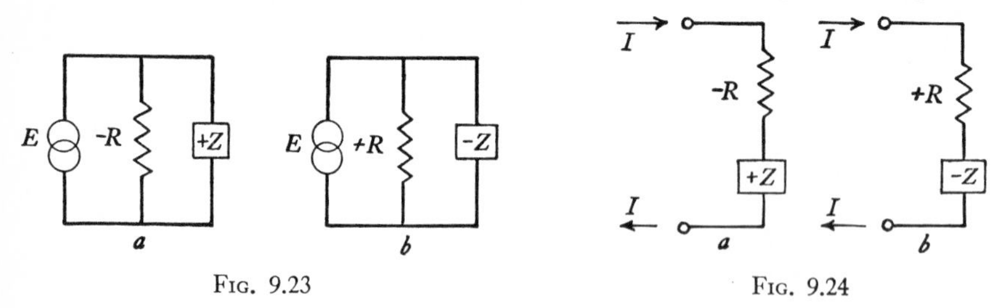

FIG. 9.23 FIG. 9.24

resistance. The combination is shown by Fig. 9.23*a*. Similarly, if we write Y as $G_1 + (Y - G_1)$ the complete impedance appears as a positive resistance in parallel with a negative impedance. This is illustrated by Fig. 9.23*b*. If we begin with a function of Class III*b* the analysis is essentially the same, except that we are now led to a series combination of a positive or negative resistance and a negative or positive impedance, as shown by Figs. 9.24*a* and 9.24*b*. The results can be summarized as the

Theorem: If an active network is stable with an energizing source of zero internal impedance, the impedance facing the source can be represented either by a negative resistance in parallel with an ordinary passive network or by a positive resistance in parallel with the negative of a passive network. If the network is stable with an energizing source of infinite internal impedance, the network impedance can be represented either by a negative resistance in series with a passive network or by a positive resistance in series with the negative of a passive network.

This discussion has been advanced specifically for functions of Class III. It is apparent, however, that it is equally valid for functions of Classes I and II. We need only recognize that functions of these classes are both open-circuit stable and short-circuit stable so that they can be represented in any one of the four ways shown by Figs. 9.23 and 9.24. It may also be interesting to notice that the methods of representation can be combined to give still other possible configurations. For example, since the negative impedance in Fig. 9.23*b* is open-circuit stable as well as short-circuit stable it can itself be represented in the form shown by Fig. 9.24*a*, leading to a representation of the original expression by a positive impedance and an L of positive and negative resistances.

As a matter of emphasis it may be desirable to say once more that the circuits of Figs. 9.23 and 9.24 do not necessarily constitute either a unique way or a physically desirable way of constructing active impedances. They are introduced merely as a convenient method of expressing the physical significance of the conditions on active and passive driving point immittances laid down in Chapter VII. It will be seen that the difference between an active and a passive driving point immittance amounts essentially to a single negative resistance, appropriately located. There is a close analogy between this result and a result derived later for the distinction between active and passive transfer immittances.

9.8. *Combinations of Active Impedances*

In dealing with passive circuits we are accustomed to thinking of the individual passive impedances as units which can be combined with one another and associated with a driving generator in any way we like. Whatever arrangement is chosen, the circuit as a whole will remain passive, and therefore stable. In active circuits, on the other hand, no such freedom is possible. Impedances which are stable for one energizing source may become unstable if the source is altered and two impedances which are individually stable for a given source may become unstable when they are added together, even if the source itself is unchanged. *In dealing with active circuits, therefore, it is necessary to study the stability of the structure in terms of the complete impedance or admittance facing the current or voltage source, including the self-impedance or self-admittance of the source itself.*

This is evidently a grave restriction. It affects both the freedom with which the active network itself can be designed and the freedom with which the energizing source can be chosen. The latter is perhaps particularly important. The analysis thus far has assumed that the self-impedance of the source would be either zero or infinite, whereas most practical sources have a finite, non-zero, self-impedance. The problem of relaxing these restrictions will be attacked here through a consideration of the open-circuit or short-circuit stability of a combination of two immittances in series or parallel, as illustrated by Figs. 9.25 and 9.26. Each of the two immittances can be regarded as an active structure if we wish, or one of them can be taken as a representation of the actual self-immittance of a physical generator.

The two situations illustrated by Fig. 9.25 can be dismissed easily. If an impedance is to be short-circuit stable, as in Fig. 9.25*a*, none of its zeros can lie in the right half-plane. But since the zeros of an impedance obtained from a number of branches in parallel are the same as the zeros of the separate branches, each of the individual branch impedances must be

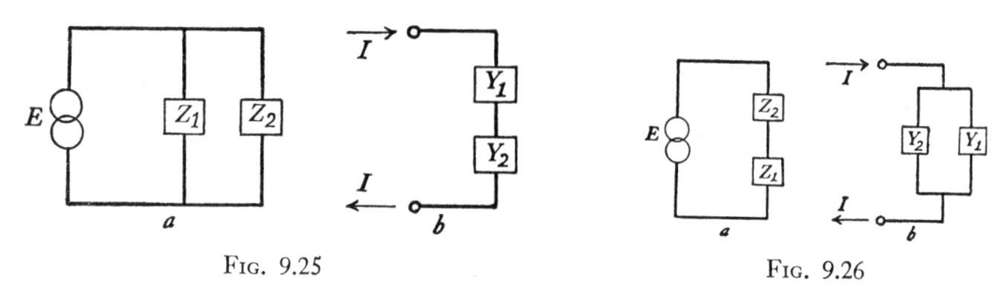

FIG. 9.25

FIG. 9.26

similarly restricted. Correspondingly, the zeros of admittance, or poles of impedance, in the structure of Fig. 9.25*b* are the same as the admittance zeros of the component structures and must be excluded from the right half-plane if the complete structure is to be stable. We therefore have the obvious

Theorem: A parallel combination of impedances will be short-circuit stable if and only if all the individual impedances are short-circuit stable. Similarly, a series combination will be open-circuit stable if and only if all the individual impedances are open-circuit stable.

The combinations illustrated by Fig. 9.26 present a more difficult problem. The discussion here will present only a few elementary rules which may be useful in some situations. To give the problem a physical context, we may suppose that Z_1 and Y_1 in Figs. 9.26*a* and 9.26*b* are respectively short-circuit stable and open-circuit stable structures and that Z_2 and Y_2 represent allowances for the self-impedance or admittance of the actual generator. The question which will be attacked is that of estimating under what circumstances Z_2 and Y_2 can be introduced without upsetting the stability of the circuit.

If Z_2 and Y_2 are real constants their effect on the stability of structure is most easily determined from an inspection of the Nyquist diagram of the original Z_1 or Y_1. The addition of a constant Z_2 or Y_2 is equivalent to a lateral translation of the whole diagram. It is clear that the lateral translation will not affect the stability of the circuit as long as it is not large enough to carry any of the points of intersection between the Nyquist path and the horizontal axis from one side of the origin to the other. This leads to the

Theorem: The series combination of a short-circuit stable impedance and a positive or negative resistance is itself a short-circuit stable impedance if the addition of the resistance leaves the sign of the real component of the impedance unchanged at every point on the real frequency axis at which the imaginary component of the impedance vanishes. Similarly, an open-circuit stable structure will remain open-circuit stable when combined in parallel with a positive or negative resistance for the same condition on the real and imaginary components of the initial and final admittance.

If Z_2 or Y_2 are functions of frequency rather than real constants the problem is more difficult, but it is still possible to show that they will not affect the stability of the circuit if they meet certain conditions. The situation can be expressed by the

Theorem: The series combination of a short-circuit stable impedance Z_1 and an open-circuit stable impedance Z_2 will be short-circuit stable if $|Z_1| > |Z_2|$ at all points on the real frequency axis. Similarly, the parallel combination of an open-circuit stable admittance Y_1 and a short-circuit stable admittance Y_2 will be open-circuit stable if $|Y_1| > |Y_2|$ at all real frequencies.*

The wording of the theorem is not intended to imply that an immittance which is specified, for example, as short-circuit stable cannot also be open-circuit stable. The stability of the immittances for the non-specified conditions is a matter of indifference.

The theorem is easily demonstrated by methods similar to those used for the first theorem at the end of the preceding chapter. If we consider in particular the relation between Z_1 and Z_2, for example, we can write

$$Z_1 + Z_2 = Z_1\left(1 + \frac{Z_2}{Z_1}\right). \tag{9-24}$$

The quantity $Z_1 + Z_2$ can have no zeros in the right half-plane if it is to be short-circuit stable and its poles must be the same as those of Z_1 since Z_2, being open-circuit stable, has no poles in this region. The Nyquist plot of $Z_1 + Z_2$ must therefore encircle the origin the same number of times in the

* Throughout this discussion it is assumed for simplicity that none of the zeros and poles of the various immittances occurs exactly on the real frequency axis, including infinity. The theorems are not necessarily invalid even when this assumption is violated, as it might be, for example, in circuits controlled at high frequencies by parasitic capacities, but such situations evidently require careful handling.

same direction as the plot of Z_1 alone. It is evident, however, that the number of times the plot of $Z_1 + Z_2$ encircles the origin is equal to the sum of the encirclements obtained by plotting the factors Z_1 and $1 + (Z_2/Z_1)$, on the right-hand side of (9–24), separately. Since the plot of $1 + (Z_2/Z_1)$ cannot encircle the origin at all under the assumed conditions, as Fig. 8.30 in the preceding chapter shows, this establishes the theorem.

It is evident from the proof of the theorem that the condition $|Z_1| > |Z_2|$ or $|Y_1| > |Y_2|$ does not necessarily fix the actual upper limit of values which may be assumed by the added Z_2 or Y_2. In many circumstances the circuit will remain stable even if the condition is violated over a portion of the frequency spectrum. If we disregard one special case, however, there is a final upper limit beyond which the added immittance cannot go without necessarily producing instability. This is shown by the following

Theorem: The series combination of a short-circuit stable impedance Z_1 and an open-circuit stable impedance Z_2 cannot be short-circuit stable when $|Z_2| > |Z_1|$ at all points on the real frequency axis unless Z_1 is also open-circuit stable and Z_2 is also short-circuit stable. Similarly, a parallel combination of an open-circuit stable admittance Y_1 and a short-circuit stable admittance Y_2 can be open-circuit stable when $|Y_2| > |Y_1|$ at all real frequencies only if both Y_1 and Y_2 are actually both short-circuit stable and open-circuit stable.

The proof of this theorem is essentially similar to that of the preceding theorem. We begin by writing the total impedance as

$$Z_1 + Z_2 = Z_2\left(1 + \frac{Z_1}{Z_2}\right). \tag{9–25}$$

Under the assumed conditions the plot of the factor $1 + (Z_1/Z_2)$ cannot encircle the origin. The total number of encirclements by the plot of $Z_1 + Z_2$ must therefore be the same as those by the plot of Z_2. They must be in the direction appropriate for zeros since by hypothesis Z_2 is open-circuit stable and has no poles in the right half-plane. Just as in the preceding theorem, however, the plot of $Z_1 + Z_2$ must encircle the origin the same number of times and in the same direction as the plot of Z_1 if $Z_1 + Z_2$ is to have no zeros in the right half-plane. This must be in the direction corresponding to poles since Z_1 is short-circuit stable. Evidently the requirements cannot be met unless neither plot actually encircles the origin at all, which is the same as saying that each of the impedances Z_1 and Z_2 must be both short-circuit stable and open-circuit stable.

The preceding theorems cover all combinations of the two impedances except those in which both impedances are open-circuit stable, but not short-circuit stable, or vice versa. A guide to this last situation is furnished by the

Theorem: A series combination of two impedances cannot be short-circuit stable and a parallel combination of two impedances cannot be open-circuit stable, when both impedances are either short-circuit stable but not open-circuit stable or vice versa, if the absolute magnitude of either impedance is greater than that of the other at all points on the real frequency axis.

It is assumed that the degenerate case in which the two immittances have strictly coincident poles in the right half-plane can be disregarded.

The proof is similar to those of the preceding theorems. If we suppose, for example, that $|Z_2| > |Z_1|$ and that Z_1 and Z_2 are short-circuit stable their sum will be short-circuit stable only if the plot of $Z_1 + Z_2$ encircles the origin as many times as there are poles of Z_1 and Z_2 in the right half-plane. In accordance with (9–25), however, the actual plot will encircle the origin only as many times as there are poles of Z_2 alone in this region. The two conditions cannot be reconciled except for the trivial case when Z_1 and Z_2 have identical poles in the right half-plane.

A curious feature of this result is the conclusion that the stability of a short-circuit stable impedance will not be disturbed by the addition of a small open-circuit stable impedance but it may be entirely upset if the added impedance, even though very small, is also short-circuit stable.

Neither of the last two negative theorems applies to combinations of impedances which are both open-circuit stable and short-circuit stable. It is natural to expect that this combination is more likely to give a stable result than any other. If the two impedances are passive, for example, they can be combined in any proportion. In more general cases, however, it is still necessary to pay attention to the possible instability of the final circuit. An example is furnished by a final

Theorem: If Z_1 and Z_2 are respectively a positive impedance and a negative impedance it is always possible to find values of the positive constant multiplier λ such that the series combination of Z_1 and λZ_2 will not be short-circuit stable and their parallel combination will not be open-circuit stable unless Z_1 and Z_2 are exactly proportional to one another.

The proof is obvious from a Nyquist plot of $(Z_1 + \lambda Z_2)/Z_1$.

CHAPTER X

Topics in the Design of Impedance Functions

10.1. *Introduction*

The preceding chapter was essentially an attempt to explore the general physical significance of the list of restrictions on driving point immittance functions given in Chapter VII. The present chapter continues this discussion but in a different way. The material selected consists chiefly of devices and conceptions of direct application in design work. The chapter is thus intended broadly as a resumé of design methods, but its scope is limited by the fact that it includes no material not easily related to the analytic framework already established. The discussion is directed primarily at driving point immittance functions, but many of the results apply also to network functions of other types. Unless otherwise specified a passive network will be assumed.

Since the chapter does not contribute directly to the theoretical structure of the book as a whole it can be omitted, if necessary, especially if the reader is reasonably familiar with elementary passive network theory. If the omission is made, however, note should at least be taken of the frequency transformations described near the end of the chapter, since they will be used in several later discussions.

10.2. *Inverse Networks*

The duality between the impedance and the admittance methods of analyzing a network suggests a conclusion which was mentioned briefly in Chapter I but has not otherwise been dealt with explicitly. This is the proposition that to every network there corresponds an inverse. The result arises, of course, from the fact that the requirements on physical driving point functions are the same whether we consider an impedance or an admittance. If we are dealing with a passive structure, for example, the requirement that the real component of the impedance be positive at real frequencies implies that the real component of the admittance must also be positive. Moreover, the restrictions on the zeros and poles are symmetrical, so that the interchange of zeros and poles which occurs when an impedance is replaced by its reciprocal does not affect the satisfaction of the conditions of physical realizability. It therefore follows that if a passive impedance is physically realizable, its reciprocal is also realizable.

In ordinary networks, a suitable structural form for the reciprocal impedance can be found by the familiar procedure exemplified by Fig. 10.1.* Each series connection is replaced by a parallel connection, and vice versa. The individual elements are found by replacing resistances by resistances, inductances by capacities, and capacities by inductances, in such a way that the product of corresponding resistances or corresponding inductances and stiffnesses is always constant. In Fig. 10.1 the constant product of corresponding impedances, including the driving point impedances, is taken as R_0^2.

We can regard the type of inverse network illustrated by Fig. 10.1 as the *structural inverse* of the original network. Evidently the procedure which has been suggested for finding the structural inverse is not a general one. For example, since it considers only series and parallel connections, it offers

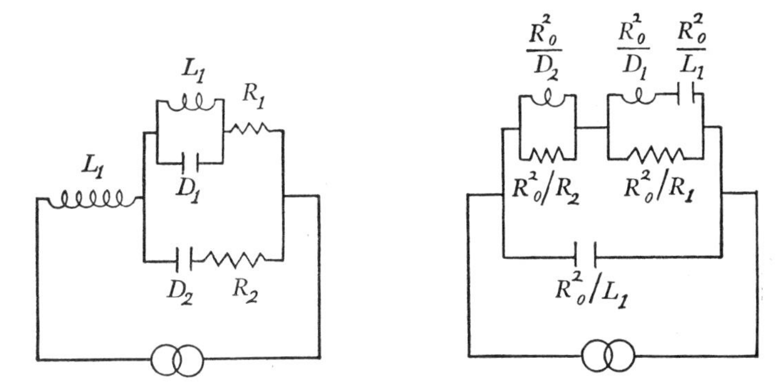

Fig. 10.1

no means of finding the inverse of a Wheatstone bridge. A structural inverse of a bridge network can, however, still be found by an extension of the original process. The extension depends upon the consideration of the network as a geometrical diagram of lines and points by means of which the plane is divided into areas. Physically, the points represent network junctions and the lines the various elements connecting them, while the areas represent closed meshes in the circuit. The process of finding the inverse network consists broadly in an interchange of areas and points. A new point is taken in each area and each such new point is connected with each new point in the neighboring areas by a branch which is the inverse of the branch separating the corresponding areas. The process is illustrated by Fig. 10.2, the new points being A, B, C, and D. It will be seen that the inverse of the Wheatstone bridge is another bridge.

* See, for example, O. J. Zobel, *B.S.T.J.*, Jan., 1923, and July, 1928. A good textbook reference is Guillemin, " Communication Networks," Vol. II, p. 203.

In spite of this generalization *a structural inverse cannot be found for every network*. No structural inverse exists, for example, for the Brune network described in the previous chapter since we cannot find the equivalent of a pair of perfectly coupled capacities to represent the reciprocal of the coupled coils in the original network. Moreover, as R. M. Foster has shown,* certain kinds of network configurations may not be representable as configurations of points, lines, and areas on a plane, in the manner assumed by the preceding discussion. No structural inverse exists for such networks even when mutual inductance is ignored.

Although a structural inverse is not always obtainable, the analytic argument remains valid. If we disregard the structural relationship, therefore, we can always find some network whose impedance is the reciprocal of the impedance of any given network. For example, the inverse of a Brune network is another Brune network. This can be illustrated by the networks shown by Figs. 9.15 and 9.17 of the preceding chapter. The first of these corresponds to the impedance $Z = (2p^2 + p + 1)/(p^2 + p + 2)$. The second was developed to represent the impedance Z_1 of (7–17) in Chapter VII. If we remove the parallel resistance at its input, however, it represents the impedance Z_2 of the same set of expressions, and satisfies the equation $Z_2 = \frac{1}{2}(p^2 + p + 2)/(2p^2 + p + 1)$. Thus if this branch is removed the two networks become inverse structures of impedance product $\frac{1}{2}$.

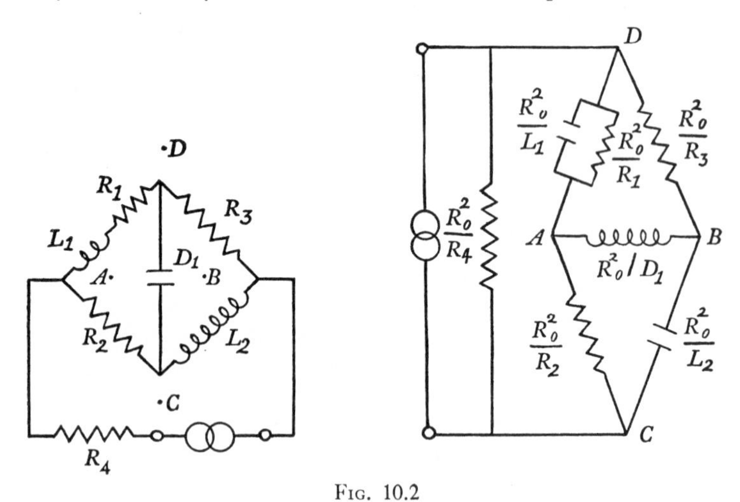

FIG. 10.2

This discussion has been directed, for simplicity, at passive networks. There is evidently no difficulty, however, in extending it to negative

* "Geometrical Circuits of Electrical Networks," Trans. A.I.E.E., June, 1932.

impedances or to active impedances belonging to what was described as Class II in the preceding chapter. If we turn to Class III, on the other hand, the restrictions on the zeros and poles of immittance are no longer symmetrical. Only the zeros need be confined to the left half-plane. Nevertheless, the impedance functions of Class III*a* and the admittance functions of Class III*b* are evidently inverse in a certain sense. The difference is merely that in going from Class III*a* to Class III*b* or vice versa, the source as well as the network itself must be reciprocated, while we have thus far assumed that the source itself would remain unaltered. If this change in the source is regarded as permissible, therefore, the general result can be summed up in the

Theorem: Corresponding to any physically realizable impedance expression there is an identical physically realizable admittance expression, and vice versa. The transformation from one mode of expression to the other need not include the generator if the original impedance or admittance is both open-circuit stable and short-circuit stable.

If active impedances are represented by combinations of passive networks and negative resistances, as was done in the preceding chapter, the previous remarks on the structural inverse of a given network can evidently be carried over to the general case without change. The problem of finding the structural inverse of a circuit containing vacuum tubes explicitly has not been studied.

10.3. *Complementary Networks*

In addition to the inverse of a given immittance function we can also speak of its complement. The complement may be defined by the requirement that the sum of the original function and its complement must be a real constant. The complement will exist as a passive impedance, provided we meet the requirements of the following

Theorem: A passive complement can be found for any immittance function if the prescribed function has no poles in the right half-plane or on the real frequency axis and if the sum of the prescribed function and its complement is chosen at least as great as the maximum value of the real component of the prescribed function on the real frequency axis.

The proof of the theorem is omitted here, since it can readily be obtained by a repetition of the methods used in the previous chapter. If we take as an example a passive impedance the requirement means simply that the impedance must be of minimum reactance type and that the final resistance must be at least as great as the maximum resistance of the original structure.

The familiar constant resistance combinations of ordinary network theory represent simple special cases of the complementary relationship. An example is given by Fig. 10.3.

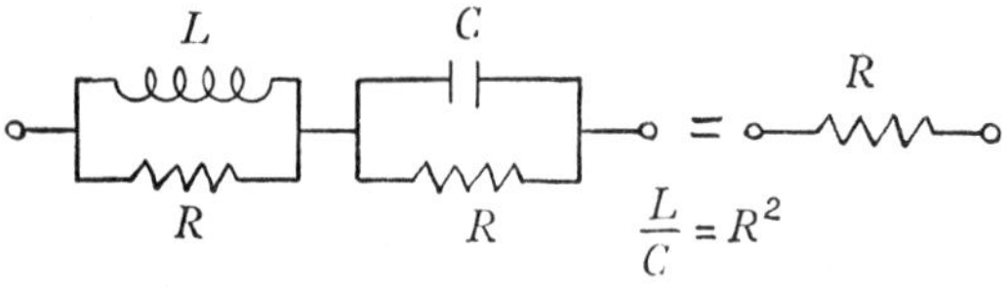

FIG. 10.3

10.4. *Partial Fraction Expansion of a General Impedance*

We saw in the previous chapter that poles of impedance or admittance on the real frequency axis could be detached from the complete impedance expression and represented separately by reactive networks in series or parallel with the structure as a whole. The same process can be extended, at least formally, to the other poles of impedance or admittance also. The representation of the network impedance which is thus secured is particularly valuable for theoretical purposes. Its utility in practical problems is restricted by the fact that in the most important special case, that of passive circuits, it does not invariably lead to a passive network to represent a passive immittance function. Even so, however, it is useful in many situations.

It will simplify discussion to restrict our attention to passive circuits and to assume that the prescribed function is an impedance. Let it be supposed, then, that the poles of the impedance are represented by the points $p_1 \cdots p_n$. In order to avoid complications in exposition, we will also assume that all the poles are simple. The procedure is essentially similar to that which was followed in connection with equation (9–8) of Chapter IX. Corresponding to any particular pole p_j, we can define a quantity C_j by

$$C_j = [(p - p_j)Z]_{p=p_j}. \tag{10–1}$$

It is easily seen that C_j is equivalent to the quantity which was called A_0 in the preceding equation (9–8). We can therefore conclude from the discussion of this equation that $C_j/(p - p_j)$ affords a representation of the pole p_j. In other words, the quantity $Z - C_j/(p - p_j)$ will have no pole at p_j. Let us suppose that all the poles are removed from the original impedance expression by the repeated application of this process. The quantity which remains then has no poles anywhere in the complex plane, and it follows from general function theoretic principles that it must be a constant.* We can easily show that the constant is a real quantity or, in other words, a resistance.† If we represent it by R_0 this is equivalent to saying that the impedance can be represented by the formal expansion

$$Z = \frac{C_1}{p - p_1} + \frac{C_2}{p - p_2} + \cdots + \frac{C_n}{p - p_n} + R_0. \qquad (10\text{–}2)$$

As equation (10–2) stands, it suggests that the impedance can be represented by a number of networks in series, each network corresponding to one term in the expansion. Whether or not such a representation is actually possible with a passive network depends essentially on the constant R_0. In order to represent any term in the expansion as a simple passive network, it must, of course, meet the condition that its individual resistance characteristic be positive at all real frequencies. If the individual term fails to meet this condition as it stands, it may still be possible to represent it as a passive network if we can add to it a sufficiently high

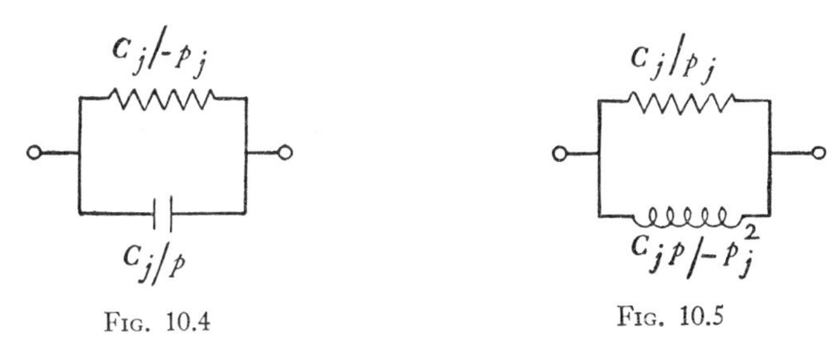

FIG. 10.4 FIG. 10.5

resistance, which must, of course, be subtracted from the R_0 term, to satisfy the resistance condition. The essential requirement which must be satisfied is, therefore, that R_0 be large enough to allow all the constituent networks to furnish a positive resistance at real frequencies without leaving a negative resistance in series with the structure as a whole. There is a close analogy between this result and a proposition in four-terminal network theory. As we will see later, the transmission characteristics of a general four-terminal network can always be represented by a number of simple structures in tandem provided the general level of loss in the original network is high enough to allow each of the constituents to furnish a positive loss at all frequencies.

In order to illustrate this relationship, let us suppose that p_j is found on the negative real axis. It is then easy to show that the corresponding C_j must be a real quantity. If C_j is positive, the term $C_j/(p - p_j)$ can be

* Liouville's Theorem — see any text on function theory.

† As (10–2) indicates, the constant is equal to the resistance of the network at infinite frequency.

easily identified with the parallel combination of resistance and capacity shown by Fig. 10.4. If C_j is negative this representation is non-physical. By adding the resistance C_j/p_j, however, the expression becomes $C_jp/p_j(p - p_j)$, which corresponds to the inductance-resistance network shown by Fig. 10.5.

If the pole is complex, a more elaborate analysis is required. Complex poles, of course, occur in conjugate pairs, and the pairs must be kept together if we are to secure a physical network. Let us suppose that a particular pair of conjugate poles is written as $p_a \pm ip_b$. It is easily shown that the corresponding C's must also be conjugate quantities. If we represent them as $C_a \pm iC_b$ we can write the component impedance Z_j as

$$Z_j = \frac{C_a + iC_b}{p - (p_a + ip_b)} + \frac{C_a - iC_b}{p - (p_a - ip_b)}$$
$$= 2\,\frac{C_ap - (C_ap_a + C_bp_b)}{p^2 - 2p_ap + (p_a^2 + p_b^2)}\,. \tag{10–3}$$

In many cases, the real component of (10–3) will not be positive for all real frequencies. If we add enough resistance, however, a passive structure

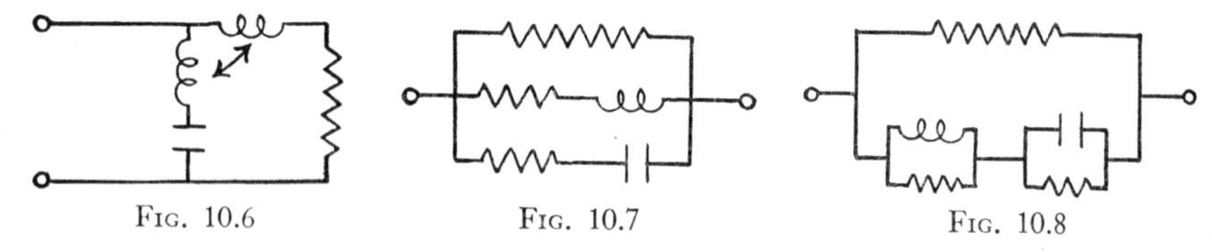

FIG. 10.6 FIG. 10.7 FIG. 10.8

can be secured. When the added resistance is the least possible, the structure will take the form of the last stage of a Brune network, as shown by Fig. 10.6. If the resistance component is great enough, other configurations are also possible. In general, they will contain one inductance, one capacity and three resistances. The particular configurations which can be used, however, depend upon the numerical values of the constants in (10–3). Typical circuits are illustrated by Figs. 10.7 and 10.8.

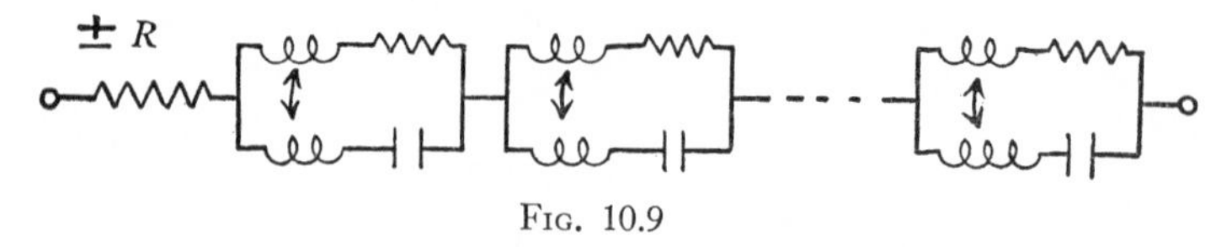

FIG. 10.9

These considerations can evidently be extended to all the poles. If we adopt in particular the Brune representation of the complex poles and regard the structures of Figs. 10.4 and 10.5 as special cases of the Brune network, the complete circuit takes the form shown by Fig. 10.9. The corresponding parallel combination obtained from an admittance analysis is given by Fig. 10.10.

As the figures show, the resistance or conductance which remains after all the poles of immittance have been represented may be either positive or negative. It will, of course, be positive if the original resistance or conductance is large enough. Since the minima of the various component resistance or conductance characteristics will ordinarily occur at different frequencies, on the other hand, we may expect that the sum of the component characteristics will be substantially greater than zero at all points on the real frequency axis. We may therefore expect that the final branch will be negative if the original immittance approximates the limiting minimum resistance or minimum conductance type. This is, of course, a serious practical limitation. In theoretical work, however, the fact that the complete immittance is exhibited as the sum of a number of very simple terms may still make the structure quite useful. For these applications, at least, we can therefore formulate the result as the

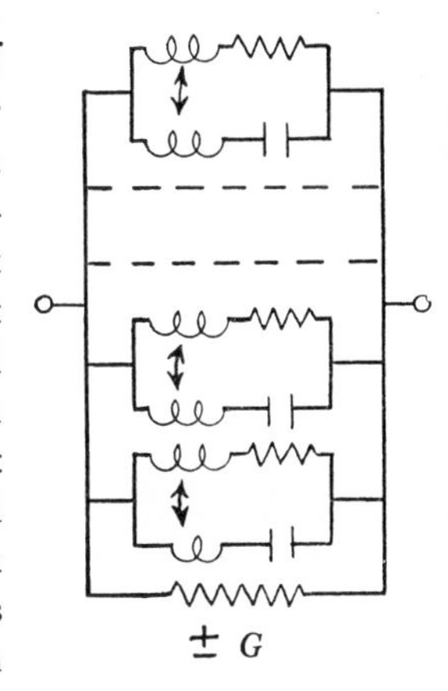

Fig. 10.10

Theorem: A passive immittance having no multiple poles can always be represented as the sum of a number of passive immittances, each of which is at most of the second degree, and a positive or negative real constant.

The extension of this analysis to active impedances involves only two considerations. In the first place, if the impedance is not both short-circuit stable and open-circuit stable some of the poles either of its impedance or admittance will be found in the right half-plane. In the corresponding expansion the component networks representing these poles can still be built, but they will not be passive structures. The second consideration is the obvious one that if we are dealing with an active circuit anyway the fact that the final resistance or conductance term may be negative should be of no particular consequence.

10.5. *Reconstruction of a Passive Impedance from a Knowledge of Either Component**

The discussion in the previous chapter shows that the resistance and reactance characteristics of a passive network can be varied independently

* As a general reference to transformations of this sort, see Darlington, " Synthesis of Reactance 4-Poles," Journal of Mathematics and Physics, Sept., 1939.

within certain limits. Thus, we can change the resistance characteristic of a network by a constant amount without changing its reactance, and we can add or subtract a reactance corresponding to poles on the real frequency axis without affecting the resistance. These are, however, the only two ways in which the two components can be varied independently. If we restrict ourselves to minimum resistance and minimum reactance networks, the resistance and reactance are uniquely related. If we know either one, we can determine the other, and therefore the impedance as a whole.

Since we are considering the real and imaginary components of the impedance at real frequencies, it is simplest to write Z as a function of ω rather than as a function of p. In general, of course, Z can be represented as the ratio of two polynomials in p. On the real frequency axis the even powers in each polynomial will be real quantities and the odd powers pure imaginaries. We can therefore write

$$Z(\omega) = \frac{A + i\omega B}{C + i\omega D}, \tag{10–4}$$

where A, B, C, and D are polynomials in ω^2 with real coefficients. If we rationalize this expression in the usual manner by multiplying the numerator and the denominator by $C - i\omega D$, the result becomes

$$Z(\omega) = \frac{AC + \omega^2 BD}{C^2 + \omega^2 D^2} + i\omega \frac{BC - AD}{C^2 + \omega^2 D^2}. \tag{10–5}$$

The resistance is thus an even rational function of ω with real coefficients, while the reactance is a similar function multiplied by ω.

Our problem is that of finding the complete expression for Z from a knowledge of either of its components. Let it be supposed that we know the even rational function representing the resistance. We begin by expanding this expression in partial fractions in the manner described in the preceding section. Since the denominator is an even function of ω, the poles must occur in positive and negative pairs. To each pole, moreover, must correspond its conjugate since the coefficients in the denominator are all real quantities. The poles thus occur in sets of four symmetrically placed about the origin. In the special case in which poles are found on the imaginary frequency axis the sets of four may reduce to pairs. The poles might also reduce to pairs, on the face of the situation, if they occurred on the *real* frequency axis, but if the assumed resistance characteristic corresponds to a physical network, there can be no such poles.

The poles of the resistance function which lie below the real frequency axis* were introduced when the numerator and denominator of the original

* That is, below the real axis in the frequency plane, or to the right of the imaginary axis in the p-plane. Cf. the relations described in connection with Fig. 2.2.

impedance were multiplied by $C - i\omega D$. They must be eliminated in reconstructing the expression for Z if the final result is to correspond to a physical network. Let us suppose that the poles above the axis are represented by $\omega_1 \cdots \omega_n$ and the corresponding residues, i.e., the C_j's of (10–2), by $C_1 \cdots C_n$. The poles below the axis will then be the conjugate points $\overline{\omega}_1 \cdots \overline{\omega}_n$, while it is easily shown that their residues will be the corresponding conjugate quantities $\overline{C}_1 \cdots \overline{C}_n$. If we assign the constant R_0 of (10–2) equally to the two groups of poles this allows us to write the complete partial fraction expansion corresponding to (10–2) in the symmetrical form

$$R(\omega) = \left[\sum_1^n \frac{C_j}{\omega - \omega_j} + \frac{R_0}{2}\right] + \left[\sum_1^n \frac{\overline{C}_j}{\omega - \overline{\omega}_j} + \frac{R_0}{2}\right]. \tag{10–6}$$

The two bracketed expressions in (10–6) evidently represent conjugate quantities on the real frequency axis. Each, therefore, provides half the final resistance characteristic. If we multiply the first by two we secure the required impedance expression in the form

$$Z = \sum_1^n \frac{2C_j}{\omega - \omega_j} + R_0. \tag{10–7}$$

The fact that this is actually the sought-for expression for the impedance is easily established. It evidently gives the right resistance characteristic and its poles are in the proper portion of the plane. The fact that the zeros are also in the proper half of the plane follows at once if we remember that the resistance must be positive on the real frequency axis and make use of the general theorem on the location of the maxima and minima of an analytic function. It is easily shown also that (10–7) is the only valid impedance corresponding to the original resistance characteristic if we exclude the possibility of introducing pure reactance networks by the addition of poles on the real frequency axis.

If we begin with the reactance characteristic, the procedure is essentially the same. The only distinction arises from the fact that because of the presence of the multiplier $i\omega$, the residues of the poles below the real frequency axis are the negative conjugates of the residues above the real frequency axis. Along the real axis, therefore, the sums of the contributions of the two groups of poles have real components of opposite sign and imaginary components of the same sign. A constant real quantity can therefore be added to one group and its negative to the other without affecting the result. This corresponds, of course, to the fact that the reactance component of any network is not changed by the addition of an additive constant to its resistance.

The extension of the analysis to active impedances evidently presents, in general, no great difficulty. It is necessary to assume, however, that the desired type of stability is appropriate for the restrictions on the poles of the given functions. Thus if we begin with a resistance we can readily construct a corresponding complete impedance function which will be open-circuit stable. It is not so easy, however, to determine an impedance which is short-circuit stable but not open-circuit stable since the poles of the short-circuit stable function may occur in both halves of the plane and there may be several ways of separating the partial fraction expansion of the resistance into two halves.

10.6. *Choice of Coefficients in Impedance Expressions*

Thus far in our discussion we have considered the physical restrictions on possible impedance expressions and some of the ways in which a definite circuit corresponding to any particular impedance can be obtained. We have not, however, considered the design problem, which is that of choosing an expression for the impedance to simulate a characteristic which has already been prescribed. There are a number of ways in which this problem can be attacked, especially when the characteristic we have in view is in some analytically simple form. Space does not permit consideration of all these possibilities. For the sake of completeness, however, the simplest and most direct attack is outlined below.*

Let it be supposed that the rational function representing the impedance is written as

$$Z = R + iX = \frac{A_0 + A_1 p + A_2 p^2 + \cdots + A_m p^m}{B_0 + B_1 p + B_2 p^2 + \cdots + B_m p^m}. \tag{10-8}$$

If we replace p by $i\omega$ on the real frequency axis and multiply through by $(B_0 + \cdots + B_m p^m)$, we can equate real and imaginary parts separately to secure the pair of equations

$$\begin{aligned}(A_0 - A_2\omega^2 + A_4\omega^4 - \cdots) &- R(B_0 - B_2\omega^2 + B_4\omega^4 - \cdots) \\ &+ X\omega(B_1 - B_3\omega^2 + B_5\omega^4 - \cdots) = 0, \\ (A_1 - A_3\omega^2 + A_5\omega^4 - \cdots) &- R(B_1 - B_3\omega^2 + B_5\omega^4 - \cdots) \\ &- \frac{X}{\omega}(B_0 - B_2\omega^2 + B_4\omega^4 - \cdots) = 0.\end{aligned} \tag{10-9}$$

Now let ω, R, and X in these expressions be assigned particular values chosen from the characteristic we are trying to meet. If we choose a sufficient number of sets of values of these three quantities the result will be a system of simultaneous equations in the A's and B's whose solution

* The method which is described is essentially a modification of a method due to O. J. Zobel. See "Distortion Correction in Electrical Circuits," *B.S.T.J.*, July, 1928.

gives a network approximating the desired impedance. Since the equations are all linear the solution is relatively simple.

The most straightforward process is obtained if we use both of equations (10–9) at each matching frequency. In some instances, however, a better overall characteristic is found if we choose twice as many matching frequencies and apply the equations alternately. Since equation (10–8) will obviously not be affected if the numerator and denominator are divided through by any constant, one of the A's or B's is arbitrary and can be conveniently set at the value unity. The process evidently carries with it no guarantee that the resulting impedance expression will be physical. Since, as we have already seen, the resistance and reactance characteristics of a physical network can be chosen independently only within narrow limits, this is inherent in the nature of the problem.

The same general method can also be applied to the simulation of either component separately. For example, if we begin with a resistance function of the form

$$R = \frac{A_0 + A_1\omega^2 + A_2\omega^4 + \cdots + A_m\omega^{2m}}{B_0 + B_1\omega^2 + B_2\omega^4 + \cdots + B_m\omega^{2m}}, \tag{10–10}$$

we can evidently choose appropriate values of the constants by means of the set of simultaneous linear equations obtained by substituting special values of ω and R in the equation

$$(A_0 + A_1\omega^2 + \cdots + A_m\omega^{2m}) - R(B_0 + B_1\omega^2 + \cdots + B_m\omega^{2m}) = 0. \tag{10–11}$$

The expression for the complete impedance can then be built up from the formula for R by the method described previously.

With this procedure the requirements for physical realizability are much less onerous than they were before. We must still be careful, however, that the rational function which is obtained for R has no poles of any order, and no zeros of odd order, on the real frequency axis. Although this procedure appears to take cognizance of only one component, it may still be appropriate for the simulation of a complete impedance. Since the minimum reactance and the resistance characteristic of a network are always dependent on one another, there is no essential loss of generality in restricting ourselves initially to the resistance characteristic alone. We can always control the reactance characteristic to some extent by the final addition of a series reactance network.

The process of resistance simulation is particularly simple if we make use of the fact that networks whose physical configuration is that of a " constant k " high-pass or low-pass filter terminated in a resistance furnish input resistances of the type of (10–10) in which all the terms in the numerator except the first or last are zero.* The analytic problem is then that of simulating a prescribed characteristic by a polynomial, and ordinary polynomial or Taylor's series methods are applicable.

10.7. *Transformations of the Frequency Variable*

If we turn back to such general equations as (1–2) of Chapter I, we observe that aside from the resistance terms, every quantity is either of the form $L_{ij}p$ or of the form D_{ij}/p. The impedance as a whole, of course, is some function of p which depends upon the particular values assigned to the L's, D's, and R's. Now suppose that in the given network we replace each inductance by an impedance varying with frequency as some function $f(p)$ and each capacity by an impedance varying as $1/f(p)$. We will also suppose that the various impedances replacing the original inductances or capacities are in the same proportions as the original inductances or capacities themselves. Evidently this merely replaces p by $f(p)$ in every equation, so that the impedance $Z(p)$ becomes transformed into $Z[f(p)]$. In other words, if we know the impedance function of a given structure, we can find immediately the impedance function of the structure obtained when each inductance is replaced by a proportional impedance of some other type, and each capacity by the related inverse impedance. It is merely necessary to replace p in the original impedance function by the expression for the impedance which replaces the inductances. While the result has been stated only for driving point impedances, it evidently holds also for the transmission properties of a network.

So far as the formal statement of the principle goes, each inductance might be replaced by a dissipative impedance, such as that illustrated by Fig. 10.11. In practical applications, however, the principle is of importance chiefly when each inductance is replaced by a network of pure reactances. This can be explained from the fact that if we deal with a network of pure reactances, both the original variable p and the new variable $f(p)$ assume only pure imaginary values at real frequencies. The real frequency characteristics of the transformed network can therefore be obtained from the real frequency characteristics of the original structure merely by correlating corresponding values of p and $f(p)$, whereas if we use a dissipative network the characteristics of the transformed structure must be obtained by computation. Since the most elaborate reactive network can merely run through all reactance values from $-\infty$ to $+\infty$ repeatedly, where the original variable p ran through such values only once, the transformed characteristics are, at

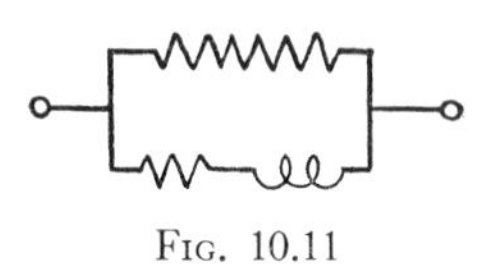

FIG. 10.11

* Further details are given in "A Method of Impedance Correction," H. W. Bode, *B.S.T.J.*, Oct. 1930.

most, repeated copies of the original characteristics, with some distortion of the frequency scale and perhaps an inversion in frequency.

The best illustrations of this principle are found in filter theory. For example, if we begin with the low-pass structure shown by Fig. 10.12*A*, the simplest transformation is effected if we make $f(p) = k/p$ where k is a real constant. This replaces each inductance by a capacity and each capacity by an inductance as shown by Fig. 10.12*B*. The characteristics are the same as those of the original structure except that the frequency scale is inverted and positive and negative frequencies are interchanged. In other words, the new structure is a high-pass filter. The relation between any two corresponding frequencies, such as the cutoffs of the two structures, on the absolute frequency scale, can, of course, be controlled by means of the constant k.

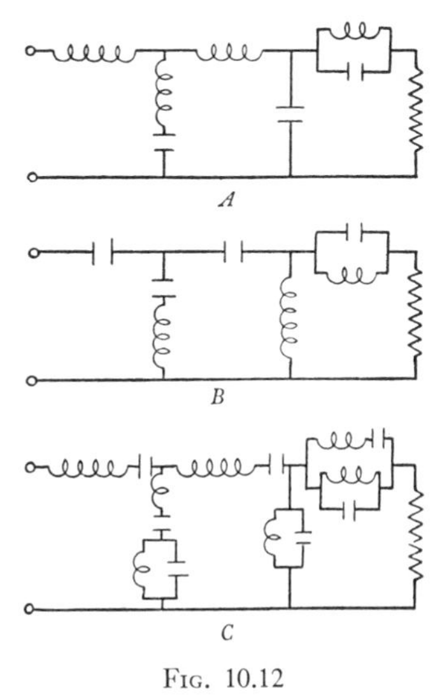

FIG. 10.12

The next simplest transformation is $f(p) = k(p/\omega_r + \omega_r/p)$. This replaces each inductance by a series resonant circuit, and each capacity by an anti-resonant circuit, as indicated by Fig. 10.12*C*. The result is easily seen to be a band-pass filter. The resonant frequencies of the networks replacing the original coils and condensers correspond to zero frequency in the low-pass filter and represent the center of the transmitted band. As we go either way from this frequency, we secure a distorted replica of the original low-pass filter characteristics. The frequency at which the center of the band is found is, of course, determined by the constant ω_r, while the width of band can be controlled by the constant k.

These relations are shown in more detail in Fig. 10.13. The solid and broken lines at the top of the figure represent respectively the real and imaginary components of the complete filter characteristic. As the figure is drawn the characteristic itself is regarded as fixed and the changes which occur in going from one type of filter to another are expressed by distorting the frequency scale, as indicated by the horizontal axes at the bottom of the drawing. The topmost axis represents the scale in the low-pass case. Since it may be taken as a reference it has been drawn in the usual arithmetic fashion, without distortion.

In order to express the correspondence among the three characteristics completely it is necessary to draw both the positive and negative halves of the real frequency axis in the low-pass case. The fact that the positive half is the one of direct design interest is indicated by drawing it very heavily. Since the real and imaginary components of the characteristic must be respectively even and odd functions of frequency in accordance with the general principle outlined in previous chapters, the relations between the two halves are easily determined.

The second horizontal axis gives the scale appropriate for the high-pass filter. The constant k has been chosen as unity. The transformation is essentially merely a matter of replacing the frequencies in the low-pass case

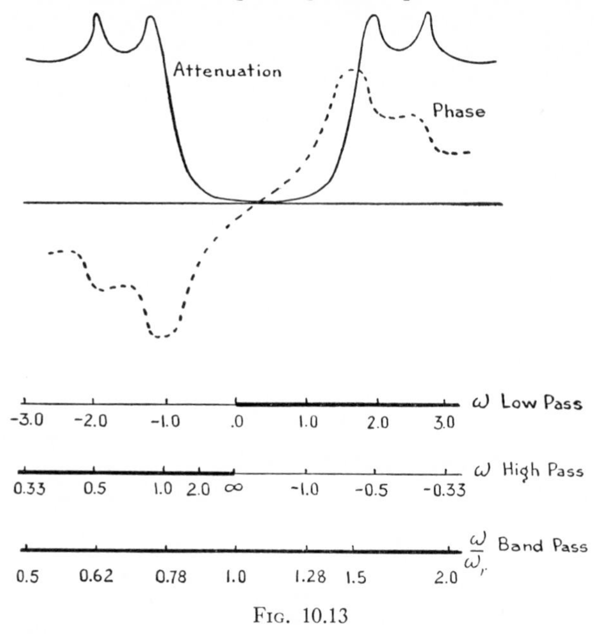

FIG. 10.13

by their reciprocals, but in order to secure an exact correspondence the *positive* frequency half of the high-pass scale must be identified with the *negative* frequency half of the low-pass scale. The bottom axis gives the band-pass scale, the constant k being chosen as two. Here the positive and negative halves of the low-pass scale correspond respectively to positive frequencies above and below the center of the band in the band-pass scale.

10.8. *Frequency Transformations in Amplifier Design*

These frequency transformations will be used in later chapters to simplify the discussion of amplifier design methods. Most practical amplifiers are called upon to transmit a band extending from one finite non-zero frequency to another. For purposes of analysis, however, we will take as our point of departure a structure transmitting from direct current up to some prescribed frequency. This will be called *the equivalent low-pass amplifier.*

The modification of the characteristics of the equivalent amplifier to suit the actual requirements can be made by either of two methods, depending upon the band width of the actual amplifier on a logarithmic frequency scale. If the band is relatively broad it is simplest to suppose that the characteristics of the equivalent amplifier are the same as those of the actual structure at all high frequencies and to superimpose upon them a set of low-frequency characteristics to take account of the fact that the transmission band of the actual amplifier does not extend to zero frequency. The required low-frequency characteristics can be obtained from any suitable high-frequency design by drawing the characteristics on a reciprocal frequency scale, using the transformation from low-pass to high-pass filters which was described in the preceding section. This is illustrated by Fig. 10.14. The solid line represents the loop gain characteristic in the original equivalent low-pass design and the broken line the modification in the characteristic near the lower edge of the useful band.

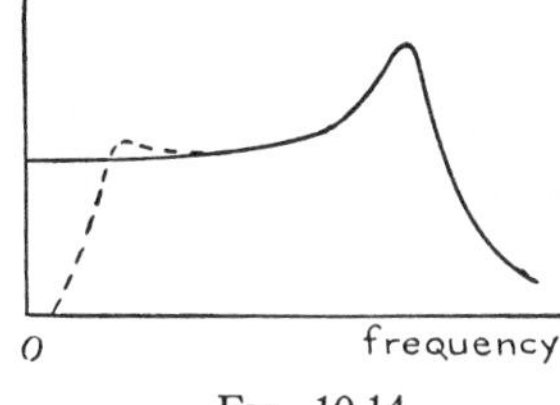

Fig. 10.14

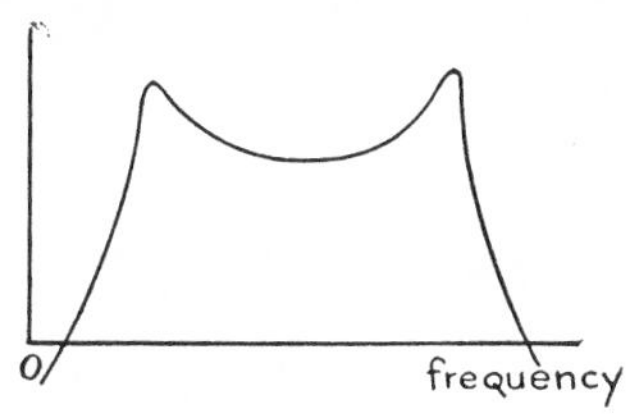

Fig. 10.15

If the band of the actual amplifier is relatively narrow, on the other hand, it is more desirable to treat the complete characteristic as a single unit, obtaining it from the equivalent low-pass structure by means of the transformation relating low-pass and band-pass filters. Fig. 10.15, for example, shows a band-pass characteristic corresponding to the low-pass characteristic of Fig. 10.14. Since the low-pass to band-pass transformation always leads to characteristics which are symmetrical about the center of the band, this leaves amplifiers with dissimilar characteristics at the upper and lower edges of the band to be treated directly. Narrow-band amplifiers with dissymmetrical requirements, however, are very exceptional.

These frequency transformations have been introduced here as an analytic simplification. They are, however, frequently convenient also in the preliminary stages of an actual design, since the branches of the equivalent amplifier are usually more easily computed than those of the actual structure.

10.9. *Principle of Conservation of Band Width*

The low-pass to band-pass transformation has one simple property of considerable importance. This is the fact that the transformation from a coil to a resonant circuit or from a condenser to an anti-resonant circuit does not affect the band width, in cycles, over which the impedance or admittance of the branch stays within any prescribed limits if we keep the coil unchanged in the first case and the condenser in the second. For example, in a low-pass circuit the susceptance of a given capacity C will be less than some fixed value B_0 between zero and a point ω_0 for which $B_0 = \omega_0 C$. In the band-pass circuit the susceptance of the corresponding branch can be written in general as

$$\omega B = \omega^2 C - \frac{1}{L}. \tag{10–12}$$

B will assume the values $\pm B_0$ at two points on opposite sides of the band. At these points, which may be indicated by ω_1 and ω_2, (10–12) becomes

$$\begin{aligned} \omega_2 B_0 &= \omega_2^2 C - \frac{1}{L}, \\ -\omega_1 B_0 &= \omega_1^2 C - \frac{1}{L}. \end{aligned} \tag{10–13}$$

Subtracting the second equation from the first gives

$$(\omega_2^2 - \omega_1^2)C = (\omega_2 + \omega_1)B_0 = (\omega_2 + \omega_1)\omega_0 C$$

or

$$\omega_2 - \omega_1 = \omega_0. \tag{10–14}$$

The frequency interval between corresponding points in the band-pass characteristic is thus the same as the equivalent interval* in the low-pass characteristic no matter how the mid-band frequency, which depends upon L, is chosen. A similar result evidently follows if we keep the inductance constant in the transformation from a simple coil to a series resonant circuit.

The transformation to a single band-pass circuit is the only one of particular engineering interest. As a matter of fact, however, similar relations also hold if we replace an individual coil or condenser by a reactive network of any arbitrary complexity, subject only to the condition that the network becomes equal to the element that it replaces at infinite frequency. The impedance or admittance of the branch will

* This interval is, of course, only the positive frequency part of the low-pass band. Since the band-pass characteristic was compared with the sum of the positive and negative frequency characteristics of the low-pass structure in Fig. 10.13 it may appear at first sight that the band-pass interval should be doubled. The apparent discrepancy is explained by the fact that there must be a negative frequency band-pass characteristic also. The total interval on the complete real frequency axis in the two cases is the same.

then lie within specified limits in a number of discrete bands, whose breadth and arrangement depend upon the resonances and anti-resonances chosen for the branch. The sum of all these intervals, however, is equal to the corresponding interval for the original inductance or capacity.

The importance of these conclusions will appear more clearly in later chapters. It will be shown that, broadly speaking, most of the characteristics of feedback amplifiers are ultimately limited by the parasitic elements in the circuit, which are principally shunt capacities to ground and secondarily series inductances. For example, tube gains are ultimately limited by interstage capacities. Input and output transformers, at least at high frequencies, are restricted principally by leakage inductance and high side capacity. The amount of feedback which can be secured is limited in the same way by the miscellaneous parasitic elements in the feedback loop. Evidently, in all these cases the result just established can be applied to the parasitic elements when they are resonated as part of the transformation from a low-pass to a band-pass system. Since the relative impedance levels of the various branches in the complete circuit are not affected by the transformation, however, the reactance or susceptance of any branch containing a parasitic element is correlated with any* overall response characteristic of the circuit in the same way after the transformation as it is in the low-pass structure. With the understanding that this is what is meant, therefore, the general result can be expressed as the

Theorem: The width of the frequency band, in cycles, over which a given response can be maintained in a circuit of given general configuration containing prescribed series inductances and shunt capacities is independent of the location of the band in the spectrum.

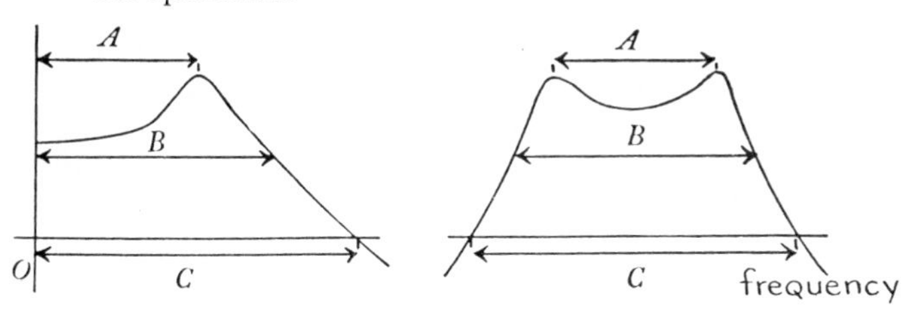

FIG. 10.16

* That is, any characteristic which can be determined from single frequency impedance values of the branches. This would evidently eliminate a delay, for example, since the result here depends both upon the impedances of the branches and upon the rate at which they vary with frequency. It is also assumed, of course, that the fact that the sign of such a response characteristic as a reactance may be opposite, on one side of the band, to that obtained from a low-pass circuit is immaterial.

The conservation of band width in the low-pass to band-pass transformation is illustrated by Fig. 10.16. The characteristics are the same as those originally shown in Figs. 10.14 and 10.15. Typical equal intervals in the two cases are indicated by the horizontal lines A, B, and C.

10.10. *Frequency Transformations to Dissipative Impedances*

It was suggested in connection with Fig. 10.9 that frequency transformations which replaced the reactive elements in the original structure by dissipative impedances were of comparatively little value. This is generally true. There are, however, two particular cases of such transformations of somewhat special interest. The first occurs when the original structure is composed only of reactances. In this case the transformation method can be used to generalize Foster's results for networks of pure reactance to include networks of any two types of impedance elements whatever. It is not necessary to assume, as was done in the previous discussion, that the impedance elements replacing the coils and condensers, respectively, in the original structure are inverse.

The rule for making the transformation can be expressed most easily in terms of equation (9–12) of Chapter IX. The structure to which this equation refers reduces to an inductance at high frequencies. Evidently, the p which multiplies the whole right-hand side of the equation can be thought of as the expression for the impedance of this inductance. Similarly, the p^2 terms which appear in the various factors of numerator and denominator correspond to resonances between the inductances and capacities of the network and can be thought of as the ratio between the impedance of an inductance and that of a capacity. It can be shown by a more detailed analysis that this identification is correct. Evidently, therefore, if we replace the inductances and capacities in a network of pure reactances by proportional impedances of any other two types the new impedance expression can be obtained from the

Theorem: The expression for the impedance of a network made up of any two kinds of impedance elements can be obtained from the expression for the impedance of a corresponding network of pure reactances by replacing the multiplier p in the pure reactance expression by the impedance which corresponds to a unit inductance and by replacing the p^2 terms in the rest of the pure reactance expression by the ratio of the impedances corresponding to a unit inductance and to a unit capacity.

Since the original reactance expression was derived for an L–L configuration it is assumed in the statement of the theorem that a structure of this type is in view. Modifications to suit other cases, however, are easily made by the methods described in the preceding chapter.

As an example of this theorem we may consider a network of inductances and resistances. The transformation to such a structure from a network of pure reactances leaves a unit inductance as a unit inductance but a unit capacity is replaced by a unit resistance. Thus the multiplier p in the expression for a pure reactance network is unchanged, but each p^2 is replaced by p. Substituting in (9–12) of Chapter IX, the new impedance expression becomes

$$Z = kp\,\frac{(p - p_2^2)(p - p_4^2)\cdots(p - p_m^2)}{(p - p_1^2)(p - p_3^2)\cdots(p - p_{m-1}^2)}\cdot \qquad (10\text{–}15)$$

As a second example, let the network be composed of capacities and resistances. This leaves a unit capacity as a unit capacity while a unit inductance is replaced by a unit resistance. In the impedance formula, the multiplier p is replaced by unity and each p^2 is replaced, as before, by p. The result is

$$Z = k\,\frac{(p - p_2^2)(p - p_4^2)\cdots(p - p_m^2)}{(p - p_1^2)(p - p_3^2)\cdots(p - p_{m-1}^2)}\cdot \qquad (10\text{–}16)$$

In both (10–15) and (10–16) the zeros and poles are found on the negative real p axis and occur alternately. The only distinction between the two expressions is the fact that as we proceed along this axis, starting from the origin, the alternation begins with a zero when the network is made up of inductances and resistances and with a pole when the network is made up of capacities and resistances.

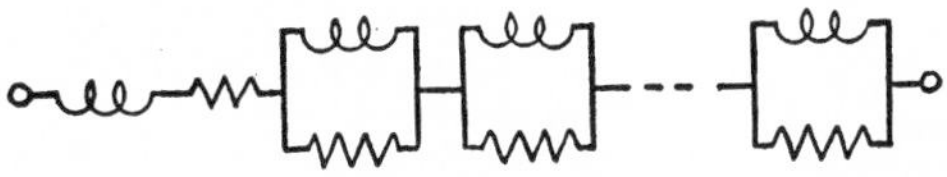

Fig. 10.17

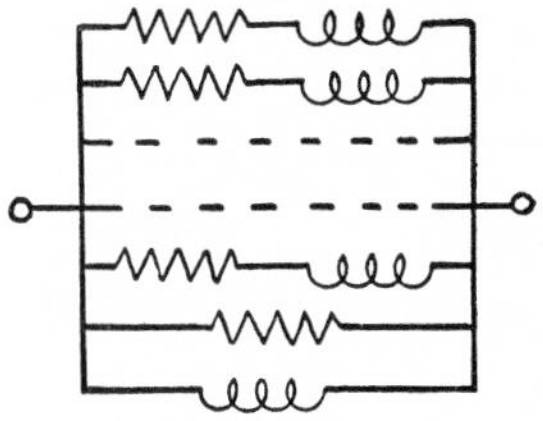

Fig. 10.18

Both types of networks can be represented in partial fraction form. Corresponding to the network of inductances and resistances, for example, we may secure either of the configurations shown by Figs. 10.17 and 10.18. These expansions have already been described in substance, in connection with Figs. 10.3, 10.4 and 10.5 of the present chapter. As the analysis shows, the poles of inductance-resistance and capacity-resistance networks, although they are both found on the negative real axis, correspond to C_j's, or residues, of opposite sign. When we add together corresponding terms from a capacity-resistance and an inductance-resistance network, as in Fig. 10.3, therefore, the poles may cancel out, leaving merely a constant.

10.11. *Effects of Parasitic Dissipation*

The second situation in which frequency transformations which replace reactive elements by dissipative impedances may be useful occurs when we are trying to express the effects of the normal parasitic dissipation of coils and condensers in the formulae for the network. For example, if R is the parasitic resistance associated with a coil L we can write the impedance of the coil as $pL + R = (p + R/L)L$. The effect of dissipation can thus be represented by replacing p by $p + R/L$ in the impedance of the non-dissipative coil. Similarly, the impedance of a capacity including a parasitic conductance G can be written as $1/(pC + G) = 1/(p + G/C)C$, and is the same as the impedance of a non-dissipative capacity with $p + G/C$ substituted for p.

In most networks the ratio R/L is about the same for all coils and the ratio G/C is about the same for all condensers. If, in addition, the two ratios are equal to one another the network may be spoken of as one having *uniform* dissipation. It is less often true that this second requirement is satisfied by actual circuits. In ordinary networks, however, the effects of dissipation are much the same whether we regard the dissipation as being concentrated principally in the coils alone or the condensers alone or assume it to be equally divided between elements of the two types.* Under these circumstances we can evidently represent the effects of dissipation by replacing p by $p + \frac{1}{2}(R/L + G/C)$ in the impedance expressions for both coils and condensers. This therefore leads to the

* This can be taken as a matter of experience, but it can also be justified, for many networks, theoretically. Thus if we go back to the energy analysis of Chapter VII it is evident that the effects of parasitic dissipation must be attributed to the power loss in the dissipative elements. The ratio of the power loss, I^2R, in a dissipative coil to its stored energy, $\frac{1}{2}I^2L$, however, is simply $2R/L$, while in a dissipative condenser the ratio is $2G/C$. In a complete network, therefore, the dissipated power must be $(2R/L)T + (2G/C)V$, which can also be written as $(T + V)(R/L + G/C) + (T - V)(R/L - G/C)$. The first term of this expression evidently represents the average dissipation assumed above while the second term gives the error in this assumption. Since $T - V$ is proportional to the input susceptance by (7–31) of Chapter VII, the error will be negligible for any network whose impedance is approximately a pure resistance. Even if this condition is not met the second term will be negligible in comparison with the first, as shown by (9–15) to (9–17) of Chapter IX, if the network is a sharply varying two terminal reactance, or, as shown by later equations of similar type, if the network is any electrically long filterlike structure.

Theorem: If a network can be regarded as uniformly dissipative any of its actual characteristics can be obtained by replacing p by $p + \frac{1}{2}(R/L + G/C)$ in the equations for the corresponding characteristics in the absence of dissipation.

In a mathematical sense the theorem states in effect that the changes due to dissipation can be represented by evaluating the function on a line somewhat to the right of the real frequency axis rather than on the real frequency axis itself. This is illustrated by Fig. 10.19. The light solid line represents the new axis when $R/L + G/C$ is constant with frequency and the broken line the result if $R/L + G/C$ increases with frequency, which is the usual case in practice. As an alternative, we can of course say that the computations are still made on the real frequency axis but that the function itself, including its zeros, poles, and other reference points, has been displaced an equivalent distance to the left.

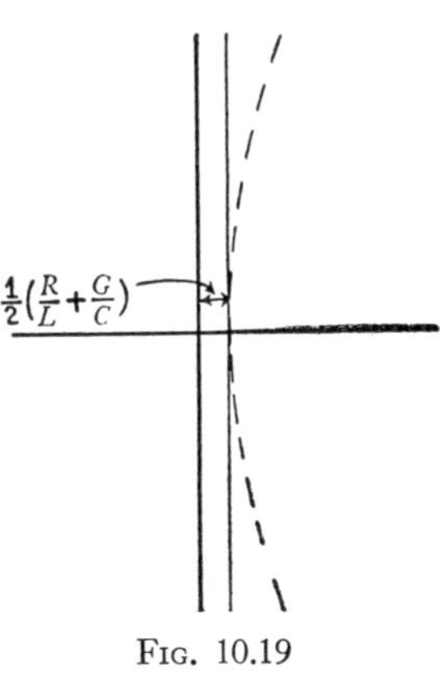

Fig. 10.19

These relations lead to a simple method of designing networks to give automatic compensation for the effects of parasitic dissipation. The method was first used by Darlington* in the design of filters which would give flat transmission bands when constructed with dissipative elements. It consists in designing the network without regard to parasitic dissipation and then translating all the zeros and poles in the impedance expressions which result $\frac{1}{2}(R/L + G/C)$ units to the right in the p plane. When the effects of parasitic dissipation are included the zeros and poles move back, of course, to their proper positions. If R and G are constant with frequency the required displacement is the same for all poles and zeros. Otherwise, it is usually sufficiently accurate to displace each pole or zero by the appropriate value of $\frac{1}{2}(R/L + G/C)$ at the adjacent real frequency. An example is shown by Fig. 10.20, which represents the distribution of zeros and poles of the transfer impedance, Δ/Δ_{12}, through a low-pass filter. The heavy line indicates the approximate transmission band. The crosses represent poles or infinite loss points, and the circles represent zeros, or points of infinite

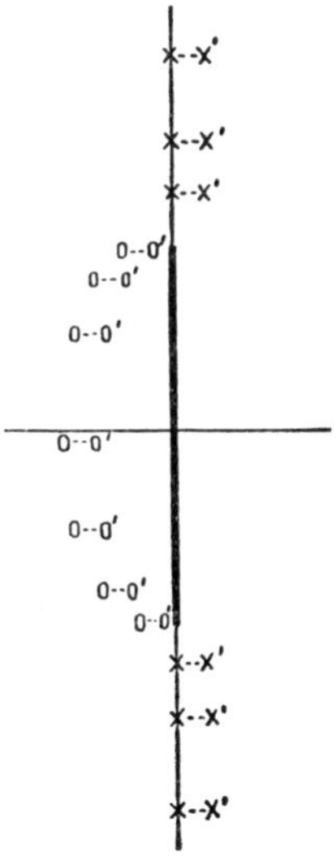

Fig. 10.20

* loc. cit., pp. 335 ff.

gain.* The predistortion of the characteristic to compensate for parasitic dissipation is accomplished by moving the poles and zeros to the positions indicated by the primes.†

In translating the zeros and poles to the right in this way it is of course necessary to make certain that the resulting network will not be non-physical. For example, in the illustration just described the zeros are the roots of Δ and cannot be moved into the right half-plane, even in the preliminary design, if we are dealing with a passive network. In this particular example there is no essential limitation on the location of the poles of the function. If the method were applied to a passive driving point impedance, however, it would be necessary to suppose that both the zeros and poles of the original design were found at least $\frac{1}{2}(R/L + G/C)$ units to the left of the real frequency axis in order to prevent critical frequencies of either type from entering the right half-plane as a result of the shift. The area between the imaginary axis and a line $\frac{1}{2}(R/L + G/C)$ units to the left thus represents a forbidden ground within which we may not be able to permit zeros and poles of the original design to lie if the method is to work. Otherwise, however, the application of the method is quite general.

This frequency transformation can also be used to provide a convenient way of estimating the effects of parasitic dissipation directly from an inspection of the real frequency characteristics of the structure. To show this, let it be supposed that we are interested in some particular characteristic $\Phi = A + iB$. It will be assumed that Φ is an analytic function of frequency in the neighborhood of the point which we are investigating. If we exclude such isolated frequencies as poles or cut-offs, this still allows us to consider almost any network characteristic we please. The method can be applied, for example, to such diverse functions as an impedance, a voltage ratio, an actual transmission characteristic, or an image transfer constant. It is necessary to remember, however, that if Φ is to be analytic both its real and imaginary components must be represented. In other words, if we are interested in such functions as the resistance or attenuation of a network, we must also include in Φ the associated reactance or phase shift.

The method depends upon the representation of the change in Φ by means of a Taylor's series. As we have already seen, the introduction of dissipation in the network is equivalent to replacing p, or $i\omega$, by $i\omega + \frac{1}{2}(R/L + G/C)$. The variable ω is therefore changed by an

* This is discussed in more detail in the next chapter. The reasons why a distribution of poles and zeros of this type should be appropriate for a low-pass filter are beyond the scope of the present treatment.

† In practice, the poles are usually not moved since the change in their location has relatively little effect on the distortion in the transmission band and requires an increase in the structural complexity of the network.

amount $\Delta\omega = - i\frac{1}{2}(R/L + G/C)$. In terms of the customary symbol Q, representing the average dissipation in coils and condensers, this change in ω can be written as $-i\omega/Q$. The Taylor's series expansion for Φ therefore appears as

$$\Phi = \Phi_0 + \left(-i\frac{\omega}{Q}\right)\frac{d\Phi_0}{d\omega} + \frac{1}{2!}\left(-i\frac{\omega}{Q}\right)^2 \frac{d^2\Phi_0}{d\omega^2} + \cdots, \qquad (10\text{–}17)$$

where Φ represents the characteristic corresponding to the actual parasitic dissipation, and Φ_0 the characteristic when dissipation is neglected. In order to apply the series, it is necessary, of course, to know the numerical values of the derivatives. The change in ω is imaginary, while ordinarily the behavior of Φ will be known only along the real frequency axis. Since Φ is analytic, however, its derivatives are the same in every direction. We can therefore evaluate them by means of the equations

$$\frac{d\Phi}{d\omega} = \frac{dA}{d\omega} + i\frac{dB}{d\omega}; \quad \frac{d^2\Phi}{d\omega^2} = \frac{d^2A}{d\omega^2} + i\frac{d^2B}{d\omega^2}; \cdots, \qquad (10\text{–}18)$$

where the differentiations are supposed to be made at real frequencies. This is illustrated by Fig. 10.21. The actual displacement of ω is from P_1 to a point P_2, off the real frequency axis. It is legitimate, however, to construct the Taylor's series on the assumption that we are concerned with an equivalent real frequency displacement to either of the points P_3 or P_4, obtaining the final answer by rotating the change in ω through 90° in each term of the series. The result is secured analytically by substituting (10–18) in (10–17). This gives

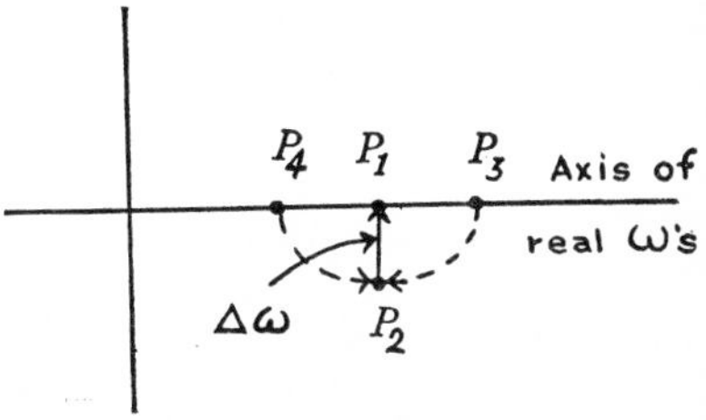

Fig. 10.21

$$A + iB = A_0 + iB_0 - i\frac{\omega}{Q}\left(\frac{dA}{d\omega} + i\frac{dB}{d\omega}\right) - \frac{1}{2!}\frac{\omega^2}{Q^2}\left(\frac{d^2A}{d\omega^2} + i\frac{d^2B}{d\omega^2}\right)$$
$$+ \frac{1}{3!}i\frac{\omega^3}{Q^3}\left(\frac{d^3A}{d\omega^3} + i\frac{d^3B}{d\omega^3}\right) + \cdots. \qquad (10\text{–}19)$$

Now equating reals and imaginaries separately, we find

$$A = A_0 + \frac{\omega}{Q}\frac{dB}{d\omega} - \frac{1}{2!}\frac{\omega^2}{Q^2}\frac{d^2A}{d\omega^2} - \frac{1}{3!}\frac{\omega^3}{Q^3}\frac{d^3B}{d\omega^3} + \cdots, \qquad (10\text{–}20)$$

$$B = B_0 - \frac{\omega}{Q}\frac{dA}{d\omega} - \frac{1}{2!}\frac{\omega^2}{Q^2}\frac{d^2B}{d\omega^2} + \frac{1}{3!}\frac{\omega^3}{Q^3}\frac{d^3A}{d\omega^3} + \cdots. \qquad (10\text{–}21)$$

Since the effects of dissipation will ordinarily be small the terms of higher order can be dropped, leaving the convenient formulae

$$A - A_0 \doteq \frac{\omega}{Q}\frac{dB}{d\omega}, \tag{10–22}$$

$$B - B_0 \doteq -\frac{\omega}{Q}\frac{dA}{d\omega}. \tag{10–23}$$

In numerical applications it is important to remember that the Q in these expressions represents the average dissipation of the coils and condensers and must be set equal to twice the Q of the coils alone when the dissipation of the condensers can be neglected.

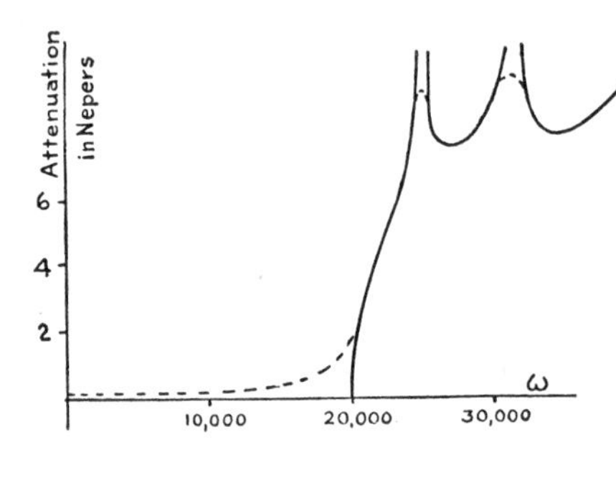

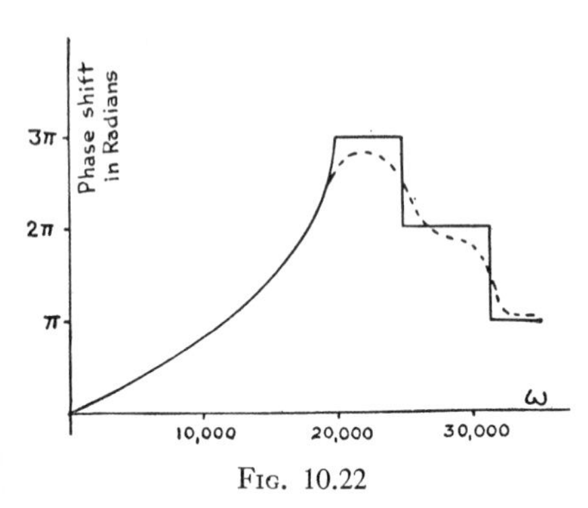

FIG. 10.22

Equations (10–22) and (10–23) show that, to a first approximation, the change produced by dissipation in the real component of a network characteristic is proportional to the slope of its imaginary component and vice versa. For example, if we interpret A as the resistance and B as the reactance of a network, we see that the resistance introduced by dissipation should be proportional to the derivative of the reactance characteristic and, conversely, the reactance change is proportional to the derivative of the resistance. If we interpret A and B as the loss and phase of a network, on the other hand, (10–22) shows that the change in attenuation produced by dissipation should be proportional to the "time of delay." Similarly, (10–23) shows that the effect of dissipation upon the phase displacement depends upon the rate of change of the attenuation characteristic.

An example of these relations is given by Fig. 10.22. The solid lines in the figure give the real and imaginary components of the transfer constant of a non-dissipative low-pass filter. This function is an unfortunate choice, in one sense, since it has singularities at the cut-off and at the points of infinite loss. As the figure indicates, the slope of the attenuation characteristic is infinite at each of these points. In addition, the phase characteristic exhibits discontinuities at the infinite loss points, corresponding to the change in the sign of the current delivered to the load when it passes through zero. The formulae cannot, of course, be applied at any singularity. Theoretically, they should also be inapplicable at any frequency so close to a singularity that the singularity falls within the interval P_3P_4 in Fig. 10.21, since the series in (10–20) and (10–21) will fail to converge in this event, while for slightly more remote frequencies we should expect the convergence to be so slow that (10–22) and (10–23) would not be useful approximations. It turns out, however, that these formulae are at least qualitatively correct even at frequencies very close to the singularities.

The dissipative phase and attenuation characteristics of the filter are shown by the broken lines in Fig. 10.22. In order to make the example roughly quantitative let it be supposed that the filter is a voice frequency structure with a cut-off at $\omega = 20{,}000$. It will also be supposed that dissipation in the condensers can be neglected but that the coils have a Q which is equal to 20 at the cut-off.* The average Q which appears in (10–22) and (10–23) is therefore 40 at the cut-off and if we suppose Q to be proportional to frequency the factor ω/Q can be replaced by the constant 500.

Turning first to the effects of dissipation on the phase characteristic, we observe that inside the transmission band the slope of the attenuation characteristic is negligible. In accordance with (10–23), the dissipative and non-dissipative phase characteristics are almost identical in this region. Between the cut-off and the first peak of attenuation the slope of the attenuation characteristic is positive and, as (10–23) indicates, parasitic dissipation reduces the phase shift. About halfway between the cut-off and the first peak, where the slope is least, we can estimate that $dA/d\omega$ is about 1 neper per thousand units of ω. At this point, therefore, the reduction in phase shift is about half a radian, but it grows progressively greater as we go toward either the cut-off or the peak. In the region just beyond the first peak, on the other hand, the attenuation slope is negative, and the phase shift is increased by dissipation, and so on.

Turning now to equation (10–22), we observe that dissipation increases the attenuation in the transmission band, where the phase characteristic has a positive slope. With the three-section filter assumed here the phase shift at the cut-off is 3π radians. This corresponds to an average $dB/d\omega$ over the band of about 5×10^{-4}, or with the given value of ω/Q, to an average attenuation of about 0.25 neper. At low frequencies, where $dB/d\omega$ is only about half this average, the attenuation is correspondingly reduced, but it is much greater near the cut-off, where the phase slope is high.

* A low Q is assumed here in order to make the effects of parasitic dissipation appreciable in an overall plot like Fig. 10.22. Even so, however, no attempt has been made to draw the curves exactly to scale.

Beyond the cut-off the phase slope is generally zero and dissipation has relatively little effect on the attenuation. Dissipation does, however, reduce the peaks of attenuation from infinite to finite values, which may be regarded as corresponding qualitatively to the associated breaks in the phase characteristic.

10.12. *Parasitic Dissipation in Distortionless Media*

Equations (10–22) and (10–23) give particularly interesting results when they are applied to a network whose dissipationless characteristics approximate those of an ideal medium. In general, it appears that the characteristics of such a structure will not be seriously impaired by dissipation, or, in other words, *a network whose characteristics approach the ideal is roughly self-compensating for the effects of uniform dissipation.* For example, if the impedance of a network approximates the ideal constant resistance characteristic, the derivatives of its resistance and reactance with frequency will ordinarily be quite small.* The changes produced by dissipation in resistance and reactance, as found from (10–22) and (10–23), must of course be correspondingly small. As judged from these formulae, therefore, the impedance should be about the same whether it is computed on a dissipative or a non-dissipative basis.

If the network is to have an ideal transmission characteristic as well as an ideal impedance, its attenuation must be constant and its phase shift must vary linearly with frequency.† By the previous argument, the constancy of the attenuation shows that the phase characteristic will be disturbed only slightly by dissipation. We cannot use the same logic to show that the attenuation is unchanged by dissipation since linearity of phase shift means a constant, but not in general a zero, value of $dB/d\omega$. We can, however, at least see from (10–22) that over narrow frequency ranges the percentage distortion in a circuit with constant delay can be no greater than the percentage band width unless Q actually decreases with frequency. Over broader ranges the loss introduced by dissipation will depend upon the variation of the factor ω/Q. Since Q is directly proportional to frequency when the resistances of the coils and leakages of the condensers are constant, the structure will also be distortionless over broad ranges in this limiting case.

These relations are most easily exemplified in transmission line theory. It is well known, for example, that an ideal non-dissipative transmission line is distortionless and that it remains distortionless if dissipation is added in accordance with the relation $R/L = G/C$, or, in other words,

* Impedance characteristics which fluctuate rapidly, without ever departing far from the ideal value, must, of course, be excepted in this argument.

† J. R. Carson, "Electric Circuit Theory and the Operational Calculus," p. 183.

uniformly. Actual lines, which do not satisfy this relation, exhibit marked distortion at low frequencies. They tend to approximate distortionless lines, however, as soon as the frequency is high enough to give reasonably large Q's for the distributed series impedance and shunt admittance, even though the distortion remains non-uniform.* For practical application, the relations are probably most useful for complicated aggregations of filters, equalizers, and phase correctors having an overall characteristic which is substantially distortionless. Evidently the effects of parasitic dissipation in the individual units should tend to be compensatory so that labor will be saved by postponing consideration of this problem until preliminary designs of the complete system are available.

10.13. *Variations in a Network Characteristic Produced by Changes in a Single Element*

In many network design problems it is convenient to study the effects of the most important elements on the network characteristic individually by assigning them various values while the remaining elements are held fixed. In such circumstances the study may be considerably facilitated by the use of certain elementary propositions from function theory. Broadly speaking, the applications of function theory are similar to those we have seen before, except that the independent variable is taken as a complex branch impedance rather than as a complex frequency.

The simplest proposition we can use depends merely upon the general form of the functional relationship between the network characteristics of greatest interest and any individual branch impedance. For example, if Z is either a driving point or a transfer impedance, it follows from (1–11) and (1–12) of Chapter I that it must be related to any given branch impedance, z, by an equation of the type

$$Z = \frac{A + Bz}{C + Dz} \tag{10–24}$$

where A, B, C, and D are quantities which depend upon the other elements of the circuit. They will, of course, normally vary with frequency. If we keep the frequency fixed, however, so that A, B, C, and D are merely constants, equation (10–24) represents a so-called " bilinear transformation " of the variable z. It is a property of such a transformation that if z assumes values lying on a circle (including as a special case a straight line) the corresponding values of Z will also lie on a circle. If z is a resistance, we can

* This assumes, of course, that R and G do not vary with frequency. In physical lines R and G usually increase with frequency, so that the attenuation also increases instead of flattening out. This corresponds to the variation in the factor ω/Q discussed previously.

regard the " circle " on which it lies as the real axis, including both positive and negative portions, while if z is a reactance, the " circle " will similarly be the complete imaginary axis.

The circle described by Z, corresponding to either of these cases, is determined as soon as we know three points on it. In most circumstances two of these points can be found readily by assigning z the special values zero and infinity. The third can be found by choosing any convenient intermediate value, or the circle can frequently be located directly by conditions of symmetry. For example, if we are dealing with a variable resistance in a network all of whose remaining elements are reactances, the portions of the Z circle corresponding to positive and negative resistances must evidently be located symmetrically about the axis of pure imaginaries. An example is furnished by the network and associated impedance plot shown in Fig. 10.23. The solid and broken line portions of the plot corre-

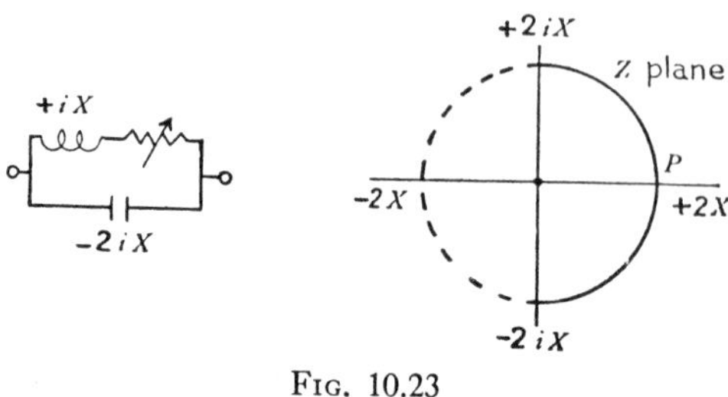

FIG. 10.23

spond respectively to positive and negative values of the variable resistance in the network. The structure is a so-called " constant impedance " device since it has the property that the absolute value of its impedance is independent of the variable resistance. This can be verified by direct computation, but we may notice that it must follow from the symmetry of the plot about the imaginary axis if the network is so chosen that the reactances corresponding to zero and infinite values of the variable resistance are equidistant from the origin.

A second example, this time showing symmetry about the real axis, is shown in Fig. 10.24. The broken line represents the locus of Z when the condenser is replaced by an inductance.

Some assistance in making studies of this sort can frequently be obtained merely from the broad fact that, except possibly for isolated points, any ordinary network characteristic must be an analytic function of any one of the branch impedances. If we vary this impedance, therefore, the network characteristic must vary " conformally." This means that if we know the effect on the characteristic produced by a slight variation of the branch impedance in any given direction, we can find the effect produced by a slight variation in the branch impedance in any other direction by rotating the original change in the characteristic through the same phase angle as that by which the variation in the branch impedance is rotated. For example, the effects on a network impedance produced by a slight change in the resistance of one branch and by a slight change in its reactance are at right

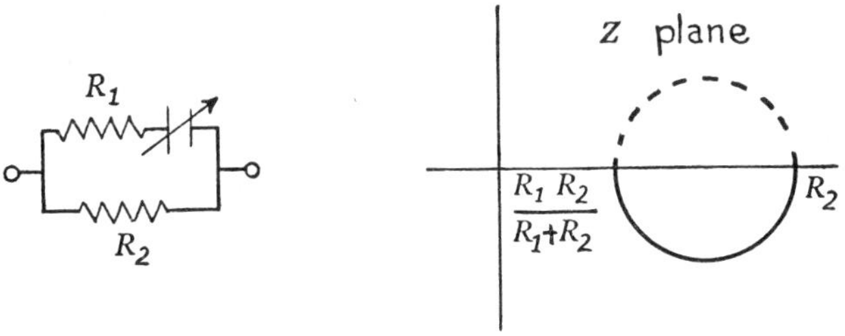

FIG. 10.24

angles to one another. Thus in Fig. 10.23 if we vary the inductance while we hold the resistance fixed at any assigned value, the new circle must cut the original circle of Fig. 10.23 orthogonally. This is illustrated by Fig. 10.25 for a resistance equal to X, which corresponds to the point P in Fig. 10.23. The original circle of Fig. 10.23 is reproduced by the broken lines.

We can also study the effect of a single branch impedance on the complete network by means of the theorem on the maxima and minima of analytic functions described in Chapter VIII. For example, if we assign z to

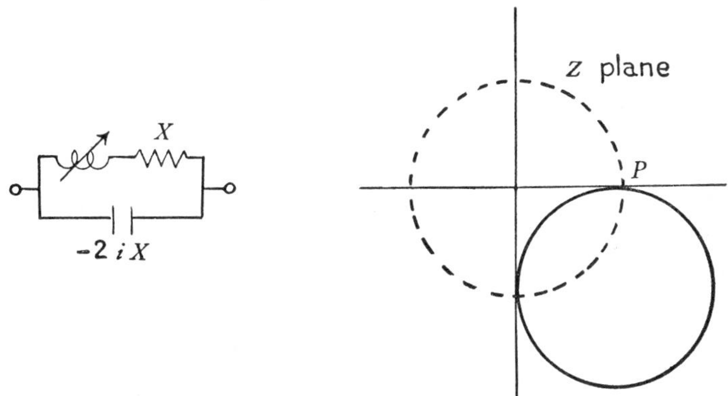

FIG. 10.25

larger and larger circles in the right half-plane the corresponding circles for Z also grow larger, so that variations in Z produced by changes in z become more extreme. The largest possible " circle " for z, in a passive network, is the axis of pure reactances and the maximum and minimum for either component of Z must consequently be found when z is a pure imaginary. This has already been discussed in Chapter VIII.

CHAPTER XI

Physical Representation of Transfer Impedance Functions

11.1. *Introduction*

Viewed broadly, the analysis of the last several chapters has consisted of an attempt to construct a general network theory upon the postulate that a realizable network must be stable. Chapters VII and VIII gave the essential framework of such a theory and the formal requirements to which it leads for the various network functions. Chapters IX and X were an effort to clothe the driving point immittance requirements with physical meaning by deducing from them a number of particular consequences for more or less specialized circuits. The present chapter and the one which follows attempt to do the same thing for transfer immittance functions. In particular, the present chapter can be looked upon as the analogue, for transfer immittances, of the discussion of driving point immittances in Chapter IX. It consists essentially in an attempt to show that the requirements for transfer functions laid down in Chapter VII are sufficient as well as necessary by a demonstration that any function meeting these conditions can be realized in a physical circuit of a certain type.

There is a very close parallel between the theory of driving point immittances and the theory of transfer immittances. The logical analogue of a driving point immittance, however, is not a transfer immittance itself but its logarithm. Thus we may look upon attenuation and phase in the transfer analysis as taking the place of resistance, or conductance, and reactance, or susceptance, in the driving point analysis. The present discussion attempts to stress this analogy as much as possible. Thus the initial operations of resistance, or conductance, reduction and reactance, or susceptance, reduction in Chapter IX are replaced here by the corresponding operations of attenuation reduction and phase reduction. As in the discussion of driving point functions, attention is first restricted to passive networks. In the driving point analysis the solution for passive circuits was extended to the general case by the addition of a negative resistance which made it possible to disregard the limitation that the resistance or conductance component of a passive driving point immittance cannot be negative. Similarly, the solution for passive transfer functions can be extended to the general case by the addition of an ideal amplifier, which allows us to realize negative attenuations. In the next chapter the analogy is carried further by the representation of the general transfer function by a number of simple structures in tandem. This corresponds to the representation of the general driving point function by a number of simple impedances in series or parallel.

The analogy just described breaks down in only one important respect. The general discussion thus far has been carried forward in dual terms to take account of the fact that the analysis may employ either mesh or nodal methods. In the consideration of driving point functions this mathematical dualism is of some physical consequence since it leads naturally to alternative series and parallel representations for a given function. It leads also to such complexities as occurred in Chapter IX when we attempted to determine the short-circuit stability of impedances in series or the open-circuit stability of impedances in parallel. In the analysis of transfer functions, on the other hand, the mathematical dualism has no particular physical significance. There is no inverse to a tandem combination of networks, in the sense that a series combination of networks is the inverse of a parallel combination. To simplify the language, therefore, the discussion will treat only of transfer impedances.

11.2. *Statement of the Problem*

In previous chapters transfer impedances and admittances have been used rather generally as measures of the response which would be obtained at one point of the network if a current or voltage source were introduced at some other point. So far as this formulation of the problem goes, the two points may be any two branches or nodes chosen at random. The self-impedances or admittances at the two points need not be sharply distinguishable from the rest of the network. In practical situations, however, the two points are usually the actual source of the signals in which we are ultimately interested and the actual receiving device, and the problem is that of interpolating some network which will control the transmission between them in some desired way. Since the source and receiver are usually given while the network is still to be found, this makes it desirable to distinguish between the network proper and its terminations, as indicated by Fig. 11.1. The network proper is represented by the box and the terminations by the two resistances R_1 and R_2.*

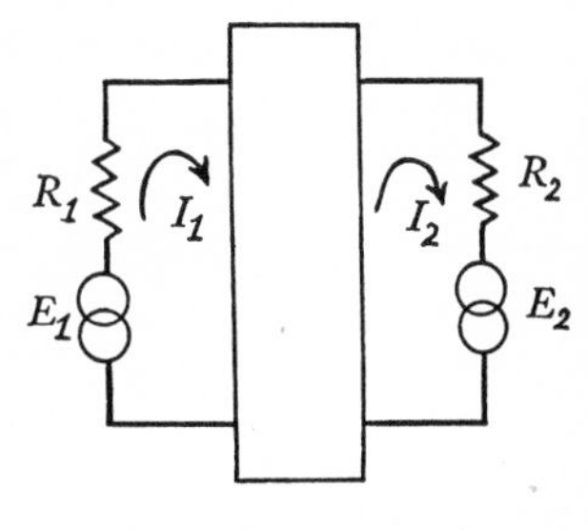

FIG. 11.1

* For descriptive purposes the terminations may as well be general impedances, since any reactances they include can be regarded as part of the network. They are assumed to be resistances here, however, to avoid any restrictions on the network when we come to the problem of simulating any possible transfer impedance.

The formulation of the situation given by Fig. 11.1 raises a number of questions which have not previously appeared. In two-terminal networks, for example, the specification of the driving point impedance of the structure fixes it completely so far as its participation in the overall operation of the complete circuit in which it appears is concerned. The choice of the transfer impedance of a four-terminal network, on the other hand, specifies the network only partially. In Fig. 11.1, for example, it fixes only the I_2 which will flow in response to the generator E_1. We may also be interested in the input current I_1 which would be caused by the same generator or either the I_1 or the I_2 which would flow if a second generator E_2 were added in the output circuit. Evidently, before taking further steps it is necessary to know how many parameters are required to fix the network completely and what disposition of the additional parameters will be made in the present situation.

This problem is most easily investigated by means of the mesh equation solution for I_1 and I_2 in terms of E_1 and E_2. If we suppose that the input and output circuits are chosen respectively as the first and second meshes, the result from (1–7) and (1–9) of Chapter I is easily seen to be

$$I_1 = E_1 \frac{\Delta_{11}}{\Delta} + E_2 \frac{\Delta_{21}}{\Delta},$$
$$I_2 = E_1 \frac{\Delta_{12}}{\Delta} + E_2 \frac{\Delta_{22}}{\Delta}, \tag{11–1}$$

where Δ is the determinant of the complete network, including the terminations R_1 and R_2. We can, however, also write the equations in a form which segregates the properties of the network itself from its terminations. Using the expansion methods indicated by such equations as (1–11) or (1–12) of Chapter I, this results in

$$\left[R_1 + \frac{\Delta_{22}^0}{\Delta_{1122}}\right] I_1 - \frac{\Delta_{21}}{\Delta_{1122}} I_2 = E_1,$$
$$-\frac{\Delta_{12}}{\Delta_{1122}} I_1 + \left[R_2 + \frac{\Delta_{11}^0}{\Delta_{1122}}\right] I_2 = E_2, \tag{11–2}$$

where Δ_{11}^0 and Δ_{22}^0 represent Δ_{11} and Δ_{22} when $R_1 = R_2 = 0$. The superscripts are immaterial for the other determinants.

Equations (11–2) show that if the operation of the network is to be specified completely for any choice of the E's and the R's it is necessary, in general, to know the four quantities $\Delta_{22}^0/\Delta_{1122}$, $\Delta_{21}/\Delta_{1122}$, $\Delta_{12}/\Delta_{1122}$, and $\Delta_{11}^0/\Delta_{1122}$. In passive networks, to which the discussion is restricted at the moment, one of these can be eliminated by the principle of reciprocity, which allows us to write $\Delta_{12} = \Delta_{21}$. The remaining three quantities can, of course, be replaced by other sets of three functionally related to them. For example, if we interpret equations (11–2) as the mesh equations of the structure shown in Fig. 11.2, the network is specified in effect by the three branches of an equivalent *T*. This is a familiar device. We may also analyze the network in terms of its image parameters or its iterative parameters. In any event, however, the complete specification of the network requires at least three parameters and we must know all of them in order to determine its operation for all possible terminal conditions.

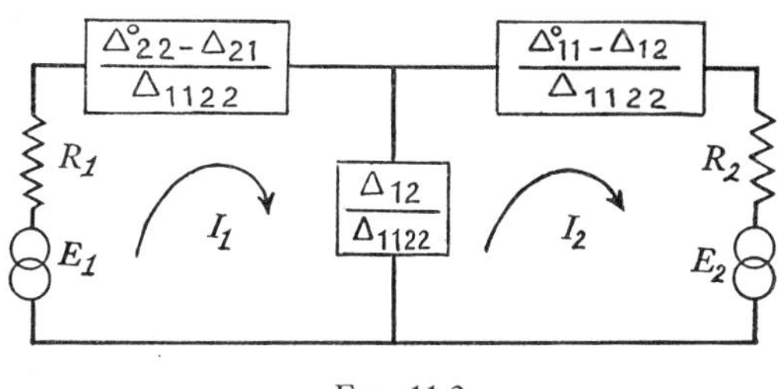

FIG. 11.2

An elaborate and somewhat unwieldy solution of the general problem of designing the network when the three parameters are chosen arbitrarily, within physical limits, has been advanced by Gewertz.* For the purposes of the present discussion, however, it is sufficient to demonstrate that a specified transfer impedance Δ/Δ_{12}, from input to output, can be obtained when the terminations have their prescribed values. This leaves two parameters which can be chosen arbitrarily and by choosing them in different ways a rich variety of solutions can be obtained. All the solutions, of course, will be alike, so far as the specified transmission characteristic is concerned, but they may differ widely in such properties as the impedance which the network presents to the source or the load. One possibility is furnished by a method due to Darlington.† Here the two arbitrary parameters are specified, by implication, by the assumption that the network is to contain only reactive elements. This solution is particularly applicable to filter problems.

The solution developed here will be based upon the assumption that the network is to have a constant resistance image impedance at each end. This choice is a particularly convenient one for theoretical purposes, since it allows us to ignore reflection effects in evaluating the transmission characteristic. This will be especially useful later when we come to the problem of representing a complete characteristic by a number of simple structures in

* "Synthesis of a Finite, Four-Terminal Network," *Journal of Mathematics and Physics*, Vol. 12, 1932–33, pp. 1–257.

† "Synthesis of Reactance 4-Poles," *Journal of Mathematics and Physics*, Sept., 1939, pp. 257–353.

tandem. It has the additional advantage, for the purposes of this book, that it converts the analysis, in effect, into a theory of equalizers. The material thus becomes directly pertinent to problems of pre-equalization or β circuit equalization in amplifier design, as well as being more remotely pertinent to the design of such structures as interstage networks, which are broadly like equalizers.

11.3. *Construction of a General Transfer Impedance*

The transfer impedance Δ/Δ_{12} between R_1 and R_2 in Fig. 11.1 will be symbolized by Z_T. Since Z_T represents a transmission it is also convenient to measure it in logarithmic units. The most efficient possible transmission between R_1 and R_2 with passive networks would be obtained if the two were matched by an ideal transformer, and corresponds to $Z_T = 2\sqrt{R_1R_2}$. If this value of Z_T is used as a reference, the logarithmic measure of Z_T is given by $\theta = \log (Z_T/2\sqrt{R_1R_2})$, where $\theta = A + iB$ may be called the *transfer loss and phase.* Since Z_T is evidently a rational function of p these relations can also be written as

$$Z_T = \frac{\Delta}{\Delta_{12}} = 2\sqrt{R_1R_2}\, e^{\theta} = 2\sqrt{R_1R_2}\, e^{A+iB}$$

$$= 2\sqrt{R_1R_2}\, k\, \frac{(p - a_1)(p - a_2)\cdots(p - a_n)}{(p - b_1)(p - b_2)\cdots(p - b_n)}. \tag{11–3}$$

The a's and b's in (11–3) are, of course, the zeros and poles of Z_T, or the points of infinite gain and infinite loss in terms of θ. The conditions which they must meet if Z_T is to represent a physical circuit are given by the general list in Chapter VII. The requirements are, broadly speaking, that both zeros and poles must either be real or occur in conjugate complex pairs, and that the zeros must be found only in the interior of the left half-plane. The poles, however, may occur in any part of the plane.* As long as the discussion is restricted to passive circuits it is necessary, in addition, to satisfy requirement *6b*, which states, in effect, that the network cannot serve as a source of power. In the present instance, this means that the constant k must be large enough to make the absolute magnitude of the last expression in (11–3) at least equal to $2\sqrt{R_1R_2}$ at all points on the real frequency axis. In other words, the transfer loss A cannot be negative.

* It will be observed that the " minimum phase " condition, *5c* in the list of Chapter VII, is not involved here. Minimum phase networks are discussed later. It is also assumed, in accordance with the discussion of Chapter VII, that none of the zeros lies exactly on the real frequency axis.

In comparing this formulation of the restrictions on passive transfer impedances with those developed for passive driving point impedances, we notice two important differences. The first is the fact that the previous requirement that the real component of the impedance cannot be negative along the real frequency axis has been eliminated. It is replaced by the requirement that the real component of θ cannot be negative at real frequencies. The second is the fact that the poles of the function are no longer confined to the left half-plane. As later discussion will show, these are the changes which are necessary if the real and imaginary components of θ are to be taken as the analogues of the real and imaginary components of a driving point impedance function.

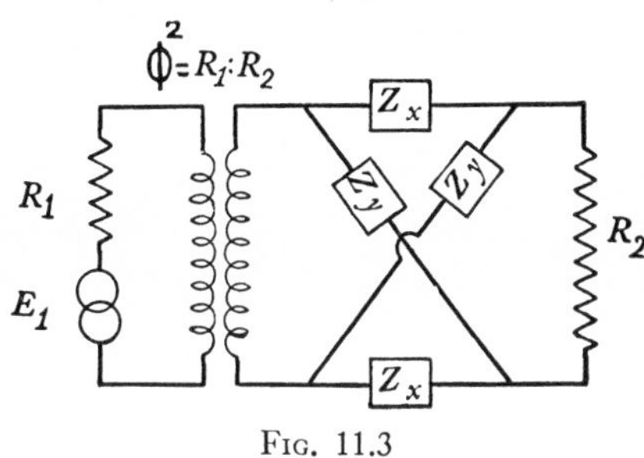

FIG. 11.3

The structure which will be used to represent this general passive transfer function is the combination of a symmetrical lattice network* and ideal transformer shown by Fig. 11.3. In terms of its branch impedances, Z_x and Z_y, the image impedance and image transfer constant of the lattice can be written in general as

$$Z_I = \sqrt{Z_x Z_y} \tag{11–4}$$

and

$$\tanh \frac{\theta}{2} = \sqrt{\frac{Z_x}{Z_y}}. \tag{11–5}$$

As suggested in the previous discussion, the image impedance of the lattice will be assumed to be a constant resistance. It can be set equal to the terminating impedance R_2 by choosing Z_x and Z_y as inverse networks of impedance product $Z_x Z_y = R_2^2$ in (11–4). With this choice the input impedance of the lattice is, of course, also R_2. The transformer in Fig. 11.3 is introduced to provide a final impedance match between this resistance

* For the benefit of readers unfamiliar with the lattice configuration it may perhaps be helpful to point out that if the structure is unfolded it takes the form of a Wheatstone bridge in which opposite arms are equal. The lattice is much used in network analysis both because of the simplicity of its design equations and because it is capable of representing any characteristics obtainable from any other symmetrical structure. Further details of its properties will be given in the next chapter. For a more complete discussion, especially of the use of the lattice in filter design, the reader may also refer to Guillemin, "Communication Networks," Vol. II, Ch. X. The introduction of the lattice structure into network theory appears to be due originally to Campbell, "Physical Theory of the Electric Wave Filter," *B.S.T.J.*, Nov., 1922.

and the generator resistance R_1. It can be omitted if the loss due to the mismatch between the two resistances is not of importance.

With these assumed impedance relations it is clear that the θ of equation (11–5) representing the transfer constant of the lattice can be identified with the θ representing the so-called " transfer loss and phase " in equation (11–3). Since Z_y can be expressed in terms of Z_x and R_2 from the image impedance condition, however, (11–5) is readily rewritten in either of the forms

$$e^{\theta} = \frac{1 + \dfrac{Z_x}{R_2}}{1 - \dfrac{Z_x}{R_2}} \tag{11–6}$$

or

$$Z_x = R_2 \frac{e^{\theta} - 1}{e^{\theta} + 1}. \tag{11–7}$$

The problem thus reduces to that of choosing a Z_x from equation (11–7) which will give the prescribed transmission characteristic. Since e^{θ} is a rational function of frequency, it is clear that Z_x will be a rational function also. To complete the analysis we must show that this rational function can be represented as a physical two-terminal impedance when e^{θ} meets the conditions we have established for transfer impedances.

The proof that Z_x can be constructed depends upon an application of the preceding theorem on the maxima and minima of analytic functions. Although e^{θ} may have poles in the right half of the p plane its reciprocal, at least, will be an analytic function in this region. The absolute value of the reciprocal function is therefore greater at some point on the real frequency axis than it is anywhere in the interior of the right half-plane. This is the same as saying that the minimum value of the transfer loss A in the whole right half of the p plane is found on the real frequency axis. We have already seen, however, that if the network is passive the minimum A on the real frequency axis cannot be less than zero. Within the right half of the plane, therefore, $A > 0$. It follows from equation (11–7) that Z_x can have neither zeros nor poles in this range. Moreover, if we write $e^{\theta} = e^{A} \cos B + ie^{A} \sin B$ the real component of Z_x is readily found to be

$$R_x = R_2 \frac{e^{2A} - 1}{(e^{A} \cos B + 1)^2 + (e^{A} \sin B)^2}. \tag{11–8}$$

Under the assumed conditions, this will evidently be positive on the real frequency axis. Z_x thus meets all the conditions of physical realizability and can be represented as a two-terminal Brune network or some equivalent structure. Since the inverse impedance Z_y is obviously also physical, this allows us to state the

Theorem: The transfer impedance of any passive network* can be represented by a symmetrical constant resistance lattice network with resistance terminations.

This conclusion is of engineering as well as of theoretical interest. It indicates, for example, that any filter characteristic can be duplicated in a constant resistance structure, thus avoiding the erratic impedances which ordinarily characterize filters. The difficulties with the method lie in the fact that the two-terminal impedance branches of the lattice may be complicated and difficult to adjust, and that the constant resistance structure as a whole requires appreciably more elements than would a conventional filter. The first of these difficulties can be avoided by the decomposition method described in the next chapter, at the cost of a considerable increase in the fixed attenuation of the network. As the method stands thus far, of course, the constant attenuation characteristic can be made as small as any passive network can give if we include the ideal transformer matching the resistances R_1 and R_2.

11.4. *Examples of the Representation of Transfer Functions by Lattices*

As an elementary example of these processes we may consider the circuit shown by Fig. 11.4. The transfer impedance from one resistance to the other is given by $Z_T = 2 + p$. Since $2\sqrt{R_1R_2} = 2$ in this circuit, the corresponding transfer loss and phase is given by $e^\theta = 1 + p/2$. Substituting in (11–7) gives the result

$$Z_x = \frac{p}{p+4} = \frac{p/4}{p/4+1}, \qquad (11\text{–}9)$$

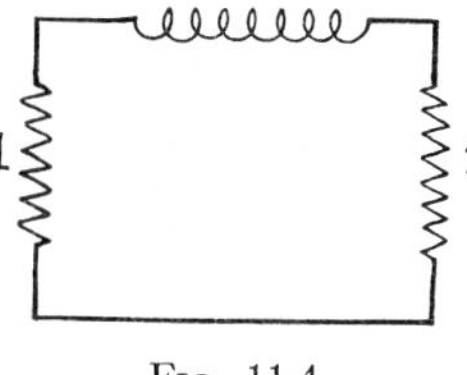

Fig. 11.4

which represents the impedance of a unit resistance in parallel with an inductance of one quarter unit. The complete lattice is shown by Fig. 11.5.†

* It is assumed that none of the zeros of Δ lies exactly on the real frequency axis. Otherwise, however, the phraseology is somewhat too restrictive since, as later discussion shows, an active transfer impedance can also be represented by a passive lattice if the lattice terminations are allowed to be different from those in the original circuit.

† The broken lines in this and subsequent lattice diagrams indicate series and cross-arm impedances identical with those shown explicitly.

The example is made slightly more complicated by including a parallel capacity in the original circuit, as shown by Fig. 11.6. The transfer impedance is readily found as

$$Z_T = p^2 + 2p + 2 \tag{11–10}$$

and is again just twice e^{θ}. The corresponding Z_x therefore appears as

$$Z_x = \frac{p^2 + 2p}{p^2 + 2p + 4}. \tag{11–11}$$

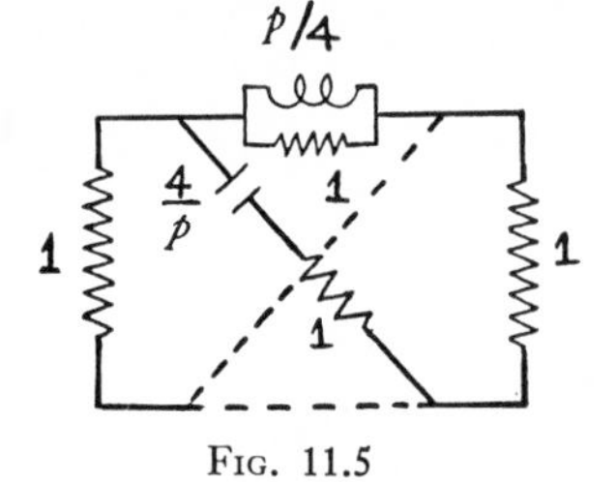

FIG. 11.5

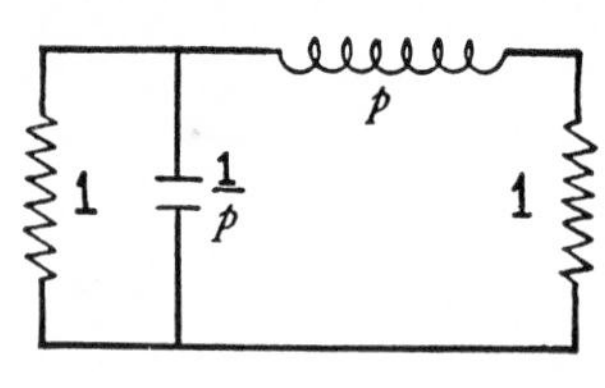

FIG. 11.6

It will be noticed that Z_x has a zero at the origin. We can conveniently begin the process of representing the impedance with a susceptance reduction at this point. With this beginning the complete network is easily determined. In admittance form, it appears as

$$Y_x = \frac{2}{p} + \frac{p/2}{1 + p/2}, \tag{11–12}$$

which represents an inductance in parallel with a series combination of a capacity and a resistance. The lattice is shown by Fig. 11.7.

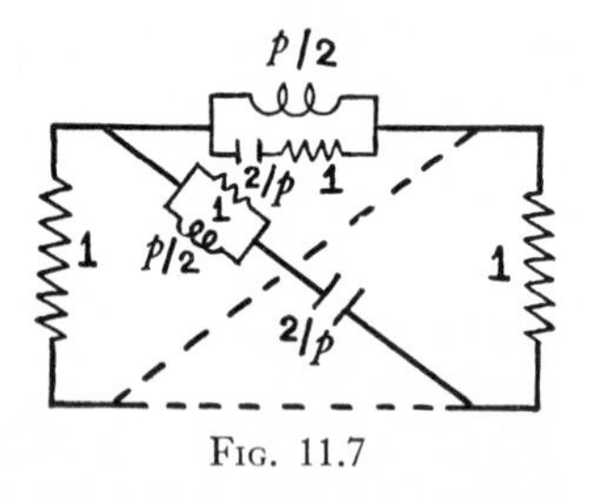

FIG. 11.7

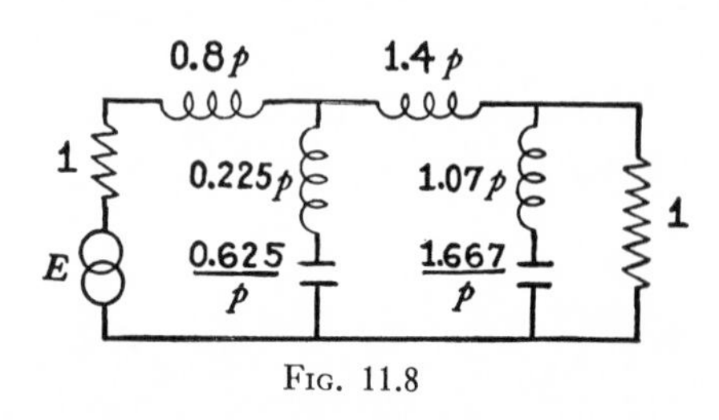

FIG. 11.8

The structure of Fig. 11.6 can evidently be regarded as an elementary filter. If we begin with more complicated filters the general procedure can still be carried out, but the degree of the impedance expression is higher and the numerical work becomes much more onerous. It is convenient, however, to include one example of a more complicated filter in order to pave the way for the description of the alternative procedure given in the next chapter. The structure is shown by Fig. 11.8. It is a conventional one and one-half section low-pass filter with a cut-off at $\omega = 1$ and with the loss characteristic shown by Fig. 11.9.* The transfer impedance expression, as

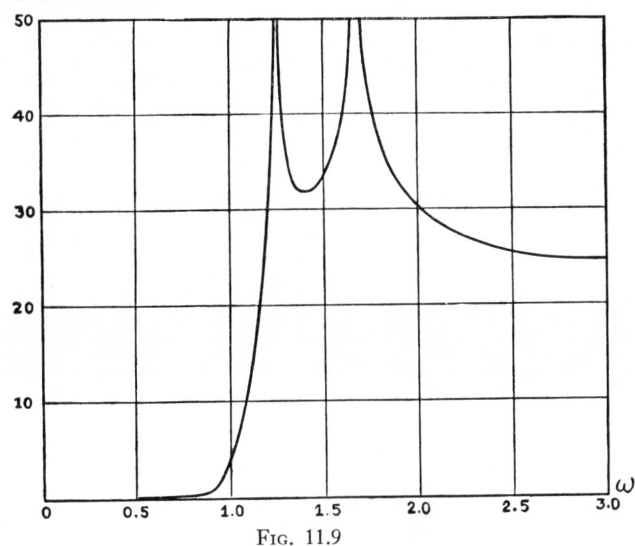

FIG. 11.9

determined by the ordinary mesh computation methods used for filters, is given by

$$Z_T = 2e^{\theta} = \frac{1.654p^5 + 4.264p^4 + 6.576p^3 + 6.84p^2 + 4.4p + 2}{0.23p^4 + p^2 + 1} \cdot \quad (11\text{–}13)$$

The corresponding Z_x is obtained as

$$Z_x = \frac{1.1p(1 + 1.1p + 1.495p^2 + 0.864p^3 + 0.376p^4)}{1 + 1.1p + 2.21p^2 + 1.644p^3 + 1.181p^4 + 0.413p^5} \cdot \quad (11\text{–}14)$$

Following Brune's methods this can be developed in the form shown by Fig. 11.10.

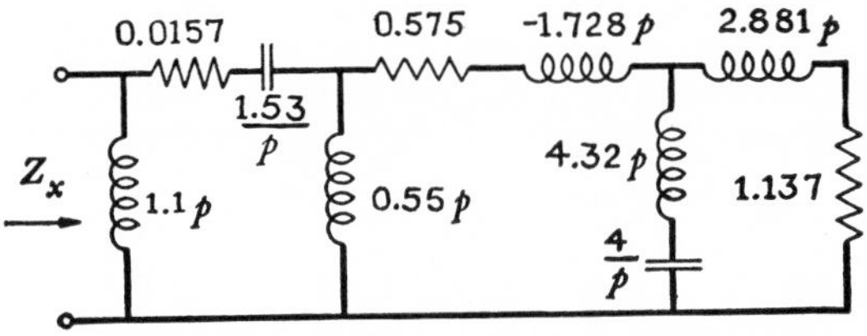

FIG. 11.10

* The filter consists of a full section with $m = 0.8$ and a half section with $m = 0.6$. The transfer impedance and loss characteristics shown later correspond to the exact element values for a structure of this type, rather than to the approximate values given by Fig. 11.8.

11.5. *Loss and Phase Reduction of the Transfer Impedance*

In discussing two-terminal networks, it was pointed out that the resistance and reactance characteristics could ordinarily be reduced to certain minimum values independently of one another. For example, we could always subtract resistance from a network until the resistance characteristic became zero at some point on the real frequency axis. Correspondingly, we could always subtract pure reactance elements until all the poles at real frequencies were eliminated. Similar transformations are possible in four-terminal networks if we consider attenuation and phase shift instead of resistance and reactance.

The possibilities of attenuation reduction follow immediately from the discussion of the previous section. Evidently, the proof given there remains valid if the transfer loss is changed by any constant, provided only that it does not become negative at any point on the real frequency axis. This can be expressed by the

Theorem: A passive transfer loss and phase will continue to meet the conditions of physical realizability in passive networks if the transfer loss is diminished by any real constant as long as it does not become negative at any real frequency.

A transfer function will be called a *minimum loss* or *minimum attenuation* expression if the minimum transfer loss on the real frequency axis is zero, so that no further diminution is possible without violating the passive conditions.

The phase shift reduction of the network requires a more elaborate discussion. In this reduction the analogue of a pole on the real frequency axis in a driving point impedance is a pole anywhere in the right half of the p plane in the expression for Z_T, while the analogue of a two-terminal network of pure reactances is an all-pass phase correcting structure.

In order to show the correspondence in detail, let us suppose that one of the poles, b_j, of Z_T in (11–3) is found on the positive real p axis. Z_T will evidently be unchanged if we replace the corresponding factor, $p - b_j$, by $p + b_j$, and at the same time multiply the complete expression by $(p + b_j)/(p - b_j)$. This leads to

$$Z_T = Z'_T \frac{p + b_j}{p - b_j} \tag{11–15}$$

where Z'_T represents Z_T after $p - b_j$ is replaced by $p + b_j$. But since p is imaginary on the real frequency axis while b_j is a real constant, the absolute value of $(p + b_j)/(p - b_j)$ at real frequencies must be unity. Thus the minimum transfer loss of Z'_T is the same as that of Z_T, and it is obvious that Z'_T meets all the requirements of physical realizability if Z_T is physically realizable. Moreover, it is apparent from (11–6) that the quantity $(p + b_j)/(p - b_j)$ can be identified with an all-pass phase correcting section of the type shown by Fig. 11.11, in which $Z_x = R_2(b_j/p)$. Since the multiplication of Z'_T and $(p + b_j)/(p - b_j)$ is equivalent to the addition of the corresponding loss and phase characteristics, Z_T can thus be constructed by combining the network shown in Fig. 11.11 in tandem with a network representing Z'_T. This is illustrated by Fig. 11.12.

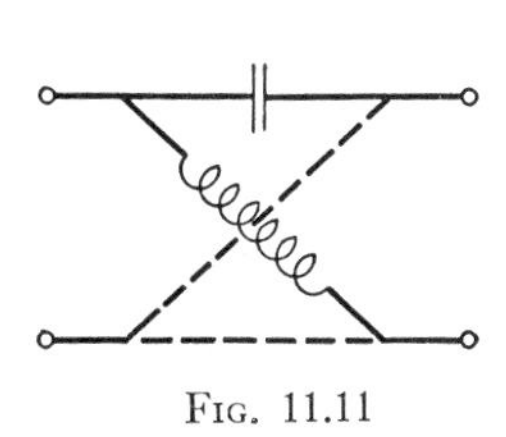

FIG. 11.11

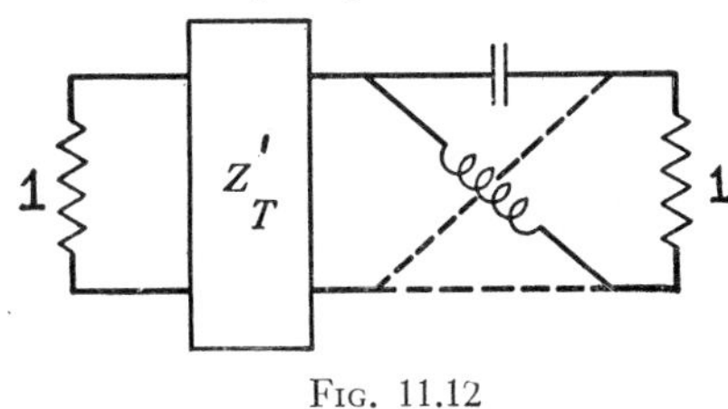

FIG. 11.12

The elimination of a pair of conjugate complex poles in the right-hand half-plane can be performed in the same manner. If we represent the poles as $b_{j1} \pm ib_{j2}$ the equation corresponding to (11–15) is

$$Z_T = Z'_T \frac{(p + b_{j1} + ib_{j2})(p + b_{j1} - ib_{j2})}{(p - b_{j1} - ib_{j2})(p - b_{j1} + ib_{j2})}$$

$$= Z'_T \frac{1 + \dfrac{2b_{j1}p}{p^2 + (b_{j1}^2 + b_{j2}^2)}}{1 - \dfrac{2b_{j1}p}{p^2 + (b_{j1}^2 + b_{j2}^2)}}. \tag{11–16}$$

Evidently, the expression $2b_{j1}p/[p^2 + (b_{j1}^2 + b_{j2}^2)]$ in this equation represents an anti-resonant circuit and can be identified with Z_x/R_2 in (11–6). The corresponding phase shifting network is therefore of the type shown by Fig. 11.13.* By continuing step-by-step in this way all the poles in the right-hand half of the plane can be replaced by their negatives in the left half of the plane. We will eventually secure a number of structures of the types illustrated by Figs. 11.11 and 11.13 in tandem with a network whose transfer imped-

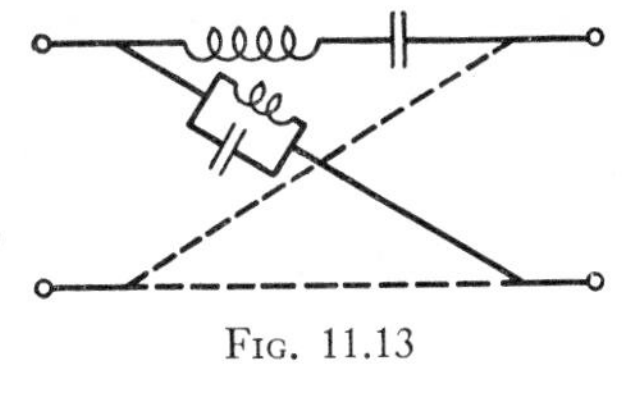

FIG. 11.13

* In Fig. 11.13 the anti-resonant branch appears in the diagonal rather than the series branch. It is apparent from an inspection of either the lattice structure itself or equations (11–4) and (11–5) that interchanging the series and diagonal branches of the lattice merely reverses the sign of the output current, without otherwise affecting the situation. In view of this simple relation no systematic attempt to distinguish between series and diagonal branches is made in future discussion.

ance has zeros and poles only in the left half of the plane. In accordance with the definition enunciated in Chapter VII, the residual network will be called a *minimum phase shift* structure.

This discussion has emphasized the substitution of poles in the left half-plane for poles in the right half-plane because the minimum phase condition will play an especially important role in our future analysis. It is, however, equally possible to transfer poles in the other direction. Each time a real pole or a pair of conjugate complex poles is moved from the left half-plane to the right half-plane the phase shift is, of course, increased by an amount corresponding to one all-pass section. This is of some practical importance because the complexity of the network will depend in general upon the number of the poles and not upon the sides of the plane in which they appear.* By permitting any of the poles to lie on either side of the plane, therefore, we can secure some control of the phase characteristics of equalizers having given loss characteristics without adding to the number of elements in the structure. This general possibility can be formulated as the

Theorem: A passive transfer impedance will continue to meet the requirements of physical realizability in a passive network if any of its real poles or any pair of its conjugate complex poles are replaced by their negatives. The change is equivalent to increasing or decreasing the transfer function by the phase shift of a corresponding all-pass section.

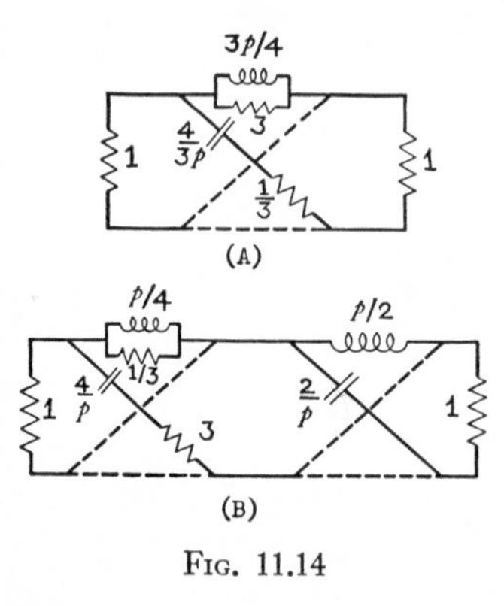

FIG. 11.14

A simple example of these transformations is given by the function

$$e^{\theta} = -2\frac{p+1}{p-2}. \qquad (11\text{–}17)$$

Upon making use of (11–7) and assuming that $R_1 = R_2 = 1$, for simplicity, the corresponding network is found in the form shown by Fig. 11.14*A*. Its attenuation and phase characteristics are shown by Fig. 11.15 and the solid line in Fig. 11.16, respectively. To perform the phase reduction, the function is written as

$$e^{\theta} = \left[-2\frac{p+1}{p+2}\right]\left[\frac{p+2}{p-2}\right]. \qquad (11\text{–}18)$$

* It is assumed here that the structure will be built as a lattice. With unbalanced configurations the statement is still true in a purely theoretical sense, but changes in the locations of the poles may affect the ease with which a circuit with positive elements can be found. This question is discussed in the next chapter.

The two terms on the right-hand side correspond respectively to the equalizer and phase corrector in Fig. 11.14B.* The attenuation characteristic, which, of course, is furnished entirely by the equalizer, is still that given by Fig. 11.15. The phase characteristics of the two components are shown

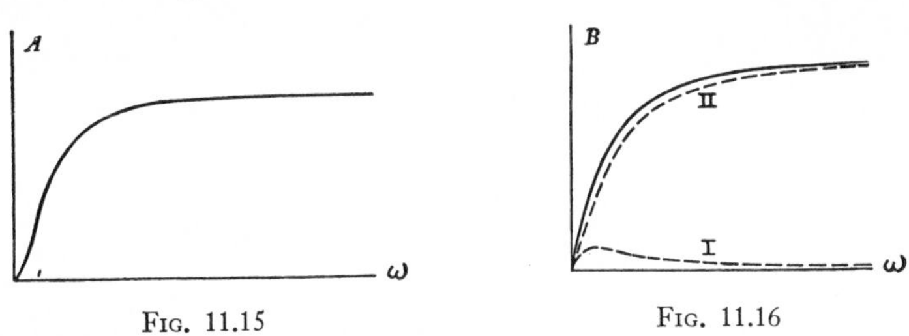

Fig. 11.15

Fig. 11.16

respectively by the broken lines I and II in Fig. 11.16. In this circuit there are only two possible phase characteristics which can be associated with the additional loss characteristic without the use of extra elements. In an equalizer whose transfer impedance contained more poles, however, the number of options is evidently much greater.†

11.6. *Properties of All-Pass Structures*

In addition to the specific networks shown on Figs. 11.11 and 11.13, all-pass networks can also be constructed in a variety of other forms. For example, it is clear that a lattice will be an all-pass network provided its Z_x and Z_y branches are inverse reactances of any complexity. Since a purely reactive Z_x will always be an odd function of frequency, it is easy to see from equation (11–6) that any such structure will have the property, which we previously established for the simple networks of Figs. 11.11 and 11.13, that *the zeros and poles of the transfer impedance will be negatives of one another.* This will be taken as a definition of what is meant by an all-pass network. A typical arrangement is shown by Fig. 11.17. The zeros are represented by circles and the poles by crosses, corresponding zeros and poles being identified by corresponding letters P, Q, etc.

In a broad sense, the all-pass sections play the same role in four-terminal

* As the reader may have observed, replacing a pole by its negative, as in equation (11–15), reverses the sign of Z'_T with respect to Z_T at zero frequency. This is compensated for by a similar reversal at zero frequency in the extracted all-pass section. Since it is usually desirable to keep the phase shifts of all components equal at zero frequency for comparative purposes, however, additional phase reversals to zero have been introduced in both networks of Fig. 11.14B by interchanging their Z_x and Z_y branches.

† For additional examples of optional phase characteristics in simple circuits see O. J. Zobel, "Distortion Correction in Electrical Circuits," *B.S.T.J.*, July, 1928.

network theory as pure reactance networks play in two-terminal theory. In their respective fields, both types of structures represent the essential ways we have available for changing the imaginary component of a network characteristic without affecting its real component. Although all-pass sections of great complexity may exist, the fact that their zeros and poles must occur in positive and negative pairs makes it possible to treat them very simply, since it is obvious that the individual combinations of zeros and poles can be represented separately by elementary networks of the types shown by Figs. 11.11 and 11.13. This can be stated as the

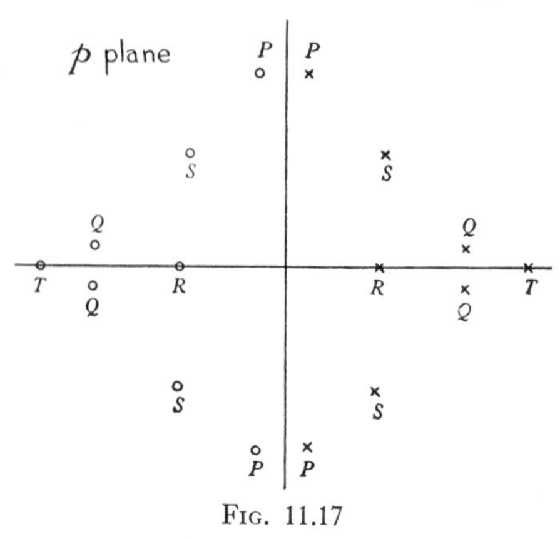

FIG. 11.17

Theorem: Any all-pass network is equivalent to a number of first and second degree all-pass networks in tandem.

An illustration showing the resolution of an all-pass network of the fifth degree (i.e., having five zeros and five poles in its transfer impedance) into simpler constituents is shown by Fig. 11.18.

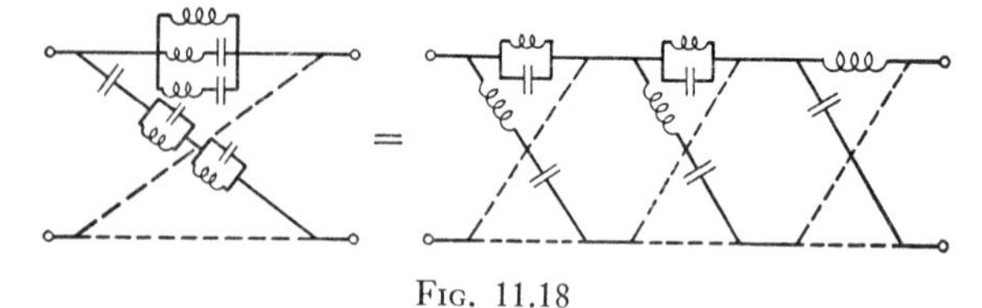
FIG. 11.18

From the point of view of the general analogy between all-pass networks and two-terminal reactances this proposition may be said to correspond to the theorem that a general two-terminal reactance can always be represented by a number of simple anti-resonant circuits in series, as illustrated, for example, by Fig. 9.8 of Chapter IX. The two-element structure of Fig. 11.13 may thus be said to correspond to an anti-resonant circuit, while the single element structure of Fig. 11.11 is equivalent to a single coil or condenser in series. Since the development in terms of all-pass networks may lead to a number of simple networks in tandem, the analogy is not quite exact. The formal analogy can be continued, however, if we combine the simple structures in pairs to secure two-element networks, by means of an equivalence described in the next chapter. In essentials, the parallelism fails at only one point. In two-terminal network theory, the existence of inverse relationships allows us to choose between a development in terms of a number of anti-resonant circuits in series and a development in terms of a number of resonant circuits in parallel. In all-pass structures, on the other hand, there appears to be no equivalent to this inverse relationship, and pairs of reciprocal developments therefore do not exist.

The analogy between two-terminal reactances and all-pass structures can be extended to include their energy relationships also. Corresponding to equation (9–16) of Chapter IX, for example, it is possible to establish the expression

$$\frac{dB}{d\omega} = \frac{2}{R_0}(T + V), \qquad (11\text{–}19)$$

where B represents phase shift, R_0 represents the image impedance of the network, and the energy functions are evaluated on the assumption that a current of unit maximum amplitude flows into the structure.

Since the energy functions are necessarily positive quantities, it follows from the equation in Chapter IX that the reactance of a physical reactive network is always an increasing function of frequency. Correspondingly, we see from equation (11–19) that the phase characteristic of an all-pass structure must always have a positive slope. Typical characteristics are shown by Fig. 11.19.* Curve I corresponds to a " single-element " section of the type shown by Fig. 11.11. With only one element in the series branch of the lattice, sections of this type have only one design parameter, and this is consumed in fixing the unit of frequency. Thus the characteristics of all sections of this type are of the same general shape. They satisfy the equation $B = 2 \tan^{-1} kf$.†

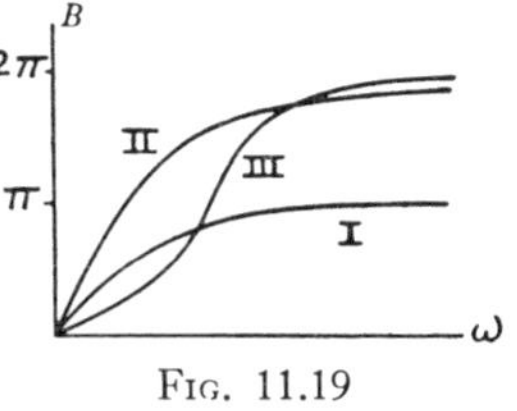

Fig. 11.19

In the two-element sections we can regard the unit of frequency as being established by the resonances of the lattice branches. This leaves one parameter which can be employed to control the shape of the curve. The additional parameter can be taken as the relative stiffness of the anti-resonant branch impedance, say, or as the phase angle of the complex roots and poles of the transfer function, the relation between the two

* In Fig. 11.19 the phase characteristics are taken as zero at zero frequency as a matter of convenience. With the usual conventions, the phase shift at zero in the structures of Figs. 11.11 and 11.13 is actually $\pm\pi$. This difference, of course, is only a phase reversal such as might be secured by interchanging either the input or output terminals.

† For a more complete discussion of the design of all-pass structures, and of their uses in communication systems, see S. P. Mead, " Phase Distortion and Phase Distortion Correction," *B.S.T.J.*, April, 1928, or H. Nyquist, " Phase Compensating Network," U. S. Patent No. 1,770,422, July 15, 1930.

being easily understood from (11–16). If the anti-resonant circuit is relatively stiff the roots and poles will be nearly real,* as typified by the points Q in Fig. 11.17, and the phase characteristic will be nearly equal to twice the phase characteristic of some single-element structure. This is illustrated by Curve II of Fig. 11.19. At the other extreme, an anti-resonant circuit of low stiffness leads to zeros and poles which are almost pure imaginary, such as the points P in Fig. 11.17. The zeros and poles are substantially opposite the point on the real frequency axis at which the anti-resonance occurs and the phase characteristic changes rapidly as we move along the axis in this vicinity. This is illustrated by Curve III of Fig. 11.19.

11.7. *Minimum Phase Shift Networks*

In four-terminal network theory a minimum phase shift network is similar to a two-terminal impedance after all the poles on the real frequency axis have been extracted. Once the minimum condition has been reached, we can make no further change in the phase characteristic without at the same time affecting the attenuation. Since both the zeros and the poles of a minimum phase transfer impedance must be found in the left half of the p plane, the analytical restrictions on such an impedance are the same as they are for a two-terminal impedance, except that there is no necessity that real frequency poles be simple or that the real component of the function be positive at all points on the real frequency axis.

Since minimum phase shift networks will be postulated frequently in later discussion, it is important to know when a structure is actually of minimum phase shift type. This is not always an easy question to answer. Some assistance, however, can be obtained from two general rules. The first can be expressed as the

Theorem: A transfer impedance which has poles of multiplicity n_1 and n_2 at zero and infinite frequency respectively is of minimum phase shift type if and only if the net phase displacement between zero and infinity is $(n_1 + n_2)(\pi/2)$ radians.

In particular, if the attenuations at zero and infinity are both finite the net phase change must be zero. In a non-minimum circuit the net change is, of course, always positive. The theorem is easily established from a consideration of the Nyquist diagram of the structure.

The second distinction is structural. It will be recalled that the poles of the transfer impedance are frequencies at which the current delivered

* With a very stiff anti-resonant circuit all the zeros and poles are real. In this case, of course, the two-element structure can be represented by two single-element structures and contributes nothing new.

to the load is zero. In a ladder network, however, the current delivered to the load impedance can become zero only because some shunt impedance becomes zero or because some series impedance becomes infinite. Since the zeros and poles of the branch impedances must be found in the left half of the plane if the branch impedances are passive, this leads at once to the

Theorem: Any passive ladder network is a minimum phase shift structure.

This, of course, includes the transmission through a series of unilateral vacuum tubes with ladder-type interstages.

Circuits which are broadly not of the ladder type are those in which the current can reach the load by alternative paths. This is shown symbolically by Fig. 11.20. Specific examples, in addition to the lattice network, are given by the bridged-T and the ladder with inductive coupling shown by

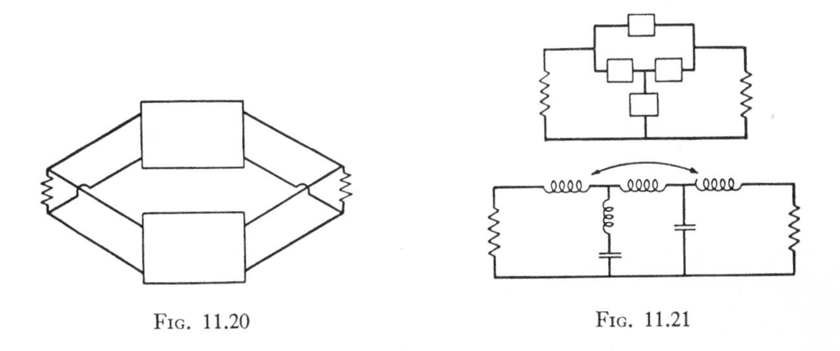

Fig. 11.20 Fig. 11.21

Fig. 11.21. In such structures the poles of the transfer impedance are not necessarily coincident with zeros or poles of the branch impedances. Zero received current can also be obtained because the currents delivered to the load by various paths cancel out. The poles are consequently not necessarily restricted to the left half-plane and the network may have a non-minimum phase characteristic. Whether or not the given network actually has such characteristics of course depends upon the particular values of the elements it happens to contain. In default of any other remedy it may be necessary to compute the poles directly.

The structures just discussed can be described broadly as bridge-type circuits. The lattice itself is, of course, a true Wheatstone bridge while the other structures at least depend upon a balance. The discussion can thus be looked upon as a statement of the essential design distinction between a bridge and a ladder or series-shunt circuit. Evidently, the distinction is one between the available phase characteristics for any given loss characteristic. The possible loss characteristics by themselves are theoretically the same for the two types of structures.*

In practical engineering, this last conclusion should be qualified in one respect. As we saw in the preceding chapter, the introduction of parasitic dissipation is equivalent to a displacement of all the critical frequencies of the network, including its frequencies of infinite attenuation, slightly to the left in the p plane. If a network is originally of the minimum phase shift type, therefore, it cannot produce infinite attenuation at real frequencies† when parasitic dissipation is taken into account. A non-minimum phase shift network, on the other hand, can be assigned frequencies of infinite attenuation which will fall on the real frequency axis after the dissipation shift is made. A simple example is furnished by the phase correcting section of Fig. 11.13. At the resonance frequency both branches of this structure become resistances when dissipation is taken into account. With proper proportioning the two resistances can be made equal, so that the structure will give infinite attenuation at this frequency. In this particular circuit, of course, the proper relation will normally lead to extreme values of the elements. In other structures, however, the same result can be secured with more reasonable element sizes. This use of non-minimum phase shift networks is of importance chiefly in filter problems and similar situations, where extremely sharp selectivity may be required.

11.8. *Representation of Active Transfer Impedances*

In dealing with driving point impedance and admittance functions it appeared that the essential distinction between active and passive functions could be represented by the addition of a negative resistance in series or parallel with the rest of the network. The negative resistance takes account of the fact that the real component of a passive driving point function must be positive at real frequencies and allows all the rest of the structure to be built as a passive circuit.

Active transfer impedances can be treated in a similar way. Evidently, they are exactly the same as passive transfer impedances except that it is not necessary to assume, as was done in connection with (11–3), that the absolute magnitude of the function is so chosen that the transfer loss is positive at all real frequencies. This limitation can be overcome by adding a negative loss, or, in other words, an ideal flat gain amplifier, to the passive circuit. In the driving point discussion, however, it was necessary to consider alternative series and parallel combinations of a negative resist-

* This can be shown rigorously by the methods used in the next chapter if the absolute level of loss is not regarded as important.

† Aside possibly from zero and infinity, depending largely upon the way in which dissipation is supposed to take place.

ance and a passive circuit, as indicated by Figs. 9.23 and 9.24 of Chapter IX, to take account of the distinction between an impedance and an admittance specification of the complete structure. In discussing transfer functions the passive and active constituents can be placed directly in tandem with either analysis, as shown by Fig. 11.22. This result can be summarized as the

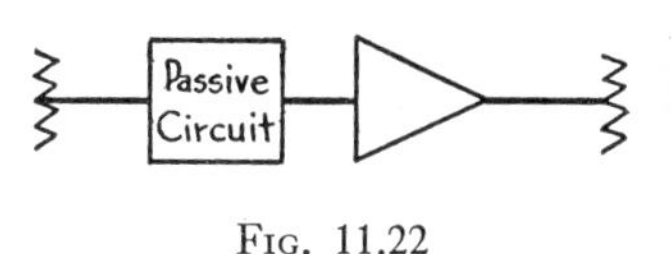

FIG. 11.22

Theorem: A general transfer immittance function can always be represented by a passive circuit and an ideal flat amplifier in tandem.

This theorem is of service chiefly in resolving apparent paradoxes in active circuit theory. Since all this analysis depends fundamentally upon the postulate that the network is stable, we can at once suspect that any particularly wonderful or unusual transmission characteristic, departing radically from the characteristics of ordinary experience, was computed from an unstable circuit. We may take as an example the problem of constructing a negative all-pass network or a negative length of line.* Since the gain of a feedback amplifier is the same as the loss of its β circuit in the region of high feedback, we should be able to simulate such a characteristic over a reasonable frequency range by building an amplifier with a corresponding positive structure in its feedback circuit. We might also attempt to obtain such a characteristic through the use of one or more negative elements. Figure 11.23, for example, shows the equivalent of a negative all-pass circuit secured with the help of a negative resistance.

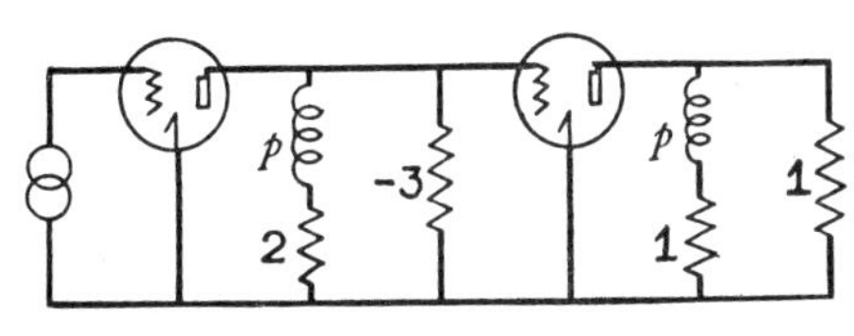

FIG. 11.23

There is nothing actually impossible about the problem of simulating either a negative all-pass section or a negative length of line over a modest frequency range. Either characteristic can, in fact, be approximated by ordinary equalizers. If we use equalizers, however, we know that this apparent reversal of normal behavior at low frequencies is obtained only at the cost of a tremendous change in the nature of the characteristic beyond the range of approximation. The change is in the direction of a decreasing loss at high frequencies and is usually sufficient to nullify whatever result we might hope to secure from such a device. If we simulate a negative line, for example, the envelope delay at low frequencies will be negative, but the

* That is, a structure whose attenuation and phase characteristics at every frequency are exactly the negatives of those of an ordinary all-pass network or transmission line.

response to the high frequency components of any suddenly impressed signal will be so greatly enhanced that the low frequency delay is not a true measure of the actual delay of the signal. Whatever the signal may be, the circuit will not actually exhibit a transient at negative time. To take a perhaps less obvious situation, we may suppose that either the line or the all-pass structure is to be used to cancel the phase shift of a low-pass filter. If the phase shift is actually cancelled the change in loss at high frequencies is so great that the original discriminating properties of the filters are also cancelled.

The point of the theorem is that limitations exactly similar to these must hold in an active circuit, *provided the circuit is stable.* In the feedback amplifier representing a negative line or a negative all-pass network, for example, any choice of μ and β which will provide the representation and also give a stable circuit must lead to an actual gain $\mu/(1 - \mu\beta)$ which rises beyond the useful band in the same violent and uncontrollable way as does the equalizer characteristic. A circuit like that of Fig. 11.23, which has a constant gain characteristic, is unstable, as we can easily see by inspection of the resonance around the first interstage loop.

As an example of another aspect of the theorem, we may consider the provision of a very narrow band-pass characteristic by the use of a very narrow band-elimination structure in the β circuit of a feedback amplifier. In practice, a very narrow band-pass characteristic is not obtainable with purely passive elements, whereas the inverse characteristic can be secured fairly easily by the use of some type of bridge circuit varying rapidly through a balance point. The theorem, however, states flatly that the final amplifier transmission characteristics can be duplicated, except for a constant loss, by a passive circuit. The point here is that the theorem is stated for idealized passive elements. It takes no account of limitations due to element sizes or, what is more important for this problem, limitations due to parasitic dissipation in the elements. The advantage of the feedback design, in a broad sense, is that it provides an easy and convenient way of supplying energy to neutralize element dissipation.

11.9. *Constituents of General Driving Point and Transfer Functions*

Most of the work of the remaining chapters is based upon a discussion of the relations which must necessarily exist between the real and imaginary components of driving point and transfer functions if the functions are to represent physical networks. This discussion is complicated by the fact that no altogether exact and universal relation between the two components can exist. For example, if we begin with a given resistance characteristic we can always secure a variety of corresponding reactance characteristics by adding pure reactance networks to the circuit. Chapter IX and the present chapter have been devoted chiefly to an examination of the ways in which the real and imaginary components of driving point and transfer functions can be varied independently, in an effort to clear up ambiguities of this sort before proceeding with the general problem. The results of both chapters are summarized in Fig. 11.24.

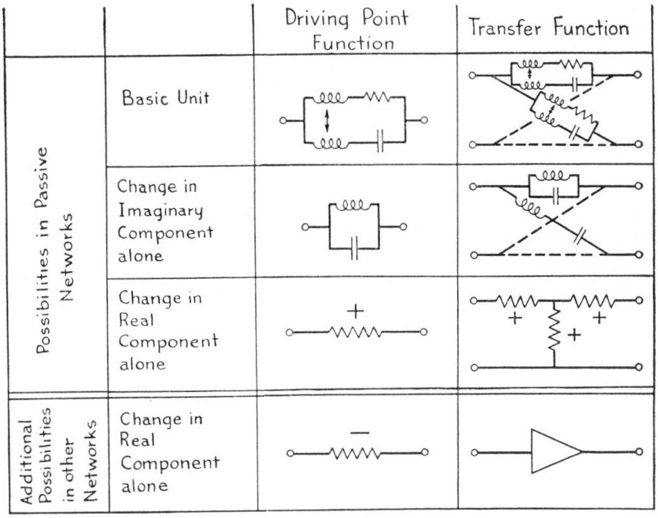

		Driving Point Function	Transfer Function
Possibilities in Passive Networks	Basic Unit		
	Change in Imaginary Component alone		
	Change in Real Component alone		
Additional Possibilities in other Networks	Change in Real Component alone		

Fig. 11.24

The top of the figure shows a minimum resistance and minimum reactance structure in the driving point column and a minimum loss and minimum phase structure in the transfer column. The particular circuits shown utilize the simplest form of Brune's network. More complicated functions can be represented by extending the network. In virtue of the discussion of Chapter X, however, we can also represent more complicated driving point functions, to within an additive resistance, by summing up a number of the elementary structures. It is shown in the next chapter that a corresponding result holds for transfer functions. The networks thus represent, in some sense, the principal ways in which physical driving point and transfer impedances can behave. In these networks, moreover, the real and imaginary components of the driving point or transfer function are uniquely related. Granted either component, the other can be found exactly.

The remaining portions of the figure show the possible ways of changing one component of the driving point or transfer function of the basic network without affecting the other. Thus we can change the imaginary component by the addition of anti-resonant networks or all-pass sections, as indicated by the second line of the figure. The real component can be changed by the addition of a positive resistance or a positive loss, as indicated by the third line. Finally, if we include active elements as well as passive elements the real component of the original functions can be changed by the addition of a negative resistance or a negative loss. If the diagram is allowed to symbolize parallel as well as series combinations of driving point units, the list gives a complete statement of all possible* driving point and transfer functions.

* It must be remembered, of course, that the analysis has been simplified at various points by ignoring multiple poles, zeros and poles exactly on the real frequency axis, etc.

CHAPTER XII

Topics in the Design of Equalizers

12.1. *Introduction*

This chapter continues the discussion of transfer functions, with special reference to equalizers, in terms of the foundation laid down in Chapter XI. The chapter is intended as a summary* of miscellaneous methods and ideas of interest in practical equalizer design. It is thus broadly similar to Chapter X, which contained a similar summary for driving point functions, and like Chapter X it can be omitted without injury to the general theoretical development of the book. If it is undertaken, however, it will facilitate study to recognize that much of the material it contains is essentially parallel to the material in Chapter X, except that attenuation and phase shift replace resistance and reactance.

12.2. *Complementary Characteristics*

In discussing two-terminal impedances, it was shown that if a given impedance is of the minimum reactance type it is always possible to find a second impedance such that the sum of the two will be a constant resistance. A similar relation can be developed for minimum phase shift transfer functions, if we exclude the limiting case for which points of infinite attenuation occur on the real frequency axis itself. With this restriction, both the zeros and poles of the original transfer impedance must be found within the left half of the p plane, excluding its boundary. The reciprocal transfer impedance, which, of course, will produce complementary phase and attenuation characteristics, will evidently have the same properties. This allows us to state the

Theorem: Corresponding to any minimum phase shift transfer function having no poles of attenuation on the real frequency axis there exists a complementary function such that the sum of the two gives a constant loss and zero phase shift at all frequencies. The complementary function will be realizable in a passive network if the final constant loss is at least equal to the maximum loss of the original function on the real frequency axis.

* There is no existing treatment of equalizers which covers all the ground of the present chapter. For a much more thorough treatment of many of the topics, however, see O. J. Zobel, loc. cit.

A simple example is given by Fig. 12.1.

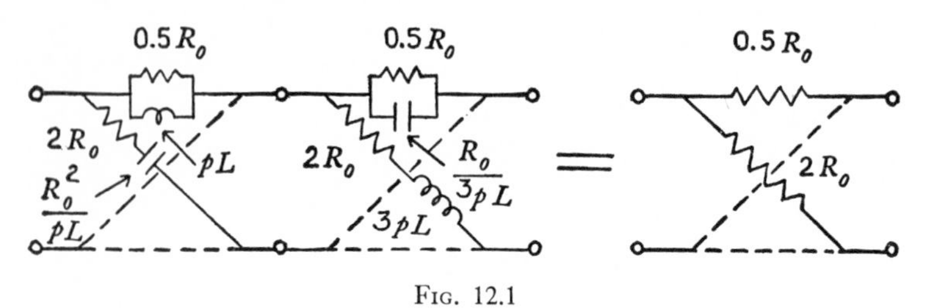

FIG. 12.1

12.3. *Partial Product Expansion of a General Transfer Impedance*

In discussing two-terminal impedances we considered two general ways in which the impedance might be represented. The first led to the construction of the complete impedance as a single elaborate Brune network. We also saw, however, that it is possible to represent the impedance as a combination of much simpler networks in series, by means of a partial fraction expansion, provided the resistance component of the total characteristic is sufficiently great. In a somewhat similar fashion, it is possible to replace the single elaborate lattice which we have heretofore used to represent a transfer impedance by a number of simpler structures in tandem, provided a sufficiently high constant attenuation can be tolerated. Since a constant change in attenuation is frequently not of great significance, this feature of the process is not as important as it was in the discussion of two-terminal impedances.

The expansion into the tandem section configuration can be obtained merely by rewriting the original Z_T of equation (11–3) in Chapter XI as the expression

$$Z_T = \left[k_1 \frac{(p - a_1) \cdots (p - a_j)}{(p - b_1) \cdots (p - b_j)}\right]\left[k_2 \frac{(p - a_{j+1}) \cdots (p - a_n)}{(p - b_{j+1}) \cdots (p - b_n)}\right], \quad (12\text{–}1)$$

where the product $k_1 k_2$ is equal to the k of the original equation. Evidently each of the terms in the right-hand side of this expression is itself of the proper form to represent a transfer impedance. The equation thus suggests that the original transfer impedance can be represented by two networks in tandem, each corresponding to one of the terms in (12–1). The representation will be physical if we satisfy two conditions. The first is that the original k, which fixes the constant loss of the network, must be large enough to allow each of the constituent networks to be assigned a positive attenuation on the real frequency axis. Since the constituent networks will not ordinarily have attenuation minima at the same frequencies, this implies in general that the composite network will exhibit a greater fixed loss than would be necessary to construct the structure as a single lattice. The second condition is merely that both members of any conjugate complex pair of zeros or poles must be assigned either to one network or the other. Since the order in which the zeros and poles in (12–1) are arranged is otherwise arbitrary, and no special requirement need be placed upon the relative numbers of the factors assigned to the two constituent networks, these requirements still allow us to break up the complete structure in a tremendous variety of ways.

The decomposition of the network into a number of simpler structures in tandem can evidently be continued by the decomposition of either of the structures first found. For theoretical purposes particular interest attaches to the result secured when this process is carried as far as possible. In this event, many of the final structures will be of the first degree, with a transfer impedance expression containing a single real zero and a single real pole. Since a pair of conjugate zeros or poles must be kept together, some of the final structures may also have transfer impedances of the second degree. It is easy to see, however, that no more complicated cases need be considered. This result can be formulated as the

Theorem: Any physically realizable transfer impedance can be represented, to within a constant loss, by a combination of passive constant resistance lattice sections in tandem, each of the constituent sections being of at most the second degree.

A list of elementary first and second degree structures, corresponding to the elementary transfer impedances to which this reduction may lead, is shown by Figs. 12.2 and 12.3. In each instance it is supposed that the elementary structure will have zero loss at one frequency. In general, the physical configurations of the networks might be altered appreciably if greater losses were allowed. As an aid to the use of the structures in practical design, the figures also include rough plots of their attenuation and phase characteristics, the attenuation and phase being represented, respectively, by the solid and broken line curves at the right of the figures.

The two necessary first degree networks are given by structures III and IV of Fig. 12.2. It will be seen that together these two structures include all possible arrangements of one real zero and one real pole. Figure 12.2 also includes the two phase correcting sections shown previously in Figs. 11.11 and 11.13 of Chapter XI. In view of their presence we can assume that the attenuating structures are of the minimum phase shift type. All the structures can, however, be assigned non-minimum phase shift characteristics if we so desire. Since the physical configurations of the structures remain the same when they are assigned non-minimum characteristics, this is evidently of importance if we wish to simulate a non-minimum phase shift transfer impedance without using unnecessary elements.

The second degree structures are shown by Fig. 12.3. Together, they are sufficient to represent all possible second degree transfer impedances, except for certain cases in which both the zeros and poles are real. These cases are omitted since, of course, any such transfer impedance can be represented by two first degree networks.* As Fig. 12.3 indicates, struc-

	Structure	Requirements for Physical Realizability	Element Values	Typical Attenuation and Phase Characteristics
I	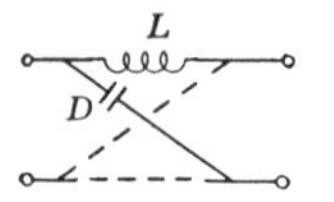 L, D	$a = -b$	$L = \frac{R_o}{b}$ $D = R_o^2/L$	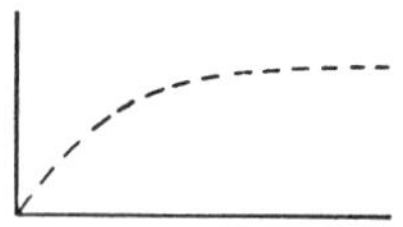
II	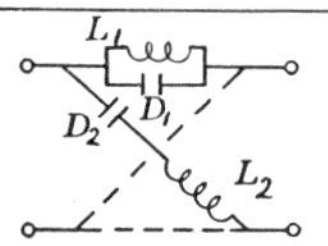 L_1, D_1, D_2, L_2	$a_1 = -b_1$ $a_2 = -b_2$	$L_1 = R_o(\frac{1}{b_1} + \frac{1}{b_2})$ $D_1 = R_o(b_1 + b_2)$ $L_2 = R_o^2/D_1$ $D_2 = R_o^2/L_1$	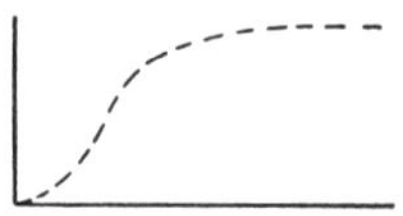
III	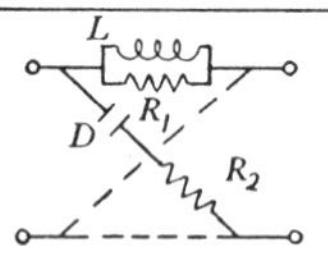 L, R_1, D, R_2	$\lvert a\rvert \leq \lvert b\rvert$	$R_1 = \frac{b-a}{b+a} R_o$ $L = \frac{a-b}{2ab} R_o$ $R_2 = R_o^2/R_1$ $D = R_o^2/L$	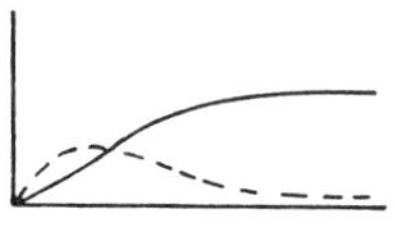
IV	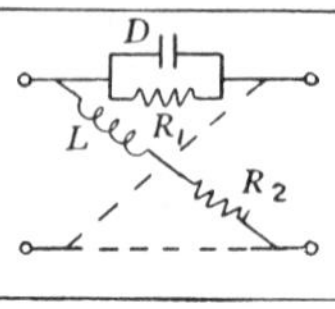 D, L, R_1, R_2	$\lvert a\rvert \geq \lvert b\rvert$	$R_1 = -\frac{b-a}{b+a} R_o$ $D = \frac{1}{2}(b-a)R_o$ $R_2 = R_o^2/R_1$ $L = R_o^2/D$	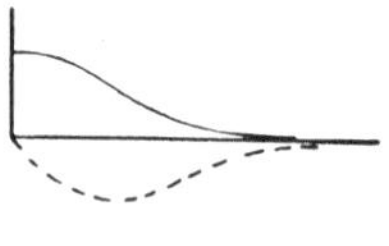

FIG. 12.2

tures V and VI will usually be required when the poles are complex and the zeros are real, or nearly so, and VII and VIII are appropriate for complex zeros and real poles, while any one of the structures may be needed when both poles and zeros are complex. This correlation, however, is only approximate.

* Naturally, corresponding second degree structures can also be found. In order to cover all possible second degree functions we must include in Fig. 12.3 two additional networks, which are similar to V and VI except that the reactive elements in each lattice branch are both inductances or both capacities. The conditions for physical realizability for these two networks in terms of the a's and b's are the same as for the corresponding network V or VI having a reactive element of the same type in parallel with the Z_x branch.

The element values of the first degree networks are given by explicit formulae in Fig. 12.2. The element values of the second degree networks are less easily written. For the structures of V and VI they can, however, be computed, and are shown, for the Z_x branch, by Figs. 12.4 and 12.5. In the Brune networks represented by structures VII and VIII reasonably explicit formulae are hardly possible. It is simplest to give formulae for the lattice branch impedance as a whole, leaving the individual elements to be

	Structure	Requirements for Physical Realizability	Typical Attenuation and Phase Characteristics
V	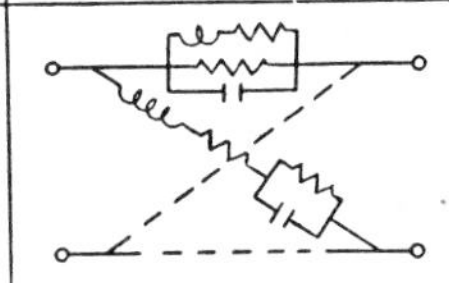	$\lvert a_1a_2\rvert \geq \lvert b_1b_2\rvert$ $b_1^2+b_2^2 \leq a_1^2+a_2^2$ The b's are ordinarily complex. The a's may be real or complex.	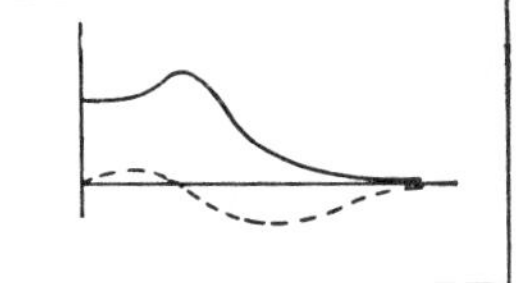
VI	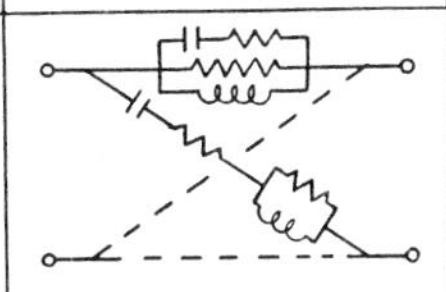	$\lvert a_1a_2\rvert \leq \lvert b_1b_2\rvert$ $\frac{1}{b_1^2}+\frac{1}{b_2^2} \leq \frac{1}{a_1^2}+\frac{1}{a_2^2}$ The b's are ordinarily complex. The a's may be real or complex.	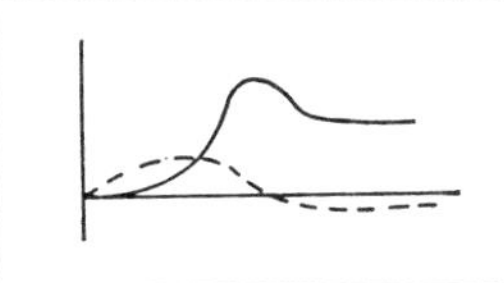
VII	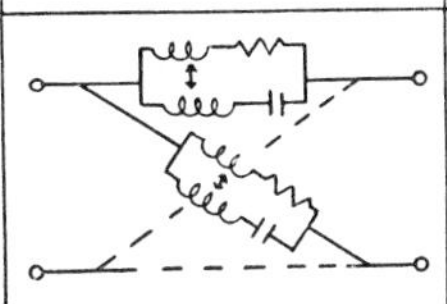	$\lvert a_1a_2\rvert \geq \lvert b_1b_2\rvert$ $b_1^2+b_2^2 \geq a_1^2+a_2^2$ The a's are ordinarily complex. The b's may be real or complex.	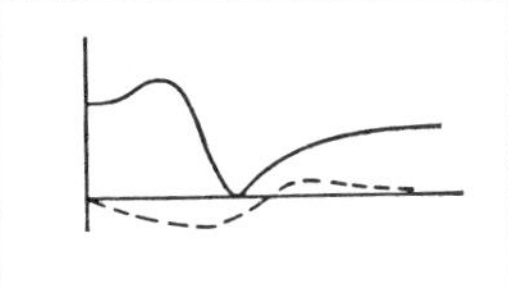
VIII	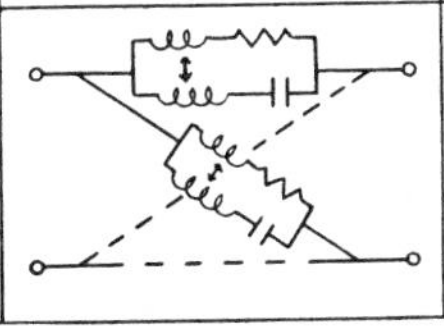	$\lvert a_1a_2\rvert \leq \lvert b_1b_2\rvert$ $\frac{1}{b_1^2}+\frac{1}{b_2^2} \geq \frac{1}{a_1^2}+\frac{1}{a_2^2}$ The a's are ordinarily complex. The b's may be real or complex.	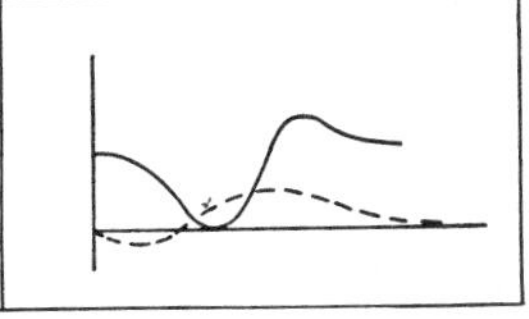

Fig. 12.3

determined subsequently from this expression. If we write the lattice branch Z_x as

$$Z_x = R_0 \frac{A_1 + A_3p + A_5p^2}{A_2 + A_4p + A_6p^2}, \tag{12–2}$$

the coefficients $A_1 \cdots A_6$ must satisfy the system of equations

$$\begin{aligned} A_1 - A_2 &= b_1b_2(A_5 - A_6), \\ A_1 + A_2 &= a_1a_2(A_5 + A_6), \\ A_3 - A_4 &= -(b_1 + b_2)(A_5 - A_6), \\ A_3 + A_4 &= -(a_1 + a_2)(A_5 + A_6), \end{aligned} \tag{12–3}$$

where, of course, a_1, a_2, b_1, and b_2 are the zeros and poles of the second degree function which is to be represented, and are supposed to satisfy the inequalities given on Fig. 12.3. The four conditions (12–3) allow us to

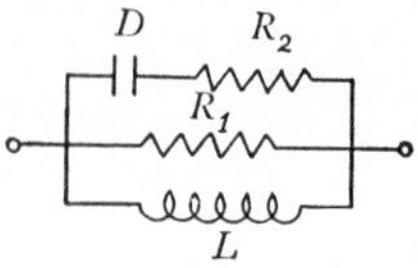

$$L = \frac{R_0}{2}\left[\frac{b_1 + b_2}{b_1 b_2} - \frac{a_1 + a_2}{a_1 a_2}\right]$$

$$R_1 = R_0 \frac{\left[\dfrac{b_1 + b_2}{b_1 b_2} - \dfrac{a_1 + a_2}{a_1 a_2}\right]^2}{\left(\dfrac{1}{a_1^2} + \dfrac{1}{a_2^2}\right) - \left(\dfrac{1}{b_1^2} + \dfrac{1}{b_2^2}\right)}$$

$$R_2 = \frac{R_0}{\dfrac{b_1 b_2 + a_1 a_2}{b_1 b_2 - a_1 a_2} - \dfrac{R_0}{R_1}}$$

$$D = \frac{(b_1 + b_2)a_1 a_2 - (a_1 + a_2)b_1 b_2}{b_1 b_2 - a_1 a_2} R_2$$

FIG. 12.4

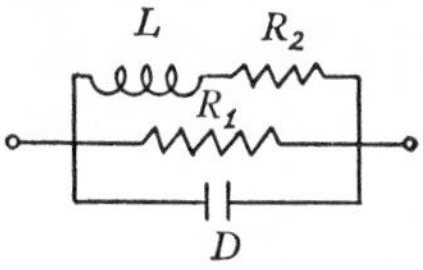

$$D = \frac{R_0}{2}[(b_1 + b_2) - (a_1 + a_2)]$$

$$R_1 = R_0 \frac{[(b_1 + b_2) - (a_1 + a_2)]^2}{(a_1^2 + a_2^2) - (b_1^2 + b_2^2)}$$

$$R_2 = \frac{R_0}{\dfrac{a_1 a_2 + b_1 b_2}{a_1 a_2 - b_1 b_2} - \dfrac{R_0}{R_1}}$$

$$L = \frac{(b_1 + b_2) - (a_1 + a_2)}{a_1 a_2 - b_1 b_2} R_2$$

FIG. 12.5

solve for the six A's as soon as any two, say A_5 and A_6, are known. Since (12–2) will not be altered if numerator and denominator are multiplied by any constant, however, one of the A's is arbitrary. We can conveniently suppose that $A_6 = 1$. A_5 is then given by

$$K_1 x^2 + K_2 x + K_3 = 0, \tag{12–4}$$

where

$$K_1 = \tfrac{1}{16}[(a_1^2 + a_2^2) - (b_1^2 + b_2^2)]^2$$

$$K_2 = \tfrac{1}{4}[(a_1^2 + a_2^2)^2 - (b_1^2 + b_2^2)^2] - (a_1^2 a_2^2 - b_1^2 b_2^2)$$

$$K_3 = \tfrac{1}{4}[(a_1^2 + a_2^2) + (b_1^2 + b_2^2)]^2 - 2(a_1^2 a_2^2 + b_1^2 b_2^2)$$

and $x = A_5 + 1/A_5$. In solving (12–4), the larger root must be taken, but it makes no difference which value of A_5 we choose to correspond to the x thus determined, since replacing A_5 by its reciprocal merely interchanges Z_x and Z_y. Once the A's are determined, the elements of the Brune network can, of course, be found by the methods described previously. The solution for the elements can be expedited by the fact that the minimum resistance point is given by $\omega_0^4 = A_1 A_2 / A_5 A_6$.

12.4. *Partial Product Expansion of an Illustrative Transfer Function*

The methods just discussed will be exemplified by the filter structure shown originally by Fig. 11.8 of Chapter XI. The transfer impedance of the structure is given by equation (11–13) of the same chapter. In order to break the impedance up into a product of simpler expressions it is first necessary to determine its roots and poles. This can be done by any of the standard methods of solving for the roots of a polynomial. In the present instance the result can be written as

$$e^{\theta} = \tfrac{1}{2}Z_T = 3.59\frac{(p^2+1.127p+1.043)(p^2+0.268p+0.981)(p+1.183)}{(p^2+1.5625)(p^2+2.778)}. \tag{12–5}$$

The quadratic factors, such as $p^2 + 1.127p + 1.043$ or $p^2 + 1.5625$, represent pairs of conjugate complex zeros or poles. There is in addition a single real zero represented by the factor $p + 1.183$ and a single pole at infinity.

It is apparent from an inspection of (12–5) that the complete transfer function can be represented by three elementary structures in tandem. If we accept the factors in numerator and denominator in the order in which they appear in (12–5) this is equivalent to rewriting the equation as

$$e^{A_0}e^{\theta} = e^{\theta_1}e^{\theta_2}e^{\theta_3} \tag{12–6}$$

where

$$e^{\theta_1} = k_a\frac{p^2 + 1.127p + 1.043}{p^2 + 1.5625}, \tag{12–7}$$

$$e^{\theta_2} = k_b\frac{p^2 + 0.268p + 0.981}{p^2 + 2.778}, \tag{12–8}$$

$$e^{\theta_3} = k_c(p + 1.183). \tag{12–9}$$

In these expressions the constant multipliers k_a, k_b, and k_c must be supposed to have such values that the attenuation of each constituent network is positive or zero at all points on the real frequency axis. The quantity A_0 measures the net increase in the attenuation of the complete network which may be required to satisfy this condition. It is evident from a comparison of the behavior of (12–5) and (12–6) at infinite frequency that $e^{A_0} = k_ak_bk_c/3.59$. The k's need not be known in order to follow through the design method outlined in Figs. 12.2 to 12.5. They are ordinarily determined most easily by inspection of the final networks. In anticipation of the calculation, however, it may be stated that they turn out to be respectively 1.498, 7.034, and 0.845. Thus $e^{A_0} = 2.48$, which corresponds to a net increase in loss of about 8 db.

It is convenient to begin with the construction of a network to represent e^{θ_3}. The function has a zero at -1.183 and a pole at infinity. Since these can be identified with the quantities a and b in Fig. 12.2 it is clear from the formulae that the required lattice is of the type indicated by III in the figure. The solution for the elements gives the specific circuit shown by Fig. 12.6.*

The discussion of the other constituent networks is facilitated if we make use of the relations between the roots of a quadratic and its coefficients.

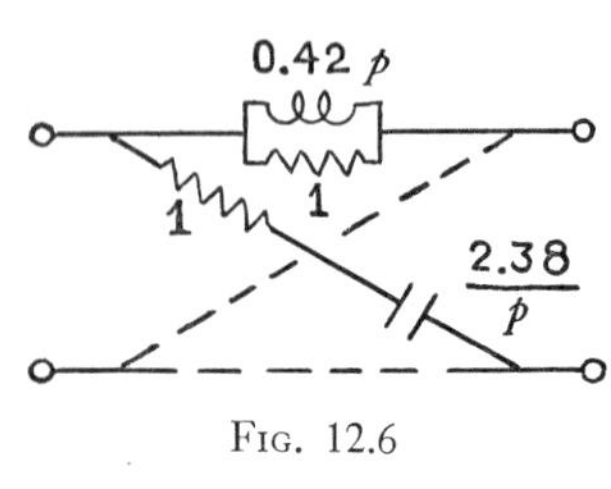

FIG. 12.6

If r_1 and r_2 are the roots of the quadratic $p^2 + \alpha p + \beta$, for example, it will be recalled that $\beta = r_1 r_2$ and $\alpha = -(r_1 + r_2)$. In equation (12–7) this evidently signifies that $a_1 a_2 = 1.043$ and $b_1 b_2 = 1.5625$, so that the corresponding lattice must be one of the types indicated by VI and VIII in Fig. 12.3. To determine which should be chosen, it is convenient to write the numerator and denominator of (12–7) in negative powers of p. Thus if the numerator is written as

$$\left(\frac{1}{1.043} + \frac{1.127}{1.043} p^{-1} + p^{-2}\right) 1.043\, p^2$$

we evidently have

$$\frac{1}{a_1 a_2} = \frac{1}{1.043} \quad \text{and} \quad \frac{1}{a_1} + \frac{1}{a_2} = -\frac{1.127}{1.043},$$

from which we can conclude that

$$\frac{1}{a_1^2} + \frac{1}{a_2^2} = \left(\frac{1.127}{1.043}\right)^2 - \frac{2}{1.043}.$$

With the help of a similar computation for the denominator it appears that the required structure is of type VI. The element values for its Z_x branch, as determined from the formulae in Fig. 12.4, are shown by Fig. 12.7. Equation (12–8) is treated in the same way except that it leads to a structure of the type indicated by VIII in Fig. 12.3. The element values for its Z_x branch, computed by the method outlined in connection with equations (12–2) to (12–4), are shown by Fig. 12.8.

As a check on this analysis, the attenuation characteristics of the three constituent networks have been computed and are shown, respectively, by Curves I, II and III of Fig. 12.9. The total attenuation is shown by Curve IV. It is, of course, the same as the attenuation characteristic for the filter given originally in Chapter XI except for an additional constant loss of 8 db.

In developing this solution, the quadratic factors in the numerator and

* All illustrative circuits, except where otherwise noted, are drawn on the assumption that $R_0 = 1$.

denominator of (12–5) have been paired off in the order in which they are written in that equation. We can evidently develop an alternative solution

FIG. 12.7 FIG. 12.8

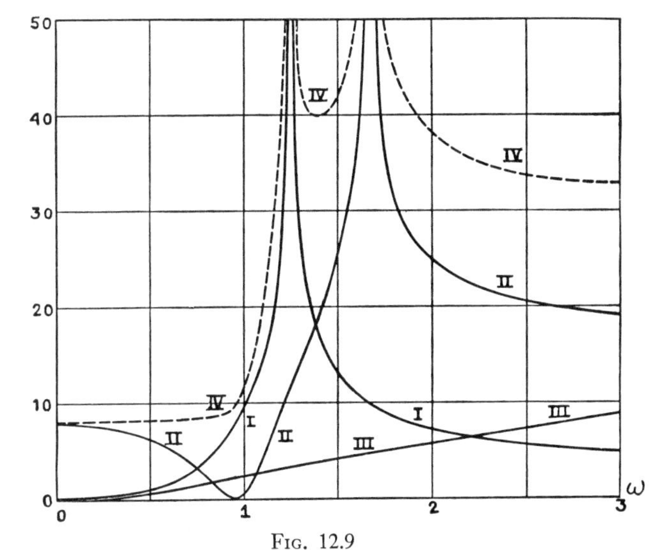

FIG. 12.9

by reversing the order in which the numerator and denominator factors are paired off. This is equivalent to replacing (12–7) and (12–8) by

$$e^{\theta_1'} = k_a' \frac{p^2 + 1.127p + 1.043}{p^2 + 2.778} \tag{12–10}$$

and

$$e^{\theta_2'} = k_b' \frac{p^2 + 0.268p + 0.981}{p^2 + 1.5625}. \tag{12–11}$$

With the help of the methods already described it is found that (12–10) represents a structure of type VI* in Fig. 12.3 and (12–11) a structure of

* Strictly speaking, the required structure is of type VIII. Since it lies very close to the boundary line between the two types, however, the simpler type VI has been chosen instead. Opportunities of simplifying in this way, or of going still further by simulating a whole group of constituents with a single elementary network, are not uncommon with the technique.

type VIII. The corresponding Z_x branches are shown by Figs. 12.10 and 12.11 and the various attenuation characteristics by Fig. 12.12. It will be

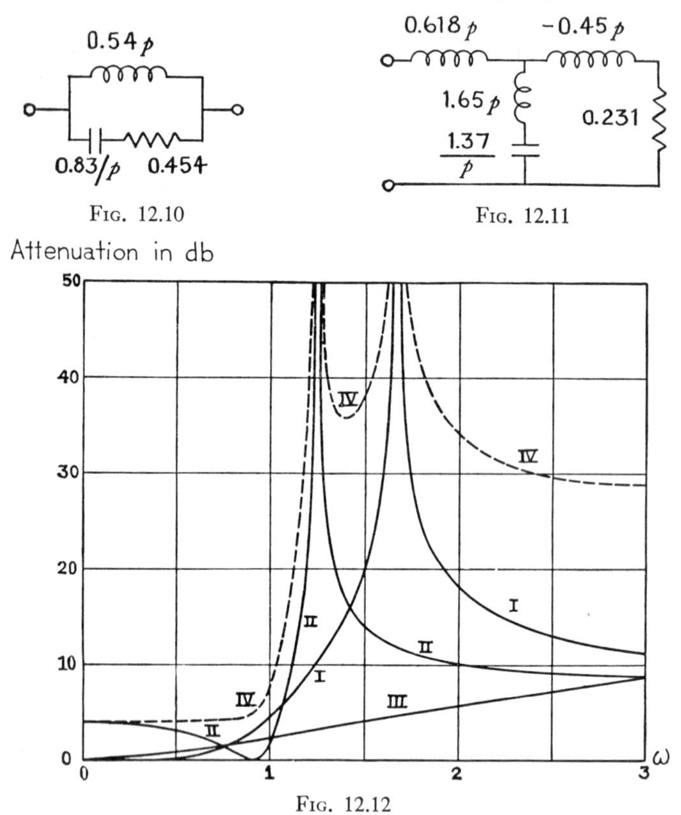

FIG. 12.10

FIG. 12.11

FIG. 12.12

seen that the characteristics are of essentially the same type as those shown previously by Fig. 12.9 but the additional constant loss in the circuit has been reduced from 8 to 4 db.

12.5. *Introduction of Surplus Factors*

The preceding analysis has shown that any transfer impedance with sufficient flat loss can be represented as a composite of a number of first and second degree lattices. Even with this restriction on the complexity of the constituent structures, however, the networks corresponding to any particular transfer impedance will not ordinarily be unique. For example, one possibility of changing the individual constituent networks consists merely in varying the order in which the factors in the numerator and denominator of the original transfer function are paired off. This was illustrated in the preceding section. If there are n pairs of factors to be established this leads to $n!$ possible combinations of constituent sections.

A still wider variety of constituent sections can be obtained if we include the possibility of multiplying both the numerator and denominator of the transfer function by additional arbitrary factors before the order of the factors is rearranged. This procedure was used in Chapter XI, in connection with equation (11–15), in order to reduce a general transfer function to the minimum phase case. An example of its application to an ordinary equalizer is shown by Fig. 12.13. Structure A in the figure corresponds to

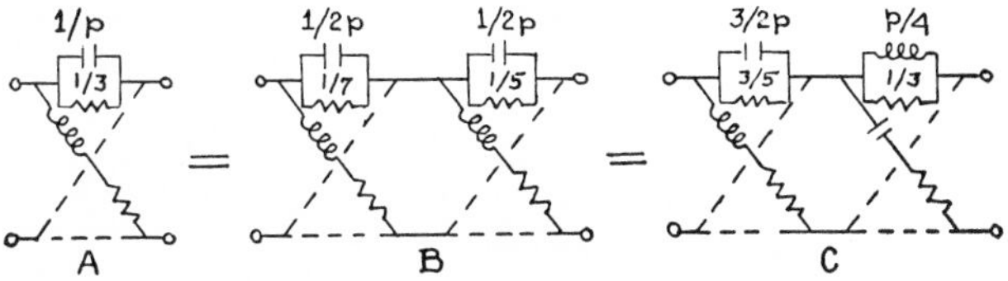

Fig. 12.13

the transfer function $(p + 4)/(p + 2)$ while B and C are the equivalent structures which we can secure by rewriting the transfer function respectively as $\dfrac{p+4}{p+3}\,\dfrac{p+3}{p+2}$ and $\dfrac{p+4}{p+1}\,\dfrac{p+1}{p+2}$. In forming structure C, it is necessary to suppose that an additional constant loss in the circuit can be tolerated.

For practical purposes, the use of surplus factors suffers from the obvious disadvantages that it increases the number of elements in the circuit and may also increase its flat loss. The method may, however, be of occasional value in simplifying the networks which must be constructed. As an example, let it be supposed that the mutual inductance coupling required for the Brune networks used in realizing the transfer function of (12–11) is objectionable. The difficulty can be avoided by writing the function as

$$e^{\theta_2'} = k_b' \frac{p^2 + \lambda p + 0.981}{p^2 + 1.5625} \, \frac{p^2 + 0.268p + 0.981}{p^2 + \lambda p + 0.981}. \tag{12–12}$$

If we choose λ greater than about 0.85 the first rational function on the right-hand side meets the requirements for construction in the form shown by VI of Fig. 12.3. The second can be represented by the first of the structures shown later in Fig. 12.14.

If we carry the process illustrated by (12–12) far enough, paying no regard either to the number of elements in the network or to its flat loss, it is possible to show that a general transfer impedance can be represented by a much simpler set of elementary constituent sections than those shown by Figs. 12.2 and 12.3. Thus, in discussing second degree functions previously the possibilities we were forced to consider included a pair of conjugate zeros in association with a pair of real poles, a pair of conjugate poles in association with a pair of real zeros, and a pair of conjugate zeros in association with a pair of conjugate poles. But if we multiply and divide a transfer impedance of the last type by appropriate real factors, it can evidently be represented as a product of transfer impedances of the first two types. In dealing with second degree networks, therefore, we need

Structure	Conditions for Physical Realizability	Element Values	Typical Characteristics
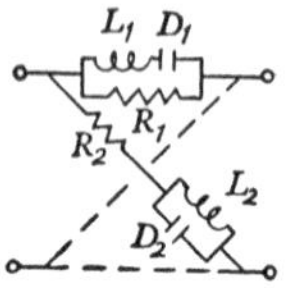 L_1 D_1 R_1 R_2 L_2 D_2	$a_1 a_2 = b_1 b_2$ $\lvert a_1+a_2 \rvert < \lvert b_1+b_2 \rvert$ In typical cases a's are complex, b's are real.	$R_1 = R_o \frac{(b_1+b_2)-(a_1+a_2)}{(b_1+b_2)+(a_1+a_2)}$ $L_1 = \frac{D_1}{b_1 b_2} = R_o \frac{(b_1+b_2)-(a_1+a_2)}{-2(a_1+a_2)(b_1+b_2)}$ $R_2 = R_o \frac{(b_1+b_2)+(a_1+a_2)}{(b_1+b_2)-(a_1+a_2)}$ $D_2 = b_1 b_2 L_2 = R_o \frac{-2(a_1+a_2)(b_1+b_2)}{(b_1+b_2)-(a_1+a_2)}$	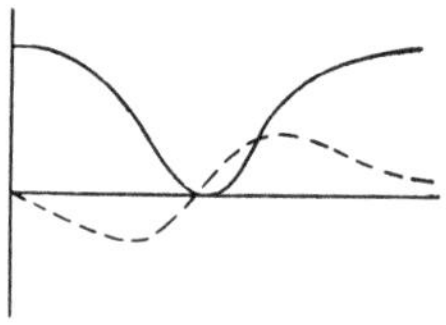
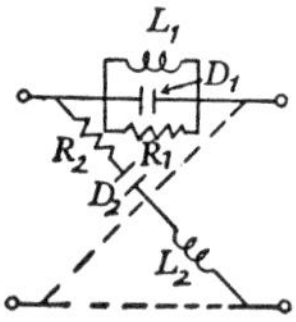 L_1 D_1 R_1 R_2 D_2 L_2	$a_1 a_2 = b_1 b_2$ $\lvert a_1+a_2 \rvert > \lvert b_1+b_2 \rvert$ In typical cases a's are real, b's are complex.	$R_1 = R_o \frac{(a_1+a_2)-(b_1+b_2)}{(a_1+a_2)+(b_1+b_2)}$ $D_1 = b_1 b_2 L_1 = -\frac{R_o}{2}\left[(a_1+a_2)-(b_1+b_2)\right]$ $R_2 = R_o \frac{(a_1+a_2)+(b_1+b_2)}{(a_1+a_2)-(b_1+b_2)}$ $L_2 = \frac{D_2}{b_1 b_2} = \frac{-2R_o}{(a_1+a_2)-(b_1+b_2)}$	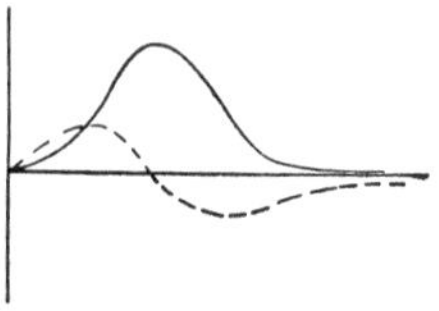

FIG. 12.14

consider only functions of these types. Moreover, even with these functions, the introduction of additional surplus factors evidently allows us to choose the real zeros or poles arbitrarily, provided we compensate for the errors thus produced with first degree networks. The only essential problem is that of representing the complex zeros or poles.

With the help of these possibilities the most general structures which are required in constructing second degree functions can be reduced to the two shown by Fig. 12.14. The first is appropriate for a pair of complex zeros associated with real poles, and the second for a pair of complex poles associated with real zeros. As the figure shows, in both networks the products of the poles and zeros must be equal. In applying the networks, it is of course assumed that the complex zeros or poles will be specified from the transfer impedance to be represented and the real zeros or poles then assigned any convenient values consistent with this restriction. Since all the networks of Fig. 12.2 are special cases of these two, Fig. 12.14 can be regarded as presenting a complete list of the elementary constituents of a general transfer impedance.

12.6. *Reconstruction of the Transfer Impedance from a Knowledge of Either Component*

We saw in a preceding chapter that while the resistance and reactance components of a physical two-terminal network can be varied with respect to one another, the ways in which they can be varied are defined within narrow limits. For example, if the reactance characteristic is fixed, the resistance can be changed only by a constant, while if the resistance characteristic is fixed, the reactance can be changed only by an amount corresponding to the addition of an ordinary series reactance. For a minimum resistance, minimum reactance structure, therefore, the complete impedance expression can be reconstructed if we know either component alone. A similar situation exists with respect to transfer impedances. The loss and phase characteristics of the network can be varied with respect to one another only by amounts corresponding to a constant loss or to an added all-pass network. If we assume that the network is of the minimum loss, minimum phase shift type, the complex transfer impedance characteristic can therefore be obtained if we know either the loss or the phase shift separately.

The process of reconstructing the characteristic is similar to that which we have previously described. Along the real frequency axis the even powers in the rational function representing Z_T will be real quantities while the odd powers will be pure imaginary. We can therefore write

$$Z_T = \frac{C_1 + i\omega C_2}{C_3 + i\omega C_4} \tag{12–13}$$

where C_1, C_2, C_3, and C_4 are polynomials in ω^2 with real coefficients. The attenuation and phase can consequently be expressed as

$$e^{2A} = \frac{C_1^2 + \omega^2 C_2^2}{C_3^2 + \omega^2 C_4^2} = \frac{(C_1 + i\omega C_2)(C_1 - i\omega C_2)}{(C_3 + i\omega C_4)(C_3 - i\omega C_4)} \tag{12–14}$$

and

$$\tan B = \omega \frac{C_2 C_3 - C_1 C_4}{C_1 C_3 + \omega^2 C_2 C_4}. \tag{12–15}$$

The latter of these can be more conveniently written as

$$\frac{1 + i \tan B}{1 - i \tan B} = \frac{(C_1 + i\omega C_2)(C_3 - i\omega C_4)}{(C_3 + i\omega C_4)(C_1 - i\omega C_2)}. \tag{12–16}$$

The forms in which equations (12–14) and (12–16) have been written indicate immediately how the process of reconstruction may take place. Suppose, for example, that the formula for e^{2A} is given. If the expression is to correspond to a physical network, it must be a rational function of

ω^2.* When we determine the zeros and poles, therefore, we will find that they occur in positive and negative pairs, one member of each pair lying in each half of the plane. The formula for e^{2A} can consequently be written as

$$e^{2A} = \left[k\,\frac{(p-a_1)(p-a_2)\cdots(p-a_n)}{(p-b_1)(p-b_2)\cdots(p-b_n)}\right]\left[k\,\frac{(p+a_1)(p+a_2)\cdots(p+a_n)}{(p+b_1)(p+b_2)\cdots(p+b_n)}\right] \tag{12–17}$$

where the first bracketed expression includes the zeros and poles in the left half of the p plane and the second bracketed expression includes their counterparts in the other half of the plane. Evidently the first bracketed expression can be identified with Z_T and is the transfer impedance expression which we seek.

The reconstruction of the complete transfer impedance from a knowledge of the phase characteristic proceeds similarly. If the expression for $\tan B$ corresponds to a physical network it must be an odd rational function of frequency with real coefficients. We begin by constructing the expression $(1 + i \tan B)/(1 - i \tan B)$ as indicated by equation (12–16) and calculating its zeros and poles. Since $i \tan B$ is an odd function of frequency, the points at which it assumes the values $+1$ and -1 are negatives of one another. In other words, the zeros of $(1 + i \tan B)/(1 - i \tan B)$ must be the negatives of its poles. Suppose that the zeros and poles are computed and arranged into groups corresponding to their locations in the right and left sides of the p plane. The zeros in the right side of the plane will then be the negatives of the poles in the left side, and vice versa. A result consistent with (12–16) will evidently be obtained if we identify $C_1 + i\omega C_2$ with the product of the factors corresponding to zeros in the left side of the plane and $C_3 + i\omega C_4$ with the product of factors corresponding to poles in the left side of the plane. The ratio of these quantities, from (12–13), is then the desired expression for the transfer impedance. Since the fixed loss cannot be determined from the phase characteristic this ratio can be multiplied by any suitable constant.

In both of these reconstructions, the resulting transfer impedance is unique only if we assume that the structure is of the minimum phase shift type. This is, of course, obvious when we begin with the attenuation characteristic. In addition to the Z_T specified by equation (12–17) an infinite number of other solutions can be obtained by interchanging the poles on the left-hand side of the p plane with their negatives or by adding extra zeros and poles symmetrically located with respect to the real frequency axis. When we begin with the phase characteristic itself, on the other hand, we

* In addition, the coefficients must, of course, be real and there can be no zeros and no odd order poles on the real frequency axis.

might expect that there would be no difficulty in determining whether the network is of minimum or non-minimum phase shift type. Uncertainty arises, however, when we select the zeros of Z_T from the zeros of $(1 + i \tan B)/(1 - i \tan B)$. While it is clear that only zeros in the left side of the p plane are admissible, it is not, in general, necessary that all the zeros in this region be chosen as zeros of Z_T. Some zeros can be omitted from Z_T by regarding them instead as zeros of $C_3 - i\omega C_4$ in (12–16). In this case the corresponding poles of Z_T, as determined from the rule suggested by (12–16), will lie in the right-hand side of the plane, so that a solution which is of the non-minimum phase shift type is obtained. Evidently, several solutions may be possible by omitting various combinations of zeros.* This is illustrated in the next section.

12.7. *Networks with Equal Phase Shifts*

The discussion just finished suggests that it should be possible to duplicate the phase characteristic of a non-minimum phase circuit with a minimum phase circuit. This is a question of some special interest, since it represents a point at which the analogy between driving point and transfer functions breaks down. Evidently we cannot duplicate the reactance of a pure reactance network with a minimum reactance structure. Moreover, it implies that although we cannot obtain a varying attenuation without a corresponding phase shift we can arrange two transmission paths which will have a varying difference in attenuation with no relative phase displacement. If the attenuation characteristics of the two paths were made approximately equal to one another over a specified range and a device were added to balance the outputs of the paths against one another such a circuit might conceivably be used as an alternative to ordinary filters in providing frequency selectivity.

As an example of the possibility of securing equal phase characteristics from minimum and non-minimum phase shift devices we may consider the function $(1 + iX)^2$, where X is some reactance. This expression evi-

* Each time a zero is omitted, however, the degree of the numerator of the corresponding Z_T goes down while that of the denominator goes up. Since the rational function representing a physical transfer impedance can have no zeros at infinity this sets a limit on the total number of zeros which can be omitted. Evidently, no zeros of $(1 + i \tan B)/(1 - i \tan B)$ in the left half-plane can be omitted in constructing Z_T unless the total number of zeros in the region exceeds the number of poles by at least two. This can be correlated with the net phase displacement between zero and infinity through contour integral considerations. If the net phase shift is negative, the characteristic is non-physical. If it is either zero or 90°, the characteristic must be of the minimum phase type. Beyond this point ambiguity arises because a displacement of 180° can be attributed either to an all-pass section or to a minimum phase network having infinite loss at the ends of the spectrum.

dently represents the transfer function through the two identical lattices in tandem shown by Fig. 12.15*a*. The associated phase shift, $2 \tan^{-1} X$, however, is the same as that of the all-pass network shown by Fig. 12.15*b*. Evidently, therefore, the fact that a network has an all-pass phase characteristic is not sufficient to ensure that it is actually an all-pass network. It may be a combination of simple equalizing structures.

The result just established can be made somewhat more general. If we set $iX = \alpha p$ the quantity $(1 + iX)$ can be regarded as the factor representing a real zero in a general transfer function. Similarly, if $iX = \alpha p + \beta/p$ we can regard $(1 + iX)$ as a representation of a pair of conjugate complex zeros. The relation illustrated by Fig. 12.15 is thus equivalent to the statement that the phase shifts associated with the zeros of a general transfer function are equal to half the phase shifts of a number of elementary phase correctors of the types illustrated by Figs. 11.11 and 11.13 of Chapter XI. Since the same result must hold for the poles of the function except that the phase shifts are negative we are thus led to the

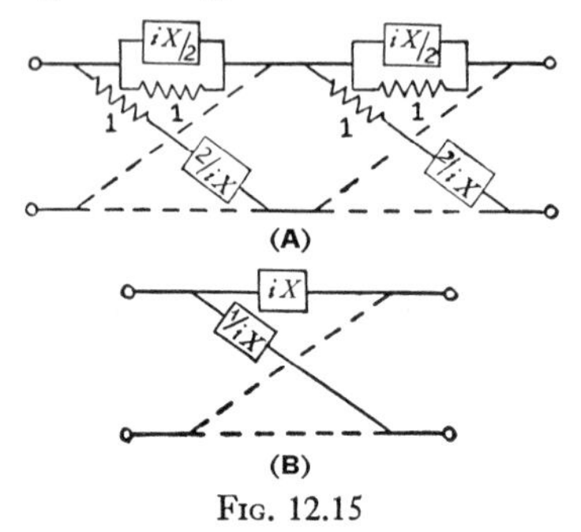

FIG. 12.15

Theorem: A general transfer phase characteristic is always half the characteristic of a number of elementary positive or negative phase correctors.

With this theorem as a basis it is easy to formulate the relations which must hold between two transmission paths if they are to have the same phase characteristic but different attenuation characteristics. The principal requirement is that the transfer functions in the two paths be selected initially so that their ratio or product is the square of a rational function of frequency. This is accomplished if the two transfer functions appear as $e^{\theta_1}e^{\theta_2}$ and $e^{\theta_1}e^{\theta_3}$, where e^{θ_2} and e^{θ_3} represent complementary characteristics and e^{θ_1} is any arbitrary transfer function. It is apparent from the complementary relationship and the preceding theorem that the difference between the phase characteristics in the two paths must then be the characteristic of a number of integral positive or negative phase correctors. In order to make the phase difference zero it is merely necessary to add corresponding positive all-pass sections in one path or the other.

12.8. *Choice of Parameters*

The choice of the coefficients in the rational function representing the transfer impedance to meet a prescribed characteristic can evidently be accomplished by methods similar to the linear equation scheme described in connection with two-terminal impedances. For example, if we are attempting to simulate a given attenuation characteristic and a given phase characteristic simultaneously, we can write

$$\frac{a_0 + a_1(i\omega) + a_2(i\omega)^2 + \cdots}{b_0 + b_1(i\omega) + b_2(i\omega)^2 + \cdots} = Z_T = e^A \cos B + ie^A \sin B, \quad (12\text{–}18)$$

or, equating real and imaginary parts separately,

$$(a_0 - a_2\omega^2 + a_4\omega^4 - \cdots) - e^A \cos B\,(b_0 - b_2\omega^2 + b_4\omega^4 - \cdots) + \omega e^A \sin B\,(b_1 - b_3\omega^2 + b_5\omega^4 - \cdots) = 0; \quad (12\text{–}19)$$

$$\omega(a_1 - a_3\omega^2 + a_5\omega^4 - \cdots) - \omega e^A \cos B\,(b_1 - b_3\omega^2 + b_5\omega^4 - \cdots) - e^A \sin B\,(b_0 - b_2\omega^2 + b_4\omega^4 - \cdots) = 0. \quad (12\text{–}20)$$

If we substitute sets of values of ω, A, and B in these expressions, by the use of selected points taken from the prescribed characteristic, we will evidently secure a set of simultaneous linear equations whose solution determines the a's and b's.

We can also deal with the attenuation characteristic and phase characteristic separately. Thus if we are particularly interested in the attenuation we may write

$$\frac{c_0 + c_1\omega^2 + c_2\omega^4 + \cdots + c_n\omega^{2n}}{d_0 + d_1\omega^2 + d_2\omega^4 + \cdots + d_n\omega^{2n}} = e^{2A}, \quad (12\text{–}21)$$

or

$$(c_0 + c_1\omega^2 + \cdots + c_n\omega^{2n}) - e^{2A}(d_0 + d_1\omega^2 + \cdots + d_n\omega^{2n}) = 0 \quad (12\text{–}22)$$

and, of course, as in the general case, this basic linear relation gives rise to a set of simultaneous equations for the determination of the c's and d's. The complex transfer impedance expression can then be reconstructed by the method described in the preceding section. For the reasons discussed in connection with the corresponding problem in two-terminal impedance design, this is an appropriate method even when we are finally interested in the simulation of phase shift as well as attenuation. Reliance in meeting the phase requirements is based upon the final design of a separate phase corrector.*

The desirability of using these methods in practical circumstances depends largely upon the particular problem in hand. In many instances a structure which will furnish a required characteristic with sufficient accu-

* For a more detailed exposition see Zobel, loc. cit.

racy can be determined by inspection and the design accomplished without the labor of setting up auxiliary mathematical machinery. The simultaneous equation process, however, furnishes a simple and systematic design method when the straight cut-and-try procedure fails.

12.9. *Networks Equivalent to the Lattice*

For purposes of theoretical analysis, the lattice, which is the only structure we have considered thus far, is particularly valuable both because of its generality and because of the simplicity and symmetry of its design equations. In practical application, however, other types of circuits are frequently preferable. It will be the object of this section to list a number of network equivalences by means of which the application of the lattice analysis to other types of structures can be facilitated.

The basic equivalence between the lattice and any other symmetrical four-terminal network is that illustrated broadly by Fig. 12.16*. The T

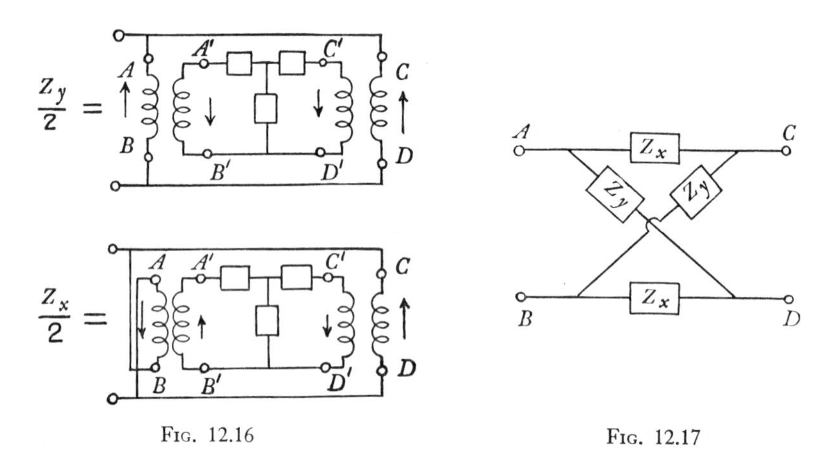

FIG. 12.16 FIG. 12.17

structure appearing in the figure is introduced merely for definiteness and is not intended to imply that the equivalence is restricted to any particular configuration. The equivalence is easily understood if we notice that the branches of an actual lattice can be obtained directly from external impedance measurements if we introduce appropriate short circuits between pairs of external terminals to eliminate one pair of branches at a time. For example, if we short-circuit terminals A and C and also B and D in the

* This is a slight modification of the equivalence originally described by G. A. Campbell. See "Physical Theory of the Electrical Wave Filter," *B.S.T.J.*, Nov., 1922.

lattice of Fig. 12.17, the impedance between *AC* and *BD* will obviously be $Z_y/2$. Similarly, if we connect *A* to *D* and *B* to *C*, the impedance between *AD* and *BC* will be $Z_x/2$. Figure 12.16 states, in effect, that the branches of the lattice equivalent to a general symmetrical network can be determined by making these two measurements on the corresponding terminals *A*, *B*, *C*, and *D* of the general structure.

The ideal transformers at the ends of the structure in Fig. 12.16 are of unity ratio. They are introduced merely to take account of the fact that the network whose lattice equivalent we are determining is not necessarily a balanced structure, and it is only its side circuit properties that are considered here. The arrows in Fig. 12.16 indicate the proper orientations of the transformer windings. Since a reversal in the direction of one winding amounts merely to an interchange of Z_x and Z_y in the equivalent lattice, however, or to a phase reversal in going through the network, this is almost a matter of indifference.

The transformers can evidently be omitted when the network under consideration is completely balanced. If we change the diagram slightly they can also be omitted for a completely unbalanced network, such as the particular T structure shown in Fig. 12.16. We notice that the only difference between the measurements determining Z_x and Z_y is the fact that the current in one transformer is reversed in going from one measurement to the other. From symmetry, however, the currents in the two transformers must be of equal magnitude in each measurement. In determining Z_y the currents in the secondaries flow in the same direction, so that the voltage between A' and B' is equal to that between C' and D', or in other words terminals A' and C' are at the same potential. The impedance $Z_y/2$, which is measured between *AC* and *BD*, is consequently the same as that which would be found if we omitted the transformers and measured directly between terminal B' and terminals A' and C' strapped together. When we determine Z_x, on the other hand, the currents in the two secondaries are in opposite directions, so that no current enters or leaves the network through the ground wire. The measurement would consequently be unchanged if the bottom terminals of the transformer secondaries were connected directly together rather than to terminals B' and D'. If we take account of the fact that a four-to-one impedance transformation results from the fact that with this connection the primary windings of the transformer are in parallel while their secondaries are effectively in series, we can therefore conclude that the impedance $Z_x/2$ is just one-fourth the impedance which would be found between terminals A' and C' if no external connections were made to any other part of the circuit, including terminal B'. This leads to the equivalence between a lattice and a symmetrical unbalanced network shown in Fig. 12.18, where Z_1 represents the impedance between A' and C' which has just been described, and Z_2 represents the impedance between A' and B', with C' strapped to A', which was described earlier.*

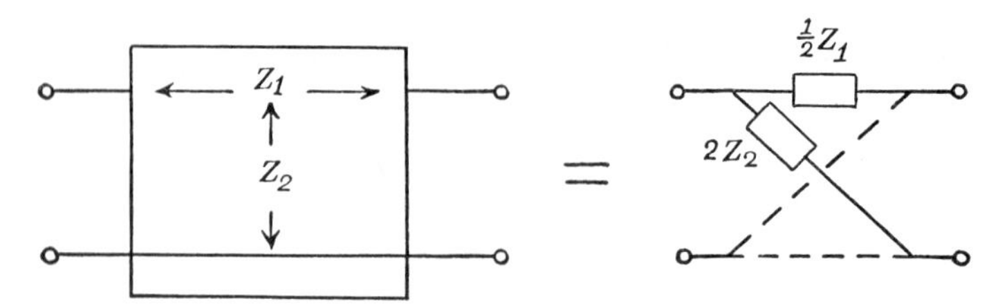

FIG. 12.18

12.10. *Illustrative Lattice Equivalences*

The application of the equivalence of Fig. 12.18 to T and π networks is shown in Figs. 12.19 and 12.20. The central branches of the T and π structures are represented in two equal parts, to illustrate the fact that the

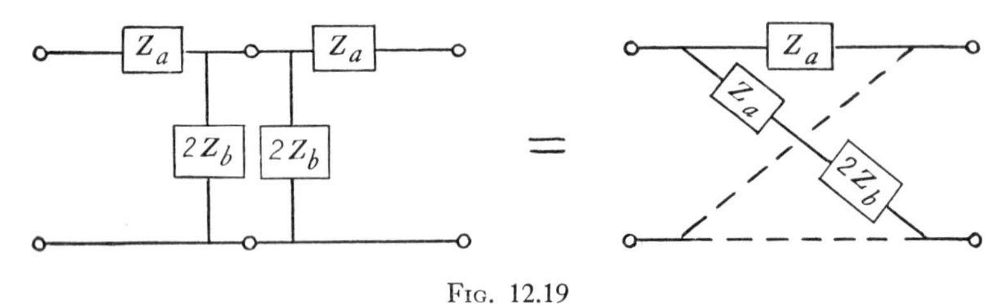

FIG. 12.19

Z_x and Z_y branches of the equivalent lattice are respectively equal to the short-circuit and open-circuit impedances of the half T or π sections. It is easy to see that a physical lattice can always be obtained for any T or π structure, but that the converse is not necessarily true.

* Essentially the same relationships are expressed by the so-called bisection theorem, due to Bartlett ("The Theory of Electrical Artificial Lines and Filters," p. 28). Bartlett's theorem states that the Z_x and Z_y impedances of the lattice equivalent of a given symmetrical network can be found by bisecting the network along the plane of symmetry and measuring the input impedance of either half when the terminals which would normally connect it to the other half are first short-circuited and then left open. This is an obvious relation from Fig. 12.18 since it follows from symmetry that in the measurement symbolized by Z_1 all the terminals on the plane of symmetry are at the same potential, so that they can be connected together without affecting the result, while in the Z_2 measurement the wires connecting the two halves of the network carry no current, so that they can equally well be opened. The equivalence of Fig. 12.18, however, applies also to the exceptional circuit which has symmetrical external characteristics without being structurally symmetrical.

Other examples of these equivalences are furnished by Figs. 12.21 and 12.22. As the figures imply, an impedance which occurs either in series or

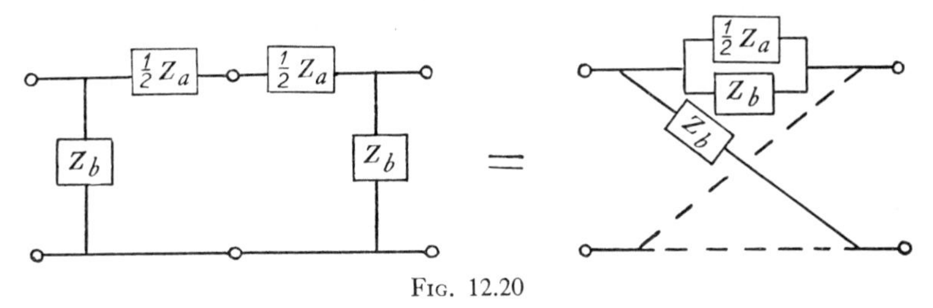

Fig. 12.20

in shunt with both lattice branches can be removed and placed in series or shunt with the lattice as a whole. For purposes of equalizer design perhaps

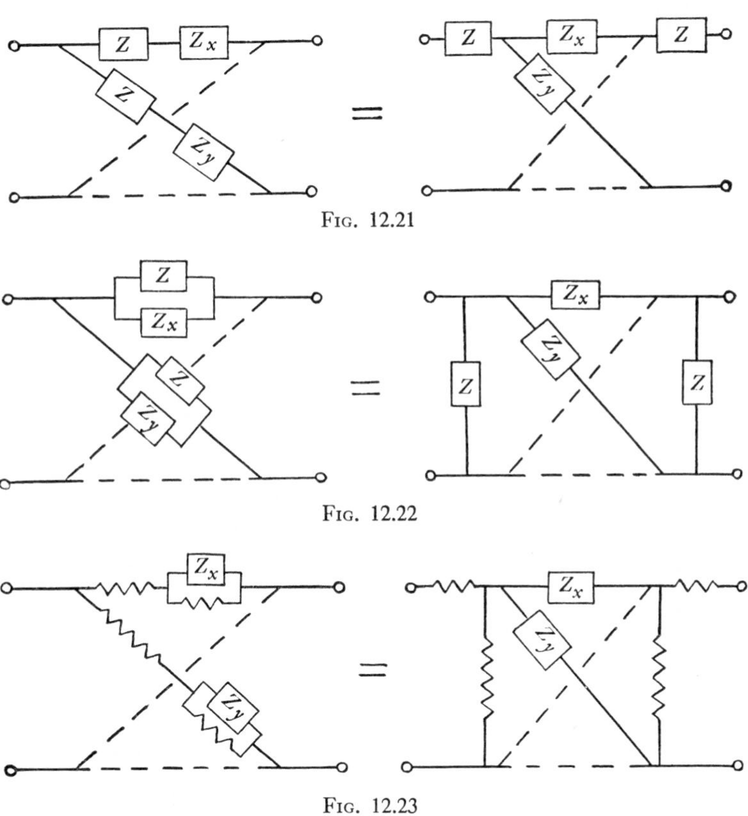

Fig. 12.21

Fig. 12.22

Fig. 12.23

the most useful application of these relations is that shown by Fig. 12.23. Since the series and shunt resistances appearing outside the lattice on the right-hand side of Fig. 12.23 can be regarded simply as attenuating pads, we notice that the essential effect of introducing a constant loss is to add series and shunt resistances to both lattice branches. Conversely, if a lattice is of the minimum loss type, either the resistance or the conductance of each branch must vanish at some point along the real frequency axis.

A more difficult example of these equivalences is furnished by Fig. 12.24, which represents the combination of two lattice networks to form a single

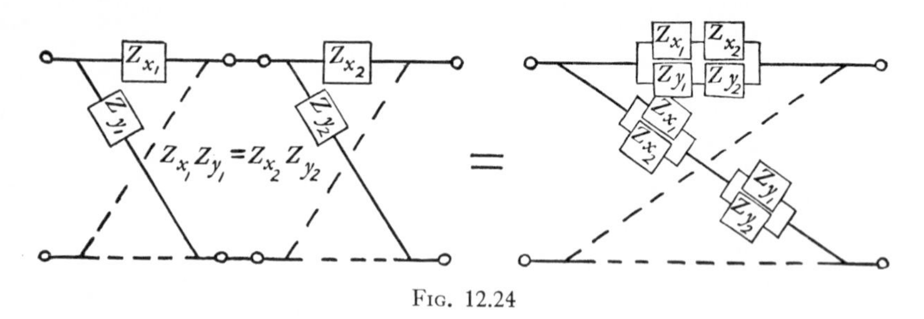

FIG. 12.24

equivalent lattice. As the relation $Z_{x_1}Z_{y_1} = Z_{x_2}Z_{y_2}$ shown in the figure implies, the original lattice structures must have the same image impedance. This condition is necessary, in general, if the resulting structure is to be symmetrical. Our preceding discussion in this chapter has been largely devoted to a description of the ways in which a general transfer impedance characteristic could be broken down to produce a number of very simple structures in tandem. The equivalence shown by Fig. 12.24 evidently represents the inverse operation, by means of which the elementary structures can be recombined as far as desired.

12.11. *Alternative Forms of Equalizing Structures*

With the help of these equivalences a lattice equalizer can be replaced by a number of alternative structures, of which two of particular interest are described in this section. The first is an equivalent of the lattice only in a restricted sense. It is obtained merely by replacing either the Z_x or Z_y branches of the original structure by simple resistances equal to the terminal impedances as shown by Fig. 12.25. The transfer impedances of the resulting networks are easily computed if we first represent them as T's or π's by means of Fig. 12.19 or Fig. 12.20. In

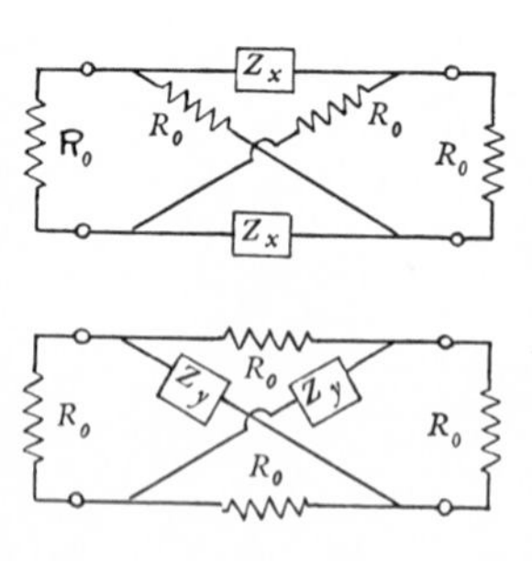

FIG. 12.25

both cases we find

$$Z_T = 4R_0 \frac{1 + \dfrac{Z_x}{R_0}}{1 - \dfrac{Z_x}{R_0}}. \qquad (12\text{–}23)$$

As we see by comparison with equations (11–3) and (11–6) of Chapter XI this is just twice the transfer impedance of the original network. In exchange for an added attenuation of 6 db, therefore, we secure a considerable simplification in the complexity of the network. It is to be observed, however, that the new networks are not of constant R type. The " equivalence " therefore holds only for the transmitted current when both terminal impedances have their assumed values. The networks cannot be used if the terminal impedances do not meet this condition, or if we must combine a number of structures in tandem.

A second alternative for the lattice is the bridged-T structure shown by Fig. 12.26.* The equivalent lattice of this network, as determined by the method of Fig. 12.18, has a Z_x branch consisting of the Z_c impedance of the bridged-T in parallel with half its Z_a impedance, while the Z_y branch consists of the Z_c impedance in series with twice the Z_b impedance. If the bridged-T is physically realizable, therefore, the equivalent lattice is always realizable, but we can convert the lattice into a bridged-T only if we can find an impedance, to represent Z_c, which is in series with one branch of the lattice and in parallel with the other.

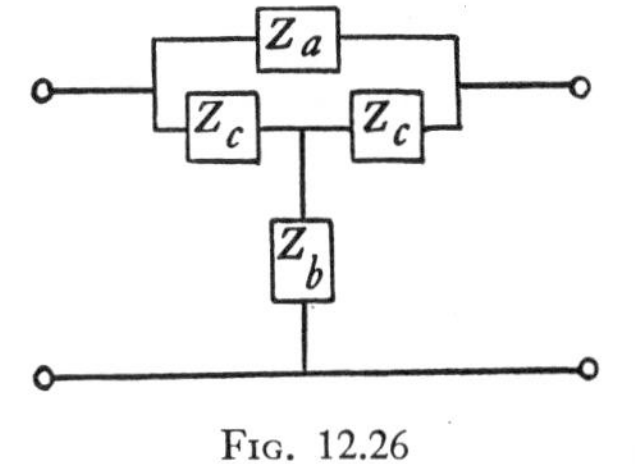

FIG. 12.26

For purposes of equalizer design, it is customary to suppose that the bridged-T is a constant resistance structure in which the Z_c impedance is equal to the terminating impedance R_0, as shown by Fig. 12.27. With this value of Z_c it is easily shown that the constant resistance condition will be met provided Z_{11} and Z_{21} are inverse networks with an impedance product

* The bridged-T is discussed here because it is the configuration which is most used in equalizer design work. In other applications, however, it is at least equally customary to convert the lattice into any one of several combinations of two impedance branches, proportional respectively to the Z_x and Z_y impedances of the original lattice, and a two or three winding transformer. A good brief list of these possible configurations is given in Starr, " Electric Circuits and Wave Filters," p. 366. A very general theoretical study of the possible ways of constructing lattice or bridge circuits with the help of transformers is given by Campbell and Foster, " Maximum Output Networks," *Trans. A.I.E.E.*, Vol. 39, Part I, 1920, pp. 231–280.

given by $Z_{11}Z_{21} = R_0^2$. When the structure is terminated at the far end by the circuit resistance R_0, the first series resistance R_0, the two inverse impedances Z_{11} and Z_{21}, and the final terminating impedance represent the four arms of a bridge whose galvanometer arm is the second series R_0. The relation $Z_{11}Z_{21} = R_0^2$, however, requires that the bridge be balanced so that no current can flow through the galvanometer arm. Strictly speaking, therefore, this element of the network is superfluous. It might be replaced by either an open circuit or a short circuit without disturbing either the driving point impedance or the transmission characteristics of the structure. These two possibilities are exhibited by Figs. 12.28 and 12.29. It is customary to include the second resistance, however, since its presence makes the circuit less sensitive to slight departures of the terminal impedances from their nominal values.

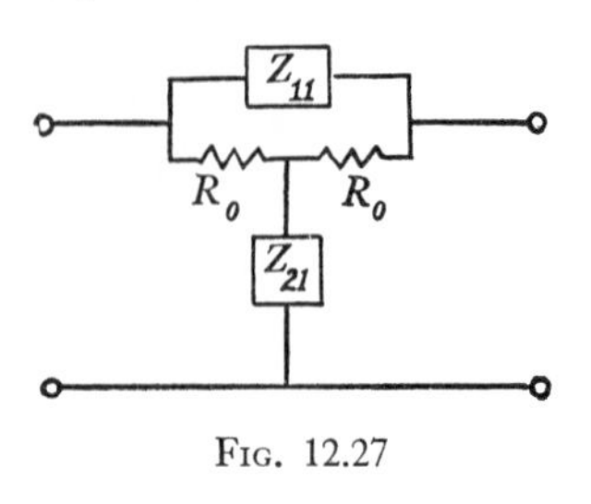

FIG. 12.27

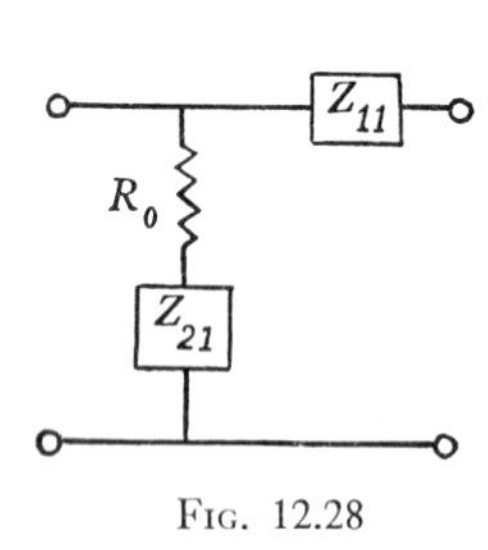

FIG. 12.28

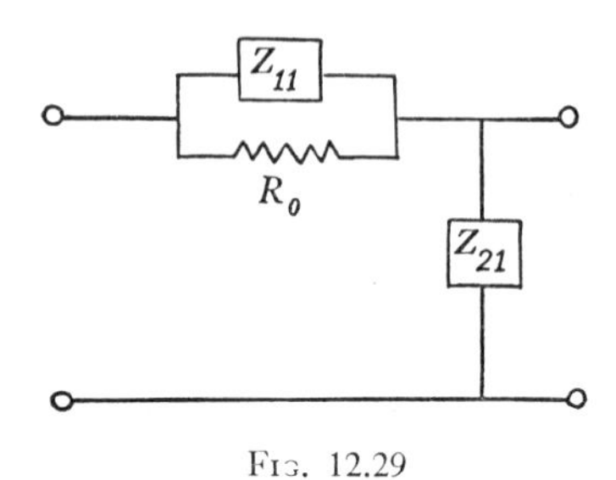

FIG. 12.29

12.12. *Design Formulae for Bridged-T Equalizers*

Although the bridged-T has been developed merely as an equivalent of the lattice, it is ordinarily easier to apply it to design problems if we deal directly with its own design equation. Upon substituting the expression for Z_x in terms of Z_{11} in equation (11–6) of Chapter XI we find

$$e^{\theta} = 1 + \frac{Z_{11}}{R_0}. \qquad (12\text{–}24)$$

Since for this circuit $Z_T = 2R_0e^{\theta}$ if both terminating impedances are equal to R_0, the transfer impedance of the bridged-T is proportional to the design impedance Z_{11} in series with a resistance. We can apply equation (12–24) immediately to develop certain properties of the bridged-T in analogy to properties we have already established for the lattice. For example, we saw in connection with Fig. 12.23 that the addition of a constant loss to the lattice was essentially equivalent to adding resistances in series and parallel with both lattice branches. In order for a lattice to be of the minimum loss type, it was necessary for either the resistance or the conductance component of each branch impedance to vanish at some real frequency. If we add a constant attenuation, A_0, to the θ defined by (12–24), on the other hand, the expression becomes

$$e^{\theta+A_0} = e^{A_0}\left(1 + \frac{Z_{11}}{R_0}\right)$$

$$= 1 + \frac{e^{A_0}Z_{11} + R_0(e^{A_0} - 1)}{R_0}. \qquad (12\text{–}25)$$

Aside from a change in scale, the addition of a constant loss to the bridged-T is therefore equivalent to the addition of a resistance in series with Z_{11}. Conversely, a constant loss can be subtracted from the bridged-T if the resistance component of its Z_{11} impedance is greater than zero at all real frequencies.

The use of equation (12–24) also allows us to replace the bridged-T by a simpler structure in somewhat the same way that a constant resistance lattice can be replaced by one of the networks shown by Fig. 12.25. In this instance, however, the substitute network is still more elementary. It consists merely of a simple series or parallel impedance proportional to the original Z_{11} or Z_{21} branch, as shown by Figs. 12.30 and 12.31. The fact

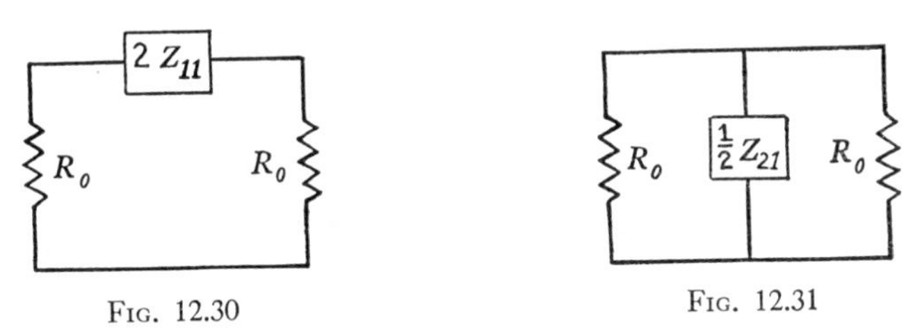

FIG. 12.30

FIG. 12.31

that the insertion loss characteristics of these circuits is the same as that defined by equation (12–24) can be seen by inspection. Although these circuits are logically analogous to those of Fig. 12.25 they have the advantage that we now no longer are required to accept an additional 6 db in the loss characteristic. Of course none of these " equivalents " can be used if the terminating impedances are not at their prescribed values or if we wish to combine a number of structures in tandem.

It is apparent from the preceding discussion that the constant resistance bridged-T of Fig. 12.27 is considerably less general than a constant resistance lattice. For example, the two can be made equivalent only if resistances R_0 are found in parallel with the Z_x branch of the lattice and in series with its Z_y branch. The significance of this structural requirement is best seen from equation (12–24). It is apparent from this equation that Z_{11} will be a physical impedance only if e^{θ} is a minimum phase shift expression, and then only if the phase shift is nowhere greater than $\pm 90°$. On the other hand, if we begin with any such expression and introduce enough constant loss a physical Z_{11} is always obtainable.

In general, the limitation on the maximum phase shift of a bridged-T becomes more troublesome as the complexity of the structure increases. In dealing with lattices, for example, we saw that two simple structures in tandem could always be replaced by one more elaborate lattice. No such relationship can exist for bridged-T's, however, since two structures whose individual phase shifts are less than 90° may easily give a total phase shift in excess of this limit. With increased complexity, therefore, the bridged-T becomes relatively less and less general. On the other hand, it is easily seen by inspection of the design formulae that when the minimum phase requirement is met, the structures of Fig. 12.14 can always be built as bridged-T's. If we begin by splitting up the characteristic into sufficiently simple components, therefore, any minimum phase shift transfer impedance can be represented by bridged-T networks.

For practical purposes, bridged-T equalizers can usually be designed most simply on a cut-and-try basis. The configuration adopted for the Z_{11} branch is most commonly a resistance in parallel with a network of pure reactances. It is evident that the resulting attenuation characteristic will reach equal maxima at every anti-resonance of the reactance network, and will become zero at every series resonance. This is illustrated by Fig. 12.32.

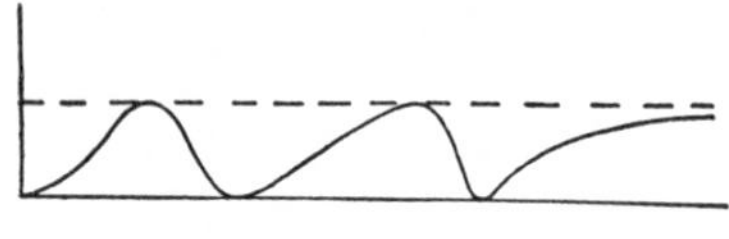

FIG. 12.32

A structure of this type is usually applied when the required loss characteristic in the frequency range of interest is similar to the characteristic of Fig. 12.32 between two successive maxima, two successive minima, or one maximum and the preceding or following minimum. Since the maximum value of attenuation is fixed by the parallel resistance, this element of the network can usually be chosen immediately. The design problem therefore reduces to the choice of a suitable two-terminal reactive structure. In the useful range, however, the resonances and anti-resonances are fixed by the location of the maxima and minima of loss. The cut-and-try work therefore consists chiefly in the selection of the constant multiplier of the reactance expression, and perhaps additional elements resonating outside the useful range, in order to shape the characteristic at intermediate points. For purposes of calculation, the equation

$$e^{2A} = 1 + \frac{1/R_0 + 2G}{R_0(G^2 + B^2)}, \tag{12–26}$$

which is easily derived from equation (12–24), may be used. In this expression G is the conductance of the (known) parallel resistance, while B represents the susceptance of the reactive network which must be found.

CHAPTER XIII

General Restrictions on Physical Network Characteristics at Real Frequencies

13.1. *Introduction*

The preceding chapters have shown that the mathematical specification of any of the usual characteristics of a network must be restricted in certain ways if the structure is to be physical. In particular, it is necessary for most network functions to behave in an especially simple way in the right-hand half of the p plane. This formulation of physical realizability is perhaps adequate in a formal sense. In practical engineering problems, however, we usually wish to be concerned only with the behavior of the structure at real frequencies. The question thus naturally arises as to the ways in which the restrictions on network performance in the right half-plane affect the characteristics which can be secured from physical circuits at points on the real frequency axis.

This problem has already been discussed at some length in Chapter VIII and Cauchy's theory of integration in the complex plane was introduced there as the principal mathematical tool which would be used in treating it. The theory was applied, however, only to the demonstration of Nyquist's stability criterion. In the present chapter and the ones which follow it the theory will be used to develop a number of additional relationships which physical network functions must satisfy. The discussion will utilize in particular Cauchy's theorem on the integral of an analytic function around a closed contour and the various special results on the integration of powers of z on circular arcs, which were described in the introduction to Chapter VIII. The student should reread this material, if necessary, before undertaking the present chapter.

13.2. *Nature of Restrictions on Physical Network Characteristics*

Before beginning the analysis, it may be profitable to consider the general nature of the relations which one should anticipate. Essentially, the problem of providing a given characteristic with a physical network is that of simulating the characteristic over a prescribed range with a rational function of frequency. If there were no restrictions on the rational function, this could always be done as accurately as we please. In general, however, the resulting function would have zeros and poles scattered in all parts of the p plane. Since only half the plane is actually available, this means that in a certain sense the conditions of physical realizability specify half of any problem. Broadly speaking, for each fact we can introduce arbitrarily, a matching fact is forced upon us if the zeros and poles are to lie in the proper half of the plane. It is as though we were Nature's tenants on a share basis. We must surrender half the crop for the privilege of farming the land.

As an example of this sort of relation, we may consider the processes of reconstructing a complete impedance from a known resistance characteristic or a complete transfer function from a known loss characteristic, which were described in Chapters X and XII. In each case it is possible to start with any even rational function of frequency to represent the given resistance or attenuation characteristic. Evidently, therefore, there are no restrictions on the problem of simulating any prescribed resistance or attenuation characteristic we choose as long as we assume even symmetry.* In reconstructing the complete driving point or transfer impedance, however, we found in general that the result is completely prescribed from the initial function. As our payment to Nature for freedom to choose the resistance or attenuation characteristic as we please, therefore, we must surrender control of the reactance or phase characteristic. Conversely, if we choose the imaginary component we find that Nature insists on specifying the real component. Our only advantage in the bargain lies in the possibilities presented by non-minimum phase or reactance networks.

Contour integral theorems can be developed to express these relations and many others besides. For example, instead of choosing as our half of the characteristic the real component alone or the imaginary component alone over the complete frequency spectrum, we may elect to specify the real component in some parts of the spectrum and the imaginary component in the rest of the spectrum. The remaining portions of the complete characteristic are then determined. We may also choose to specify only a single isolated fact about the situation. Nature's due, then, is a corresponding isolated fact. For example, if we specify that an impedance shall vanish at infinite frequency like a prescribed capacity, but impose no other restriction on the characteristic, there is a single requirement on the behavior of the impedance at finite frequencies. Similarly, if we specify, as an isolated fact, that the difference between the attenuations at two chosen frequencies shall be a prescribed amount, there exists, as an isolated fact, a corresponding single requirement on the phase characteristic of the structure.

Contour integral relations of these types exist in great variety. Unfortunately it is extremely difficult to organize all the possible relations in any very coherent way. In a purely mathematical sense most of the formulae are related to one another by such obvious transformations and changes of

* Except, of course, for the fact that if the discussion is restricted to passive structures, the resistance or attenuation cannot be negative.

variable that there is no good reason for picking out any particular set as independent. Basically they are all merely reflections of Cauchy's theorem. Thus the expressions which one chooses to regard as distinctive must be selected for their physical meaning for the particular problem in hand. It is easy to isolate a limited set which are useful for relatively common problems. Beyond this point, however, there is an almost inexhaustible list of formulae which might conceivably be useful in more specialized situations. Reliance here must evidently be placed upon the manipulative and interpretive skill of the individual engineer.

As a practical program, the present chapter will be devoted principally to theorems of the type which apply when a single isolated restriction is placed upon the function. Most of the discussion will be devoted to two of the simplest theorems. Various devices by means of which a wider variety of relations can be built up are described more briefly at the end of the chapter. Later chapters give expressions which are particularly applicable when we have chosen one half of the characteristic completely, either by specifying the real component at all frequencies, the imaginary component at all frequencies, or the two components alternately in successive frequency ranges.

13.3. *Analytic Conditions*

The contour integral will be taken over the path shown in Fig. **13.1.** This is the same path as that used in Chapter VIII to demonstrate Nyquist's criterion for stability. As in that discussion, the semicircular part of the path is supposed to be extremely large while the small indentations on the real frequency axis are included to avoid any singularities in the integrand which may happen to fall there. The integral around the complete path will be symbolized by $\oint$ and the integral around the semicircular portion of the path by $\oint$.

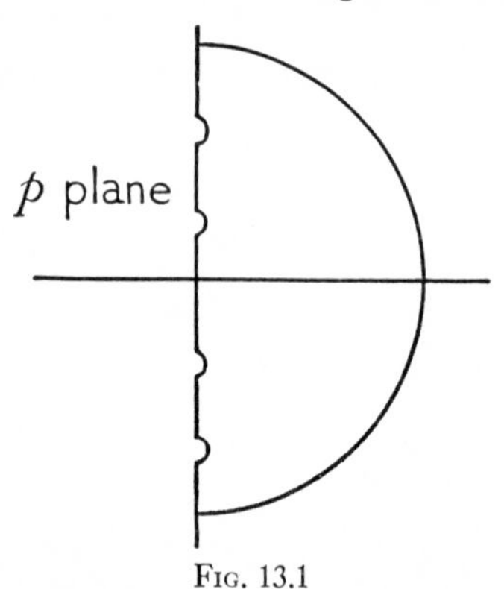

FIG. 13.1

Let the function in which we are interested be represented by $\theta = A + iB$. It will be supposed that θ satisfies the following conditions:

1. The real component, A, is an even function of frequency.
2. The imaginary component, B, is an odd function of frequency.
3. There are no singularities in the interior of the right half-plane.
4. Singularities at any finite point p_0 on the real frequency axis are of such a nature that $(p - p_0)\theta$ vanishes as p approaches p_0. This

admits logarithmic singularities and branch points but not poles on the real frequency axis.

5. In general, it will be supposed that θ is analytic at infinity. Many of the theorems, however, admit a singularity here provided θ/p vanishes when p is made indefinitely great.
6. If θ is assumed to be analytic at zero and infinite frequency, the quantities A_0, B_0, A_∞, B_∞, etc., will be defined as the coefficients in the corresponding power series expansions

$$\theta = A_0 + iB_0\omega + A_1\omega^2 + iB_1\omega^3 + \cdots \tag{13-1}$$

and

$$\theta = A_\infty + i\frac{B_\infty}{\omega} + \frac{A_1'}{\omega^2} + i\frac{B_1'}{\omega^3} + \cdots. \tag{13-2}$$

The most important functions satisfying these restrictions are passive impedances of minimum reactance type, or passive admittances of minimum susceptance type, and transfer loss and phase functions of minimum phase shift type. The transfer function, for example, is included because, in addition to satisfying the obvious requirements 1 and 2, it has no singularities in the interior of the right half-plane and the singularities, or infinite loss points, on the real frequency axis are only logarithmic. Minimum reactance impedance functions and minimum susceptance admittance functions are also included but non-minimum functions must be excluded because they have poles on the real frequency axis.

In addition to these two principal possibilities θ may also represent functions of several other types. For example, we can include active driving point functions in the analysis if we are careful to analyze a network which is open-circuit stable but not short-circuit stable as an impedance rather than as an admittance, and vice versa. We can also admit the logarithm of any passive two-terminal impedance without restriction to a minimum reactance or susceptance structure. Conversely, transfer impedances or admittances can be treated arithmetically in most cases without the necessity of expressing the transmission in terms of attenuation and phase. Since branch points on the real frequency axis are admissible, θ may also be an image impedance or an image transfer constant.

These functions are all of a type which would be appropriate for the analysis of networks of lumped elements. It is only lumped constant circuits which are of concern here. With suitable modifications, however, the contour integral theorems can be extended in many cases to circuits with distributed elements also. This question is discussed briefly at the end of the chapter.

In general, the first step in developing the theorems which follow is to combine θ with some other function in such a way that the result vanishes at infinity at least as rapidly as ω^{-1}. This makes it possible to evaluate the contribution of the large semicircular path to the complete integral. If the integrand vanishes more rapidly than ω^{-1}, it follows from the discussion in Chapter VIII that the integration along the semicircular path can be neglected entirely as soon as the path is made sufficiently large. Otherwise, this part of the loop must be taken into account, but its contribution is easily determined from equation (8–4) of Chapter VIII. The contour integration thus reduces in effect to an integration along the real frequency axis from some very large negative frequency to an equally large positive frequency. But the real and imaginary components of θ have respectively even and odd symmetry about the origin on the real frequency axis. If the same symmetry is maintained in the complete integrand the positive and negative frequency halves of the integral of the imaginary component will evidently cancel out, while the integral of the real component can be replaced by twice the integral along the positive half of the axis alone. From Cauchy's theorem, however, the integral around the complete contour is zero. In the result, therefore, the integral of the real component over all positive frequencies is set equal either to zero, if the integrand vanishes more rapidly than ω^{-1} at infinity, or to some known constant, if the integrand varies exactly as ω^{-1}.

13.4. *Resistance Integral or Attenuation Integral Theorem*

The simplest possible example of this process is obtained if we construct an integrand which varies in the desired way at high frequencies by subtracting A_∞ in equation (13–2) from θ. Since the integral around the complete loop must vanish, we can therefore write

$$\oint (\theta - A_\infty)\, d\omega = 0. \tag{13–3}$$

This can be broken up into an integration around the semicircle and an integration along the real frequency axis, and the limits of integration for the latter can be taken as $-\infty$ and $+\infty$ if the path is made indefinitely large. This gives

$$\int_{-\infty}^{\infty} (\theta - A_\infty)\, d\omega + \int (\theta - A_\infty)\, d\omega = 0. \tag{13–4}$$

In the second integral of (13–4), only the leading term, $i(B_\infty/\omega)$, of the power series for $\theta - A_\infty$ in (13–2) makes any contribution to the result. If we also break up the first integral into separate expressions for the real and imaginary components of $\theta - A_\infty$ this allows the complete expression to be written as

$$\int_{-\infty}^{\infty} (A - A_\infty)\, d\omega + i \int_{-\infty}^{\infty} B\, d\omega + \oint i \frac{B_\infty}{\omega}\, d\omega = 0. \qquad (13\text{–}5)$$

Since B is an odd function of frequency, the second integral in equation (13–5) must be equal to zero. Correspondingly, since A is even, the first integral can be replaced by twice the integral which would be obtained between the limits zero and infinity. Finally, the third integral can be evaluated as πB_∞ by the formula given in equation (8–4) of Chapter VIII. Collecting results, therefore, the expression reduces to

$$\int_0^{\infty} (A - A_\infty)\, d\omega = -\frac{\pi}{2} B_\infty. \qquad (13\text{–}6)$$

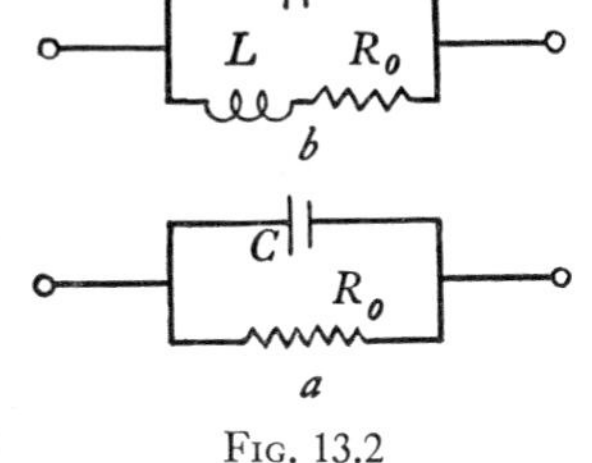

FIG. 13.2

The theorems of the chapter will be illustrated by the two networks shown in Fig. 13.2. If we let θ represent the impedance of one of the networks A and B will be respectively resistance and reactance. We see by inspection that $A_\infty = 0$ and $B_\infty = -1/C$. Equation (13–6) consequently becomes

$$\int_0^{\infty} R\, d\omega = \frac{\pi}{2C}. \qquad (13\text{–}7)$$

This result is easily confirmed by direct calculation. The resistance of the network in Fig. 13.2a, for example, is $R = R_0/(1 + \omega^2 C_0^2 R_0^2)$. Substituting in (13–7) therefore gives

$$\int_0^{\infty} R\, d\omega = \int_0^{\infty} \frac{R_0}{1 + \omega^2 C^2 R_0^2}\, d\omega = \frac{1}{C} \int_0^{\infty} \frac{d(R_0 C\omega)}{1 + (R_0 C\omega)^2}$$
$$= \frac{1}{C} [\tan^{-1} R_0 C\omega]_0^{\infty} = \frac{\pi}{2C} \qquad (13\text{–}8)$$

by ordinary integration.

The calculation for the structure of Fig. 13.2b is somewhat more difficult but it can be made by the same general method. The resistance of the structure is given in general by

$$R = \frac{R_0}{1 + (R_0^2 C^2 - 2LC)\omega^2 + L^2 C^2 \omega^4}. \qquad (13\text{–}9)$$

If this is split into partial fractions the resistance integral appears as

$$\int_0^{\infty} R\, d\omega = \frac{\alpha}{\alpha - \beta} \int_0^{\infty} \frac{R_0\, d\omega}{1 + \alpha\omega^2} + \frac{\beta}{\beta - \alpha} \int_0^{\infty} \frac{R_0\, d\omega}{1 + \beta\omega^2} \qquad (13\text{–}10)$$

where

$$\alpha = \tfrac{1}{2}(R_0^2C^2 - 2LC + R_0C\sqrt{R_0^2C^2 - 4LC}),$$
$$\beta = \tfrac{1}{2}(R_0^2C^2 - 2LC - R_0C\sqrt{R_0^2C^2 - 4LC}). \tag{13–11}$$

By integrating each term in the manner indicated by (13–8) we secure again the result $\pi/2C$. The equality of the areas under the resistance characteristics where the capacity C is fixed is illustrated by Fig. 13.3. The Curves I and I′ give typical characteristics for the structure of Fig 13.2*a*. Curves II and II′ represent characteristics obtained from Fig. 13.2*b*.

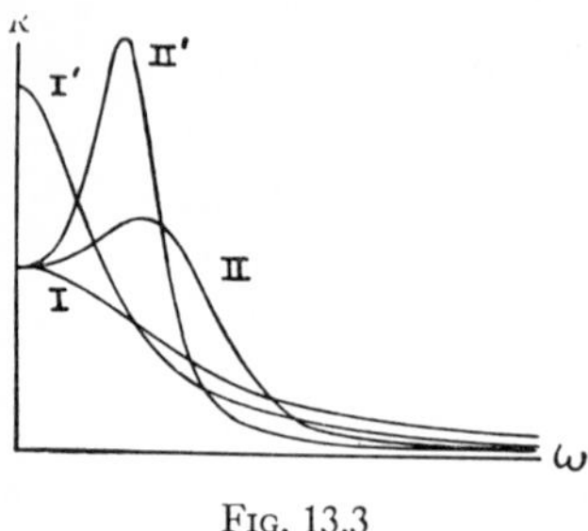

FIG. 13.3

Equation (13–7) also holds for any other minimum reactance network including the parallel capacity C. It does not hold, however, for such structures as those shown by Figs. 13.4 and 13.5 since neither of these configurations is of the minimum reactance type. In order to perform the contour integration for the impedance of such a network, it is necessary to indent the contour slightly as indicated by Fig. 13.1 in order to avoid the

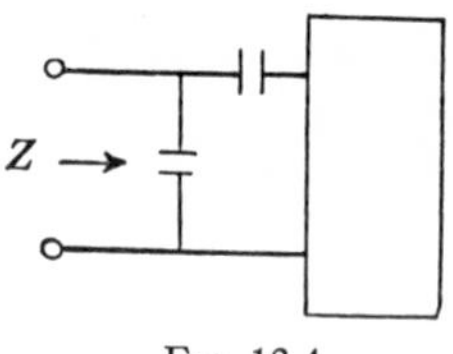

FIG. 13.4

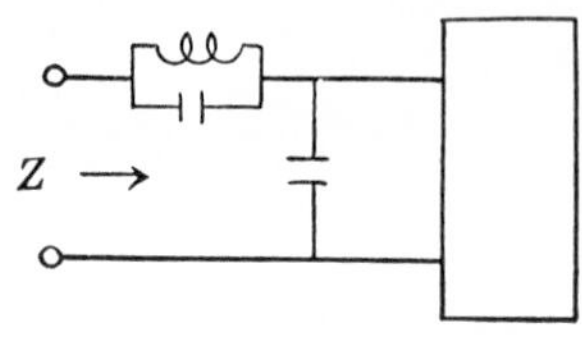

FIG. 13.5

poles of impedance, and the contribution of these small indentations to the complete loop integral also requires consideration. Since the residue at a pole on the real frequency axis is always positive, however, the sign of this contribution, at least, is known. We can if we like therefore generalize (13–7) to include both minimum and non-minimum cases by writing it in the form

$$\int_0^\infty R\,d\omega \leq \frac{\pi}{2C} \tag{13–12}$$

where the equality sign holds for minimum structures.

Equation (13–6) has been included as equation I(*a*) in the list of formulae given at the end of the chapter. The remaining equations I(*b*), I(*c*) and I(*d*) in the first group of formulae in the list are alternative forms of the same relation. For example, equation I(*b*) is the same as I(*a*) expressed on an inverse frequency scale, while I(c) and I(d) are relations obtained by integrating the first two expressions by parts.

13.5. *Equalizers and Local Feedback Circuits with Parasitic Capacities*

By interpreting θ in other ways than as an impedance, the general equation (13–6) can be made to yield a variety of other special results. Many of these are of importance in considering the characteristics obtainable from a network including some parasitic element, such as a shunt capacity, which defines its behavior at high frequencies. If θ is chosen appropriately in such a situation it is ordinarily possible to identify A with the characteristic in which we are interested at ordinary frequencies, while B_∞ can be evaluated in terms of the parasitic element from a study of the high frequency behavior of the structure. By using (13–6), then, the maximum response obtainable from a physical structure including the prescribed parasitic element can be computed.

Most of these applications depend also upon some analytic tools we have not yet developed and are most readily considered at a later point. In order to illustrate the process, however, we will consider the particular θ given by

$$\theta = \log\left(1 + \frac{Z_{11}}{R_0}\right). \tag{13–13}$$

This equation represents the loss and phase shift of a constant resistance equalizer of the general type described in Chapter XII and shown here by Fig. 13.6. In accordance with the general relations developed in Chapter XII the analysis also covers situations in which the equalizer is replaced by a simple two-terminal network inserted in series or shunt with the circuit.

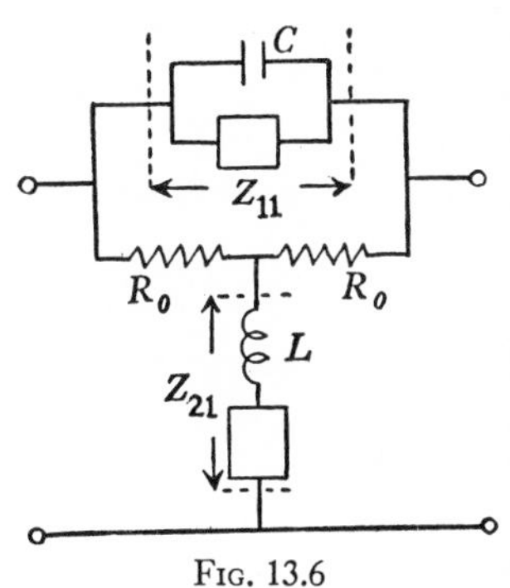

Fig. 13.6

It will be assumed that the Z_{11} impedance includes a prescribed shunt capacity C as indicated by Fig. 13.6. Obviously, if C is large Z_{11} cannot be a large impedance over a broad frequency band and in accordance with equation (13–13) the attenuation will be correspondingly small. On the other hand, as C is made smaller, Z_{11} and the attenuation A can assume larger and larger values. The theorem described in this section is concerned with the exact relation among these quantities.

The reason for considering such a problem as this is that we frequently have occasion to introduce equalizers into β circuits of amplifiers in order to control their gain characteristics. It is shown in a later chapter, however, that the amount of feedback which can be secured from the amplifier depends upon the asymptotic characteristics of the feedback at frequencies remote from the band and is diminished by anything which introduces attenuation into the feedback loop in the asymptotic region. Obviously, the behavior of the equalizer at very high frequencies depends upon the value assigned to C, and the relation between C and the general level of attenuation which can be secured from the structure is therefore useful in determining the extent to which the available feedback is reduced by the introduction of equalization into the circuit.

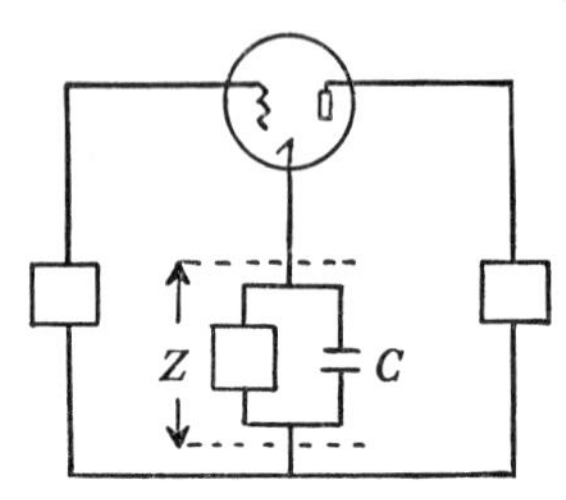

FIG. 13.7

In addition to this particular problem, the analysis can also be applied to a number of parallel problems in which the function of interest has a form similar to (13–13). An example is furnished by the introduction of local feedback through the use of an impedance between cathode and ground in one tube as shown by Fig. 13.7. The equation for the gain of such a circuit, neglecting grid-cathode and plate-cathode admittances in comparison with the other admittances of the circuit, is given by

$$\mu = \frac{G_m}{1 + G_m Z}. \tag{13–14}$$

The reduction in gain produced by the local feedback is therefore measured by $1 + G_m Z$. This is evidently the same expression as that in equation (13–13) if we replace the transconductance G_m by the reciprocal of R_0. Since Z will generally be controlled at high frequencies by the parasitic capacity C in Fig. 13.7, between cathode and ground, the situation is essentially similar to that discussed for the equalizer.

The relation between the equalizer loss, or the reduction in gain due to local feedback, and the capacity C can be established by replacing Z_{11} in (13–13) by its high frequency value $1/i\omega C$. It is easily shown that $\log (1 + 1/i\omega CR_0)$ reduces approximately to $1/i\omega CR_0$ when ω is very large. We thus have $A_\infty = 0$ and $B_\infty = -1/CR_0$. Substitution in (13–6) therefore gives

$$\int_0^\infty A\, d\omega = \frac{\pi}{2CR_0}. \tag{13–15}$$

As an example, let it be supposed that we wish to apply local feedback to a tube for which $G_m = 4 \times 10^{-3}$ mhos, and $C = 40\ \mu\mu f$. The equivalent R_0 which appears in (13–15) is $1/G_m$, or 250 ohms. An easy calculation shows that the total local feedback obtainable amounts to 1 neper over a 25 mc band or 2 nepers over a 12.5 mc band. Since the integral in (13–15) runs to infinite frequency, however, and we evidently cannot reduce A

abruptly to zero, the feedback available over a definite 12.5 or 25 mc band is slightly less than these figures would indicate.*

13.6. *Regeneration and Degeneration in a General Feedback Circuit*

The analysis just concluded can also be used to derive a second result which is at least curious, although it may not be of great practical importance. We are accustomed to thinking of feedback amplifiers as being either regenerative, in which case the external gain is increased at the cost of an increase in the effects of tube variations, or degenerative, in which case the gain is reduced in exchange for a corresponding improvement in the effects of tube variations. It is apparent, however, that the expression $\log(1 + G_m Z)$, which we have just studied, is merely a particularly simple form to which the general expression $\log(1 - \mu\beta)$ reduces for the special case of a single tube feedback amplifier. Equation (13–15) therefore measures the total reduction in gain or degeneration for such a system. In a similar fashion we might replace the θ in (13–13) by $\log(1 - \mu\beta)$ for a general amplifier and proceed with the analysis in the same way as before.

In the general case only one difference would appear. Whereas in the single tube feedback amplifier the feedback $\mu\beta$ varies, in general, inversely as the first power of the frequency at high frequencies, in a general multitube amplifier, the feedback would vanish as some higher power of frequency. If the feedback drops off as a higher power than the first, however, the contribution of the integral around the infinite semicircle is evidently zero and the right-hand side of equation (13–15) therefore vanishes. This can be formulated as the

Theorem: In a single loop feedback amplifier of more than one stage the average regeneration or degeneration over the complete frequency spectrum is zero.

In a typical amplifier, in other words, the increase in gain at high frequencies due to the fact that $|1 - \mu\beta|$ is less than one just balances the

* This example is taken from the design of a repeater amplifier used some years ago in an experimental system for long distance broad-band transmission over coaxial lines. The system was intended to transmit carrier telephone messages over a 2 mc band; a modified form of the system with a somewhat extended band to accommodate television as well as telephone signals is described by Strieby and Wentz, "Television Transmission over Wire Lines," *B.S.T.J.*, Jan., 1941. The 40 $\mu\mu f$ cathode-ground capacity mentioned in the text is much greater than the physical capacity in the actual amplifier, but the grid-cathode and plate-cathode capacities lead to an effective C of about this magnitude. The reason for maintaining the local feedback over a band as great as 12 to 25 mc is that otherwise the stability of the system is jeopardized by a decrease in the gain of the tube to which the local feedback is applied, even if the characteristics around the main loop are apparently absolutely stable. The design is described in more detail in a later chapter.

reduction in gain due to feedback in and near the useful band. It must be remembered that the comparison takes place on an arithmetic frequency scale and the high frequency region over which a perceptible increase in gain takes place may be very broad.

13.7. *Phase or Reactance Integral*

Equation (13–6) gives the integral of the real component of a network function over the real frequency axis in terms of the behavior of the imaginary component at infinite frequency. A second contour integral theorem gives an analogous relation between the integral of the imaginary component of the function over the real frequency axis and the behavior of the real component at extreme frequencies.

In developing (13–6) the integrand was made to vary as ω^{-1} near infinity, so that the integration around the large semicircle could be performed, by subtracting A_∞ from θ. We can also secure a manageable integrand at high frequencies by dividing θ by ω. This leads to

$$\oint \frac{\theta}{\omega}\, d\omega = 0. \tag{13–16}$$

When the path is made very large, the integral around the complete loop can again be broken up into an integration along the real frequency axis and an integration around an infinite semicircle. It is necessary, however, also to include the contribution of a very small indentation around the origin to take account of the fact that the integrand has a pole at this point. Equation (13–16) thus becomes

$$\int_{-\infty}^{\infty} \frac{\theta}{\omega}\, d\omega + \oint \frac{\theta}{\omega}\, d\omega + \oint' \frac{\theta}{\omega}\, d\omega = 0, \tag{13–17}$$

where the third integral represents the very small semicircle near the origin.

In evaluating the first term of (13–17) we find we need again to consider only the component having even symmetry over the positive and negative frequency ranges. In this instance, however, this component is iB/ω. The integrands in the remaining terms can be written as A_∞/ω and A_0/ω, since the contributions of the higher order terms in (13–2) disappear when the path is pushed to the limiting case. This gives

$$2i\int_{0}^{\infty} \frac{B}{\omega}\, d\omega + \oint \frac{A_\infty}{\omega}\, d\omega + \oint' \frac{A_0}{\omega}\, d\omega = 0. \tag{13–18}$$

The second and third integrals of (13–18) can be evaluated by means of equation (8–4) of Chapter VIII. They are equal to $-\pi i A_\infty$ and $\pi i A_0$, respectively. The complete expression is therefore

$$\int_{-\infty}^{\infty} B\, du = \frac{\pi}{2}\,(A_\infty - A_0), \tag{13–19}$$

where $du = d(\log \omega)$ has been written for $d\omega/\omega$. This equation is evidently exactly analogous to the integral for the real component given by (13–6) except for the fact that the integration is taken on a logarithmic frequency scale and the right-hand side involves the difference between the values of the real component at zero and infinite frequency. The reason for this latter change is physically evident from the fact that the absolute level of resistance or attenuation in a circuit can always be varied at will without affecting the rest of the circuit characteristics.

Equation (13–19) states, in effect, that the total area under the imaginary component plotted on a logarithmic frequency scale depends only upon the difference between the values assumed by the real component at zero and infinite frequency, and not upon the way in which the real component varies between these limits. This is illustrated by Fig. 13.8. If the change in the real component is concentrated in a narrow portion of the frequency spec-

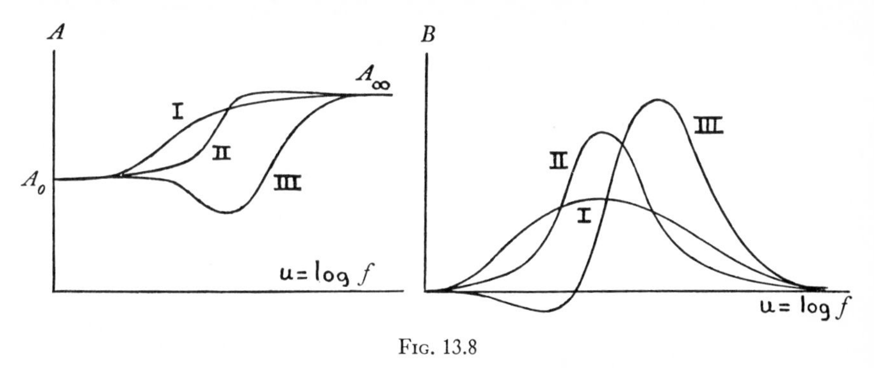

FIG. 13.8

trum the imaginary characteristic rises to a sharp peak, while if the change in the real component is more gradual the imaginary characteristic is broad and flat. For a given total change in the real characteristic, however, the area under the imaginary characteristic is always the same. If A and B are attenuation and phase the units in which (13–19) is expressed are nepers and radians and it is easily seen that the phase area is equal to 90° multiplied by a frequency interval equal to the change in loss expressed as a current ratio. For example, a low-pass filter having 40 db loss at high frequencies* has an accompanying phase area equal to 90° over a frequency range of 100 : 1.

* Taken literally, A_∞ in (13–19) represents the loss at infinite frequency, where the attenuation of any actual low-pass filter is infinite because of reflection effects. It is obvious, however, that if A_∞ is taken as the loss at some fairly representative high frequency the equation should give an approximately correct value for the phase area at lower frequencies. The difficulty can also be avoided by allowing θ to stand for the transfer constant rather than the insertion loss of the filter.

In order to exemplify the relation in detail, we may consider again the simple networks shown by Fig. 13.2, allowing A and B to represent resistance and reactance, respectively. If we choose the structure of Fig. 13.2a, we have $A_0 = R_0$, $A_\infty = 0$, and $B = -(\omega C R_0^2)/(1 + \omega^2 C^2 R_0^2)$. Equation (13–19) therefore becomes

$$\int_0^\infty - \frac{CR_0^2}{1 + \omega^2 C^2 R_0^2} d\omega = -\frac{\pi}{2} R_0, \tag{13–20}$$

which can easily be checked by ordinary integration. The analogous expression for the structure of Fig. 13.2b is

$$\int_0^\infty \frac{(L - R_0^2 C) - \omega^2 L^2 C}{(1 - \omega^2 LC)^2 + (\omega R_0 C)^2} d\omega = -\frac{\pi}{2} R_0. \tag{13–21}$$

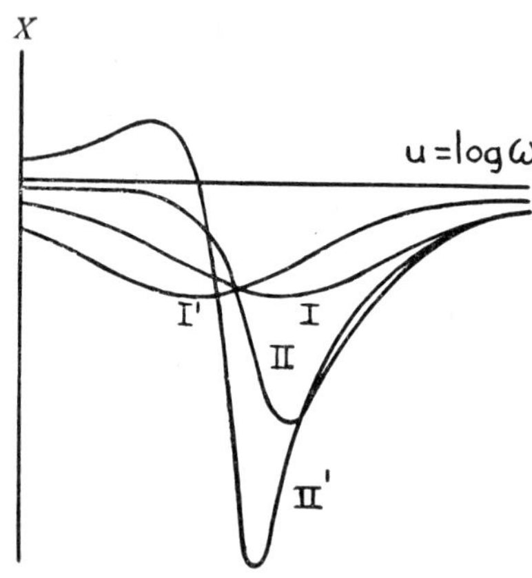

FIG. 13.9

This can also be confirmed by ordinary integration, although the algebra is somewhat more difficult. The equality of reactance areas for these networks for a specified value of R_0 is illustrated by Fig. 13.9, where the curves represent the reactance characteristics corresponding to the resistance characteristics of Fig. 13.3. The reactance corresponding to Curve I′ in Fig. 13.3 has been divided by two in order to permit all the characteristics to correspond to the same value of R_0.

13.8. *Applications of Phase Area Law in Amplifier Design*

In amplifier design, equation (13–19) can be used either in planning the general form of an overall loop cut-off characteristic or in making minor adjustments in a design which is nearly satisfactory. As an example of the first application, let it be supposed that we are dealing with an equivalent low-pass amplifier, as described in Chapter X, and let $\theta = \log T$, where T represents the return ratio for one of the tubes and is the same as $-\mu\beta$ for the usual single loop amplifier. Obviously, A_0 in (13–19) represents the effective feedback in the useful band* in nepers. Above the useful band $\mu\beta$ must decrease until it becomes less than unity beyond the amplifier cut-off. This change in gain can evidently be identified roughly with the quantity $A_\infty - A_0$ in (13–19). Associated with it must be a certain definite phase area. If the amplifier is to be absolutely stable, however, it follows from

* That is, as a negative loss. It must be remembered that $\mu\beta$ is stated as a gain while the A in (13–19) is taken to represent an attenuation.

the Nyquist plot of T given by Fig. 8.27 of Chapter VIII that the maximum phase shift at any frequency in the region below the cut-off must be less than 180°. Since the total phase area is fixed, this requirement can be met only if the area is distributed over a sufficiently wide range. For example, if the feedback in the useful range is 40 db and the phase shift is nowhere greater than 180°, equation (13–19) indicates that the phase area must extend over a frequency range of at least 10 to 1.

It is fairly evident physically that this must correspond approximately to the region of decreasing $\mu\beta$ between the useful band and the cut-off, and the calculation therefore gives an estimate of the maximum rate at which we can allow $\mu\beta$ to decrease in the feedback loop design. If the design calls for a cut-off which is more abrupt than this the peak phase shift will necessarily be more than 180° and the amplifier will be either Nyquist stable or unstable. A more precise estimate, which allows for the possibility that a certain amount of the total phase area may be found above or below the cut-off interval, can be obtained by the methods described later.

As an example of the use of the phase area law in detailed design work let it be supposed that as a result of a preliminary design the Nyquist diagram for T near the cut-off point takes the form shown by the solid line in Fig. 13.10. The corresponding separate gain and phase characteristics, plotted against log ω, are shown by the solid lines in Figs. 13.11 and 13.12. The useful band is supposed to be found at relatively low frequencies, well below the region covered by the sketches. The amplifier is, of course, unstable. It would become stable, however, if the characteristics were moved to the positions indicated by the broken lines in the three figures.*

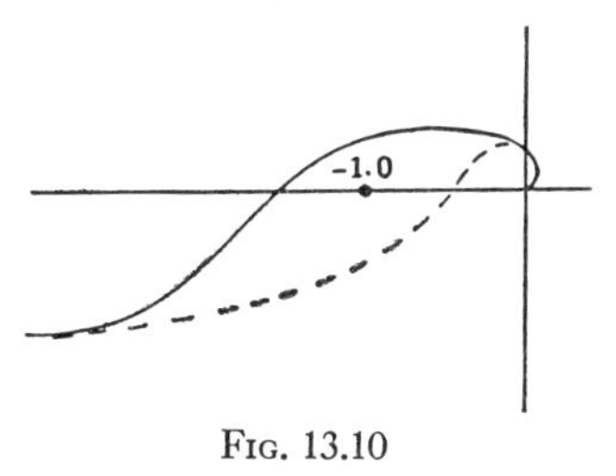

Fig. 13.10

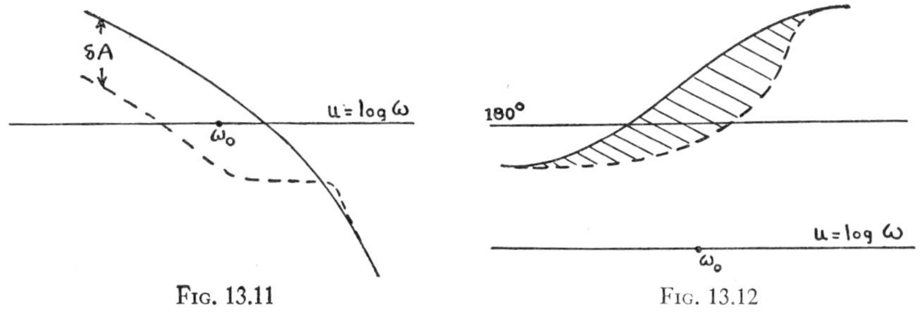

Fig. 13.11

Fig. 13.12

* The reasons why it is necessary to assume that both the loop gain and loop phase characteristics will be changed, and why the new characteristics should be chosen as they are in Figs. 13.11 and 13.12 may be seen in part from the present discussion, but they will appear more clearly from the analysis in later chapters.

Turning first to the phase characteristic, we notice that the change decreases the phase area by the amount indicated by the shading in Fig. 13.12. There must be a corresponding change in $A_0 - A_\infty$.* In a physical circuit, however, we can assume that the characteristics of the feedback loop at extremely high frequencies are determined by parasitic elements, such as interstage capacities, and are beyond our control. The change must therefore affect A_0 rather than A_∞. It is indicated by δA in Fig. 13.11 on the assumption that since the Nyquist diagram is satisfactory at lower frequencies the solid and broken line characteristics in Fig. 13.11 will remain parallel below the region covered by the drawing. The phase area law thus makes it possible to estimate what sacrifice in feedback in the useful band will be required in order to make the amplifier stable.

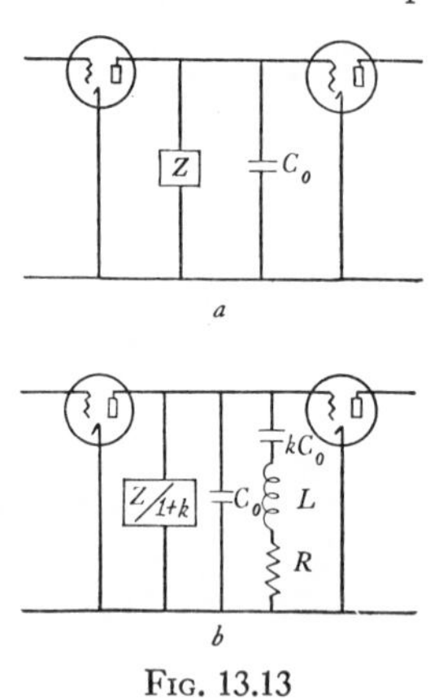

FIG. 13.13

With this clue at one's disposal the choice of an appropriate detailed design should be a relatively simple matter. Let it be supposed, for example, that the external gain of the amplifier is satisfactory. Then the feedback in the useful band must be diminished by changing the μ circuit rather than the β circuit. One possibility is afforded by the addition of a so-called " trap circuit " to one of the interstages. This is illustrated by Fig. 13.13. The original interstage is shown by Fig. 13.13*a* and the modified structure including the trap circuit by Fig. 13.13*b*. At low frequencies, where the elements L and R of the trap circuit are unimportant, the second structure evidently has the same characteristics as the first except for a constant change in level equal to log $(1 + k)$. We can therefore determine k, and consequently the trap circuit capacity C in terms of the interstage capacity C_0, from the results of the phase area computation. For example, if the phase area computation indicates that the feedback in the useful band must be decreased 12 db we must choose $k = 3$. The trap circuit inductance L is chosen to resonate with kC_0 at about the frequency indicated by ω_0 in Fig. 13.12, where the maximum phase change is to be made, and R is fixed by the phase change required at this point. Since the total phase area is correct, this should lead to a reasonably satisfactory result without further trouble in most cases, but minor improvements may be obtainable by making slight changes in L and R or by introducing part of the damping

* In a physical amplifier A_∞ must be infinite. Since the high frequency characteristics around the loop are not changed, however, it is sufficient, for the purposes of this calculation, to identify A_∞ with the attenuation at any frequency beyond the range of interest.

in shunt rather than in series with L. No special attention need be paid to the change in the gain characteristic illustrated by Fig. 13.11, since it follows automatically if the desired phase characteristic is realized.

The μ circuit gain can also be depressed by the introduction of a local feedback circuit for one of the tubes. This is illustrated by Fig. 13.14. R is chosen from (13–14) to give the required decrease in gain at low frequencies. The capacity C can at least be estimated from the relation given in a preceding section, and L and C together form a simple filter which cuts off in the general neighborhood of ω_0. It is, of course, permissible to generalize the filter, either by replacing L by an anti-resonant circuit or by adding more branches to the network, in order to control the characteristics more carefully. The reader should also understand that these illustrations are given in advance of the general design technique described later and are somewhat subordinate to considerations which have not yet appeared. For example, if the local feedback structure is used, it is necessary to consider whether the circuit will remain stable if the gain of the tube to which it applies is decreased.

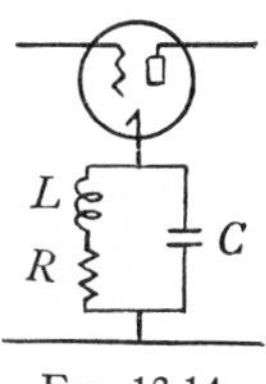

Fig. 13.14

13.9. *Other General Relationships*

The preceding discussion has emphasized the formulae for the integral of the real component and for the integral of the imaginary component both because these are the simplest possible results of the contour integral analysis and because they are of particularly broad application. If we choose more and more complicated integrands the analysis can also be made to yield an almost interminable list of other possible formulae. As the formulae become more complicated, however, their application in physical problems becomes increasingly difficult. The derivation of additional formulae will therefore not be considered in great detail. The following headings summarize some of the methods which can be used in extending the analysis. Typical results to which they lead are given in the list at the end of the chapter.

1. *Formulae Involving Coefficients of Higher Order Terms in Power Series for θ.* In deriving (13–6) we began by subtracting the first term in the series expansion for θ near infinite frequency. The leading term of the series which was left thus consisted of the second term of the original series and the coefficient of this term could be evaluated by means of the integration around the large semicircle. One possible method of extending the preceding theorems is obtained by continuing this process. If we subtract successively more and more terms of the original series the successive coefficients in the expansion can be represented one by one. Equations

III(a) and III(b) in the list at the end of the chapter, for example, show how the coefficients A_1 and A'_1 in the expansions of equations (13–1) and (13–2) can be represented.

A simple illustration of these formulae can be obtained by returning to the structures of Fig. 13.2. In Fig. 13.2a we have $A'_1 = 1/R_0C^2$, while for Fig. 13.2b, A'_1 is evidently zero. Equation III(a) for the two networks thus becomes

$$\int_0^\infty \left[-\frac{\omega^2 C R_0^2}{1 + \omega^2 C^2 R_0^2} + \frac{1}{C} \right] d\omega = \frac{\pi}{2} \frac{1}{C^2 R_0} \tag{13–22}$$

and

$$\int_0^\infty \left[\frac{\omega^2 L(1 - \omega^2 LC) - \omega^2 R_0^2 C}{(1 - \omega^2 LC)^2 + (\omega R_0 C)^2} + \frac{1}{C} \right] d\omega = 0. \tag{13–23}$$

The first of these is obvious by inspection. The second can be verified by writing it as

$$\int_0^\infty \frac{(1 - x^2)\, dx}{(1 - x^2)^2 + \dfrac{R_0^2 C}{L} x^2} = 0 \tag{13–24}$$

or

$$\int_0^1 \frac{(1 - x^2)\, dx}{(1 - x^2)^2 + \dfrac{R_0^2 C}{L} x^2} + \int_0^\infty \frac{(1 - x^2)\, dx}{(1 - x^2)^2 + \dfrac{R_0^2 C}{L} x^2} = 0 \tag{13–25}$$

where $x^2 = \omega^2 LC$. If we replace x by $1/x$ in the second integral of (13–25) it is easily seen that it is exactly the negative of the first integral.

We can express the physical meaning of equations III(a) and III(b) most easily if we rewrite III(a), for example, in either of the forms

$$\int_0^\infty \left(B - \frac{B_\infty}{\omega} \right) d(\omega^2) = \pi A'_1 \tag{13–26}$$

or

$$\int_0^\infty \left[\frac{B}{B_\infty/\omega} - 1 \right] d\omega = \frac{\pi}{2} \frac{A'_1}{B_\infty}. \tag{13–27}$$

Corresponding expressions hold for equation III(b) if ω is replaced by $1/\omega$. In (13–26) and (13–27) B_∞/ω is, of course, the imaginary characteristic which would be realized if the infinite frequency behavior of the structure were maintained over the complete frequency spectrum. If we suppose that A'_1 is zero the equations say that the average value of the actual imaginary characteristic is, in a certain sense, the same as that of this limiting infinite frequency characteristic. In (13–26), for example, the areas under the two characteristics are the same when the computation is made on a frequency squared scale. In (13–27) the average percentage departure of one characteristic from the other is zero if we make the computation on an ordinary arithmetic frequency scale.

Equation (13–27) is illustrated, for the structure of Fig. 13.2, by the curves shown in Fig. 13.15. In these networks B_∞/ω is evidently the capacity reactance $-1/C\omega$, and $B/(B_\infty/\omega)$ is therefore the ratio of the actual reactance to the capacity reactance. Curves I and I′ of Fig. 13.15 show this ratio for the reactance characteristics given originally by Curves I and I′ of Fig. 13.9. Since these curves correspond to the structure of Fig. 13.2*a*, for which A_1'/B_∞ in (13–27) is $-1/R_0C$, the area under the curves is less than that under the unit line. On the other hand, the coefficient A_1' is zero for the network of Fig. 13.2*b* and the average height of the corresponding Curves II and II′ is consequently unity. In other words, the average reactance characteristic obtained from a network of the type shown by Fig. 13.2*b* is, in a sense, unaffected by the addition of the elements R_0 and L.

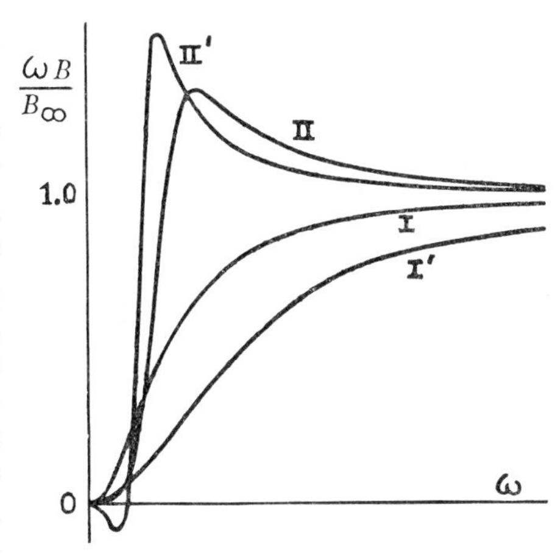

Fig. 13.15

2. *Formulae Involving Products of Functions.* A second general method of extending the list of formulae is found if we regard the original function θ as the product of two functions $\theta_1 = \alpha + i\beta$ and $\theta_2 = \gamma + i\delta$. Both θ_1 and θ_2 may themselves be " network functions " or one of them can be regarded as the particular network characteristic with which we are concerned, while the other is some arbitrary function of frequency introduced to give some desired special weighting to the various parts of the frequency spectrum. It is convenient, however, to suppose that in any case the real component γ of θ_2 vanishes at infinity. If we suppose that θ_1 and θ_2 behave otherwise at infinity in the way we have previously specified for the original function θ, this means that all the terms in the product $\theta_1\theta_2$, except $\alpha_\infty\,\delta_\infty$, vanish at least as rapidly as ω^{-2} and can be ignored in the integration over the infinite semicircle. The contribution of the infinite semicircle to the complete integral is therefore $-\pi\alpha_\infty\,\delta_\infty$. On the real frequency axis, on the other hand, we need retain only the even component $\alpha\gamma - \beta\delta$ of the integrand. The result can therefore be written in the general form

$$\int_0^\infty (\alpha\gamma - \beta\delta)\,d\omega = \frac{\pi}{2}\,\alpha_\infty\delta_\infty. \qquad (13\text{–}28)$$

The cases in which one of the two functions is chosen arbitrarily to produce a desired weighting of the results on the real frequency axis are described later. The simplest example of the use of the formula when θ_1 and θ_2 are both "network functions" is furnished if we assume $\theta_1 = \theta_2 = \theta - \theta_\infty$. This gives equation IV(*a*) in the list at the end of the chapter. On a reciprocal frequency scale the relation can also be written as equation IV(*b*). The process can of course be continued to include still higher powers of $\theta - \theta_\infty$. Equation IV(*c*), for example, gives the result when $\theta_1 = \theta_2^2 = (\theta - \theta_\infty)^2$. Although none of the resulting formulae are given in the list, equation (13–28) can evidently be applied also to situations in which θ_1 and θ_2 are network functions derived from different networks. For example, if θ_1 and θ_2 are the impedances $R_1 + iX_1$ and $R_2 + iX_2$ of two networks of the general types illustrated by Fig. 13.2, equation (13–28) evidently yields

$$\int_0^\infty R_1R_2 \, d\omega = \int_0^\infty X_1X_2 \, d\omega. \tag{13–29}$$

Instead of considering two quite distinct impedances we may also consider one impedance, $R + iX$, and the change in that impedance, $\Delta R + i\Delta X$, produced by some physical change in the network. If we assume that the impedance vanishes at infinity both before and after the change is made the result is

$$\int_0^\infty R\Delta R \, d\omega = \int_0^\infty X\Delta X \, d\omega. \tag{13–30}$$

Equations IV(*a*) and IV(*b*) are of some special interest as an indication that, in addition to meeting the general integral conditions set by the previous equations, the real and imaginary components of θ must be so related that they have approximately equal sinuosity. Thus, for example, equation (13–19) allows us to conclude that a low-pass or high-pass filter without phase shift cannot be constructed, but it gives no information on structures having the same attenuation at zero and infinite frequencies. Equations IV(*a*) and IV(*b*), on the other hand, give a much more general result. This can be formulated as the

Theorem: A network whose reactance or phase characteristic is zero at all points on the real frequency axis cannot have a resistance or attenuation characteristic which varies in any way whatsoever with frequency. Conversely, if the resistance or attenuation characteristic of the network is constant its reactance or phase characteristic can be only that which would be obtained from a two-terminal reactive network or a phase correcting structure.

3. *Formulae Involving Products of Functions with Reversed Symmetry.* As a further extension of this process, we may also suppose that the integrand appears in the general form $\theta_1\theta_2/\omega$. We can suppose that θ_1 and θ_2 have the same significance as they had before except that it is no longer necessary to assume that the real component of one of the functions vanishes at infinite frequency. The introduction of the factor $1/\omega$ has the effect of changing the symmetry of the real and imaginary components of $\theta_1\theta_2$ on the real frequency axis from even to odd or vice versa. The result which is secured is thus the complement of equation (13–28) in much the same sense that (13–19) is the complement of (13–6). We readily find that

$$\int_{-\infty}^{\infty} (\beta\gamma + \alpha\delta)\, du = \frac{\pi}{2}(\alpha_\infty\gamma_\infty - \alpha_0\gamma_0) \tag{13–31}$$

where $u = \log \omega$.

If we let $\theta_1 = \theta_2 = \theta$ this expression yields V(a) in the list given at the end of the chapter. Similarly, the choices $\theta_1 = \theta_2 = i\omega(\theta - \theta_\infty)$ and $\theta_1 = \theta_2 = (1/i\omega)(\theta - \theta_0)$ lead to V(b) and V(c), respectively. As in the previous discussion, the formula can also be applied when θ_1 and θ_2 refer to different networks. For example, the equation corresponding to (13–29) is

$$\int_{-\infty}^{\infty} (R_1X_2 + R_2X_1)\, du = -\frac{\pi}{2}R_{01}R_{02} \tag{13–32}$$

where R_{01} and R_{02} are the zero frequency values of the two impedances. Similarly, we can replace (13–30) by

$$\int_{-\infty}^{\infty} R\Delta X\, du = -\int_{-\infty}^{\infty} X\Delta R\, du \tag{13–33}$$

if we suppose that ΔR vanishes at both zero and infinite frequency.

The most interesting equation of this group is probably V(d). This is an equivalent form of V(a) which is obtained with the help of some of the preceding equations by means of the transformations

$$\begin{aligned}\int_{-\infty}^{\infty} AB\, du &= \frac{A_\infty + A_0}{2} \times \frac{\pi}{2}(A_\infty - A_0) \\ &= \frac{A_\infty + A_0}{2}\int_{-\infty}^{\infty} B\, du.\end{aligned} \tag{13–34}$$

Equation V(d) follows directly from this if we interpret $\bar{A}$ as $(A_\infty + A_0)/2$. The equation states in effect that the real and imaginary components of θ are orthogonal on a logarithmic frequency scale, if we measure the real component from this reference value. A simple example is furnished by the network of Fig. 13.2*a*. The reactance characteristic of the structure and its resistance characteristic, measured from $\bar{A}$, are shown respectively by the broken and solid lines in Fig. 13.16. In this instance the orthogonality of the two components is easily seen from the fact that they have respectively odd and even symmetry about the center point of the characteristic.

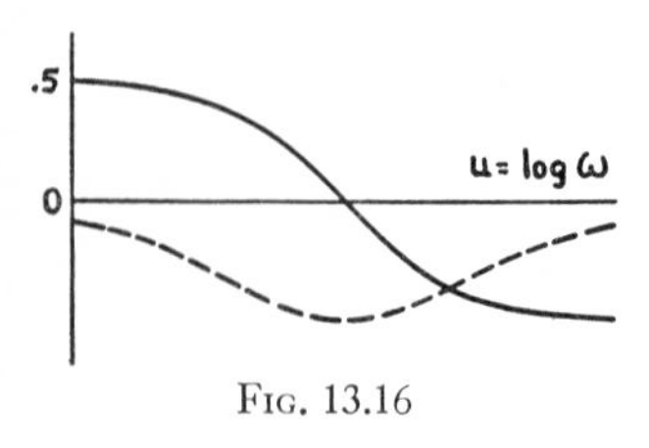

FIG. 13.16

4. *Formulae Involving A and B at Finite Points or Integrals of A and B over Finite Ranges.* The equations considered thus far fall into two general classes. In one, which may be illustrated by IV(*a*), the integrals of two aspects of the network performance are compared to one another. In the other, which may be illustrated by I(*a*), one such integral is related to a specific number which is derived from a different aspect of the characteristic. In either case, however, the integrals extend over the complete frequency spectrum, from zero to infinity, and any specific numbers which may enter the equations are descriptive of the behavior of the structure only at these extreme points.

The practical utility of the formulae would be greatly extended if these specifications could be exchanged for specifications on the behavior of the function at finite points or over finite ranges. For example, I(*a*) shows what restrictions must be placed on the real component if the imaginary component behaves in a prescribed way at infinity. For some design problems it would be more useful to know how the real component is restricted if the imaginary component assumes some chosen value at a prescribed finite point. We might also conceive of using I(*a*) the other way around, to determine how the imaginary component must behave at infinity if the real component is prescribed over the complete spectrum. In practical design problems, however, the characteristics are usually prescribed over only a finite range. For such applications a formula which stated how B must be restricted when the integration of A is carried out over only a finite interval would evidently be more valuable.

Extensions of these general types can be obtained by modifying the integrands in the earlier formulae appropriately. For example, such quantities as A_0, B_0, A_∞ and B_∞ appear in the earlier formulae because they are residues of the integrand which are evaluated by the integration around either the large semicircular portion of the complete path or the small indentation near the origin. Residues which specify A and B at other points can be obtained if we introduce corresponding poles into the integrand and indent the contour of integration appropriately. For example, we can secure an integrand with poles at $+\omega_0$ and $-\omega_0$, to preserve symmetry, by multiplying the integrands in any of the preceding expressions by $1/(\omega - \omega_0) \pm 1/(\omega + \omega_0)$. Similarly, we can restrict the range of integration of either A or B by introducing branch points, which interchange the real and imaginary components in the complete integrand.

These possibilities are mentioned here largely for the sake of completeness. They grade insensibly into the analysis presented in later chapters and it will simplify exposition to consider them from the point of view adopted there. As an example of the introduction of branch points to generalize such a formula as I(a), however, we may consider the equation

$$\oint \frac{\theta - A_\infty}{\sqrt{1 - \omega^2/\omega_c^2}} d\omega = 0, \tag{13–35}$$

where it is supposed that the "positive" square root of $\sqrt{1 - \omega^2/\omega_c^2}$ is taken. In other words $\sqrt{1 - \omega^2/\omega_c^2}$ is a positive real quantity for $-\omega_c < \omega < \omega_c$, it is a positive imaginary for $\omega > \omega_c$ and a negative imaginary for $\omega < -\omega_c$.* This is the same convention as would be used if $\sqrt{1 - \omega^2/\omega_c^2}$ represented a filter image impedance.

It is evident that the integration around the large semicircle in (13–35) can be ignored. The integral from zero to infinite frequency of the even component of the integrand must therefore vanish also. In virtue of the way in which $\sqrt{1 - \omega^2/\omega_c^2}$ behaves, however, $(A - A_\infty)/\sqrt{1 - \omega^2/\omega_c^2}$ is an even function of frequency for $|\omega| < \omega_c$ and is odd thereafter, while $iB/\sqrt{1 - \omega^2/\omega_c^2}$ is even for $|\omega| > \omega_c$ and is odd for smaller values of ω. The equation therefore reduces to

$$\int_0^{\omega_c} \frac{A - A_\infty}{\sqrt{1 - \omega^2/\omega_c^2}} d\omega = -\int_{\omega_c}^{\infty} \frac{B}{\sqrt{\omega^2/\omega_c^2 - 1}} d\omega. \tag{13–36}$$

This expression has been written as equation VI(a) in the list at the end of the chapter. The corresponding expression in terms of reciprocal frequencies is listed as equation VI(b). In addition to these two, a variety of other more or less closely related expressions can be obtained by multiplying or dividing the original integrands in VI(a) and VI(b) by ω or by applying the same methods to other formulae in the general list.

The physical application of (13–36) can be illustrated by supposing that we have an amplifier whose characteristics outside the useful band are

* In mathematical terms the branch cut between $+\omega_c$ and $-\omega_c$ must be so chosen that the integration contour lies on one sheet of the Riemann surface. These are the appropriate signs for $\sqrt{1 - \omega^2/\omega_c^2}$ if we regard $\sqrt{1 - \omega^2/\omega_c^2}$ as positive for positive real values of p and move continuously to the real frequency axis without leaving the sheet.

satisfactory but which has an unsatisfactory feedback characteristic within the useful band. For example, the feedback in the useful band may be irregular, whereas it should be flat, or it may be flat when a varying feedback would be more desirable. In order to apply (13–36) we may identify ω_c with the edge of the band in the low-pass equivalent design and let A and B represent respectively the $\mu\beta$ gain and the $\mu\beta$ phase shift. The desirable characteristics outside the band will be retained if we do not change B in the second integral of (13–36) or A_∞, which may be taken as the gain at any representative high frequency point, in the first integral. The equation thus states that the reproportioning of the feedback in the useful band must leave $\int_0^{\omega_c} A\,d\omega/\sqrt{1-\omega^2/\omega_c^2}$ unchanged. Since $d\omega/\sqrt{1-\omega^2/\omega_c^2} = \omega_c\,d\varphi$, where $\varphi = \sin^{-1}(\omega/\omega_c)$, this is the same as saying that the area under the A characteristic when plotted against φ must be kept constant. A similar rule holds for the maximum gain obtainable from an interstage network with a varying characteristic. These applications are described in more detail in later chapters.

13.10. *Extensions of Contour Integral Formulae to Other Systems*

This discussion has been directed primarily at systems of lumped electrical elements. It is reasonable to suspect from the generality of the contour integral process, however, that the formulae may apply to other systems as well. As examples we might take a system including mechanical as well as electrical elements or a system of distributed electrical elements like a transmission line.

The problem of extending the contour integral formulae to other systems can be treated very easily if we know the analytic form of the function θ which we wish to study. Evidently, it is merely necessary to examine the function to determine whether it meets the list of conditions given at the beginning of the chapter. The condition to which special attention must be paid is the one which limits the behavior of θ at infinite frequency. In many of the formulae developed in this chapter it is necessary to assume that θ remains finite at infinity. In others, and in all the formulae developed later, this restriction is not necessary, but it is generally necessary to assume, at least, that θ/ω vanishes when ω is made indefinitely great. The function θ will, of course, be finite at infinite frequency if it represents a driving point impedance or admittance of minimum type in a lumped constant circuit. If θ represents a transfer loss and phase this is not necessarily true, but since the function can increase only logarithmically, at most, the requirement on θ/ω, at least, is always met. If we are dealing with the ordinary transmission line equation $\theta = \sqrt{(R + i\omega L)(G + i\omega C)}$, on the other hand, neither requirement is met, since θ varies near infinity as $i\omega\sqrt{LC}$. The term $i\omega\sqrt{LC}$ is, of course, a linear phase characteristic corresponding to the electromagnetic delay in the propagation of the wave down the line and we naturally cannot expect it to be correlated with the attenuation characteristic of the line. In this instance, we can evidently apply the contour integral formulae merely by subtracting this linear characteristic from the total phase characteristic.

The difficulty with this attack is, of course, the fact that we frequently do not have a precise analytic formula for θ at our disposal and it is exactly in situations when our knowledge of the behavior of the function is somewhat incomplete that the additional help afforded by the contour integral relations is most useful. For example, in a physical transmission line the " constants " R, L, G, and C usually vary somewhat with frequency because of skin effects, proximity effects, etc. Although it is possible to establish formulae which describe the behavior of the line over a broad frequency range, the discovery of exact formulae which work literally to infinity is another question.

If we nevertheless postulate that there is an analytic function θ, even though the form of the function may be unknown, it is possible to conclude, on general grounds, that it should meet most of the conditions in the list given previously. For example, the symmetry of the real and imaginary components of θ, as described in conditions (1) and (2), depends, in a structure of lumped electrical elements, only upon the fact that the coefficients in the differential equations for the structure are all real quantities. Evidently the same considerations should apply to any physical system. Except for the obvious qualifications required to take care of such functions as a non-minimum transfer loss and phase, condition (3) is satisfied in the lumped electrical structure merely because the circuit is stable. The same general argument can obviously be extended to any system specified by ordinary linear differential equations analogous to the mesh equations of the electrical circuit. The argument also applies to systems of distributed constants if we suppose, as is commonly done, that such a system can be represented as the limit of a series of lumped constant systems.

As an alternative to the limiting process, we can also study the behavior of the function on the right half-plane directly. The situation is most readily expressed by the

Theorem: The input or transfer admittance of a stable physical system cannot become indefinitely great in the neighborhood of any point in the interior of the right half-plane if the corresponding indicial admittance of the system is bounded.

The theorem is easily established with the help of the familiar equation*

$$I(t) = E(0)A(t) + \int_0^t A(t - \lambda)E'(\lambda)\, d\lambda, \qquad (13\text{–}37)$$

where $E(t)$ is a voltage applied to some point in the structure at the time $t = 0$, $E'(t)$ is the time derivative of $E(t)$, $I(t)$ is the current flowing in response to $E(t)$, either at the same or at some other point in the circuit, and $A(t)$ is the indicial admittance between the two points. If M is the upper bound of $A(t)$ the equation can be written as

$$| I(t) | \leq | E_0 | M + M \int_0^t | E'(\lambda) | \, d\lambda. \qquad (13\text{–}38)$$

But the actual response must also be the sum of a steady state term and a transient term. If we let $E(t) = e^{pt}$, where p is chosen in the neighborhood in which the steady state response becomes indefinitely great, it is clear that the limit represented by (13–38) can be made an indefinitely small fraction of the envelope of the steady state response. Thus the transient term must approximate the steady state term and must increase exponentially as the steady state term does. In other words, the system is unstable.

If the admittance is a single valued function of p its only possible singularities in the right half-plane are poles or essential singularities. In either case, however, these possibilities are ruled out by the theorem just established, since the admittance will become indefinitely great at appropriately chosen points in the neighborhood of the singularity.† We may also imagine the admittance to be a multiple valued function. If the admittance is to represent something physically determinable, however, the possibility that it may have branch points in the right half-plane is greatly restricted by the consideration that we must choose one branch of the function to represent the " physical " admittance without introducing branch cuts which will give discontinuities in the physical response characteristic.‡ Even without this argument, the previous theorem excludes such possibilities as logarithmic singularities or branch points of the type represented by $(p - k)^{-1/2}$.

* See, for example, Bush's *Operational Circuit Analysis*, p. 56, or Carson's *Electric Circuit Theory*, p. 16.

† See, for example, Goursat-Hedrick, *A Course in Mathematical Analysis*, Vol. II, Part I, p. 92.

‡ This argument does not apply with equal force to branch points in the left half-plane because it is not necessarily possible to determine " steady state " characteristics by physical measurements in this region. See, for example, the discussion at the end of Chapter II.

An example of branch points which might conceivably exist in the right half-plane is furnished if we suppose that the admittance includes the factors $(p - \alpha_1)^{1/2}(p - \alpha_2)^{1/2}$. This situation is evidently not ruled out by the previous theorem. Moreover, if the rest of the function is real for real values of p, the complete function will be a pure imaginary on a branch cut extending from α_1 to α_2 on the real p axis. Thus the physical response, which is defined as the real component of $e^{pt}Y$, is zero at the cut and there is no discontinuity in moving from the top to the bottom halves of the plane. If α_1 and α_2 are almost equal the two irrational factors can be replaced approximately by an ordinary zero. Since a zero in the right half-plane in an ordinary network merely indicates a non-minimum phase shift function, the existence of this possibility is perhaps not unnatural.

This discussion has been presented for what it may be worth. It is evidently unwise to dogmatize about so vague and general a problem. The implication of the discussion, however, is that if a linear physical system is known to be stable, which is proved by its mere existence, its driving point and transfer functions must satisfy most of the conditions for the contour integral analysis. Aside from singularities of the type just described difficulties are likely to appear principally because of the existence of singularities on the real frequency axis, and especially at infinity. If we are concerned in particular with transmission, these effects may be looked upon as departures from a minimum phase condition. They are qualitatively similar to the departures which one might expect in lumped constant networks, although they may differ from possible lumped constant characteristics in detail.

TABULATION OF CONTOUR INTEGRAL FORMULAE

Group		*Integrand*	*Result*
I	(*a*)	$\theta - \theta_\infty$	$\int_0^\infty (A - A_\infty)\, d\omega = -\frac{\pi}{2} B_\infty$
	(*b*)	$\frac{\theta - \theta_0}{\omega^2}$	$\int_0^\infty \frac{A - A_0}{\omega^2}\, d\omega = \frac{\pi}{2} B_0$
	(*c*)	$\theta - \theta_\infty$	$\int_0^\infty \omega \frac{dA}{d\omega}\, d\omega = \frac{\pi}{2} B_\infty$
	(*d*)	$\frac{\theta - \theta_0}{\omega^2}$	$\int_0^\infty \frac{1}{\omega} \frac{dA}{d\omega}\, d\omega = \frac{\pi}{2} B_0$
II	(*a*)	$\frac{\theta}{\omega}$	$\int_{-\infty}^\infty B\, du = \frac{\pi}{2}(A_\infty - A_0)$

TABULATION OF CONTOUR INTEGRAL FORMULAE (*Continued*)

Group		*Integrand*	*Result*
III	(*a*)	$\omega\left(\theta - A_\infty - i\dfrac{B_\infty}{\omega}\right)$	$\int_0^\infty (\omega B - B_\infty)\,d\omega = \dfrac{\pi}{2}A_1'$
	(*b*)	$\dfrac{\theta - A_0 - iB_0\omega}{\omega^3}$	$\int_0^\infty \dfrac{B - B_0\omega}{\omega^3}\,d\omega = -\dfrac{\pi}{2}A_1$
IV	(*a*)	$(\theta - \theta_\infty)^2$	$\int_0^\infty (A - A_\infty)^2\,d\omega = \int_0^\infty B^2\,d\omega$
	(*b*)	$\dfrac{(\theta - \theta_0)^2}{\omega^2}$	$\int_0^\infty \dfrac{(A - A_0)^2}{\omega^2}\,d\omega = \int_0^\infty \dfrac{B^2}{\omega^2}\,d\omega$
	(*c*)	$(\theta - \theta_\infty)^3$	$\int_0^\infty (A - A_\infty)^3\,d\omega = 3\int_0^\infty (A - A_\infty)B^2\,d\omega$
V	(*a*)	$\dfrac{\theta^2}{\omega}$	$\int_{-\infty}^\infty AB\,du = \dfrac{\pi}{4}(A_\infty^2 - A_0^2)$
	(*b*)	$\omega(\theta - \theta_\infty)^2$	$\int_0^\infty \omega(A - A_\infty)B\,d\omega = -\dfrac{\pi}{4}B_\infty^2$
	(*c*)	$\dfrac{(\theta - \theta_0)^2}{\omega^3}$	$\int_0^\infty \dfrac{(A - A_0)B}{\omega^3}\,d\omega = \dfrac{\pi}{4}B_0^2$
	(*d*)	$\dfrac{\theta^2}{\omega}$	$\int_{-\infty}^\infty (A - \bar{A})B\,du = 0$
VI	(*a*)	$\dfrac{\theta - A_\infty}{\sqrt{1 - \omega^2/\omega_c^2}}$	$\int_0^{\omega_c} \dfrac{A - A_\infty}{\sqrt{1 - \omega^2/\omega_c^2}}\,d\omega = -\int_{\omega_c}^\infty \dfrac{B}{\sqrt{\omega^2/\omega_c^2 - 1}}\,d\omega$
	(*b*)	$\dfrac{\theta - A_0}{\omega^2\sqrt{1 - \omega_c^2/\omega^2}}$	$\int_{\omega_c}^\infty \dfrac{A - A_0}{\sqrt{1 - \omega_c^2/\omega^2}}\dfrac{d\omega}{\omega^2} = -\int_0^{\omega_c} \dfrac{B}{\sqrt{\omega_c^2/\omega^2 - 1}}\dfrac{d\omega}{\omega^2}$

In II, V(*a*) and V(*d*), $u = \log\omega$.

CHAPTER XIV

Relations Between Real and Imaginary Components of Network Functions*

14.1. *Introduction*

The theorems developed in the preceding chapters are concerned with a number of rather specialized relations between the real and imaginary components of network characteristics. The first theorem, for example, allows us to calculate the resistance or attenuation integral when the behavior of the corresponding reactance or phase characteristic at infinite frequency is known. The second theorem gives a similar relation for the integral of the imaginary component in terms of the behavior of the real component at extreme frequencies. Except for rather specific limitations of this sort, however, the theorems leave the detailed real and imaginary characteristics still to be determined.

The present chapter continues this discussion to consider the problem of determining one characteristic completely when the other is known at all frequencies. The three special problems considered are:

1. The computation of the imaginary characteristic corresponding to a real characteristic which is prescribed over the complete frequency spectrum.
2. The computation of the real characteristic corresponding to a prescribed imaginary characteristic.
3. The computation of the remaining portions of the two characteristics when the real component is prescribed in some parts of the frequency spectrum and the imaginary component is prescribed in the rest of the spectrum.

* The fact that there must be an analytic connection between the real and imaginary components of a network characteristic has been recognized by a number of previous writers. The literature of the field includes a considerable list of more or less specific results, developed usually by Fourier or operational methods. No attempt is made to review this work here, partly because the variety of attacks which have been followed are difficult to reduce to a coherent basis and partly because the formulae are frequently ambiguous, because of the authors' failure to recognize the minimum phase condition. Special mention should, however, be made of the work of Norbert Wiener and his students. See, for example, Y. W. Lee's paper in the *Journal of Mathematics and Physics* for June 1932, which includes formulae equivalent to a number of the formulae in the present chapter.

The results are stated here in terms of analytic formulae. Methods of making approximate computations graphically are considered in the next chapter.

14.2. *Applications of Formulae for Relations between Real and Imaginary Characteristics*

Formulae for the relation between the real and imaginary components in the three situations just listed are developed here principally as tools in feedback amplifier design. If we are concerned with the overall feedback loop characteristic, for example, the phase integral theorem of the preceding chapter gives some information on the loop phase characteristic which we may expect to accompany a loop cut-off characteristic of given general type. If we are to be certain that the maximum phase shift will not exceed a safe limit, however, it is necessary to secure much more detailed information concerning the relation between the two characteristics. Any one of the three formulae of the present chapter, but in particular the first and the third, may be used for this purpose. The formulae may also be used in detailed amplifier design problems. Examples here are furnished by the discussion of interstage circuits and input and output circuits given in later chapters.

The formulae may also be applied to many problems of ordinary network theory. As one illustration, we may consider the design of the Z_{11} impedance in a constant resistance equalizer of the type described in Chapter XII. Both the magnitude and phase angle of the Z_{11} impedance are determined if we specify both the loss and phase shift of the complete structure. If we deal only with the loss characteristic, however, we can secure a required attenuation, at any one frequency, from a Z_{11} impedance of any phase angle provided the magnitude of the impedance is properly chosen. This appears at first sight to add an element of flexibility to the problem. In accordance with the results of the present chapter, however, the phase characteristic of the equalizer would be completely fixed if the required loss characteristic extended over all frequencies, and it is approximately fixed throughout the center of any reasonably broad band over which the loss characteristic is prescribed. In fact, therefore, the Z_{11} impedance of many equalizers can be fairly accurately determined in both magnitude and phase angle. In many equalization problems a rough preliminary computation of this sort may serve as a useful guide to design work. Since a phase angle of more than 90° cannot be provided for the Z_{11} impedance, the preliminary computation is also useful in determining whether the prescribed characteristic is physically obtainable with a single equalizer section.

These uses of the formulae are sufficiently exemplified by the discussion in later chapters. The formulae will be illustrated in the present chapter, consequently, by a study of the general problem of providing a selective system without phase distortion. Such a system might, of course, be a linear phase shift low-pass filter. The " system " may, however, be either more or less complicated than a filter. For example, a very simple system of this type is represented by an interstage network in a non-feedback video amplifier. Here the selectivity depends upon the fact that the gain of the interstage must decrease at high frequencies because of the interstage capacities. At the other extreme, the system might consist of a length of coaxial line, complete with repeaters, equalizers, etc., transmitting television signals. In this instance, the selectivity of the system may be ascribed to the increase in the line attenuation at high frequencies and to the fact that normal repeaters cannot be expected to maintain their gain at frequencies well above or below the useful band.

In practice, satisfactory characteristics are usually obtained in situations like these by means of additional phase equalization in the systems. The formulae developed here, however, refer only to minimum phase shift networks. Thus the discussion attempts to show only what types of distortion are to be expected in selective systems not including separate phase equalization and, very roughly, how the amount of phase equalization required can be related to the selectivity characteristic.

14.3. *Phase Characteristic Corresponding to a Prescribed Attenuation Characteristic**

The equation relating the imaginary characteristic and real characteristic in general is in effect an extension of equation (13–6) in the preceding chapter. As it was discussed there, this equation was regarded as a condition imposed on the real characteristic for a prescribed variation of the imaginary characteristic in the neighborhood of infinity. On the other hand, we can equally well regard the equation as a method of determining the behavior of the imaginary component at high frequencies when the real component is known.

The reason for the appearance of B_∞ in the final expression is that the function has a residue of this amount at infinity, which is evaluated by the integration around the large semicircle. If we can create a corresponding residue at any finite frequency, it should be equally easy to determine the corresponding B at that point. Let it be supposed, for example, that we wish to evaluate B at ω_c. It is first necessary to create a pole at this point

* As a matter of simplicity of expression the real and imaginary components of the function θ are referred to frequently as " attenuation " and " phase " in the rest of this chapter. The reader will of course understand, however, that θ can be any function meeting the requirements given in the preceding chapter.

by dividing θ by $\omega - \omega_c$. In order to preserve the symmetry of the expression a term to give a pole at the complementary point $-\omega_c$ should also be introduced. If we also suppose that A_c, the value assumed by A at $\omega = \omega_c$, is subtracted from θ,* the resulting contour integral can be written as

$$\oint \left(\frac{\theta - A_c}{\omega - \omega_c} - \frac{\theta - A_c}{\omega + \omega_c} \right) d\omega = 0. \tag{14-1}$$

It is readily seen that the integrand vanishes at least as rapidly as ω^{-2} at high frequencies. The contribution of the large semicircular path to the complete integral can therefore be ignored. The remaining portion of the path consists of the real frequency axis and two small semicircular indentations of the type shown by Fig. 13.1 in the preceding chapter, which are taken to avoid the poles at $\omega = \pm\omega_c$. If the indentations are very small, θ on each of them can be assumed to be constant and equal to the value $A_c + iB_c$ or $A_c - iB_c$, which it assumes at the corresponding point $\pm\omega_c$. This allows (14–1) to be written as

$$\int_{-\infty}^{\infty} \frac{2\omega_c}{\omega^2 - \omega_c^2} (A - A_c + iB)\, d\omega + \oint' iB_c \left(\frac{1}{\omega - \omega_c} - \frac{1}{\omega + \omega_c} \right) d\omega$$
$$- \oint'' iB_c \left(\frac{1}{\omega - \omega_c} - \frac{1}{\omega + \omega_c} \right) d\omega = 0, \tag{14-2}$$

in which the first term represents the contribution of the real frequency axis and the second and third terms the contributions around the two small indentations. In the first integral we can neglect the imaginary com-

* This is done essentially to facilitate exposition. In equation (14–2), for example, it allows us to avoid consideration of the A terms which would otherwise appear in the two primed integrals. It also simplifies the consideration of (14–3) since the vanishing of $A - A_c$ at $\omega = \omega_c$ prevents the integrand from exhibiting a pole at this point. These, however, are reasons of convenience rather than necessity. Thus in (14–2) the contributions of the A terms in the two primed integrals would cancel out anyway, even if they were left in. The difficulty with (14–3) can be avoided if we notice that the method of deriving (14–3) leads to the so-called " principal value " of the integral. In other words, if the small quantity ε represents the radius of the semicircular indentations around $\pm\omega_c$, the actual limits of integration run from zero to $\omega_c - \varepsilon$ and from $\omega_c + \varepsilon$ to infinity. For these limits, it is easily shown by direct integration that the A_c term contributes nothing to the result when ε is made sufficiently small. If the integrals are defined in terms of their principal values, therefore, this term can be omitted from (14–3) and all subsequent equations. This will be of some importance later in the chapter where terms analogous to A_c are occasionally omitted to simplify the formal expressions.

ponent from considerations of symmetry In the second integral we can neglect $1/(\omega + \omega_c)$ in comparison with $1/(\omega - \omega_c)$ if we suppose that this indentation is the one near ω_c. With the help of (8–4) in Chapter VIII the integral can be evaluated as $i\pi(iB_c) = -\pi B_c$. This is also the value obtained for the third integral from similar considerations. The result is therefore

$$B_c = \frac{2\omega_c}{\pi} \int_0^\infty \frac{A - A_c}{\omega^2 - \omega_c^2} d\omega. \tag{14–3}$$

An alternative form of equation (14–3) will be developed in a succeeding section. The present form is particularly useful in studying the approximate phase characteristic corresponding to an attenuation characteristic

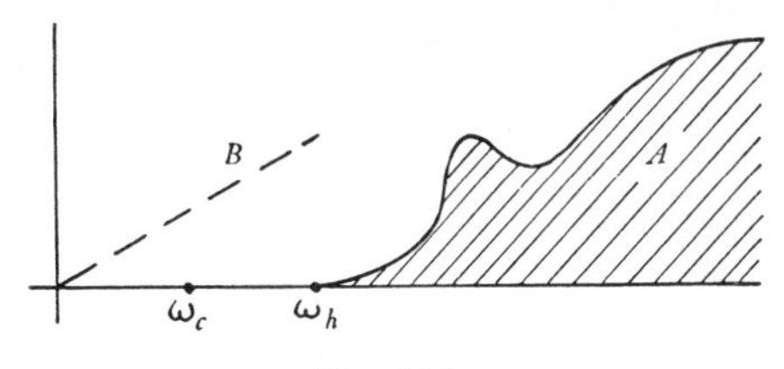

FIG. 14.1

which is nearly constant in the frequency range near ω_c but which may vary appreciably at more remote frequencies. This is illustrated by Figs. 14.1 and 14.2. In Fig. 14.1, for example, the attenuation characteristic is nearly constant in the region below some point ω_h. If ω_c is less than ω_h, $A - A_c$

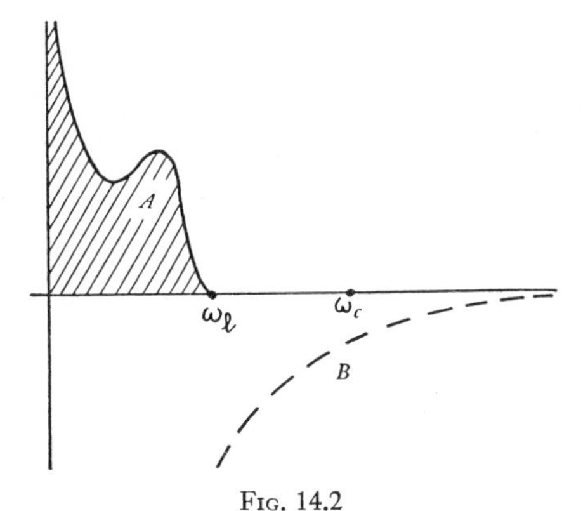

FIG. 14.2

in (14–3) will be very small throughout this low-frequency region and this portion of the total integral can be neglected. If we also ignore ω_c^2 in comparison with ω^2 in the integration beyond ω_h the equation can be written as

$$B_c \doteq \frac{2\omega_c}{\pi} \int_{\omega_h}^{\infty} (A - A_c) \frac{d\omega}{\omega^2}$$
$$\doteq \omega_c \left[\frac{2}{\pi} \int_0^{1/\omega_h} (A - A_c)\, d\left(\frac{1}{\omega}\right) \right]. \tag{14–4}$$

In other words, the low frequency phase shift is proportional to frequency and to the area under the high-frequency attenuation characteristic computed on a reciprocal frequency scale. This is illustrated by the broken line in Fig. 14.1. The result is, in form, the same as equation I(b) of the preceding chapter, but the method of derivation allows it to be used over a considerably wider range than we would be entitled to assume with the derivation used there. For further purposes perhaps the most important feature of the equation is the fact that it states that *any* high-frequency attenuation characteristic is reflected at low frequencies as a linear phase shift. This property will be much used in shaping amplifier cut-off characteristics at high frequencies, since it allows us to adjust the high-frequency characteristics with considerable freedom and still produce corresponding phase characteristics which cancel one another out over a wide low-frequency band.

If the attenuation characteristic is of the form shown by Fig. 14.2 we can proceed in the same way, except that now ω^2 must be neglected in comparison with ω_c^2 in the denominator of the integrand in (14–3). The result is

$$B_c \doteq \frac{-1}{\omega_c} \left[\frac{2}{\pi} \int_0^{\omega_l} (A - A_c)\, d\omega \right], \tag{14–5}$$

where ω_l, as shown in Fig. 14.2, is the point at which the low-frequency attenuation characteristic begins. Thus the high-frequency phase shift varies inversely with frequency and is proportional to the negative of the area under the low-frequency attenuation characteristic computed on an arithmetic frequency scale. The phase shift is shown by the broken line in Fig. 14.2.

If the attenuation characteristic is constant in the neighborhood of ω_c but varies at both high and low frequencies we can, of course, obtain the phase shift by adding together the elementary results (14–4) and (14–5). This gives

$$B_c \doteq K_1 \omega_c - \frac{K_2}{\omega_c}, \tag{14–6}$$

where the constants K_1 and K_2 are written for brevity in place of the terms enclosed by the brackets in (14–4) and (14–5). If the K's are both positive the net phase characteristic is evidently similar to the reactance characteristic of an ordinary resonant circuit.

The simplest illustrations of these formulae are furnished by filters. Let it be supposed, for example, that we are dealing with a low-pass filter which has an average attenuation of about 6 nepers over a frequency range extending from about 3000 cps to infinity. The low-frequency phase shift is, from (14–4), given approximately by

$$\begin{aligned} B_c &= \omega_c \left[\frac{2}{\pi} \int_0^{1/6000\pi} 6\, d\left(\frac{1}{\omega}\right) \right] \\ &\doteq 2 \times 10^{-4} \omega_c. \end{aligned} \tag{14–7}$$

It is to be noticed that this low-frequency delay, equal to about 0.2 millisecond, is a consequence merely of the fact that the high-frequency selectivity exists, and does not depend upon the particular configuration adopted for the filter. This is of some interest in connection with the discussion given near the end of Chapter XI on the problem of designing a negative all-pass network to cancel a filter phase characteristic.

14.4. *Phase Equalization of a Broad-Band System*

A more elaborate example of the use of equations (14–4) to (14–6) is furnished by a study of the overall phase characteristic of a complete telephone system. This was discussed briefly in one of the preceding sections. It is convenient to suppose that the system under consideration is a broad-band affair, like a coaxial line with its associated repeaters and equalizers, and that we are chiefly interested in isolating the factors which determine how much phase equalization would be required in order to fit the system for the transmission of television signals.*

If the equalizers and repeater gains are properly adjusted, the net attenuation of the system must be constant and substantially zero over a useful band extending from ω_1 to ω_2. We may, however, expect the attenuation to rise rapidly below ω_1 and above ω_2 due to the failure of the repeaters to maintain their gains outside the useful band and to the increase in the line attenuation at high frequencies. The complete attenuation characteristic thus takes the form shown by the solid line in Fig. 14.3. In a long system including many repeater points the losses below ω_1 and above ω_2 may amount to hundreds or thousands of db.

It will be supposed that the repeaters and equalizers are all of minimum phase shift type. In accordance with the discussion of the preceding chap-

* For an example of such a system, see the paper by Strieby and Wentz, referred to in the preceding chapter.

ter it will be assumed that the line can also be included in a minimum phase shift analysis if we disregard a linear phase characteristic representing the infinite frequency behavior of the structure.* Corresponding to the overall

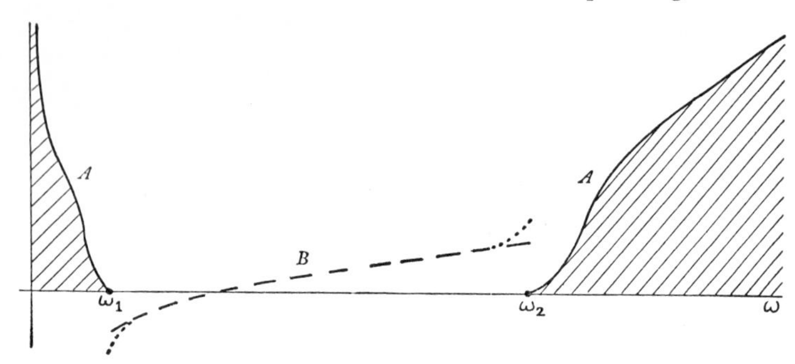

FIG. 14.3

attenuation characteristic shown by the solid line in Fig. 14.3, therefore, the net phase characteristic must take the form defined by equation (14–6). It is illustrated by the broken line in Fig. 14.3. Upon studying the relationship expressed by (14–6) we may draw the following conclusions:

1. There is a strong tendency for the attenuation equalization of the line to produce automatic compensation for its phase characteristic also. This tendency becomes more pronounced as the band width in octaves is increased. In other words, equation (14–6) shows that only the variations in the attenuation characteristic beyond the band contribute to the phase characteristic. If the band is very broad the regions of increased attenuation are so remote from the center of the useful band that the net phase characteristic in this range is very small. If the transmitted band is not over 1 or 2 octaves wide, on the other hand, the tendency of the system to provide automatic phase equalization will manifest itself only very imperfectly.
2. To a first approximation, the attenuation characteristic at high frequencies corresponds to a linear phase shift in the useful range. It is therefore not a factor in producing delay distortion. The low-frequency attenuation, on the other hand, produces a delay characteristic varying as $1/\omega^2$. In a broad-band system, therefore, the low-frequency attenuation characteristic may produce a substantial amount of delay distortion. It follows that if the final phase

* The attenuation characteristic of the line at infinite frequency of course remains. If the analysis is to apply it is necessary to assume that A/ω vanishes at infinity. This requirement is met by a coaxial line, where the attenuation varies approximately as $\sqrt{\omega}$ at high frequencies.

equalization of the system is to be as simple as possible the overall low-frequency attenuation should be substantially less than the overall high-frequency attenuation. Since the line attenuation at frequencies below the band should be much smaller than it is above the band this is fortunately not a difficult condition to achieve.

3. Near the edges of the band the approximate formula (14–6) becomes inaccurate. We note, however, that when ω_c approaches the edge of the band the integrand of equation (14–3) exceeds the approximate value assigned to it in equations (14–4), (14–5), and (14–6) throughout the range of integration. At the edges of the band, therefore, the net phase characteristic must be greater than the approximate formula indicates. This is illustrated by the dotted lines in Fig. 14.3. In virtue of this effect, we cannot conclude that the contribution of the high-frequency attenuation characteristic gives no phase distortion. It is apparent, however, that the ratio between the approximate value of the integrand in equations (14–4) to (14–6) and the exact value at any prescribed frequency ω_c is greater for the part of the total range of integration which lies near the useful band than it is for remote regions. The high-frequency phase distortion and the increase in the low-frequency phase distortion will therefore be much reduced if the loss characteristic can be made to cut off gradually just beyond the useful band. This problem is discussed at greater length later in the chapter.
4. The same considerations also lead to a second conclusion. Since the influence of the attenuation characteristic just beyond the useful band

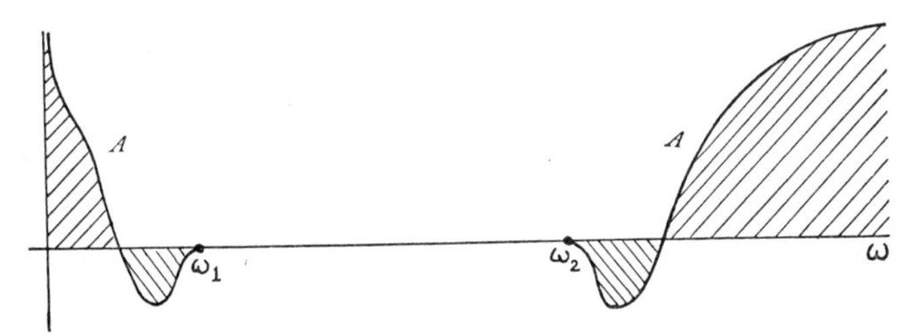

Fig. 14.4

is preponderant, a relatively small negative attenuation in this range should cancel the phase distortion due to the much larger positive attenuations which are physically inevitable at more remote frequencies. In other words, a system having a transmission characteristic of the general type illustrated by Fig. 14.4 should be substantially phase distortionless. Transmission characteristics of this type are not generally admissible for a variety of reasons. For example, in a long system the required net gain at the edges of the band, although it may be relatively small, is still so great in db that random noise picked up in this part of the spectrum will eventually overload the repeaters. The device may, however, be useful in special applications.

14.5. *Alternative Formula for the Relation between Loss and Phase*

Equation (14–3) is a useful tool in studying the phase characteristic corresponding to attenuations at relatively remote frequencies. When the attenuation characteristic varies appreciably in the neighborhood of the frequency at which the phase is to be determined, however, it is more convenient to use an alternative expression. The alternative formula is found by writing (14–3) on a logarithmic frequency scale. If we set $u = \log(\omega/\omega_c)$ the expression becomes

$$\begin{aligned} B_c &= \frac{2}{\pi}\int_0^\infty \frac{A - A_c}{\omega/\omega_c - \omega_c/\omega}\frac{d\omega}{\omega} \\ &= \frac{2}{\pi}\int_{-\infty}^\infty \frac{A - A_c}{e^u - e^{-u}}\,du \\ &= \frac{1}{\pi}\int_{-\infty}^\infty \frac{A - A_c}{\sinh u}\,du. \end{aligned} \tag{14–8}$$

This equation is next integrated by parts much as equation I(a) was integrated in the preceding chapter to secure equation I(c). The integration of (14–8), however, is simplified if we divide the complete range of integration into separate ranges above and below $u = 0$. Considering first the integration over positive values of u, we have

$$B_1 = -\frac{1}{\pi}\left[(A - A_c)\log\coth\frac{u}{2}\right]_0^\infty + \frac{1}{\pi}\int_0^\infty \frac{dA}{du}\log\coth\frac{u}{2}\,du. \tag{14–9}$$

If we replace u by $-u$ the integration over negative values of u can be performed in a similar manner* and yields

$$B_2 = \frac{1}{\pi}\left[(A - A_c)\log\coth\frac{-u}{2}\right]_{-\infty}^0 + \frac{1}{\pi}\int_{-\infty}^0 \frac{dA}{du}\log\coth\frac{-u}{2}\,du. \tag{14–10}$$

* That is, the integral of $1/\sinh u$, which was taken as $\log\coth(u/2)$ for positive values of u, is taken as $\log\coth(-u/2)$ when u is negative. The imaginary component which would appear if the integral were taken as $\log\coth(u/2)$ for negative values of u also is not actually of importance, since it cancels out when the limits of integration are introduced, but its presence complicates the discussion. A somewhat similar point is exemplified by a number of later equations, such as (14–20) and (14–28).

Near $u = 0$, the quantity $A - A_c$ must be approximately proportional to u while log coth $u/2$ will vary as $-\log (u/2)$. At the limit $u = 0$, therefore, the integrated portions of both (14–9) and (14–10) must appear in the general form $u \log u$, which is known to vanish when u vanishes. At the other limits, the log coth term approximates $2\,e^{-u}$ or $2(\omega_c/\omega)$, in equation (14–9) and $2\,e^{u}$, or $2(\omega/\omega_c)$, in equation (14–10). Since we have already restricted the permissible loss functions to those for which ωA and A/ω vanish at zero and infinite frequency, respectively, this means that the integrated portions of (14–9) and (14–10) vanish at these limits also and can be disregarded entirely. When the two equations are added together to find the complete phase shift, therefore, the result appears as

$$B_c = \frac{1}{\pi}\int_{-\infty}^{\infty} \frac{dA}{du} \log \coth \frac{|u|}{2}\, du. \qquad (14\text{–}11)$$

Although equation (14–11) may appear to be a more complicated expression than equation (14–3), it can be given a simple physical interpretation. We observe in the first place that the equation implies broadly that the phase characteristic is proportional to the derivative of the attenuation

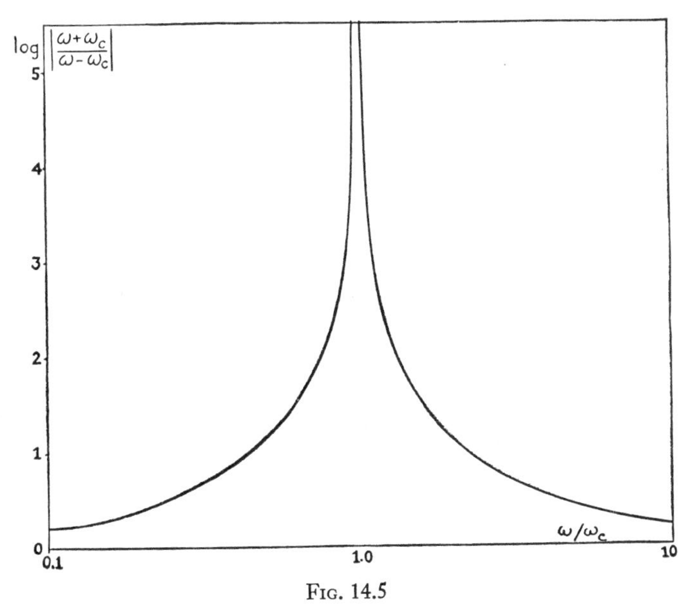

FIG. 14.5

characteristic on a logarithmic frequency scale. Thus, if we double dA/du we will also double B_c. Since the integration includes the complete frequency spectrum, however, the phase characteristic at any point depends upon the slope of the attenuation characteristic in all parts of the spectrum.

The relative importance of the slopes in various parts of the spectrum is given by the term log coth $|u/2|$ which can also be written as $\log|(\omega+\omega_c)/(\omega-\omega_c)|$. This term thus acts as a weighting factor. It is plotted in Fig. 14.5.

As we might expect physically, the weighting factor is large in the vicinity of $\omega=\omega_c$. In fact, it becomes logarithmically infinite at this point. Thus, the derivative of the attenuation characteristic in the neighborhood of the frequency at which the phase is to be computed is much more important in determining the result than the attenuation slope at more remote points. For frequencies much larger than ω_c the weighting factor is approximately $2(\omega_c/\omega)$, while at frequencies much smaller than ω_c it is approximately $2(\omega/\omega_c)$. Thus in either case the importance of a remote attenuation slope is inversely proportional to the interval, expressed as an arithmetical frequency ratio, between the point at which the slope occurs and the point at which the phase is to be computed. This is evidently in agreement with our previous result that attenuations remote from the useful range will produce a phase characteristic which is proportional to frequency if the attenuation is found above the useful band and one which is inversely proportional to frequency if the attenuation characteristic is below the useful range.

14.6. *Phase Characteristics Corresponding to Illustrative Attenuation Characteristics*

With equation (14–11) at hand, it is evidently theoretically possible to determine the phase characteristic corresponding to any attenuation characteristic. We need merely differentiate the attenuation characteristic on a logarithmic frequency scale, multiply it by the weighting curve and integrate the result, using graphical integration if necessary. If a large number of points of the phase characteristic must be obtained, however, repeated computations of this sort become quite tedious. An easier method, which applies in most situations, is described in the next chapter. For the purposes of the present discussion (14–11) will be illustrated by a number of very simple attenuation characteristics for which the corresponding phase characteristics can be found analytically.

The simplest possible illustration of (14–11) is obtained if the attenuation characteristic has a constant slope on a logarithmic frequency scale at all frequencies. If we set $dA/du=k$ in (14–11) the equation becomes

$$B=\frac{k}{\pi}\int_{-\infty}^{\infty}\log\coth\frac{|u|}{2}\,du. \tag{14–12}$$

The definite integral, however, is known* to be $\pi^2/2$. The phase shift is,

* See Bierens de Haan, "Nouvelles Tables D'Intégrales Définies," Table 256.

therefore, given by

$$B = k\frac{\pi}{2}\cdot \tag{14–13}$$

The phase characteristic is therefore constant and equal to 90° multiplied by the slope of the attenuation characteristic. These relations are illustrated by Fig. 14.6.

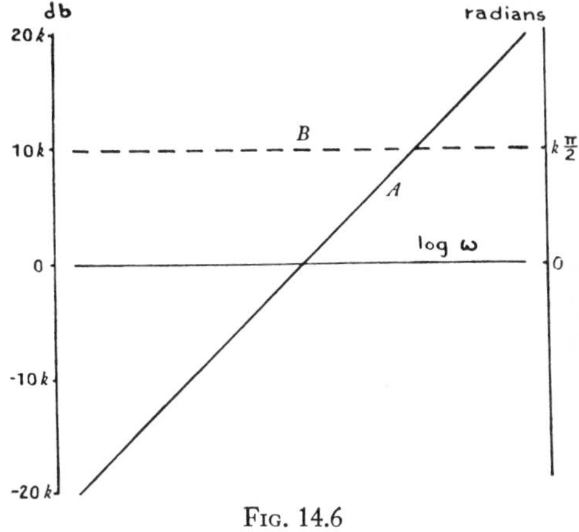

Fig. 14.6

For purposes of future discussion it is desirable to identify the units in terms of which the slope k is expressed. Since u is a natural logarithm and A is written in nepers, choosing $k = 1$ is equivalent to supposing that A will change by one neper between frequencies which are in the ratio, $e = 2.7183$. In other words, if $k = 1$, the attenuation, expressed as a current ratio, is proportional to the arithmetic frequency. This will be called a *unit slope* in future discussion. A unit slope is evidently the same as a change of 6 db per octave or 20 db per decade* and may also be referred to in these terms.

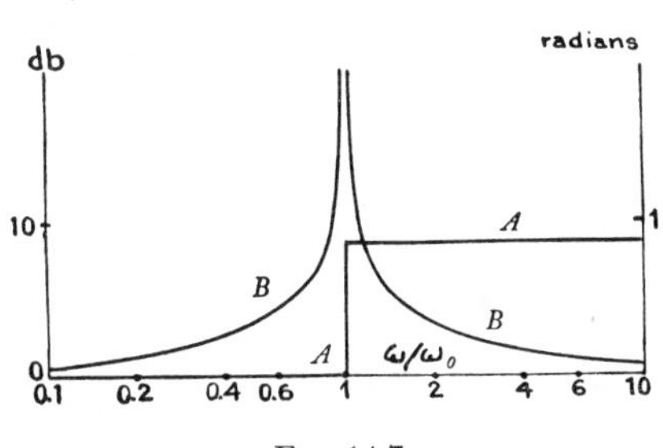

Fig. 14.7

As a second example of (14–11), let it be supposed that the attenuation is everywhere constant except for a discontinuity at one frequency. This is illustrated by Curve A of Fig. 14.7. We can represent the discontinuity, for the purpose of applying (14–11), by supposing that dA/du is very large over a very narrow range in the neighborhood of the break. Since dA/du is elsewhere zero, we need carry the integral in (14–11) only over this narrow range. Since the weighting function can be regarded as a constant over this narrow range, however, the integral reduces, in effect, to the integral of dA/du itself over the region of the break. This is the same as the total

* In accordance with a growing usage, the term decade is used here to mean a frequency interval of ten to one, or an interval of one cycle of graduations in a plot on ordinary log paper.

change in A at the discontinuity. The phase shift at any point is therefore equal to the product of the change in A and the value of the weighting function corresponding to the interval between the break frequency and the frequency at which the phase shift is computed. It can be written as

$$B = \frac{k}{\pi} \log \left| \frac{\omega + \omega_0}{\omega - \omega_0} \right|, \tag{14–14}$$

where k is the change in A in nepers and ω_0 is the break frequency. This is illustrated by Curve B in Fig. 14.7 for $k = 1$.

A third elementary characteristic of special interest is that in which the attenuation is constant on one side of a prescribed frequency ω_0 and has a constant slope thereafter. This is illustrated by Curve A in Fig. 14.8. Characteristics of this type are described in more detail in the next chapter and will be used at several points in later discussions. They will be called *semi-infinite constant slope* characteristics in future analysis.

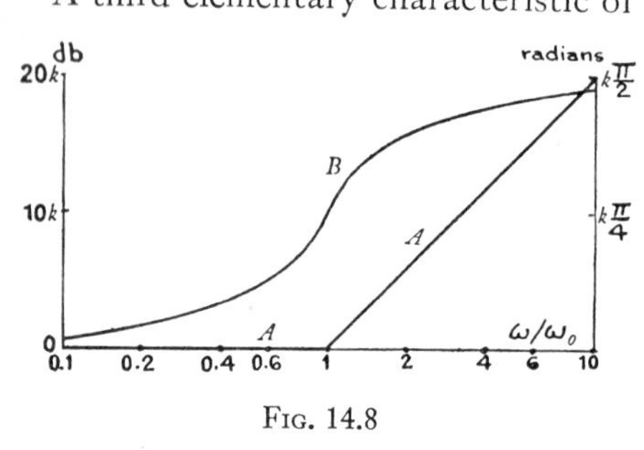

FIG. 14.8

The computation of the phase characteristic accompanying an attenuation characteristic of this sort is more difficult than it was for either of the preceding examples. A detailed analysis of the problem is consequently postponed to the next chapter. The general properties of the phase characteristic can, however, be understood from Curve B of Fig. 14.8. For example, at a frequency which is well within the sloping part of the attenuation characteristic the phase shift is only slightly less than $k(\pi/2)$, where k is the attenuation slope. It is thus almost equal to the phase shift which would be obtained with an attenuation characteristic having the constant slope k at all frequencies. It is apparent from (14–11) that this must be so, since the only difference between the two situations is the fact that in the semi-infinite case $dA/du = 0$ in (14–11) over a range of integration corresponding to one of the tails of the weighting curve. We may also observe that the phase shift at ω_0 is just half the asymptotic value $k(\pi/2)$ and that the characteristic exhibits odd symmetry on a logarithmic frequency scale about this point. The reason for this relationship is again obvious from (14–11) if it is noticed that the sum of two semi-infinite characteristics with the same slope k, but running in opposite directions from ω_0, must be equal to a constant slope characteristic. This is shown by Fig. 14.9, the two semi-infinite characteristics being identified by the solid and broken lines. The sum of the accompanying phase characteristics must, of course, be equal to $k(\pi/2)$, while it is apparent from the symmetry of (14–11) for positive and negative values of u that the two characteristics must be equal at reciprocally related frequencies.

In accordance with the earlier discussion, the low-frequency phase shift for the semi-infinite characteristic of Fig. 14.8 must be substantially linear on an arithmetic scale. The exact expression is readily obtained from (14–4) and appears as

$$B = \frac{2}{\pi} k \frac{\omega}{\omega_0}, \qquad \omega \ll \omega_0. \tag{14–15}$$

Thus if we assume $k = 1$ the linear phase characteristic extrapolated to ω_0 is equal to $2/\pi$ radians, or about 36.5°. The actual phase shift at this point, as determined from the considerations just discussed, is $\pi/4$ radians, or 45°. It is evident from these figures that the phase characteristic is at least roughly linear over the complete frequency range below ω_0. Over most of the range in fact, the approximation is even better than these figures might suggest, since the departure of the actual phase characteristic from the linear approximation occurs chiefly in the range just below ω_0. This can be seen most easily from the equation

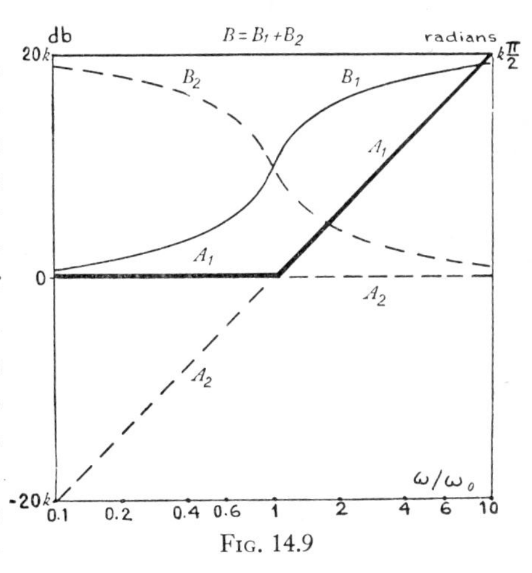

Fig. 14.9

$$\frac{dB}{d\omega} = \frac{k}{\pi\omega} \log \left| \frac{\omega_0 + \omega}{\omega_0 - \omega} \right|, \tag{14–16}$$

which is established in the next chapter. This expression is roughly constant over the first two-thirds or three-quarters of the band. At higher frequencies, however, it increases rapidly and approaches infinity logarithmically as ω approaches ω_0. The very high value of $dB/d\omega$ near ω_0 is, of course, a reflection of the artificiality of the postulated attenuation characteristic and would be avoided if the attenuation varied smoothly through ω_0.

The elementary characteristics illustrated by Figs. 14.6, 14.7, and 14.8 have been introduced principally for their application in the approximate study of attenuation-phase relations according to the methods developed later. They are also of some interest, however, in connection with the general problem of the phase distortion in selective circuits, which was discussed earlier. For example, we can evidently take Fig. 14.7 to represent an idealized low-pass filter, with infinitely sharp discrimination between the transmission and attenuation regions. Equation (14–14), then, shows the phase distortion which such a system must have in the absence of phase equalization and represents the limit approached by a physical filter as it becomes more and more sharply discriminating. On the other hand, comparison of Figs. 14.7 and 14.8 shows that the phase distortion is due primarily to the presence of a sharp rise in attenuation just beyond the useful band and not to the fact that the system discriminates, on the whole, between a wanted and an unwanted range. Thus the phase characteristic of Fig. 14.8 is reasonably linear over most of the useful band in spite of the fact that the attenuation eventually rises far beyond the highest value attained in Fig. 14.7. Moreover, even the residual phase distortion in Fig. 14.8 can be somewhat reduced if the transition between the wanted and unwanted regions is made more smoothly. These results are confirmed and extended by later examples.

14.7. *Relation between Phase and Attenuation Characteristics on an Arithmetic Frequency Scale*

Equation (14–11) has been expressed in terms of the logarithm of frequency since this is usually the scale which lends itself most appropriately to physical problems. By a direct transformation, however, the equation can also be expressed in terms of any other frequency variable z. This process is especially useful if z represents either frequency itself or the reciprocal of frequency.

The transformation to the new frequency scale z is facilitated by the fact that the term $(dA/du)du$ in the integrand of (14–11) becomes simply $(dA/dz)dz$, whatever z may be. In order to complete the transformation, therefore, it is merely necessary to express the weighting function appropriately on the new scale and to change the limits of integration so that they will continue to embrace the complete positive real frequency axis. Thus, if z represents ω, equation (14–11) is transformed into

$$B_c = \frac{1}{\pi}\int_0^\infty \frac{dA}{d\omega}\log\left|\frac{\omega+\omega_c}{\omega-\omega_c}\right| d\omega, \tag{14–17}$$

while if z represents $1/\omega$, the equation becomes

$$B_c = -\frac{1}{\pi}\int_0^\infty \frac{dA}{d\,(1/\omega)}\log\left|\frac{1/\omega+1/\omega_c}{1/\omega-1/\omega_c}\right| d\,(1/\omega). \tag{14–18}$$

As an example of these transformations, let it be supposed that the attenuation characteristic for which a corresponding phase shift is to be determined is one which has constant slope for a finite interval of an arithmetic frequency scale. Such a characteristic is shown by Curve A in Fig. 14.10 where, for convenience, the slope is supposed to begin at the origin.* The characteristic is, in a sense, the counterpart of the semi-infinite slope on the logarithmic frequency scale which was considered previously. It is important to notice, however, that in contrast to a slope on a logarithmic frequency scale, the characteristic we are now considering cannot be regarded as extending over an indefinitely large interval since

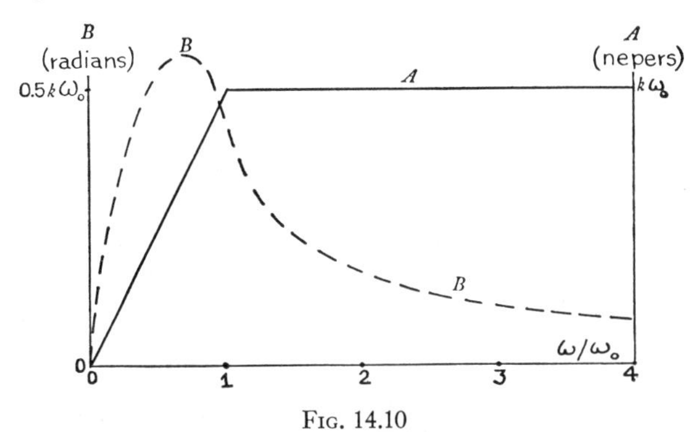

FIG. 14.10

this would violate the condition that A/ω must vanish at infinite frequency.

Let the slope $dA/d\omega$ between the origin and the point ω_0 be represented by k. Then since $dA/d\omega = 0$ at higher frequencies, equation (14–17) can be written as

$$B_c = \frac{k}{\pi}\int_0^{\omega_0} \log\left|\frac{\omega + \omega_c}{\omega - \omega_c}\right| d\omega. \tag{14–19}$$

This is readily evaluated as

$$B_c = \frac{k\omega_0}{\pi}[(x+1)\log(x+1) + (x-1)\log|x-1| - 2x\log x], \tag{14–20}$$

where x equals ω_c/ω_0.

A sketch of the function defined by (14–20) is shown by Curve B in Fig. 14.10. Its general shape is about what one would expect from (14–11) if it is recalled that a constant attenuation slope on an arithmetic scale is equivalent to a slope which gradually decreases toward low frequencies when the characteristic is plotted on a logarithmic frequency scale.

* Since, by postulate, A is an even function of frequency this means that the curve must change direction sharply at the origin. The behavior of the phase characteristic at extremely low frequencies is consequently rather peculiar, as inspection of equation (14–20) or Fig. 14.10 shows. This somewhat unnatural choice of the attenuation characteristic can be disregarded here, since its effects disappear in the applications of the analysis made later in this chapter and in the next chapter.

14.8. *Attenuation Characteristic Corresponding to a Given Phase Characteristic*

Thus far in this chapter, the problem under consideration has been that of determining the phase characteristic corresponding to a given attenuation. We will now turn to the converse problem of determining the attenuation when the phase is known. In its general features the solution of this problem differs from the preceding one in only one important respect. When the attenuation is prescribed, the corresponding minimum phase is uniquely determined. Since we can always add or subtract an arbitrary loss in a physical circuit without affecting its phase characteristic however, the attenuation corresponding to a given phase can be determined only to within an arbitrary additive constant. In the equations which follow this is taken into account by referring the attenuation characteristic to the attenuation at zero or infinite frequency.

The required formulae can be obtained most simply by replacing θ by either $i\omega(\theta - A_\infty)$ or $(\theta - A_0)/i\omega$ in all the preceding equations. The introduction of the factor $i\omega$ has, as its chief effect, the interchange of the real and imaginary components at each stage of the analysis. Thus, if we begin with $i\omega(\theta - A_\infty)$, the real component is $-\omega B$, and has even symmetry, while the imaginary component is $i\omega(A - A_\infty)$ with odd symmetry. If we replace A by $-\omega B$ and B by $\omega(A - A_\infty)$, therefore, the formulae which have been used to determine B from A can be applied equally well to determine A from B. Similarly, the adoption of the function $(\theta - A_0)/i\omega$ is equivalent to replacing the original A and B by B/ω and $-(A - A_0)/\omega$, respectively. The terms A_0 and A_∞ are included in the new expressions in order to prevent them from having a pole at zero or infinite frequency, which would be contrary to our original assumptions about the function to be integrated. Their introduction is equivalent to measuring the attenuation from its zero or infinite frequency value, as discussed previously.

With this as a basis, the development of appropriate formulae for the computation of the loss characteristic corresponding to a given phase characteristic is a matter of simple substitution. Thus, if we begin with the function $i\omega(\theta - A_\infty)$, equation (14–3) is transformed into

$$A_c - A_\infty = -\frac{2}{\pi}\int_0^\infty \frac{\omega B - (\omega B)_c}{\omega^2 - \omega_c^2}\,d\omega, \tag{14–21}$$

while if we begin with $(\theta - A_0)/i\omega$, the result is

$$A_c - A_0 = -\frac{2\omega_c^2}{\pi}\int_0^\infty \frac{B/\omega - B/\omega_c}{\omega^2 - \omega_c^2}\,d\omega. \tag{14–22}$$

Similarly, the derivative formula of equation (14–11) can be transformed into

$$A_c - A_\infty = -\frac{1}{\pi\omega_c}\int_{-\infty}^{\infty} \frac{d(\omega B)}{du}\log\coth\frac{|u|}{2}\,du \tag{14–23}$$

and

$$A_c - A_0 = -\frac{\omega_c}{\pi}\int_{-\infty}^{\infty} \frac{d\,(B/\omega)}{du} \log \coth \frac{|u|}{2}\, du. \qquad (14\text{–}24)$$

In physical problems the phase shift is frequently constant over broad intervals so that the functions $B\omega$ and B/ω will vary respectively as ω or $1/\omega$. This makes the expression of the formulae in terms of arithmetic frequency scales or reciprocal frequency scales of greater interest than it is when the known component was the attenuation. Appropriate formulae for these scales are easily obtained by modifying equations (14–17) and (14–18). If we let z represent either ω or $1/\omega$, the results of both equations can be written as

$$A_c - A_\infty = \pm \frac{1}{\pi\omega_c}\int_0^{\infty} \frac{d(\omega B)}{dz} \log \left|\frac{z + z_c}{z - z_c}\right| dz \qquad (14\text{–}25)$$

and

$$A_c - A_0 = \pm \frac{\omega_c}{\pi}\int_0^{\infty} \frac{d\,(B/\omega)}{dz} \log \left|\frac{z + z_c}{z - z_c}\right| dz \qquad (14\text{–}26)$$

where, in each expression, the negative sign must be chosen if $z = \omega$ and the positive sign if $z = 1/\omega$.

All these formulae assume that either A_0 or A_∞ will be finite. This is, of course, not invariably true. In physical systems, however, the losses at zero and infinite frequency, if they are not finite, will become infinite logarithmically. One or the other of the two losses can therefore always be made finite by the addition of a suitable constant slope characteristic. The required slope is easily determined from a consideration of the phase characteristic at the limit.

Elementary illustrations of these transformations are most readily obtained by returning to the characteristics shown previously in Figs. 14.6, 14.7, 14.8, and 14.10. We can transform any of these figures to give new relations between A and B by multiplying or dividing the characteristics as they stand by ω and interchanging the real and imaginary characteristics. As an example, consider Fig. 14.7. If we suppose that we are dealing with the transformation which replaces θ by $i\omega(\theta - A_\infty)$, Curve A in that figure can be identified with the product of $-\omega$ and the new B, while Curve B is ω times the new $A - A_\infty$. We can consequently divide the original curves by $\pm\omega$ to secure the characteristics for the new B and the new $A - A_\infty$ shown by Fig. 14.11.

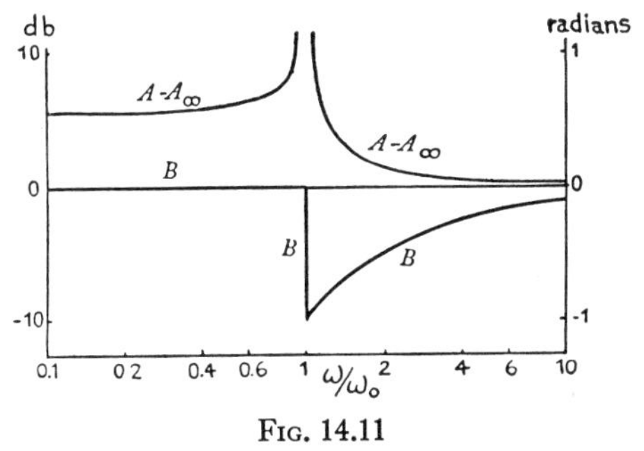

Fig. 14.11

Conversely, if we suppose that θ has been replaced by $(\theta - A_0)/i\omega$, Curves A and B in Fig. 14.7 become respectively plots of B/ω and $-(A - A_0)/\omega$ for the new function. The new B and the new $A - A_0$ consequently take the form shown by Fig. 14.12. It will be noticed that the new B becomes infinite at infinite frequency. This merely illustrates the fact that the transformations allow us to deal in some instances with a θ whose behavior at zero or infinite frequency is less restricted than was previously assumed. In Fig. 14.12, for example, the infinite B at infinite frequency indicates a departure from a minimum phase shift condition of the type which was described in the preceding chapter as appropriate for an ordinary transmission line. We can correct the phase curve if we like by subtracting a linear component or, what amounts to the same thing, by displacing the original attenuation characteristic in Fig. 14.7 to make the infinite frequency attenuation zero. This leads to the new phase curve shown by B' in Fig. 14.12. If the practical problem is that of constructing the attenuation characteristic corresponding to a prescribed phase characteristic which is known to have been derived from a minimum phase shift structure, questions of this sort naturally cannot arise.

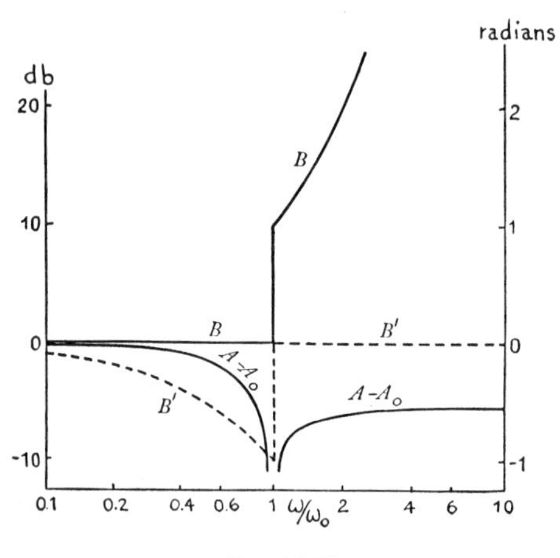

FIG. 14.12

14.9. *Linear Phase Shift Systems*

As a more elaborate example of the calculation of the attenuation characteristic corresponding to a given phase characteristic we will return again to the problem of designing a selective system without distortion in the useful range. Unless the band is infinitely broad, the requirements of zero attenuation distortion and zero phase distortion cannot be met simultaneously with minimum phase shift characteristics. In the earlier treatment of the problem, it was assumed that the attenuation characteristic over the band was ideal and we attempted to determine the residual phase distortion which remained for phase equalization. Here we will assume, on the other hand, that the minimum phase characteristic is ideal and study the residual attenuation distortion which is to be expected in consequence.

In order to simplify the problem, the lower cut-off of the system will be ignored. It will be supposed, then, that the desired phase characteristic is that shown in Fig. 14.13. The slope of the phase characteristic is taken at the constant value $dB/d\omega = a$ between zero and some point ω_0, while above ω_0 the phase shift B itself is constant and equal to $a\omega_0$. The constant value of B at high frequencies evidently means that the attenuation will eventually increase logarithmically with frequency, much like the semi-infinite slope characteristic of Fig. 14.8. As we have already seen, the semi-infinite characteristic gives a roughly linear phase characteristic at low frequencies and the approximation to linearity is improved by making a more gradual transition between the sloping and non-sloping parts of the attenuation characteristic. The present calculation thus amounts to a determination of the exact rounding off in the attenuation characteristic which is required in order to make the phase characteristic exactly linear.

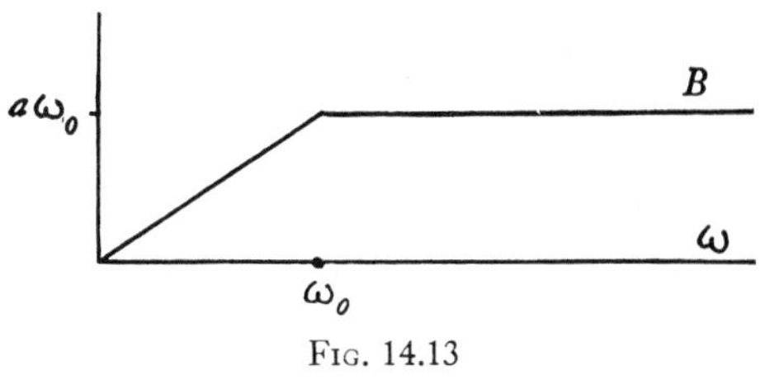

FIG. 14.13

The preceding general equations give us the option of determining the attenuation characteristic corresponding to the phase characteristic of Fig. 14.13 by a study of either $B\omega$ or B/ω. In the present instance, the function B/ω is obviously the one which it will be convenient to use. A further simplification is afforded by adoption of an inverse frequency scale. With this choice B/ω is a straight line with the slope $a\omega_0$ from $1/\omega = 0$ to $1/\omega = 1/\omega_0$ and is constant for higher values. This is indicated by the solid line in Fig. 14.14. The analysis of this characteristic has already been given in effect by (14–20). In order to adapt the result in (14–20) to the present problem it is merely necessary to replace B_c by $(1/\omega_c)(A_c - A_0)$ and make the changes called for by the inversion of the frequency scale. This gives

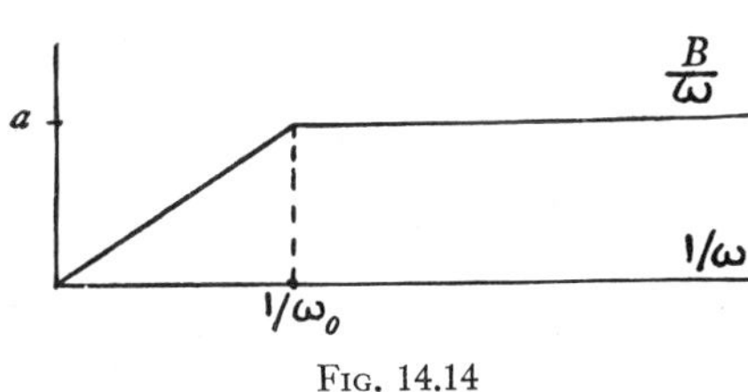

FIG. 14.14

$$\frac{1}{\omega_c}(A_c - A_0) =$$

$$\frac{a}{\pi}\left[\left(\frac{\omega_0}{\omega_c}+1\right)\log\left(\frac{\omega_0}{\omega_c}+1\right)+\left(\frac{\omega_0}{\omega_c}-1\right)\log\left|\frac{\omega_0}{\omega_c}-1\right|-2\frac{\omega_0}{\omega_c}\log\frac{\omega_0}{\omega_c}\right], \tag{14–27}$$

which can be reduced to

$$A_c - A_0 = \frac{a\omega_0}{\pi}\left[\left(1+\frac{\omega_c}{\omega_0}\right)\log\left(1+\frac{\omega_c}{\omega_0}\right)+\left(1-\frac{\omega_c}{\omega_0}\right)\log\left|1-\frac{\omega_c}{\omega_0}\right|\right]. \tag{14–28}$$

A sketch of the attenuation characteristic defined by (14–28), with the constant $a\omega_0$ chosen as unity, is shown by Fig. 14.15. The originally prescribed phase characteristic is indicated by the broken lines. It will be seen that the characteristics are much like those of a low-pass filter except for a considerable amount of attenuation distortion near the edge of the band.

A different form of attenuation characteristic is obtained if we assume that the phase shift is zero between the origin and ω_0 while it retains its high

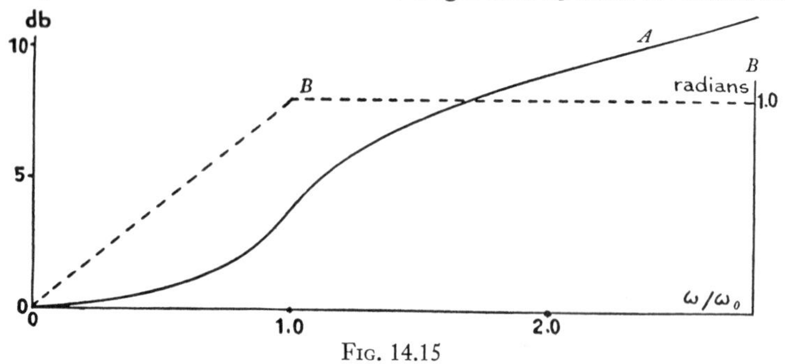

FIG. 14.15

frequency value, $a\omega_0$, beyond this point. This is equivalent to supposing that the characteristic B/ω drops abruptly to zero at the edge of the band, as indicated by the broken line in Fig. 14.14. The effect of such an abrupt break can be obtained by replacing B_c by $(1/\omega_c)(A_c - A_0)$ in the previous solution (14–14) for the phase characteristic corresponding to a discontinuous attenuation characteristic. The result is

$$(A_c - A_0)' = \frac{-a\omega_c}{\pi} \log \left| \frac{\omega_0 + \omega_c}{\omega_0 - \omega_c} \right| \qquad (14\text{–}29)$$

and this, when added to equation (14–28), gives

$$A_c - A_0 = \frac{a\omega_0}{\pi} \log \left| 1 - \frac{\omega_c^2}{\omega_0^2} \right| \cdot \qquad (14\text{–}30)$$

A sketch of the characteristics corresponding to (14–30) is shown by Fig. 14.16. It will be seen that with this solution the attenuation characteristic in the band curves downward rather than upward, as it does in (14–28). This evidently suggests that still better characteristics might be obtained from a combination of the two solutions. If we multiply (14–28) by λ and (14–30) by $1 - \lambda$ and add the equations the result is

$$A_c - A_0 = \frac{a\omega_0}{\pi} \left[\log \left| 1 - \frac{\omega_c^2}{\omega_0^2} \right| + \lambda \frac{\omega_c}{\omega_0} \log \left| \frac{1 + \dfrac{\omega_c}{\omega_0}}{1 - \dfrac{\omega_c}{\omega_0}} \right| \right] \cdot \qquad (14\text{–}31)$$

If $\lambda = 0.63$ this gives the phase and attenuation characteristics shown by the solid lines of Fig. 14.17.

The curves of Fig. 14.17 are of interest chiefly as an exemplification of the argument advanced earlier in connection with Fig. 14.4. It will be

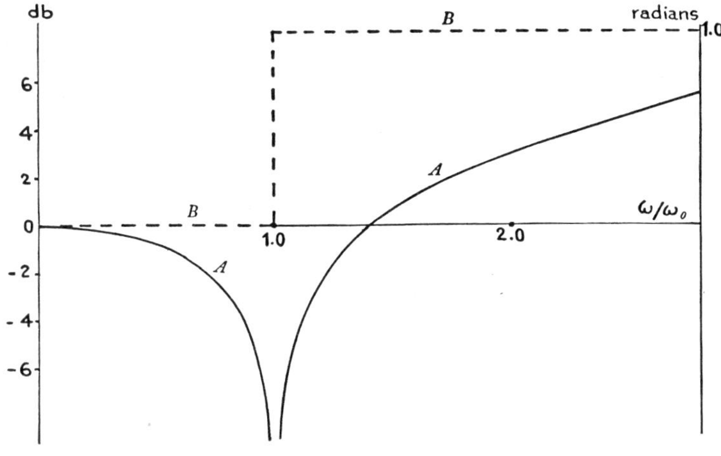

FIG. 14.16

seen that the introduction of a rather narrow region of net gain near the edge of the useful band allows the system to be designed with substantially zero attenuation and phase distortion throughout the rest of the useful band, in spite of a high loss at more remote frequencies. For practical

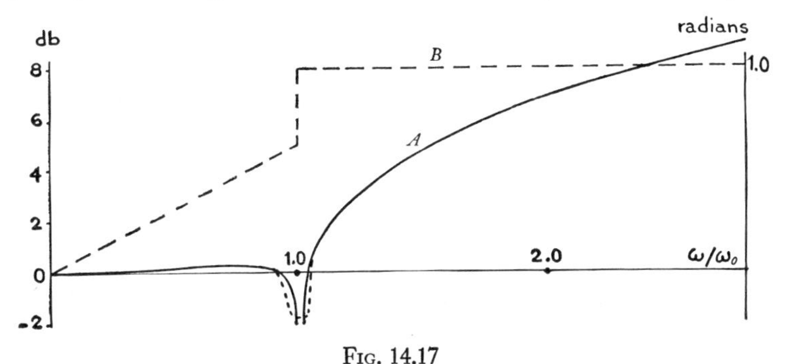

FIG. 14.17

purposes the net gain characteristic need not, of course, take exactly the form assigned to it by this analysis. It might, for example, be distorted into some such form as that indicated by the dotted lines in Fig. 14.17. If no net gain can be permitted, however, it is necessary either to accept attenuation distortion of the general type exemplified by Fig. 14.15 or to resort to phase equalization.

The simplest physical illustrations of circuits having the characteristics shown by Figs. 14.15, 14.16, and 14.17 are obtained if we imagine that we are attempting to design an interstage network for a non-feedback video amplifier. The construction of a network to simulate the characteristics of Fig. 14.16 is particularly easy, since if the multiplier $a\omega_0/\pi$ in (14–30) equals one-half, the equation will be recognized as the expression for the absolute value of the image impedance of a mid-shunt terminated low-pass filter of the constant k type.* Thus the interstage network can be constructed as a conventional filter circuit, with the interstage capacity taken as the final shunt branch.

The characteristics in the other figures can be simulated with impedances of the same general type, but using somewhat distorted values of the filter elements. As an example, we may consider the design of an interstage to represent the characteristics of Fig. 14.15. At high frequencies the network must reduce physically to the interstage capacity, so that its loss will be given by log ωC_0, where C_0 represents the capacity. We see without difficulty, however, that when ω is large the attenuation in (14–28) is approximately $(2a\omega_0/\pi)$ log ω/ω_0. We must consequently have $a = \pi/2\omega_0$. With this value at hand it is a simple matter to compute, from Fig. 14.15, the impedance which the interstage network, less the capacity, must have. The result is shown by Fig. 14.18. The impedance is very nearly equal to a mid-series filter image impedance of constant k type plus an added inductance. If this form of representation is adopted the complete interstage

* This is a reference to standard filter theory as developed largely by O. J. Zobel (*B.S.T.J.*, Jan. 1923, and later papers). Filter image impedances, and filter-like networks in general, appear frequently in the circuits used for illustrative purposes from this point on, and it will be necessary to suppose that the reader has at least a rough acquaintance with the filter field. Of a rather extensive list of possible references, Terman's " Radio Engineer's Handbook," pp. 226–244, may be mentioned for a good brief treatment, while Guillemin's " Communication Networks," Vol. II, gives a more substantial discussion. If either reference is consulted, the reader's attention is directed particularly to the sections on lattice filters. They contain general analytic formulae for available filter image impedances of the types used here. Although these image impedance formulae are developed only for lattice structures, they can also be realized in sufficiently elaborate ladder circuits, as the references given later show.

On the particular problem of designing a finite network to furnish a close approximation to a theoretical filter image impedance, the best references are perhaps Zobel's paper in the Bell System Technical Journal for April, 1931, and the writer's U. S. Patent No. 2,249,415. In addition, a number of specific designs will be given in Chapter XVII. In view of the existence of this material, it will hereafter be assumed that any given illustrative design has been finished if it can be constructed by using filter image impedances as elements.

takes the form shown by Fig. 14.19. Its phase and attenuation characteristics are shown by Fig. 14.20. The solid and broken lines represent, respec-

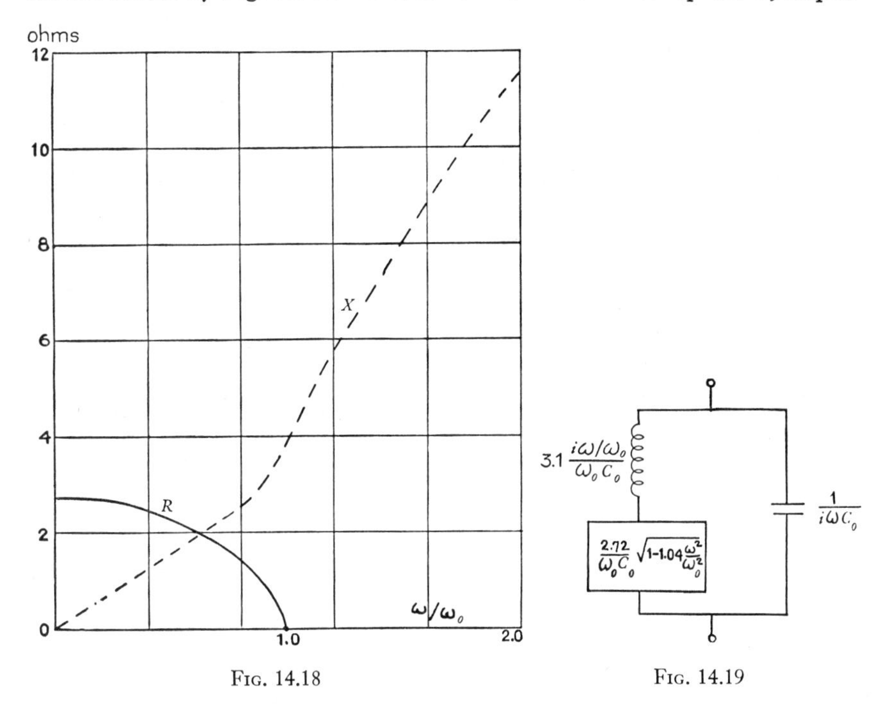

Fig. 14.18

Fig. 14.19

tively, the attenuation and phase characteristics originally specified in Fig. 14.15, but with each characteristic multiplied by $\pi/2$ to fit the value

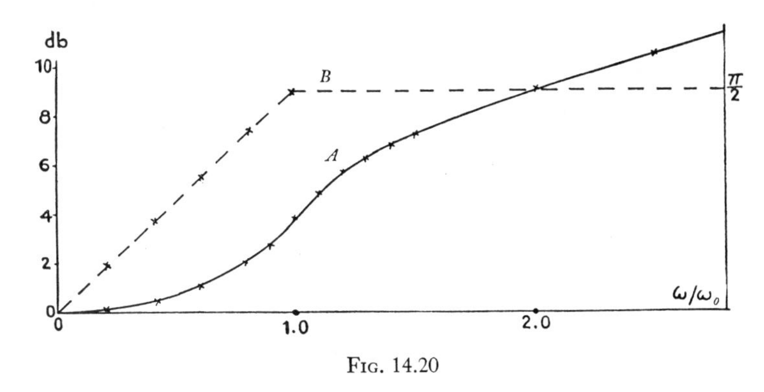

Fig. 14.20

of $a\omega_0$ adopted in this illustration. The crosses represent the characteristics actually obtained from the structure of Fig. 14.19.

14.10. *A and B Prescribed in Different Frequency Ranges*

The third general problem considered in this chapter is that of determining a complete impedance or transmission characteristic when the real component is specified in certain frequency ranges and the imaginary component in the rest of the spectrum. Let it be supposed, for example, that the attenuation is known at frequencies below ω_0 and the phase shift in the range above ω_0. The problem to be solved, then, is that of completing the characteristic by calculating the phase in the range below ω_0 and the attenuation above this point.

In each of the preceding theorems, the known component has been an even function of frequency and the component to be evaluated an odd function. Thus, in the first theorem, the attenuation, which has even symmetry, was supposed to be known and the phase was determined from it. In the second theorem, the roles of the two components were reversed by multiplying or dividing the original θ by $i\omega$.

The same procedure can be adopted for the present problem, except that the function by which θ is multiplied or divided is $\sqrt{1 - \omega^2/\omega_0^2}$ rather than $i\omega$. The properties of the function $\sqrt{1 - \omega^2/\omega_0^2}$ when the Riemann surface on which the square root is defined is chosen appropriately were described in the preceding chapter. It will be recalled that between ω_0 and $-\omega_0$ the "positive" square root is a positive real quantity and has even symmetry. In this frequency region, therefore, the introduction of the new function does not disturb the original even or odd symmetry of A and B. Above ω_0, on the other hand, the positive square root of $\sqrt{1 - \omega^2/\omega_0^2}$ is a positive imaginary while below $-\omega_0$ it is a negative imaginary. In these ranges, therefore, the function has odd symmetry, which cancels the odd symmetry of B. Thus in each part of the spectrum the portion of the integrand which has even symmetry, and is consequently retained in the final integration, depends upon the component of θ which is specified there.

This procedure can be made more definite if we write the ratio* of θ to $\sqrt{1 - \omega^2/\omega_0^2}$ as

$$\begin{aligned} \frac{\theta}{\sqrt{1 - \omega^2/\omega_0^2}} &= \frac{A}{\sqrt{1 - \omega^2/\omega_0^2}} + i\frac{B}{\sqrt{1 - \omega^2/\omega_0^2}}, \quad \omega < \omega_0 \\ &= \frac{B}{\sqrt{\omega^2/\omega_0^2 - 1}} - i\frac{A}{\sqrt{\omega^2/\omega_0^2 - 1}}, \quad \omega > \omega_0, \end{aligned} \tag{14-32}$$

* The product is not chosen in this situation since at high frequencies it reduces to $i\omega(A_\infty/\omega_0)$, with a pole at infinity. The effect of this pole could easily be discounted if A_∞ were known, but since the high frequency behavior of A is one of the functions which the analysis seeks to determine, the presence of the pole introduces a complicating feature which it is desirable to avoid.

where all the square roots on the right-hand side are positive real quantities. Any of the formulae developed previously can be applied to the present situation if we replace the original A and B, respectively, by the real and imaginary components of the expression given by (14–32). If we make these substitutions in (14–3), for example, the result is

$$\frac{2\omega_c}{\pi}\int_0^{\omega_0}\frac{A}{\sqrt{1-\omega^2/\omega_0^2}}\frac{d\omega}{\omega^2-\omega_c^2} \tag{14–33}$$

$$+\frac{2\omega_c}{\pi}\int_{\omega_0}^{\infty}\frac{B}{\sqrt{\omega^2/\omega_0^2-1}}\frac{d\omega}{\omega^2-\omega_c^2}=\frac{B_c}{\sqrt{1-\omega_c^2/\omega_0^2}},\qquad \omega_c<\omega_0$$

$$=\frac{-A_c}{\sqrt{\omega_c^2/\omega_0^2-1}},\qquad \omega_c>\omega_0,$$

where the two integrals on the left-hand side replace the single integral in (14–3)* and the terms on the right-hand side replace the original B_c. Since we originally assumed that A was known below ω_0 and B above ω_0 the two integrations can be carried out and the remaining portions of both characteristics evaluated.

It is also possible to make use of the derivative form of relationship as given by (14–11). If this formula is adopted, however, special precautions are necessary to take account of the sharp changes in the slope of the real component of $\theta/\sqrt{1-\omega^2/\omega_0^2}$ in the neighborhood of ω_0. For practical purposes it is probably simplest to flatten off the peak of the real component curve, as indicated by the broken lines in Fig. 14.21, leaving the peak itself to be treated by formulae analogous to (14–33). It may also be desirable to adjust the constant level of attenuation to give A and B the same value at ω_0, so that the peak curve will be symmetrical in the neighborhood of ω_0. This analysis can be extended in obvious ways to take account of situations in which A and B are specified in other frequency ranges. For example, if B is specified below ω_0 and A above ω_0 the function which it is appropriate to use is $i\omega\theta/\sqrt{1-\omega^2/\omega_0^2}$ and the formula corresponding to

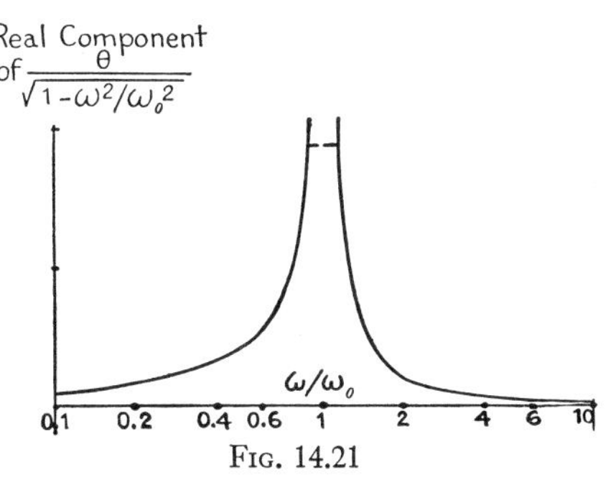

FIG. 14.21

* In equation (14–33) and also in the succeeding equations, the term corresponding to A_c in equation (14–3) has been omitted for simplicity. As shown in connection with the discussion of equation (14–1), this is permissible provided the integrals are defined in terms of their "principal values."

(14–33) is

$$\frac{2\omega_c}{\pi}\int_0^{\omega_0}\frac{-\omega B}{\sqrt{1-\omega^2/\omega_0^2}}\frac{d\omega}{\omega^2-\omega_c^2} \tag{14–34}$$

$$+\frac{2\omega_c}{\pi}\int_{\omega_0}^{\infty}\frac{\omega A}{\sqrt{\omega^2/\omega_0^2-1}}\frac{d\omega}{\omega^2-\omega_c^2}=\frac{\omega_c A_c}{\sqrt{1-\omega_c^2/\omega_0^2}},\qquad \omega_c<\omega_0$$

$$=\frac{\omega_c B_c}{\sqrt{\omega_c^2/\omega_0^2-1}},\qquad \omega_c>\omega_0.$$

Similarly, if A is specified in a band extending from ω_1 to ω_2 and B at frequencies outside the band the proper division of the spectrum is obtained if we begin with the function $i\omega\theta/(\sqrt{1-\omega^2/\omega_1^2}\sqrt{1-\omega^2/\omega_2^2})$. This leads to the formula

$$\frac{2\omega_c}{\pi}(R+S+T)=\frac{\omega_c A_c}{\sqrt{1-\omega_c^2/\omega_1^2}\sqrt{1-\omega_c^2/\omega_2^2}},\qquad \omega_c<\omega_1$$

$$=\frac{\omega_c B_c}{\sqrt{\omega_c^2/\omega_1^2-1}\sqrt{1-\omega_c^2/\omega_2^2}},\qquad \omega_2>\omega_c>\omega_1$$

$$=\frac{-\omega_c A_c}{\sqrt{\omega_c^2/\omega_1^2-1}\sqrt{\omega_c^2/\omega_2^2-1}},\qquad \omega_c>\omega_2.$$

where (14–35)

$$R=\int_0^{\omega_1}\frac{-\omega B}{\sqrt{1-\omega^2/\omega_1^2}\sqrt{1-\omega^2/\omega_2^2}}\frac{d\omega}{\omega^2-\omega_c^2}$$

$$S=\int_{\omega_1}^{\omega_2}\frac{\omega A}{\sqrt{\omega^2/\omega_1^2-1}\sqrt{1-\omega^2/\omega_2^2}}\frac{d\omega}{\omega^2-\omega_c^2}$$

$$T=\int_{\omega_2}^{\infty}\frac{\omega B}{\sqrt{\omega^2/\omega_1^2-1}\sqrt{\omega^2/\omega_2^2-1}}\frac{d\omega}{\omega^2-\omega_c^2}.$$

For simple examples of these transformations we can return again to the elementary characteristics of Fig. 14.7. Thus if we are concerned with the function $\theta/\sqrt{1-\omega^2/\omega_0^2}$ and let ω_0 represent the point of discontinuity in Fig. 14.7, Curve A in that figure can be identified with $A/\sqrt{1-\omega^2/\omega_0^2}$ below ω_0 and with $B/\sqrt{\omega^2/\omega_0^2-1}$ above ω_0. Similarly, Curve B represents $B/\sqrt{1-\omega^2/\omega_0^2}$ below ω_0 and $-A/\sqrt{\omega^2/\omega_0^2-1}$ above ω_0. An easy calculation therefore leads to the curves for the new A and the new B shown by Fig. 14.22. As in the discussion of Fig. 14.12, the new B has a pole at infinity. If a constant is subtracted from the original A curve of Fig. 14.7 to avoid this difficulty the modified characteristics take the form indicated by the broken line Curves A' and B' of Fig. 14.22. If we begin

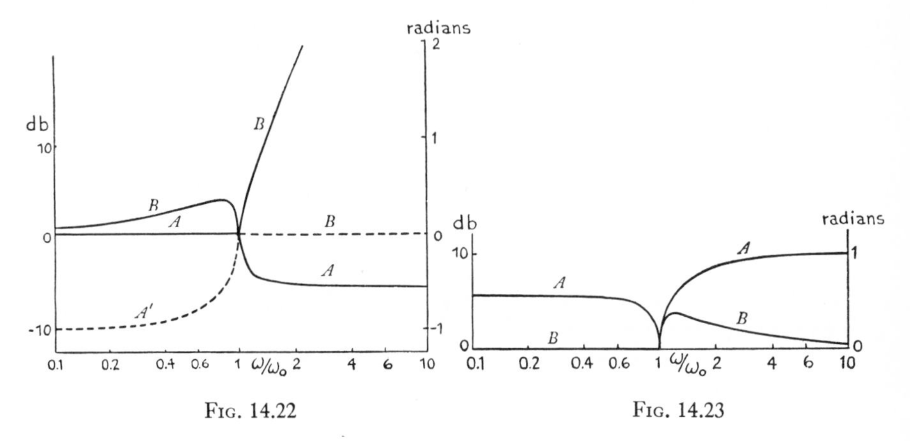

FIG. 14.22

FIG. 14.23

with the function $i\omega\theta/\sqrt{1-\omega^2/\omega_0^2}$ the analysis is essentially the same, except that there is no difficulty with the behavior of the new function at infinity, and leads to the result shown by Fig. 14.23.

14.11. *Linear Phase Systems with Prescribed Discrimination*

In the earlier discussion of selective systems with linear phase characteristics over a prescribed low frequency range it was assumed that the phase shift would be constant beyond the prescribed range. This is a convenient assumption to make for systems like the interstage network of Fig. 14.19 in which it is physically necessary for the attenuation to increase logarithmically at high frequencies. As Fig. 14.15 shows, however, it leads to a rather low discrimination just beyond the band and an unnecessarily high loss, for most purposes, at more remote frequencies. When the physical situation permits, it is consequently more desirable to specify in advance the loss which is to be realized beyond the linear phase shift range. The discussion of this problem affords a convenient example of the general methods of analysis described in the preceding section.

It will be assumed that $B = a\omega$ below ω_0 and that $A = K$ above ω_0. This is illustrated by the solid lines in Fig. 14.24. The remaining portions of the two characteristics are indicated by the broken lines. Their exact shape can be found by means of (14–34). Since the solution will evidently not be affected by the introduction of a constant gain or loss we can assume for the purpose of studying (14–34) that the constant K which fixes the high frequency attenuation is zero. This allows us to neglect the second integral in (14–34). The equation consequently becomes

$$\frac{2\omega_c}{\pi}\int_0^{\omega_0}\frac{-a\omega^2}{\sqrt{1-\omega^2/\omega_0^2}}\frac{d\omega}{\omega^2-\omega_c^2}=\frac{\omega_c A_c}{\sqrt{1-\omega_c^2/\omega_0^2}},\qquad \omega_c<\omega_0$$

$$=\frac{\omega_c B_c}{\sqrt{\omega_c^2/\omega_0^2-1}},\qquad \omega_c>\omega_0. \tag{14–36}$$

It is convenient to begin with the solution for B_c. If we split the integral in (14–36) into two parts the equation appears as

$$B_c=\frac{-2a}{\pi}\sqrt{\frac{\omega_c^2}{\omega_0^2}-1}\left[\int_0^{\omega_0}\frac{d\omega}{\sqrt{1-\omega^2/\omega_0^2}}+\int_0^{\omega_0}\frac{\omega_c^2}{\sqrt{1-\omega^2/\omega_0^2}}\frac{d\omega}{\omega^2-\omega_c^2}\right]. \tag{14–37}$$

The first integral in this expression can be evaluated immediately as $(\pi/2)\omega_0$. To evaluate the second, let ω/ω_0 be replaced by $x/\sqrt{1+x^2}$. This gives

$$\int_0^{\omega_0}\frac{\omega_c^2}{\sqrt{1-\omega^2/\omega_0^2}}\frac{d\omega}{\omega^2-\omega_c^2}=-\omega_0\int_0^{\infty}\frac{dx}{1+(1-\omega_0^2/\omega_c^2)\,x^2}$$

$$=-\frac{\omega_c}{\sqrt{\omega_c^2/\omega_0^2-1}}\frac{\pi}{2}. \tag{14–38}$$

Upon substituting in (14–37), we consequently find

$$B_c=a\omega_0\left(\frac{\omega_c}{\omega_0}-\sqrt{\frac{\omega_c^2}{\omega_0^2}-1}\right). \tag{14–39}$$

This characteristic has already been shown in Fig. 14.24.

The computation of A_c from (14–36) follows similar lines, but it is necessary to make one modification to take account of the fact that when $\omega_c<\omega_0$ the integrand in (14–36) has a pole in the range of integration. In accordance with the previous discussion, the " principal value " of the integral is to be taken in this situation. This is of importance principally in evaluating (14–38). If we set $\omega_0^2/\omega_c^2-1=1/k^2$ the pole in the integrand in (14–38) occurs at $x=k$. In order to determine the principal value of the integral we split the total range of integration into two parts, one extending from zero to $k-\varepsilon$ and the other extending from $k+\varepsilon$ to infinity, where ε is some very small quantity. This allows the second integral in

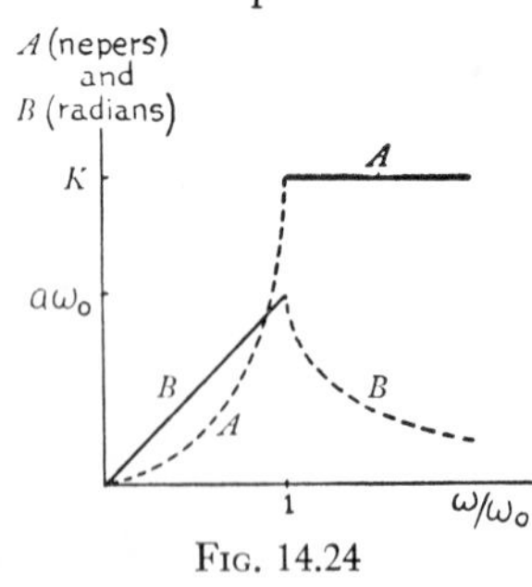

FIG. 14.24

(14–38) to be written as

$$-\omega_0\int_0^\infty \frac{dx}{1 - x^2/k^2} = -\omega_0\int_0^{k-\varepsilon} \frac{dx}{1 - x^2/k^2} - \omega_0\int_{k+\varepsilon}^\infty \frac{dx}{1 - x^2/k^2}. \quad (14\text{–}40)$$

But if we substitute $y = k^2/x$ it is easily seen that the second integral in the right-hand side of (14–40) is exactly the negative of the first. In evaluating A_c from (14–36), therefore, there is no contribution corresponding to (14–38). This gives A_c as

$$A_c = K - a\omega_0\sqrt{1 - \frac{\omega_c^2}{\omega_0^2}}, \quad (14\text{–}41)$$

where the constant loss K, which was ignored in making the analysis, has been restored to the equation. The results given by (14–39) and (14–41) can evidently be combined with the original specifications on A and B to give the complete characteristic by means of the single equation

$$\theta = A + iB = K - a\omega_0\sqrt{1 - \frac{\omega^2}{\omega_0^2}} + ia\omega. \quad (14\text{–}42)$$

A large scale plot of this characteristic with $K = a\omega_0$ is shown by Fig. 14.25.

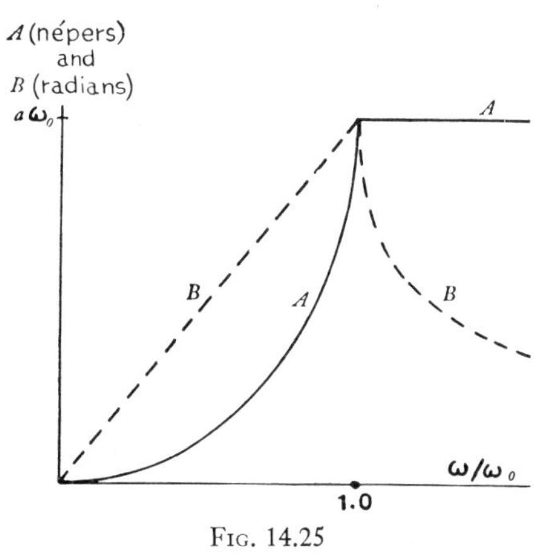

Fig. 14.25

Although the characteristic in Fig. 14.25 approximates a filter more closely than did the earlier characteristic of Fig. 14.15, it still exhibits an appreciable rounding in the transmission band. In order to secure a flatter final characteristic we might suppose that the system is to be used for vestigial sideband transmission. This requires only that the proportions of the characteristic be

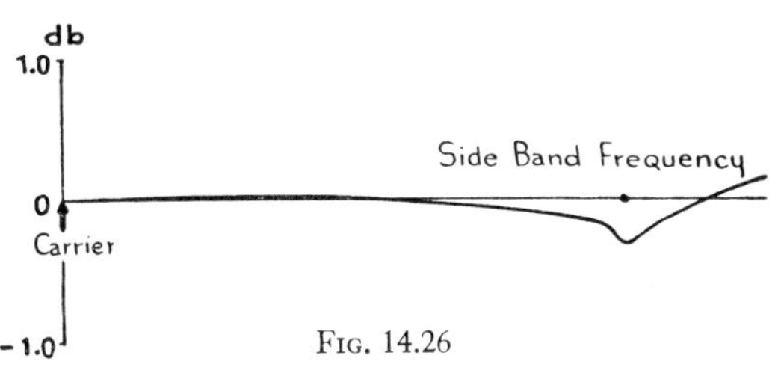

Fig. 14.26

so chosen that the carrier will fall at the point having 6 db loss. For example, if the high frequency loss is 30 db the 6 db point occurs at

$\omega = 0.6\omega_0$. This leads to the net transmission characteristic shown by Fig. 14.26.

With the proportions chosen for Fig. 14.26 the wanted sideband covers the first 60 per cent of the linear phase range and the vestigial sideband the last 40 per cent. Thus the vestigial sideband is two-thirds as great as the wanted sideband and is rather more than a " vestige." This ratio can be considerably reduced if we suppose that the actual transmission occurs in a logarithmically narrow band and that the characteristics of Fig. 14.25 represent merely the low-pass equivalent of such a circuit, in accordance with the relations described in Chapter X. In this event the region covered by Fig. 14.25 corresponds to only one-half the total band and the other half is also available for the transmission of the wanted sideband. If it is supposed that the other half can be flattened out without seriously disturbing the characteristics in the vestigial region this leads to an overall characteristic of the type shown by Fig. 14.27. It will be seen that the vestigial sideband region is now about one-fourth as broad as the region occupied by the wanted sideband.

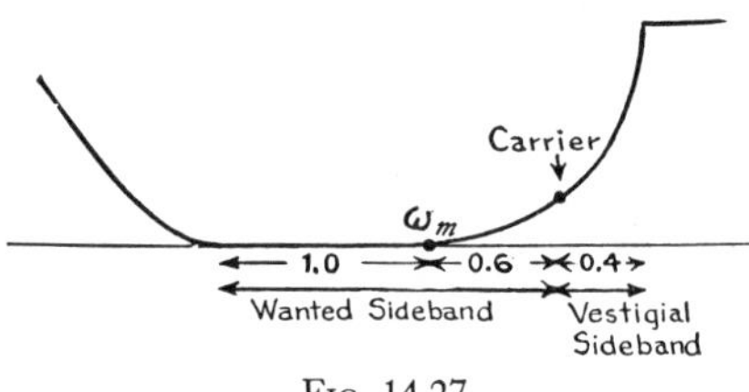

FIG. 14.27

This discussion applies, of course, only to minimum phase shift structures. We can obviously narrow the vestigial sideband region much further by using phase equalization in the final circuit. On the other hand, a minimum phase shift characteristic of the type shown by Fig. 14.27 can usually be realized relatively easily by ordinary filters and loss equalizers, while the addition of any substantial amount of phase equalization adds considerably to the total complexity of the structure. Thus Fig. 14.27 can be looked upon as at least a rough guide to the proportions which should be followed when frequency space is not at a premium but when it is important to use relatively simple network designs. Such a problem might be encountered, for example, in the short-wave transmission or reception of television signals. In practice, of course, it may be necessary to assign the vestigial sideband a frequency region even greater than the 20 per cent of the total band which is allotted to it in Fig. 14.27. For example, this estimate depends upon the assumption that 30 db attenuation outside the band is sufficient and must be increased, as inspection of Fig. 14.25 shows, if greater discrimination is required. If a linear phase characteristic must be maintained throughout the region covered by the wanted sideband it is also impossible to flatten out the characteristics in the lower half of the total band to the extent suggested by Fig. 14.27, so that the relative breadth of the vestigial region is still further increased.

TABULATION OF RELATIONS BETWEEN REAL AND IMAGINARY COMPONENTS OF NETWORK FUNCTIONS

Group		Formula
I	*(a)*	$B_c = \frac{2\omega_c}{\pi}\int_0^\infty \frac{A - A_c}{\omega^2 - \omega_c^2}\,d\omega$
	(b)	$= \frac{1}{\pi}\int_{-\infty}^\infty \frac{dA}{du}\log\coth\frac{\lvert u\rvert}{2}\,du$
	(c)	$= \frac{1}{\pi}\int_0^\infty \frac{dA}{d\omega}\log\left\lvert\frac{\omega + \omega_c}{\omega - \omega_c}\right\rvert d\omega$
	(d)	$= -\frac{1}{\pi}\int_0^\infty \frac{dA}{d\,(1/\omega)}\log\left\lvert\frac{1/\omega + 1/\omega_c}{1/\omega - 1/\omega_c}\right\rvert d\,(1/\omega)$
II	*(a)*	$A_c - A_\infty = -\frac{2}{\pi}\int_0^\infty \frac{(\omega B) - (\omega B)_c}{\omega^2 - \omega_c^2}\,d\omega$
	(b)	$= -\frac{1}{\pi\omega_c}\int_{-\infty}^\infty \frac{d(\omega B)}{du}\log\coth\frac{\lvert u\rvert}{2}\,du$
	(c)	$= \pm\frac{1}{\pi\omega_c}\int_0^\infty \frac{d(\omega B)}{dz}\log\left\lvert\frac{z + z_c}{z - z_c}\right\rvert dz$
III	*(a)*	$A_c - A_0 = -\frac{2\omega_c^2}{\pi}\int_0^\infty \frac{(B/\omega) - (B/\omega)_c}{\omega^2 - \omega_c^2}\,d\omega$
	(b)	$= -\frac{\omega_c}{\pi}\int_{-\infty}^\infty \frac{d\,(B/\omega)}{du}\log\coth\frac{\lvert u\rvert}{2}\,du$
	(c)	$= \pm\frac{\omega_c}{\pi}\int_0^\infty \frac{d\,(B/\omega)}{dz}\log\left\lvert\frac{z + z_c}{z - z_c}\right\rvert dz$
IV	*(a)*	$\frac{2\omega_c}{\pi}\left\lvert 1 - \frac{\omega_c^2}{\omega_0^2}\right\rvert^{1/2}(M + N) = B_c, \quad \omega_c < \omega_0$ $= -A_c, \quad \omega_c > \omega_0$

where

$$M = \int_0^{\omega_0} \frac{A}{\sqrt{1 - \omega^2/\omega_0^2}}\,\frac{d\omega}{\omega^2 - \omega_c^2}$$

$$N = \int_{\omega_0}^\infty \frac{B}{\sqrt{\omega^2/\omega_0^2 - 1}}\,\frac{d\omega}{\omega^2 - \omega_c^2}$$

Group	*Formula*

IV (*b*)

$$\frac{2}{\pi}\left|1-\frac{\omega_c^2}{\omega_0^2}\right|^{1/2}(P+Q) = A_c, \qquad \omega_c < \omega_0$$
$$= B_c, \qquad \omega_c > \omega_0$$

where

$$P = \int_0^{\omega_0} \frac{-\omega B}{\sqrt{1-\omega^2/\omega_0^2}}\frac{d\omega}{\omega^2-\omega_c^2}$$
$$Q = \int_{\omega_0}^{\infty} \frac{\omega A}{\sqrt{\omega^2/\omega_0^2-1}}\frac{d\omega}{\omega^2-\omega_c^2}$$

V (*a*)

$$\frac{2}{\pi}\left|1-\frac{\omega_c^2}{\omega_1^2}\right|^{1/2}\left|1-\frac{\omega_c^2}{\omega_2^2}\right|^{1/2}(R+S+T) = A_c, \qquad \omega_c < \omega_1$$
$$= B_c, \qquad \omega_2 > \omega_c > \omega_1$$
$$= -A_c, \qquad \omega_c > \omega_2$$

where

$$R = \int_0^{\omega_1} \frac{-\omega B}{\sqrt{1-\omega^2/\omega_1^2}\sqrt{1-\omega^2/\omega_2^2}}\frac{d\omega}{\omega^2-\omega_c^2}$$
$$S = \int_{\omega_1}^{\omega_2} \frac{\omega A}{\sqrt{\omega^2/\omega_1^2-1}\sqrt{1-\omega^2/\omega_2^2}}\frac{d\omega}{\omega^2-\omega_c^2}$$
$$T = \int_{\omega_2}^{\infty} \frac{\omega B}{\sqrt{\omega^2/\omega_1^2-1}\sqrt{\omega^2/\omega_2^2-1}}\frac{d\omega}{\omega^2-\omega_c^2}$$

(*b*)

$$\frac{2}{\pi\omega_c}\left|1-\frac{\omega_c^2}{\omega_1^2}\right|^{1/2}\left|1-\frac{\omega_c^2}{\omega_2^2}\right|^{1/2}(U+V+W) = B_c, \qquad \omega_c < \omega_1$$
$$= -A_c, \qquad \omega_2 > \omega_c > \omega_1$$
$$= -B_c, \qquad \omega_c > \omega_2$$

where

$$U = \int_0^{\omega_1} \frac{\omega^2 A}{\sqrt{1-\omega^2/\omega_1^2}\sqrt{1-\omega^2/\omega_2^2}}\frac{d\omega}{\omega^2-\omega_c^2}$$
$$V = \int_{\omega_1}^{\omega_2} \frac{\omega^2 B}{\sqrt{\omega^2/\omega_1^2-1}\sqrt{1-\omega^2/\omega_2^2}}\frac{d\omega}{\omega^2-\omega_c^2}$$
$$W = \int_{\omega_2}^{\infty} \frac{-\omega^2 A}{\sqrt{\omega^2/\omega_1^2-1}\sqrt{\omega^2/\omega_2^2-1}}\frac{d\omega}{\omega^2-\omega_c^2}$$

Note: In I*b*, II*b*, and III*b*, $u = \log \omega/\omega_c$. In II*c* and III*c*, z may be either ω or $1/\omega$. In either equation the plus sign must be chosen if $z = 1/\omega$ and the negative sign if $z = \omega$.

CHAPTER XV

Graphical Computation of Relations Between Real and Imaginary Components of Network Functions

15.1. *Introduction*

This chapter consists principally of a set of charts which are intended to facilitate the approximate computation of attenuation-phase relations in practical cases. The theoretical development consists merely of a statement of the methods by which the charts were prepared and the way they are to be used.

15.2. *Approximation of Actual Characteristics by Straight Lines*

The analysis of the preceding chapter is already in a form which makes it theoretically possible to determine the relationship between the real and imaginary components of network functions by graphical methods. If we make use of equation (14–11), for example, both the differentiation of A and the integration of the product of dA/du and the weighting function are operations which can be performed graphically. When a large number of points on the imaginary characteristic are to be determined, however, calculations of this sort become quite tedious.

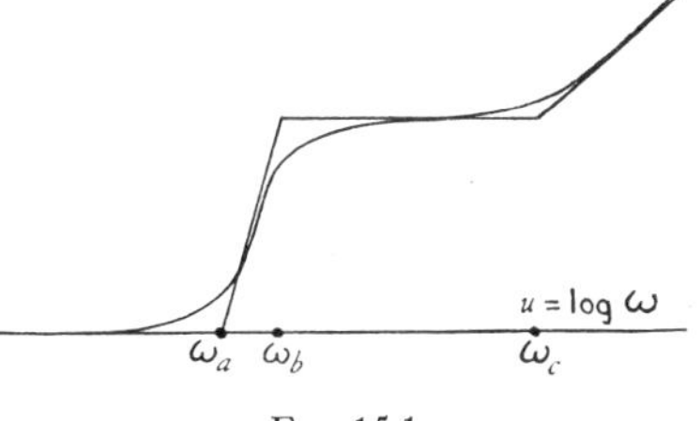

Fig. 15.1

As an alternative procedure the present chapter is based upon the assumption that the real component will be approximated by a series of straight line segments. This is illustrated by Fig. 15.1. The real characteristic which is approximated in this manner may be either a physical real component, such as an attenuation or a resistance, or an equivalent characteristic like ωB or B/ω derived by the methods described in the preceding chapter. In choosing the set of straight lines it is ordinarily sufficient to represent the major trends in the real characteristic correctly. As the discussion in the preceding chapter in connection with equation (14–11) indicated, the relation between the real and imaginary components involves in any case a smoothing out or averaging out of the real characteristic. If the major trends are correctly represented, therefore, the imaginary characteristics corresponding to the actual real characteristic and to the straight line approximation to it should be much more nearly equal than are the actual and approximate real characteristics themselves.

The advantage of the straight line approximation scheme is, of course, that it reduces the complete real characteristic to a sum of elementary characteristics. Since the imaginary component corresponding to each elementary characteristic can be computed once for all, this reduces the calculation of the complete imaginary characteristic to the addition of a number of known curves. In theory, it is sufficient to consider only one elementary characteristic, the semi-infinite slope. Figure 15.2, for example, shows how the straight line characteristic of Fig. 15.1 can be represented as the sum of three such slopes.

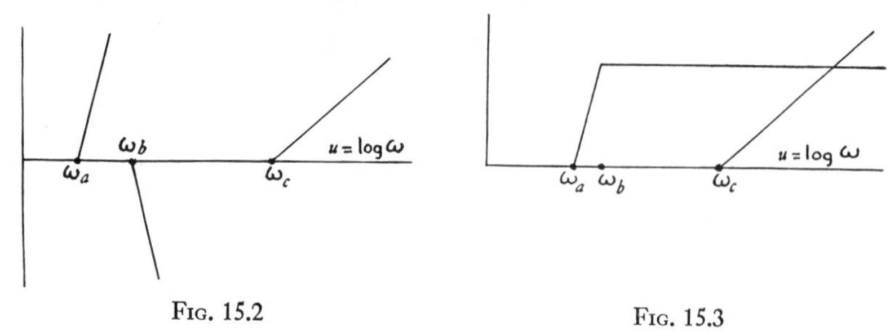

FIG. 15.2

FIG. 15.3

This form of representation reduces the work of preparing chart information to the simplest possible level, since the complete imaginary characteristic can be built up if we know one primitive curve. It suffers, however, from the disadvantage that the phase contributions of the individual slopes may be rather large positive and negative quantities even though the net phase shift is fairly small. It is consequently necessary to determine the constituent phase characteristics quite accurately in order to obtain a reasonably accurate final result. This is particularly likely to be true if the straight line approximation to the complete real characteristic includes a number of short and steeply sloping line segments. For practical purposes it is consequently preferable to regard the individual finite line segments themselves as the elementary characteristics upon which the analysis is based. As an example, Fig. 15.3 shows the representation of the characteristic of Fig. 15.1 by means of one such segment plus a semi-infinite slope.

This chapter is devoted principally to large scale plots of the phase characteristics of semi-infinite slopes and finite line segments. There is, of course, only one semi-infinite characteristic to consider, but it requires a series of curves to represent finite segments of different breadths. In addition to these curves, which assume that the real characteristic was originally plotted on a logarithmic frequency scale, a few curves of the phase characteristics corresponding to straight line segments on an arithmetic frequency scale are also included.

Although the imaginary characteristic computed by these processes should match the true imaginary characteristic quite accurately, on the whole, there will naturally be certain divergences which can be attributed to the sharp changes in slope in the straight line approximation in comparison with the smooth variations of a physical characteristic. The general situation here can be most conveniently expressed by the

Theorem: If either component of θ itself or of any derivative of θ is discontinuous at some point, the other component of θ or of the derivative must be logarithmically infinite at that point.

This relation has already been established for a discontinuity in the real component of θ itself by the discussion in connection with Fig. 14.7 of the preceding chapter. Its extension to the imaginary component or to a derivative follows readily from the methods of interchanging real and imaginary components described previously, plus the reflection that θ and its derivatives meet the same general analytic specifications.

In the straight line approximation scheme $dA/d\omega$ is discontinuous at the junctions between the line segments. This gives rise to situations of the type exemplified by Fig. 15.4. The solid lines indicate the actual characteristics and the broken lines the characteristics which appear in the approximate analysis. There is a kink in the broken line phase characteristic at the point at which the slope of the real characteristic changes, corresponding to the fact that the slope of the phase characteristic must be infinite there. Since the infinity is only logarithmic, however, the kink is very small and is scarcely perceptible in practice unless the characteristics are drawn on an extremely large scale.

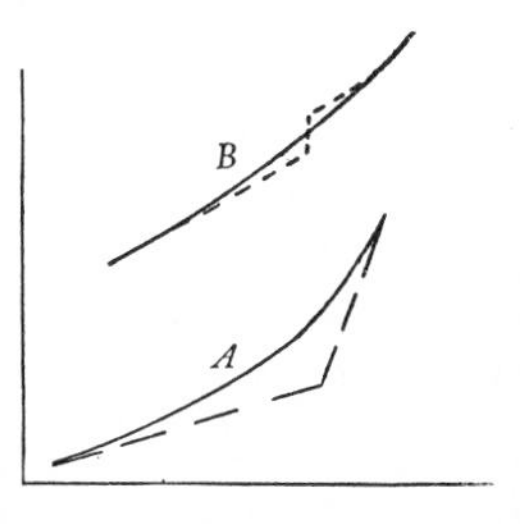

FIG. 15.4

15.3. *Summary of Charts*

Of the charts given at the end of the chapter, the first two give the imaginary characteristic corresponding to a semi-infinite real characteristic of unit slope. Chart I gives the imaginary characteristic plotted against the logarithm of frequency and is the same as Fig. 14.8 of the preceding chapter drawn on a larger scale. Chart II gives the same information on an arithmetic frequency scale. It also includes an enlarged version of the region near ω_0, where the characteristic is varying most rapidly. The formulae by means of which the characteristic is computed are somewhat complicated and are described in the next section. The curves cover only the region below ω_0 since the rest of the plot can be obtained from the relations of symmetry described in the earlier discussion of this characteristic.

Charts III and IV are similar plots of $(1/\pi) \log \coth |u/2|$, where $\log \coth |u/2|$ is the weighting function of equation (14–11) in the preceding chapter. They satisfy the equation

$$B = \frac{1}{\pi} \log \coth \frac{|u|}{2} = \frac{1}{\pi} \log \left| \frac{\omega + \omega_0}{\omega - \omega_0} \right| . \qquad (15\text{–}1)$$

The curves cover only the range below ω_0 since the function has the same value at ω and at ω_0^2/ω. As shown in connection with Fig. 14.7 of the preceding chapter, this plot also represents the phase shift corresponding to a discontinuous attenuation characteristic. To facilitate this application of the curves the imaginary component has been expressed in terms of two scales. The first gives the phase shift in radians for a change in attenuation of 1 neper and the second the phase shift in degrees for an attenuation change of 1 db. Since there are $180/\pi$ degrees in 1 radian and 8.686 db in 1 neper the scales are in the ratio $180/8.686\pi = 6.6$. The reader should note that although the degree and db relationship is applicable to attenuation and phase computations, nepers and radians are proper theoretical units which can be used also in other problems. For example, the radian scale gives the reactance, in ohms, corresponding to a 1 ohm discontinuity in a resistance characteristic.

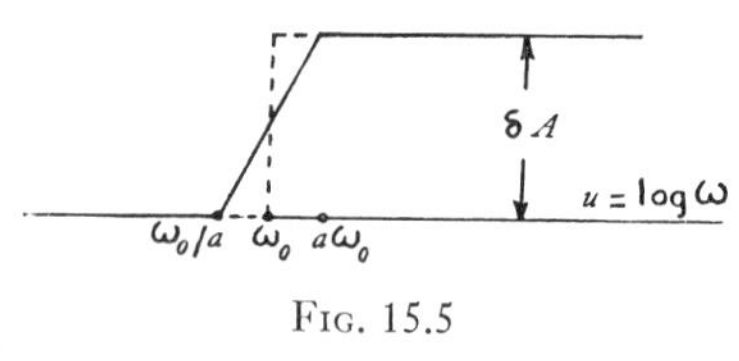

Fig. 15.5

The next series of charts gives the imaginary characteristics corresponding to finite line segments of the type shown earlier by Fig. 15.3. They are obtained by taking the difference between two semi-infinite characteristics. The reference frequency ω_0 is supposed to occur at the geometric center of the segment and the slope extends from ω_0/a to $a\omega_0$. This is illustrated by the solid line in Fig. 15.5. As in Charts III and IV, two scales for the imaginary component are shown. The first is in terms of theoretical units. If, for example, A and B are attenuation and phase, this scale gives the phase shift in radians when the total attenuation change, δA in Fig. 15.5, is 1 neper. The second scale gives the phase shift in degrees when the attenuation change is 1 db. For other attenuation changes the phase shift must, of course, be multiplied appropriately. In each chart the curves are drawn only for the region in which they differ appreciably from the curve labelled $a = 1.0$ on the charts. This limiting curve is the one which would be obtained if the real characteristic changed discontinuously by one unit at ω_0, as indicated by the dotted lines in Fig. 15.5 and is the same as the curve given in Charts III and IV. Beyond the region covered by the curves, therefore, the characteristics should be determined from these earlier charts.

Charts X and XI give the imaginary characteristic corresponding to the real characteristic shown by Fig. 15.6, where it is supposed that the frequency scale is arithmetic. This is the same characteristic as that shown by Fig. 14.10 of the preceding chapter, with $k\omega_0 = 1$, and the equation for the imaginary component was given then as

$$B = \frac{1}{\pi}[(x+1)\log(x+1) + (x-1)\log|x-1| - 2x\log x], \quad (15\text{–}2)$$

where $x = \omega/\omega_0$. The general arrangement of the charts is similar to that of the earlier plots. The only difference which need be observed is the fact that since (15–2) has no symmetrical properties it is necessary to extend the plot to cover the complete frequency range.

The remaining charts give the imaginary characteristic corresponding to a finite segment of a straight line when the frequency scale is arithmetic. The curves are intended as alternatives to those given in Charts V to IX, for situations in which the straight line approximation method is simplified by the use of an arithmetic rather than a logarithmic frequency scale.

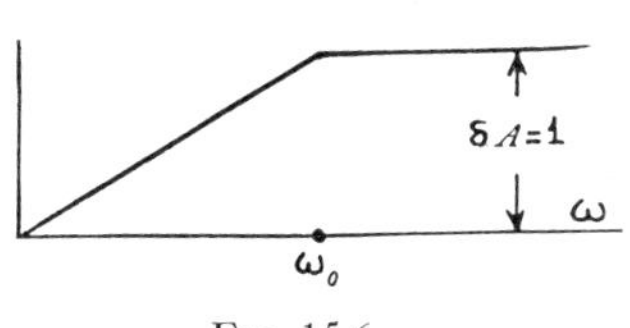

FIG. 15.6

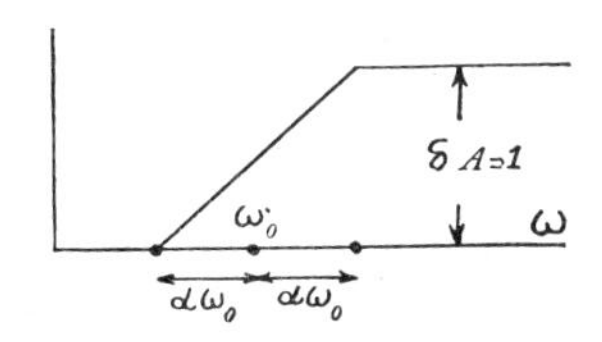

FIG. 15.7

They are, of course, obtained as differences between two characteristics of the type given by (15–2). The reference frequency ω_0 is taken as the arithmetic center of the segment and the slope is supposed to extend from $(1-\alpha)\omega_0$ to $(1+\alpha)\omega_0$. These relations are illustrated by Fig. 15.7. No curves are drawn for very small values of α since over narrow intervals straight line segments on arithmetic and logarithmic frequency scales are indistinguishable.

15.4. *Computational Methods for the Semi-Infinite Constant Slope Characteristic*

Most of the computations required to prepare the charts can be based upon explicit formulae which were given from time to time in the course of the preceding discussion. The computation of the imaginary component corresponding to a semi-infinite constant slope, however, requires special consideration.

If we suppose that the slope is unity and starts at ω_0 the imaginary component at any point ω_c is given by (14–11) of the preceding chapter as

$$B_c = \frac{1}{\pi} \int_{u_c}^{\infty} \log \coth \frac{|u|}{2} du, \tag{15–3}$$

where $u_c = \log \omega_0/\omega_c$, since in the range below u_c the slope is zero and the integrand in (14–11) vanishes. For purposes of computation (15–3) can be conveniently rewritten as

$$B_c = \frac{1}{\pi} \int_0^{x_c} \log \left| \frac{1+x}{1-x} \right| \frac{dx}{x}, \tag{15–4}$$

where $x_c = \omega_c/\omega_0$.

It appears that the result in (15–4) cannot be expressed in closed form, using elementary functions. We can, however, evaluate B_c by means of a power series expansion. The procedure is simplified by the symmetry of B_c about the point ω_0, as described previously. This allows us to restrict the computation to values of x_c below unity.

A second simplification of the same sort is provided by a relation between B at a frequency slightly below ω_0 and B at a corresponding frequency near $\omega = 0$. To develop this relation, set

$$y = \frac{1-x}{1+x} \qquad y_c = \frac{1-x_c}{1+x_c}. \tag{15–5}$$

In terms of the new variable y, (15–4) can be written as

$$B(x_c) = -\frac{1}{\pi} \int_{x=0}^{x=x_c} \log y \, d(\log x). \tag{15–6}$$

Let this equation be integrated by parts. The result is

$$B(x_c) = -\frac{1}{\pi} [\log x \log y]_{x=0}^{x=x_c} + \frac{1}{\pi} \int_{x=0}^{x=x_c} \log x \, d(\log y), \tag{15–7}$$

which is easily transformed into

$$B(x_c) = -\frac{1}{\pi} \log x_c \log y_c - \frac{1}{\pi} \int_{y=y_c}^{y=1} \log x \, d(\log y). \tag{15–8}$$

The transformation between x and y given by (15–5) is, however, symmetrical. In other words, if y is given in terms of x by (15–5), x is given in terms of y by the precisely similar expression $x = (1 - y)/(1 + y)$. Thus, the integral in (15–8) is in the same form as that in (15–6). The only difference arises from the fact that the range of integration in (15–6) extends from zero to x_c while in (15–8) it extends from y_c to one. We may, however, write the integral in (15–8) as the difference between an integration from zero to one and an integration from zero to y_c. The first of these must represent the imaginary characteristic of a semi-infinite slope at the point ω_0 and is therefore equal to $\pi/4$ by the discussion in the previous chapter. The integral from zero to y_c is the imaginary characteristic at the point y_c from (15–6). Equation (15–8) can therefore be written as

$$B(x_c) + B(y_c) = \frac{\pi}{4} - \frac{1}{\pi} \log x_c \log y_c \tag{15–9}$$

provided x_c and y_c satisfy equation (15–5).

If x_c in (15–5) is near unity, the corresponding y_c is very small but it increases as x_c decreases and the two become equal at $x_c = y_c = 0.414$. Thus, the phase characteristic can be computed at all frequencies if we know it only between zero and 0.414. Within this region, we can expect a power series expansion for B to converge rapidly. A suitable series is obtained by writing

$$\log\left(\frac{1+x}{1-x}\right) = 2\left(x + \frac{x^3}{3} + \frac{x^5}{5} + \cdots\right). \tag{15–10}$$

Upon substituting this expression in (15–4) and integrating term by term, the result is

$$B(x_c) = \frac{2}{\pi}\left(x_c + \frac{x_c^3}{9} + \frac{x_c^5}{25} + \cdots\right). \tag{15–11}$$

If we use only the first term of (15–11) in conjunction with (15–9), we can write

$$\begin{aligned} B(x_c) &\doteq \frac{2}{\pi} x_c, && 0 \le x_c \le 0.414 \\ &\doteq \frac{\pi}{4} - \frac{1}{\pi} \log x_c \log \frac{1 - x_c}{1 + x_c} - \frac{2}{\pi}\frac{1 - x_c}{1 + x_c}, && 0.414 \le x_c \le 1. \end{aligned} \tag{15–12}$$

The maximum error in B as computed from these expressions is about 2 per cent. If we use the first two terms in (15–11) the result is almost exact.

The most rapid variation in B occurs in the range near unity. In this range the behavior of the function is best characterized by its derivative. Since the derivative of an integral with respect to a variable upper limit is equal to the integrand, we see readily from (15–4) that

$$\frac{dB}{d\omega_c} = \frac{1}{\omega_0}\frac{dB}{dx_c} = \frac{1}{\pi\omega_0 x_c} \log \left|\frac{1 + x_c}{1 - x_c}\right|. \tag{15–13}$$

The delay is thus logarithmically infinite at the point at which the slope starts. This is, of course, a special case of the theorem on the effect of a discontinuity in one component, either of θ or of one of its derivatives, which was discussed earlier.

15.5. *Illustrative Application of the Charts*

In order to illustrate the use of the charts and the accuracy which may be expected from them in a simple case, let it be supposed that we are dealing with the impedance of the network shown in Fig. 15.8. Its resistance and reactance characteristics, on a logarithmic frequency scale, are shown by the broken lines in Figs. 15.9 and 15.10. A simple straight line approximation to the resistance is furnished by the solid line characteristic I in Fig. 15.9. The sloping segment in this characteristic is centered about the point $\omega = 1$ and its width is defined by the parameter $a = 2.8$. The corresponding reactance characteristic can consequently be read off immediately from the curves in Chart IX. It is shown by the solid line Curve I in Fig. 15.10.

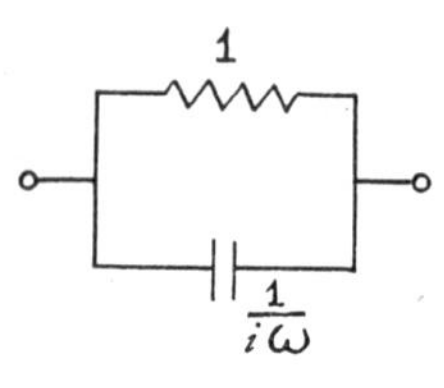

FIG. 15.8

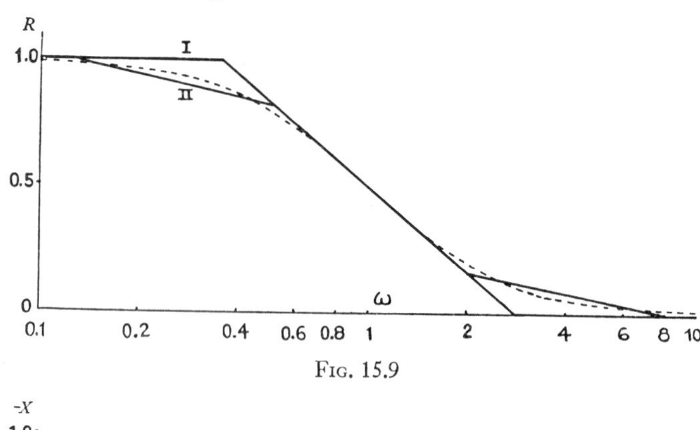

FIG. 15.9

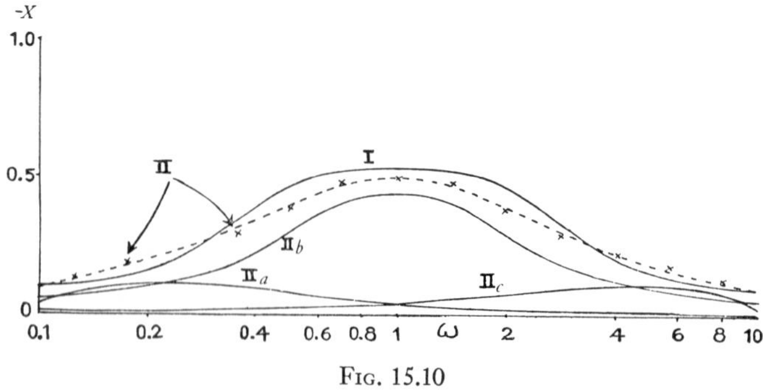

FIG. 15.10

A more elaborate straight line approximation is furnished by the solid line characteristic II in Fig. 15.9. Here the central segment and the two neighboring segments are all specified by $a = 2.0$. The corresponding reactance characteristics are found on Chart V. Allowance must be made for the facts that the central points of the side segments occur at $\omega = 0.25$ and $\omega = 4.0$ and that the three reactance characteristics must be multiplied respectively by the factors $\frac{1}{6}$, $\frac{2}{3}$, and $\frac{1}{6}$, to agree with the total resistance changes represented by the corresponding line segments. This leads to the constituent reactance characteristics shown by Curves II*a*, II*b* and II*c* in Fig. 15.10. Their sum is indicated by the crosses.

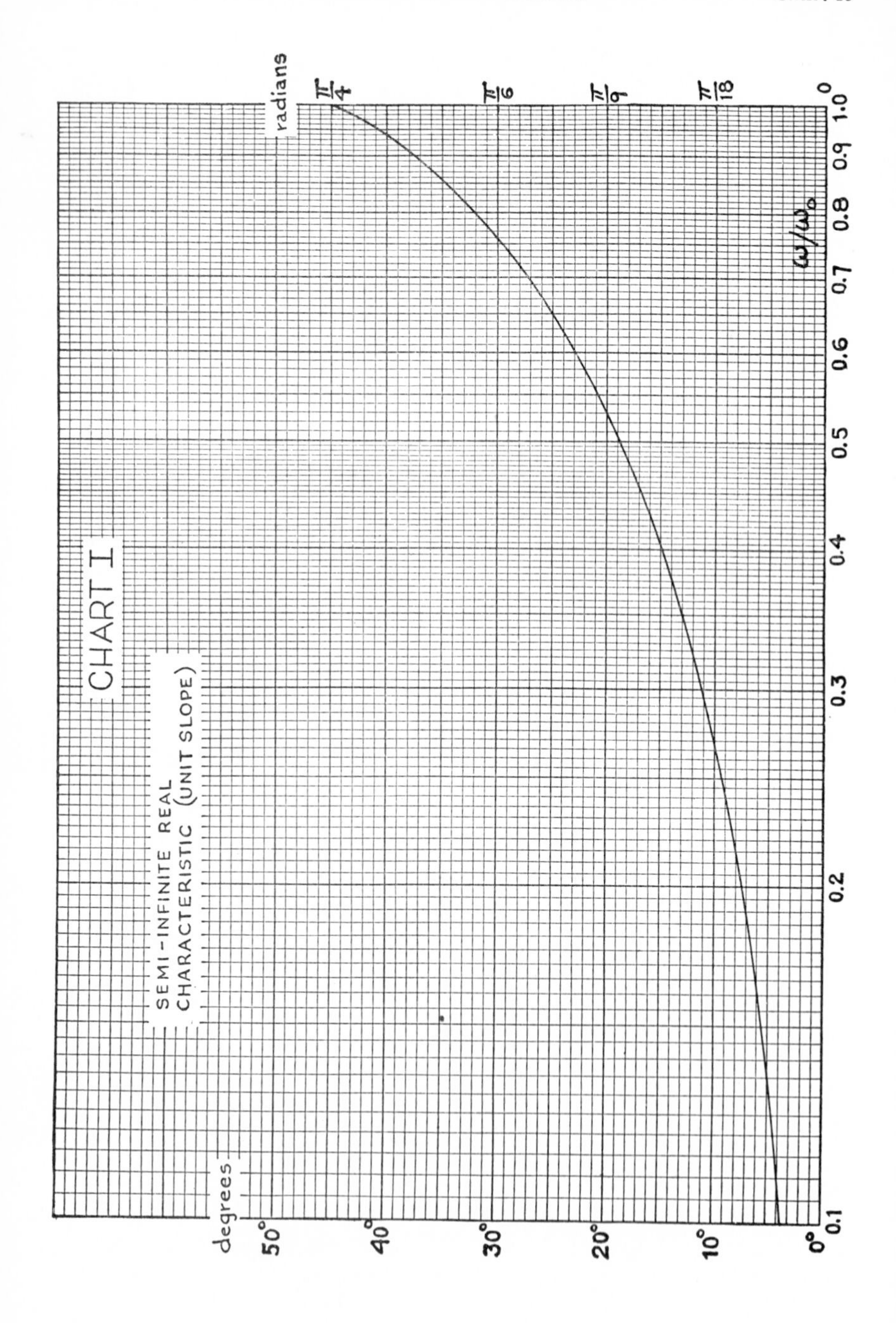
CHART I
SEMI-INFINITE REAL
CHARACTERISTIC (UNIT SLOPE)
radians
π/4
π/6
π/9
π/18
0
degrees
50°
40°
30°
20°
10°
0°
0.1
0.2
0.3
0.4
0.5
0.6
0.7
0.8
0.9
1.0
ω/ω₀

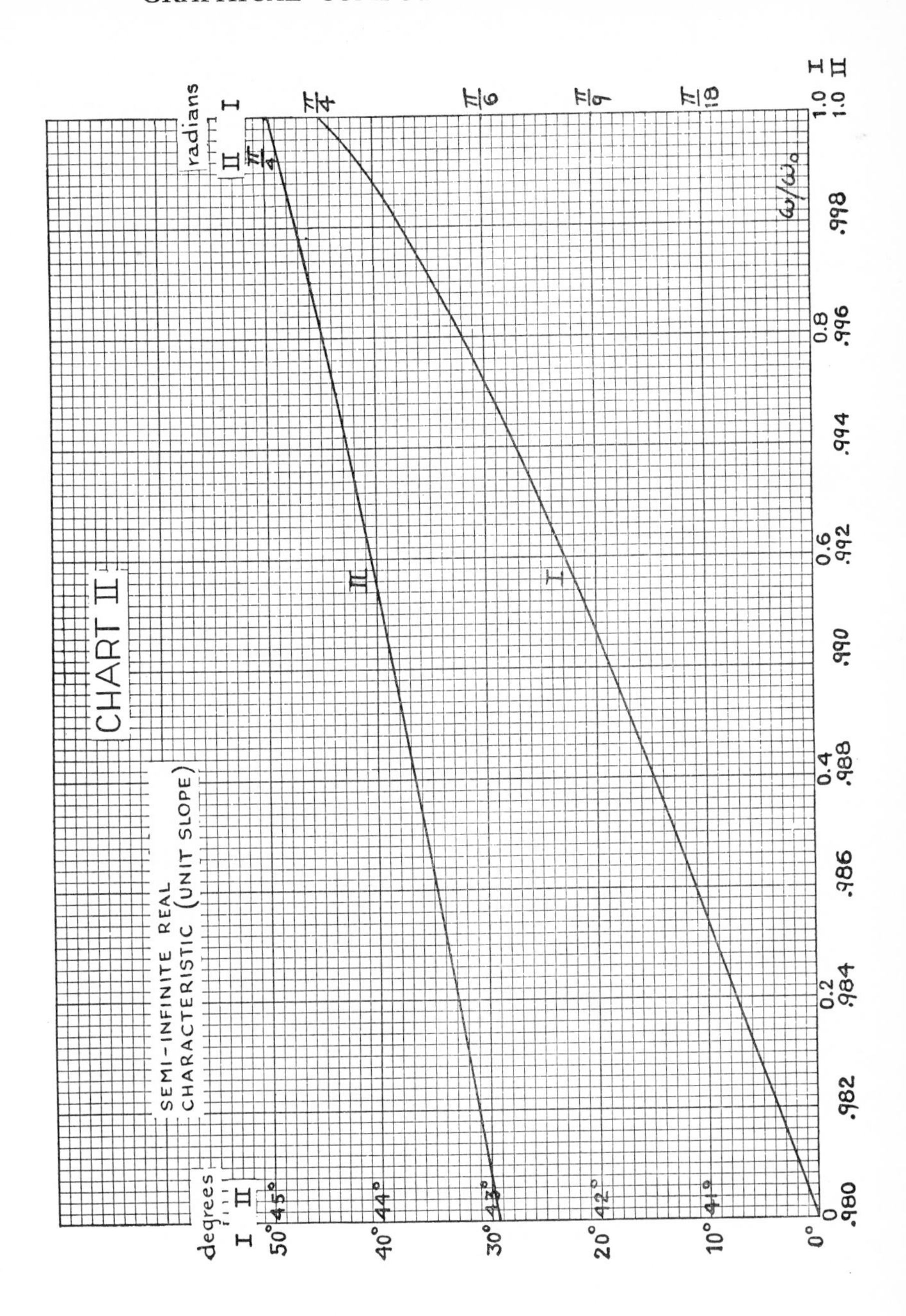
CHART II
SEMI-INFINITE REAL
CHARACTERISTIC (UNIT SLOPE)
degrees
I II
50° 45°
40° 44°
30° 43°
20° 42°
10° 41°
0°
radians
I II
π/4 π/4
π/6
π/9
π/18
0 .980
.982
0.2 .984
.986
0.4 .988
.990
0.6 .992
.994
0.8 .996
.998
1.0 1.0
I II
ω/ω₀

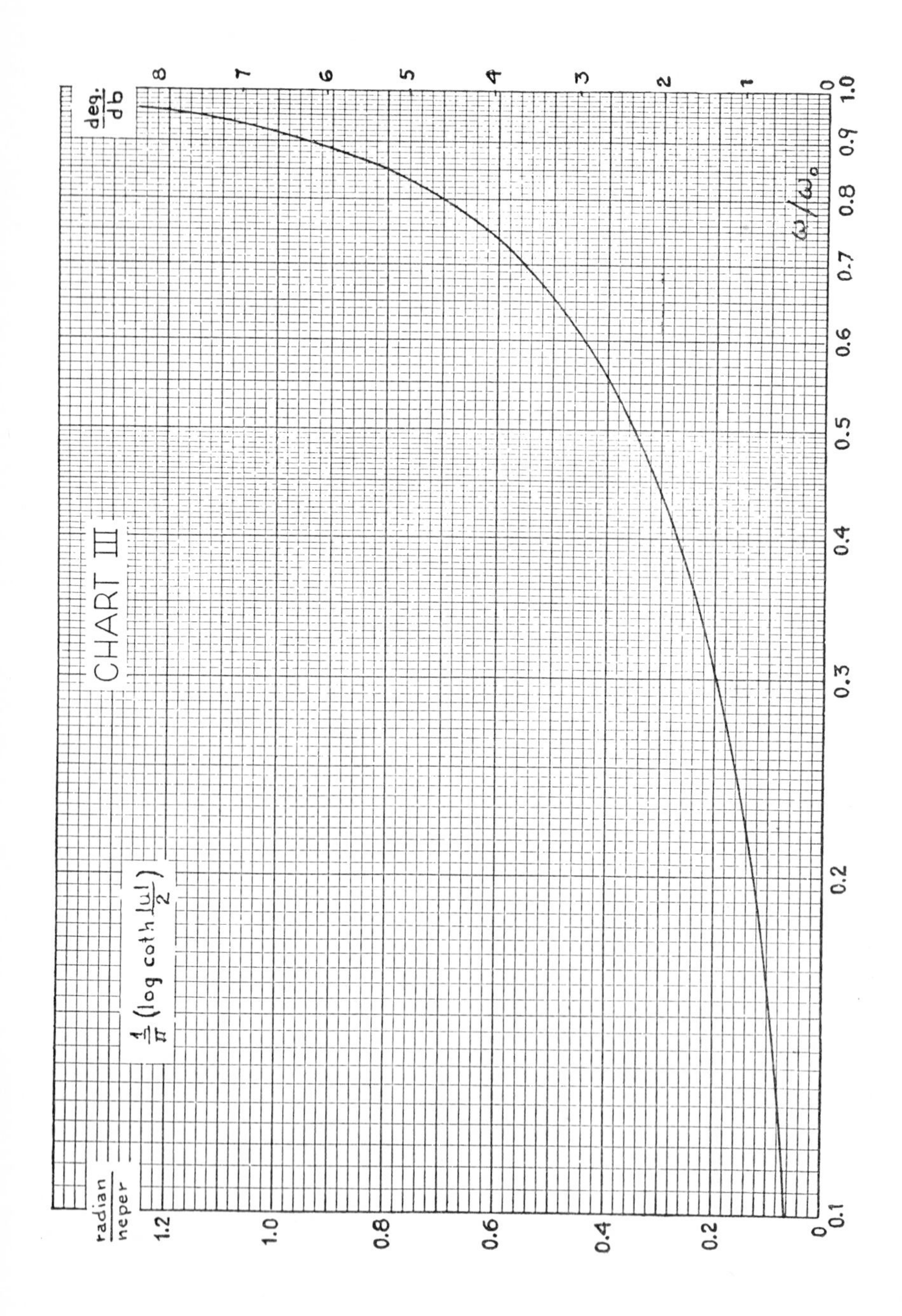
CHART III
$\frac{1}{\pi}\left(\log \coth \frac{|u|}{2}\right)$
deg.
db
radian
neper
1.2
1.0
0.8
0.6
0.4
0.2
0
8
7
6
5
4
3
2
1
0
0.1
0.2
0.3
0.4
0.5
0.6
0.7
0.8
0.9
1.0
ω/ω_0

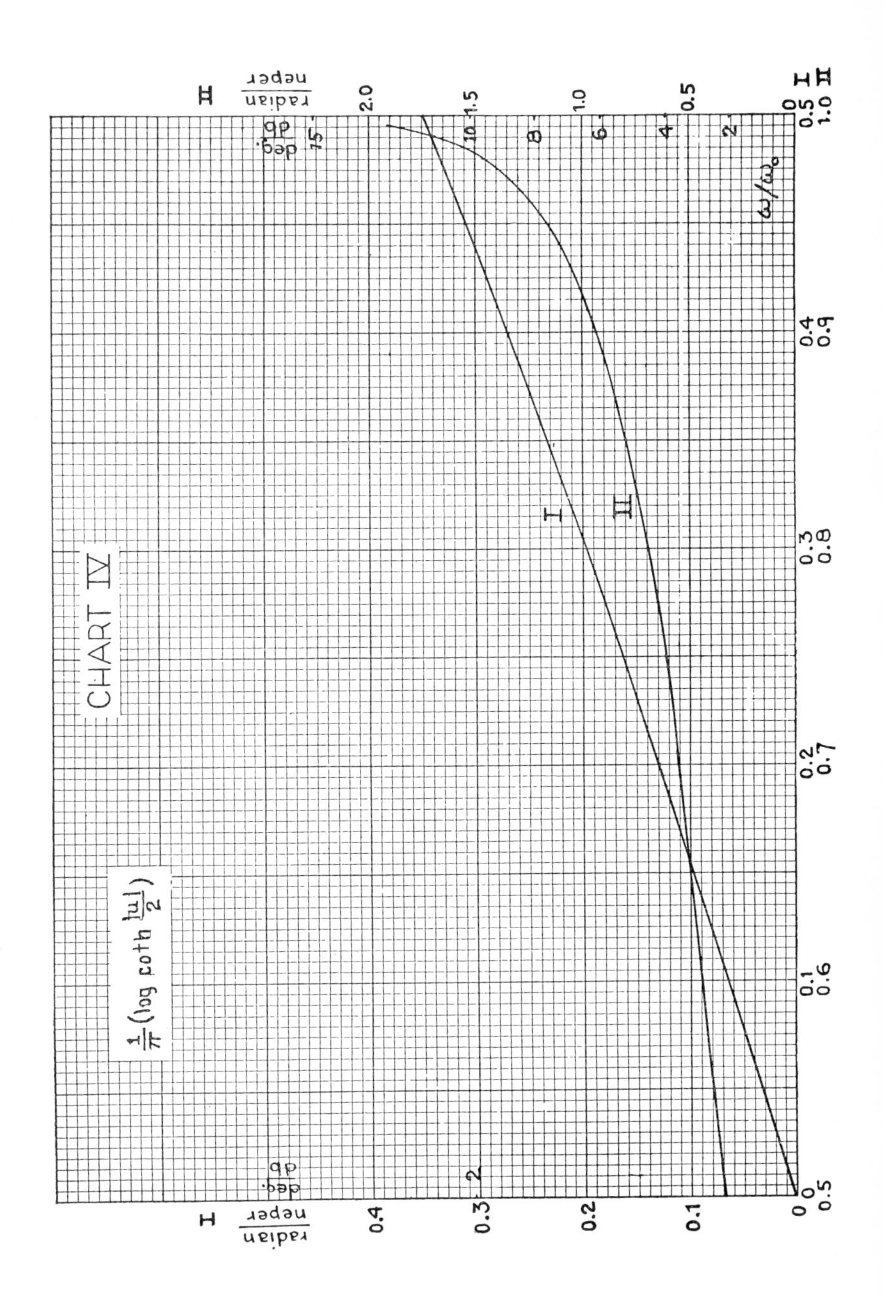
CHART IV
$\frac{1}{\pi}\left(\log \coth \frac{|u|}{2}\right)$
I
II
ω/ω₀
radian
neper
deg.
db
0.4
0.3
0.2
0.1
0
2.0
1.5
1.0
0.5
15
10
8
6
4
2
0.5 1.0
0.4 0.9
0.3 0.8
0.2 0.7
0.1 0.6
0 0.5

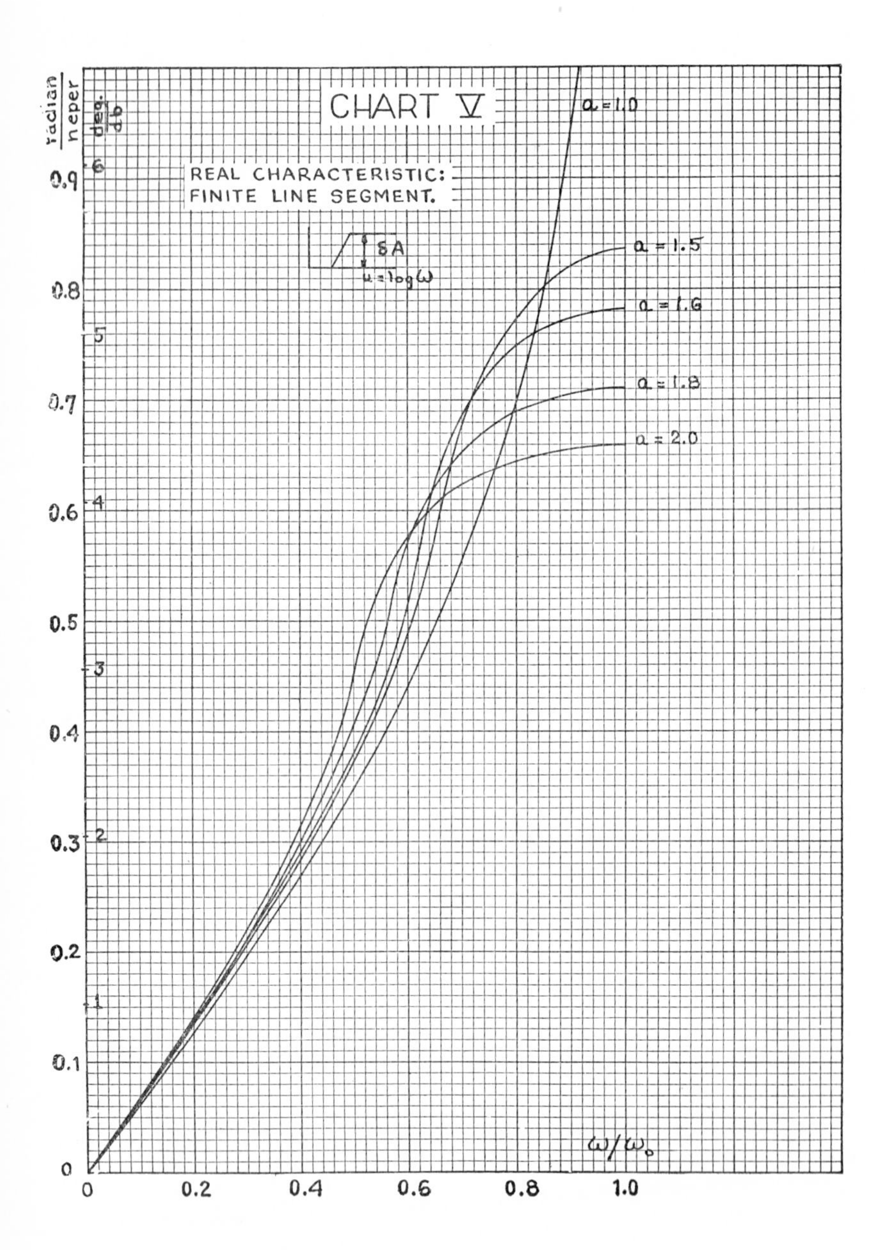
CHART V
REAL CHARACTERISTIC:
FINITE LINE SEGMENT.
δA
u = log ω
a = 1.0
a = 1.5
a = 1.6
a = 1.8
a = 2.0
radian/neper
deg./db
ω/ω₀
0
0.1
0.2
0.3
0.4
0.5
0.6
0.7
0.8
0.9
1
2
3
4
5
6
0.2
0.4
0.6
0.8
1.0

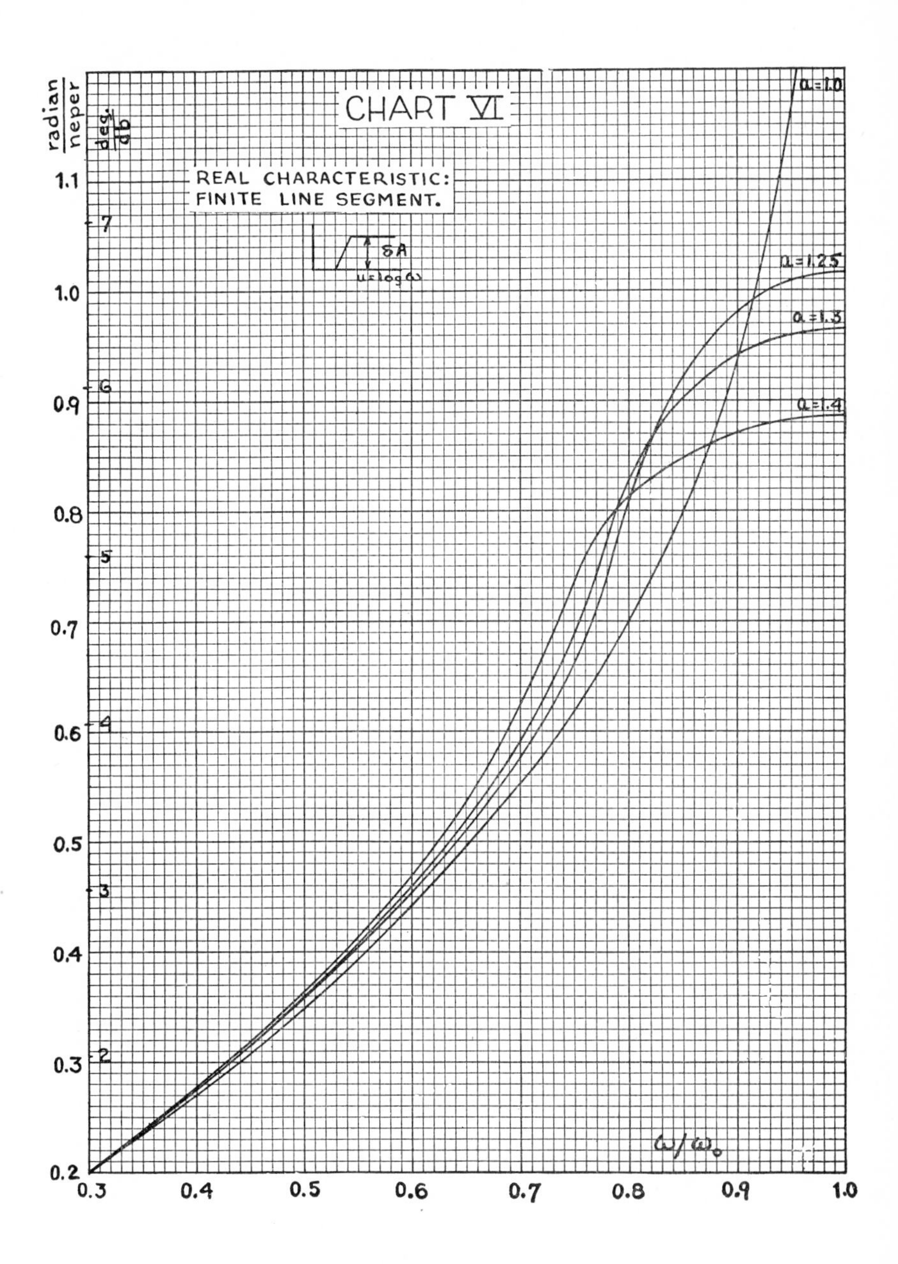
CHART VI
REAL CHARACTERISTIC:
FINITE LINE SEGMENT.
δA
u=log ω
radian/neper
deg./db
a=1.0
a=1.25
a=1.3
a=1.4
ω/ω₀
0.2
0.3
0.4
0.5
0.6
0.7
0.8
0.9
1.0
1.1
2
3
4
5
6
7

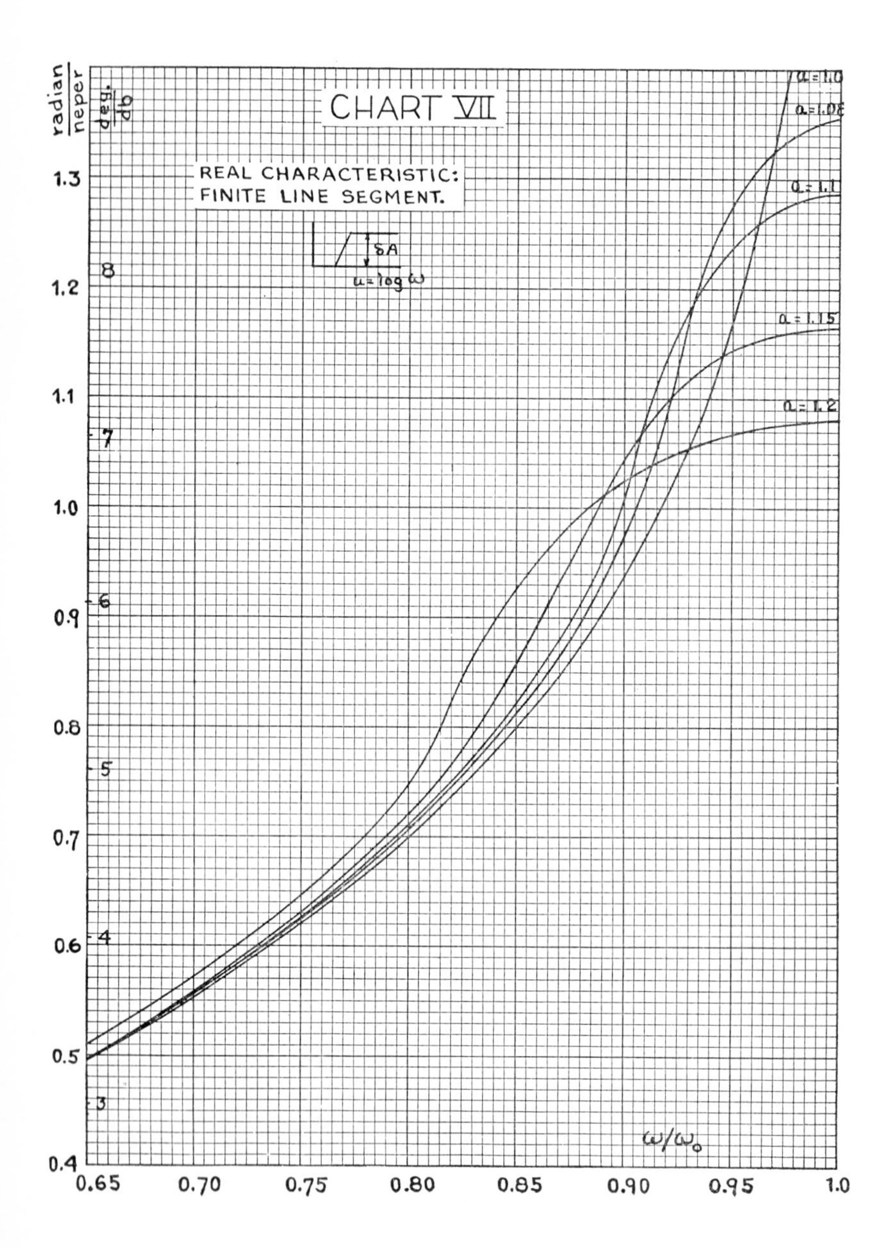

CHART VII
REAL CHARACTERISTIC:
FINITE LINE SEGMENT.
δA
u = log ω
radian/neper
deg./db
a = 1.0
a = 1.08
a = 1.1
a = 1.15
a = 1.2
ω/ω₀
1.3
1.2
1.1
1.0
0.9
0.8
0.7
0.6
0.5
0.4
8
7
6
5
4
3
0.65
0.70
0.75
0.80
0.85
0.90
0.95
1.0

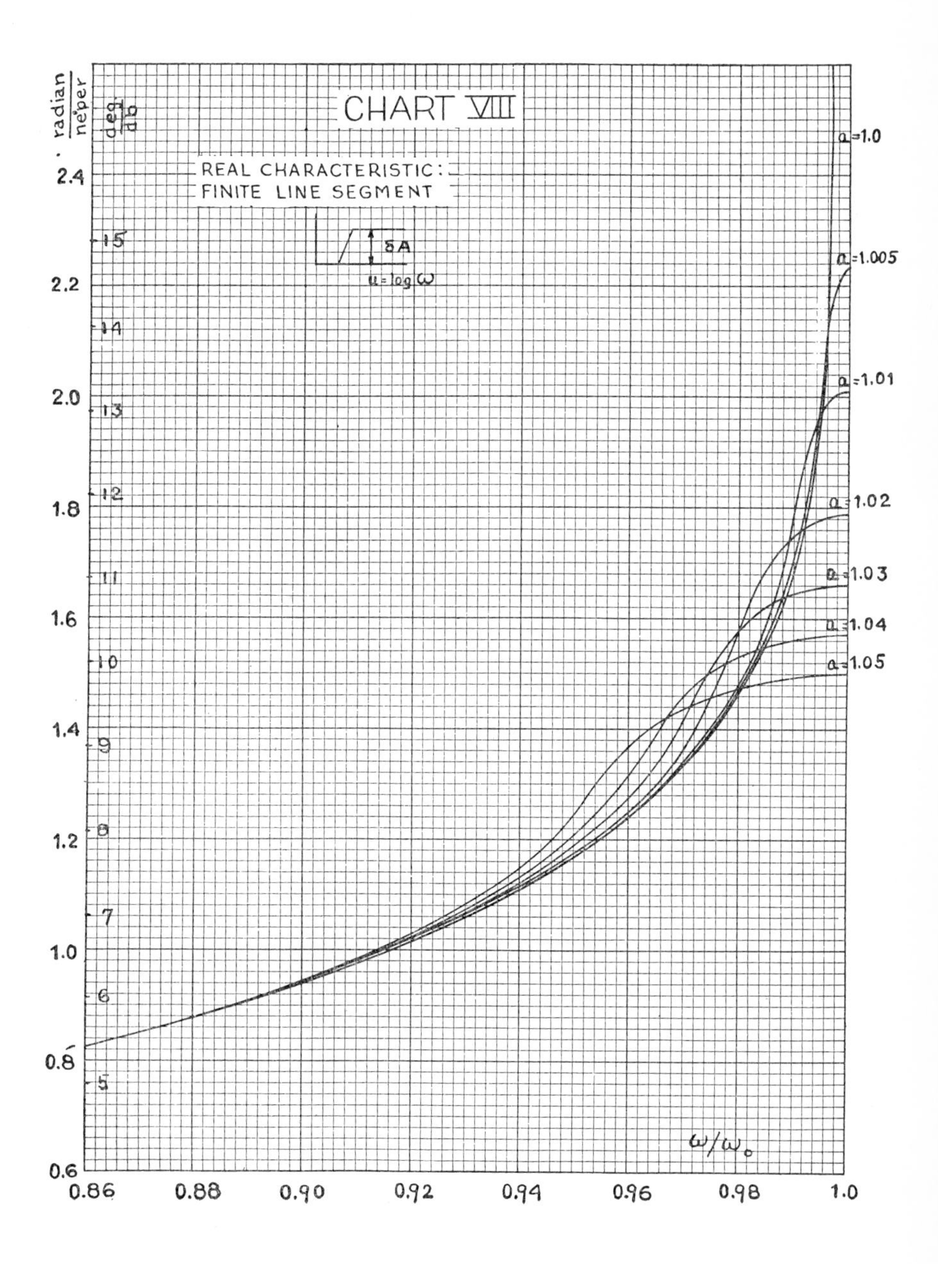
CHART VIII
REAL CHARACTERISTIC:
FINITE LINE SEGMENT
δA
u = log ω
radian/neper
deg/db
2.4
2.2
2.0
1.8
1.6
1.4
1.2
1.0
0.8
0.6
15
14
13
12
11
10
9
8
7
6
5
a=1.0
a=1.005
a=1.01
a=1.02
a=1.03
a=1.04
a=1.05
ω/ω₀
0.86
0.88
0.90
0.92
0.94
0.96
0.98
1.0

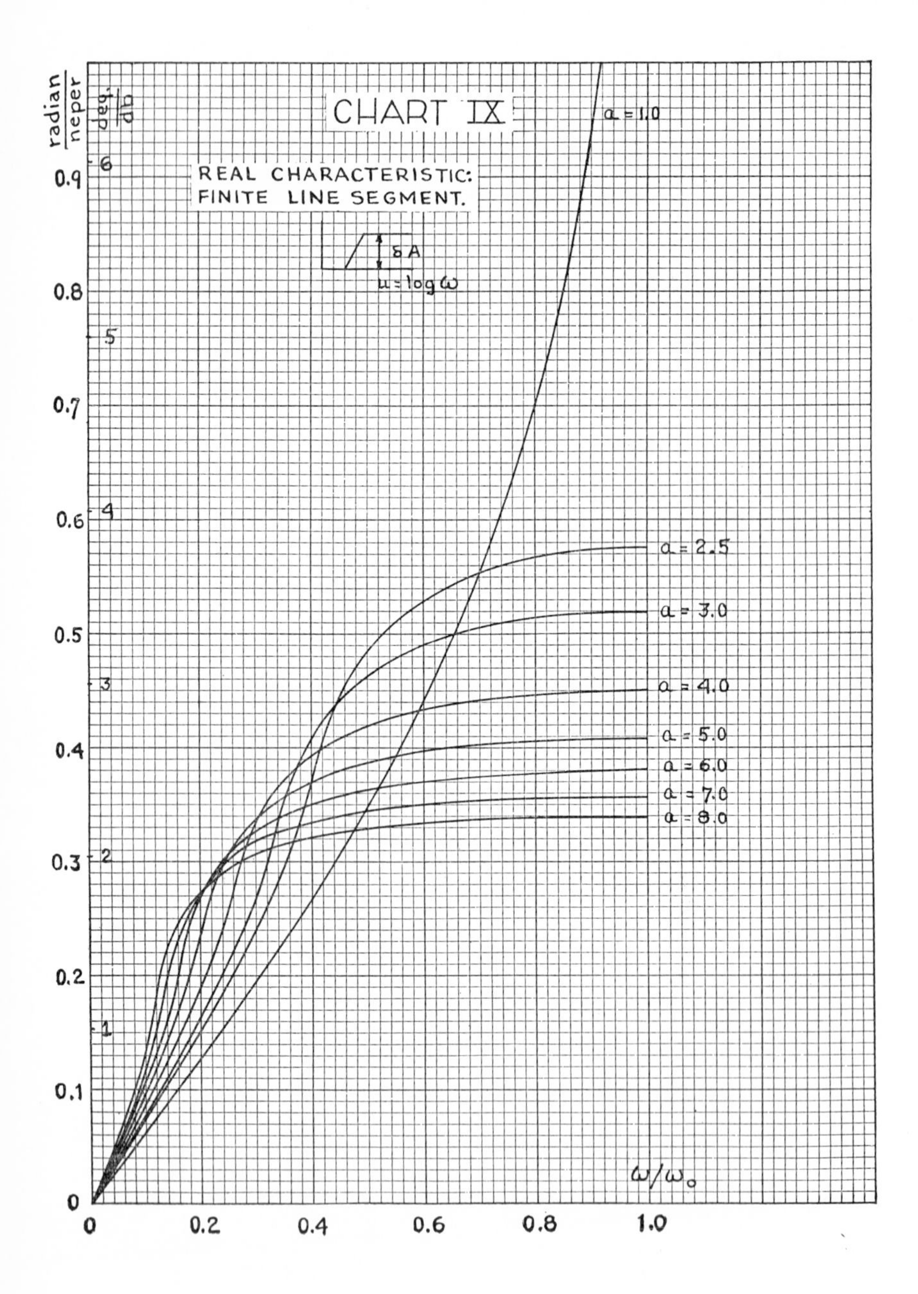
CHART IX
REAL CHARACTERISTIC:
FINITE LINE SEGMENT.
δA
u = log ω
radian/neper
deg./db
a = 1.0
a = 2.5
a = 3.0
a = 4.0
a = 5.0
a = 6.0
a = 7.0
a = 8.0
ω/ω₀
0
0.1
0.2
0.3
0.4
0.5
0.6
0.7
0.8
0.9
1
2
3
4
5
6
0.2
0.4
0.6
0.8
1.0

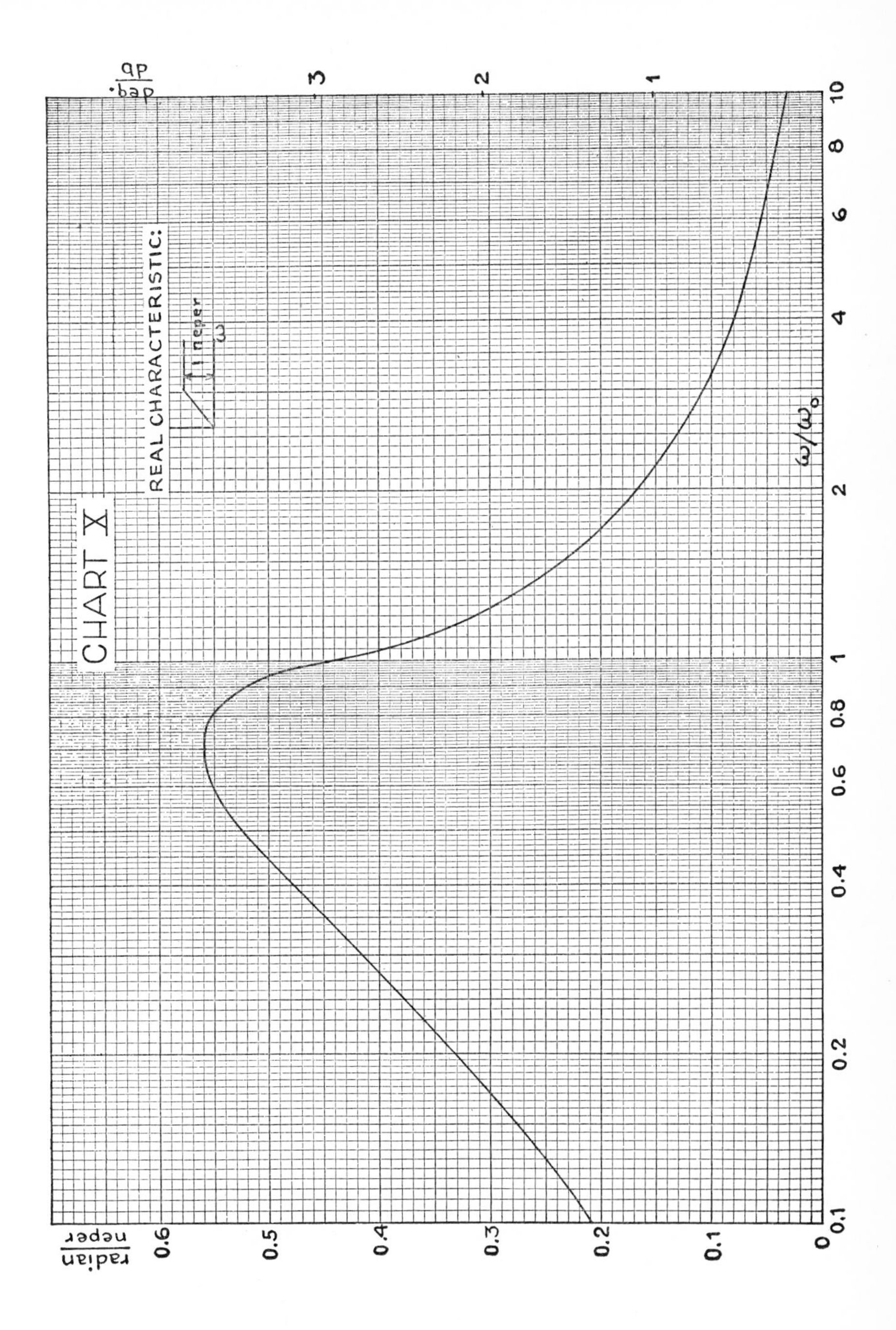
CHART X
REAL CHARACTERISTIC:
1 neper
ω
ω/ω₀
0.1
0.2
0.4
0.6
0.8
1
2
4
6
8
10
radian
neper
0.6
0.5
0.4
0.3
0.2
0.1
0
db
deg.
3
2
1

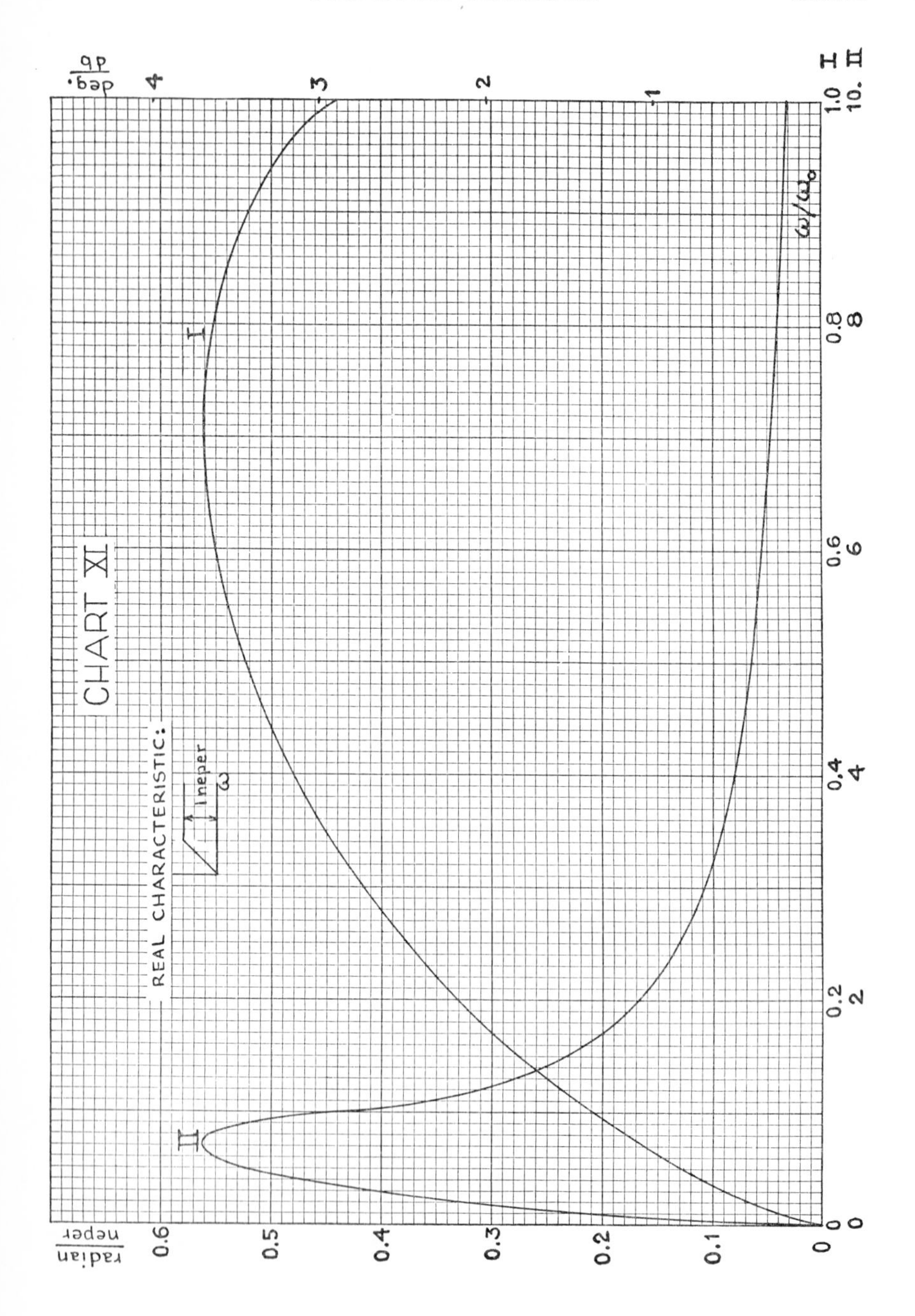
CHART XI
REAL CHARACTERISTIC:
1 neper
ω
radian
neper
deg.
db
0
0.1
0.2
0.3
0.4
0.5
0.6
1
2
3
4
I
II
0
0.2
0.4
0.6
0.8
1.0
2
4
6
8
10.
ω/ω₀

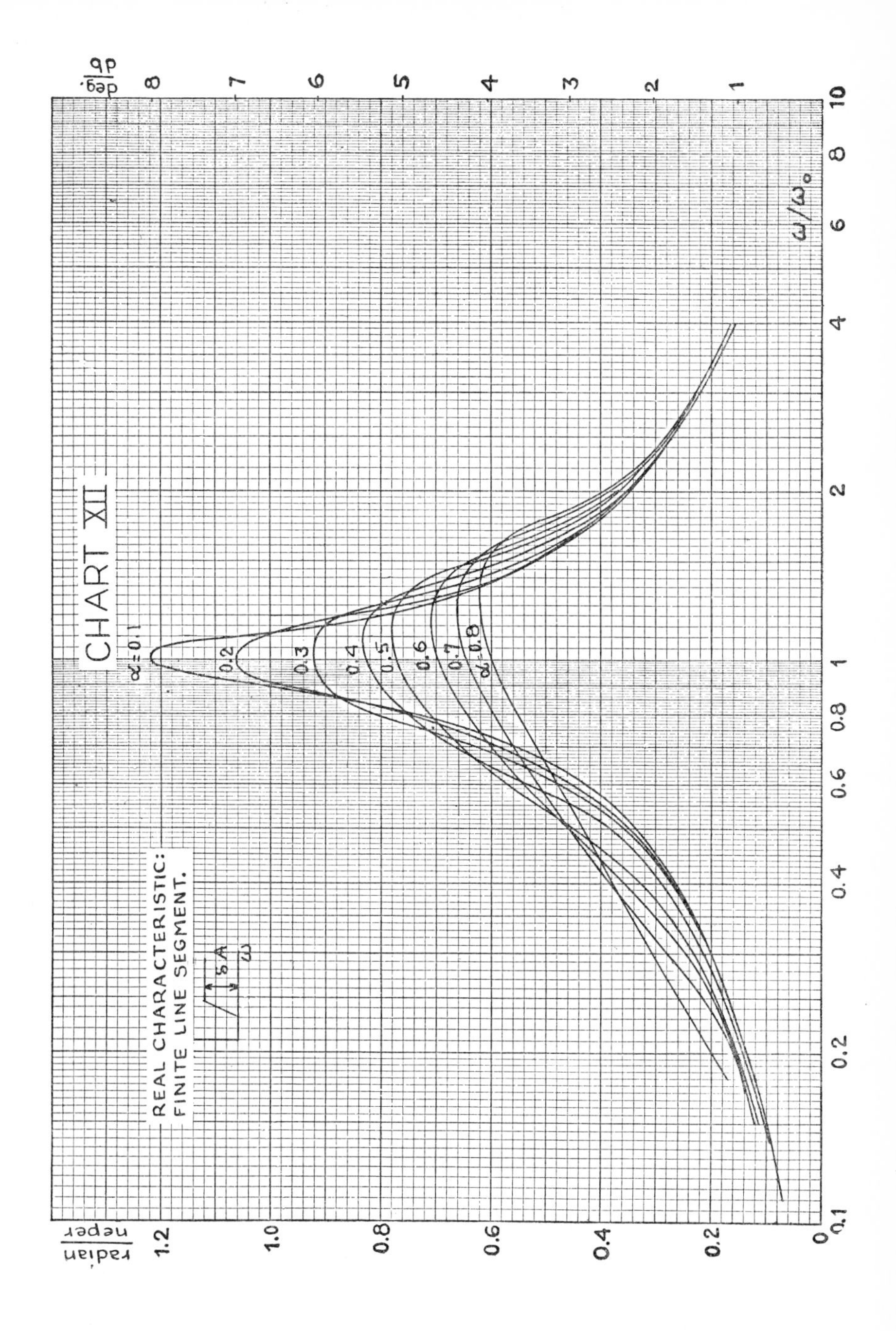
CHART XII
REAL CHARACTERISTIC:
FINITE LINE SEGMENT.
δA
ω
α=0.1
0.2
0.3
0.4
0.5
0.6
0.7
α=0.8
ω/ω₀
0.1
0.2
0.4
0.6
0.8
1
2
4
6
8
10
radian/neper
0
0.2
0.4
0.6
0.8
1.0
1.2
deg./db
1
2
3
4
5
6
7
8

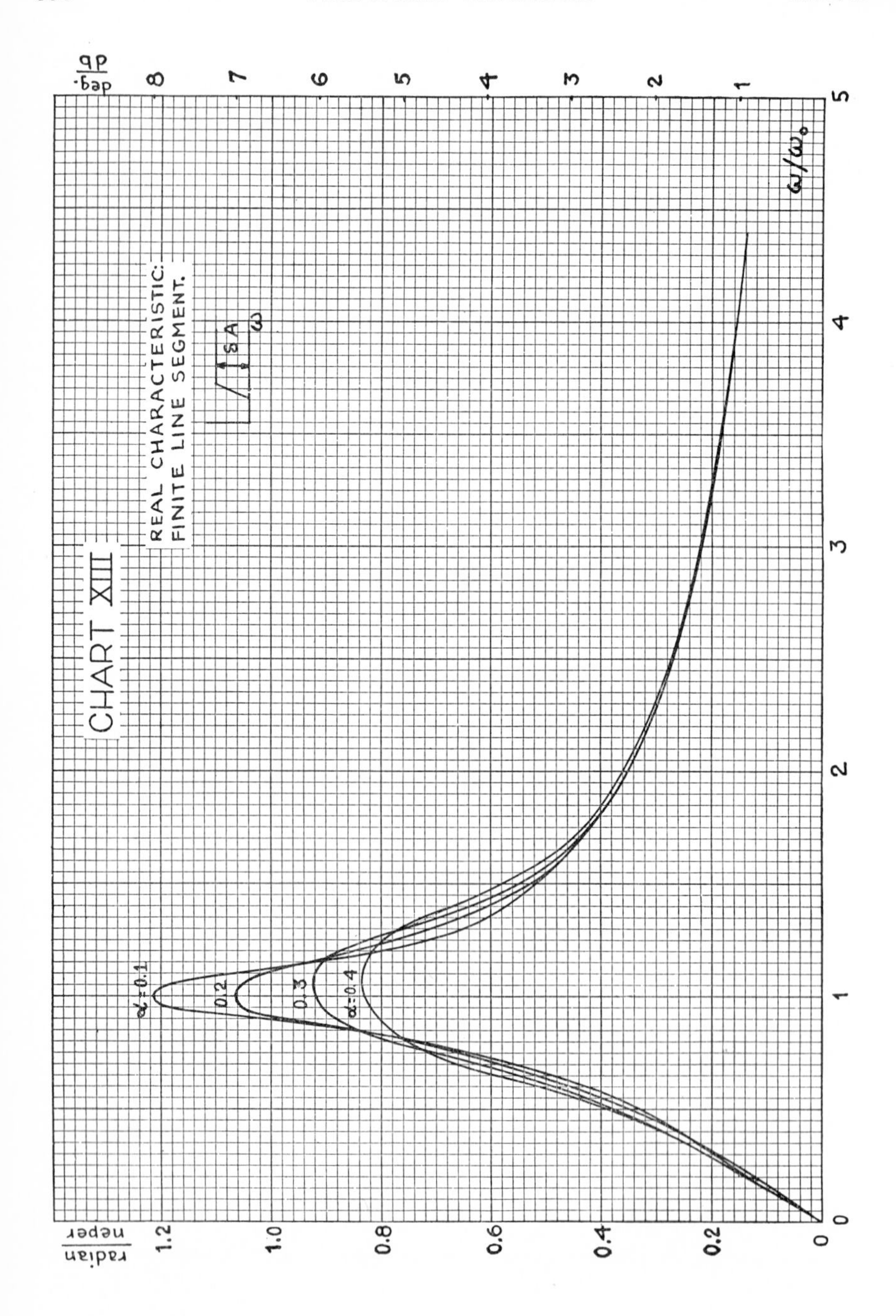
CHART XIII
REAL CHARACTERISTIC:
FINITE LINE SEGMENT.
δA
ω
α=0.1
0.2
0.3
α=0.4
ω/ω₀
0
1
2
3
4
5
radian
neper
0
0.2
0.4
0.6
0.8
1.0
1.2
deg.
db
1
2
3
4
5
6
7
8

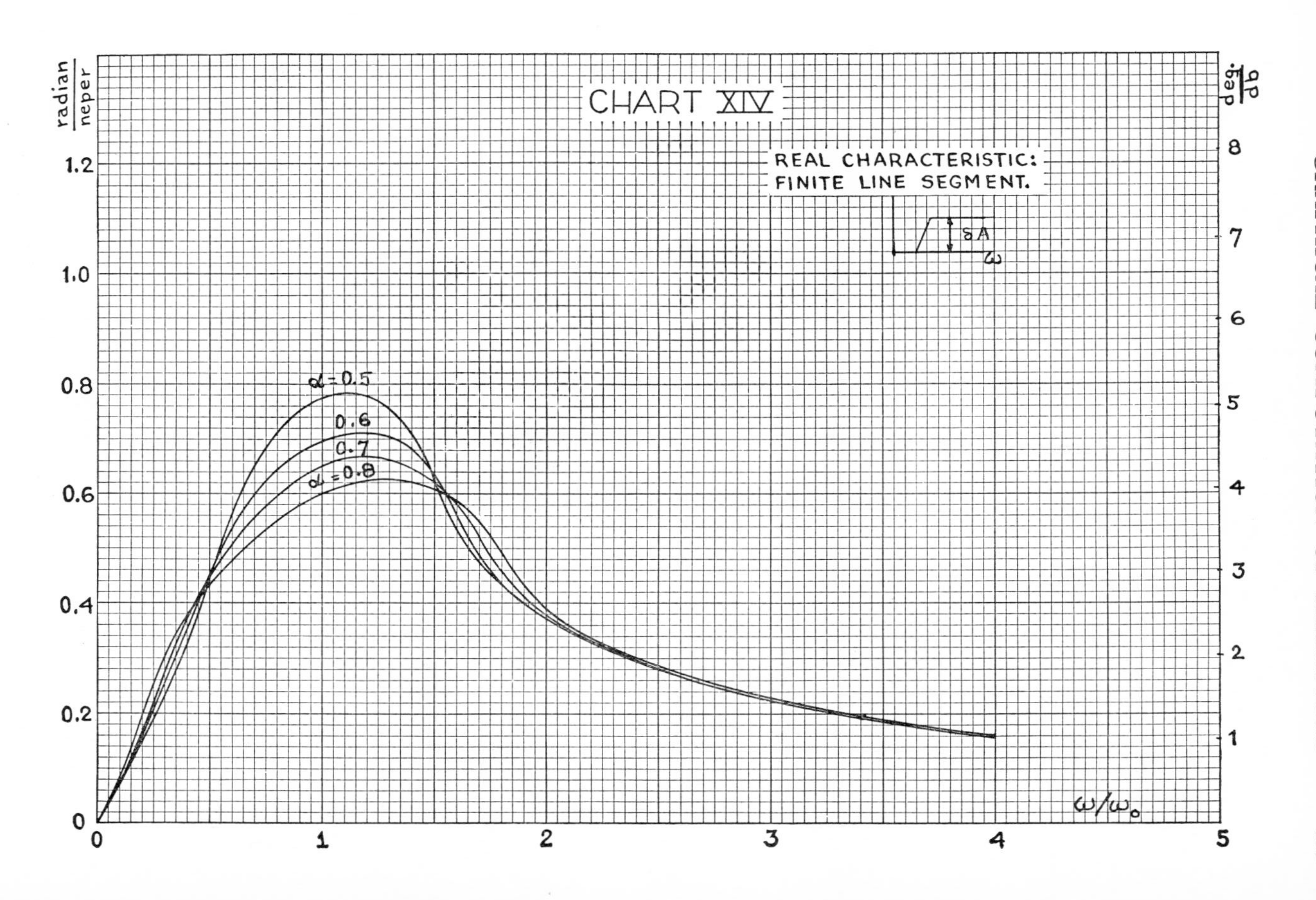
CHART XIV
REAL CHARACTERISTIC:
FINITE LINE SEGMENT.
δA
ω
ω/ω_0
radian / neper
deg. / db
0
0.2
0.4
0.6
0.8
1.0
1.2
1
2
3
4
5
6
7
8
0
1
2
3
4
5
α=0.5
0.6
0.7
α=0.8

CHAPTER XVI

Application of General Theorems to Input and Output Circuit Design

16.1. *Introduction*

Beginning with the present chapter the emphasis in the book will shift from the development of general design principles to the discussion of special problems in amplifier circuit design. As a general procedure, each chapter begins with a discussion of the application of the general methods developed in preceding chapters to the particular problem in hand and continues with one or more illustrative designs. The illustrations are based broadly upon actual past designs, but it has been necessary in many instances to simplify and modify the design somewhat in order to focus attention on the particular design procedure under discussion. The statement that any particular illustration represents a network designed for such-and-such a purpose should therefore not be taken literally.

The present chapter is based upon two theorems, one directed at the design of an input or output transformer terminated in an open circuit except for a specified parasitic shunt capacity, and the other directed at transformers terminated in a finite resistance in addition to the parasitic capacity. The theorems are illustrated by an input or output circuit design for one of the coaxial repeaters* and by an antenna coupling circuit designed for a radio transmitter. The succeeding chapter gives a similar discussion of the design of interstage networks including a specified shunt capacity.

Before beginning these two chapters it may be desirable to mention that the mathematical expressions upon which the discussion depends are not necessarily restricted in their physical application to the problems of input and output circuit design and interstage design for which they are nominally developed. For example, the principal theorem of the present chapter is one on the reflection coefficient obtainable in a circuit including a prescribed parasitic element. Since expressions having the mathematical form of a reflection coefficient appear frequently in network analysis this theorem may be useful in fields having nothing to do with an input or out-

* This is a reference to the transmission system described in Chapter XIII. (See footnote, p. 285.)

put circuit. It is therefore of some importance to pay attention to the mathematical form of the functions examined, without regard to the physical context in which they appear. It may also be observed that since the analysis always postulates a prescribed parasitic element it is governed generally by the theorem on the conservation of band width in a circuit with prescribed parasitic elements which was developed in Chapter X. This material should be re-read if necessary before the present chapter is undertaken.

16.2. *Input and Output Circuits with Infinite Terminations*

The first theorem deals with the maximum performance obtainable from an amplifier input or output circuit when the amplifier impedance itself is merely a shunt capacity. Figure 16.1, for example, represents an output network of an amplifier whose last tube is of screen grid type, so that its plate resistance can be regarded as substantially infinite in comparison with the other impedances in the structure. Figure 16.2 shows a corresponding

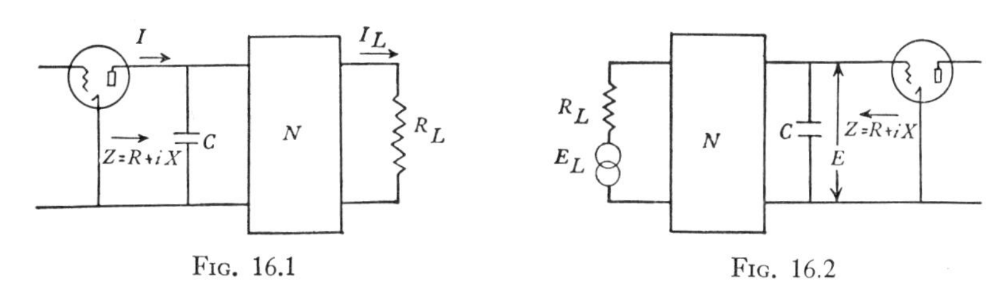

Fig. 16.1

Fig. 16.2

input circuit. In each figure the resistance R_L represents the line and N is the coupling network. Physically, N will of course be a transformer in most cases. For the purposes of this discussion, however, it will be supposed that N may include any number of tuning or shaping elements in addition to the transformer proper. Although Figs. 16.1 and 16.2 are drawn for non-feedback amplifiers, the conditions of the theorem will frequently be fulfilled also by feedback structures, especially if the feedback is of series or cathode type. With either of these feedbacks the active impedance of the amplifier proper is very high, as the discussion in Chapter V pointed out, so that the input or output circuit is effectively open-circuited. The only difference to be observed is that with feedback the capacity C in Figs. 16.1 and 16.2, instead of representing the sum of the tube capacity and the high side capacity of the input or output transformer, reduces to the transformer capacity alone.*

If the parasitic capacity C were not present we could evidently imagine that the network N consisted of an ideal transformer of indefinitely high

* See, however, the discussion of " volume performance " given later in the chapter.

turns ratio. This would allow us to make the current ratio I_L/I in Fig. 16.1 or the voltage ratio E/E_L in Fig. 16.2 as large as we pleased over any prescribed band. The capacity, however, limits the response by tending to short-circuit the transformer when its impedance ratio is made too high. The theoretical problem is that of determining how large a response can be obtained over any given band when the best possible network N, including both a transformer and additional tuning elements, is used.

This problem is easily solved by means of the resistance integral condition

$$\int_0^\infty R\,d\omega = \frac{\pi}{2C}, \tag{16–1}$$

which was originally developed as equation (13–7) of Chapter XIII. For example, if we let $Z = R + iX$ represent the impedance looking away from the output tube proper, as indicated by Fig. 16.1, the power delivered by the tube is $|I|^2R$. If the network is non-dissipative, which is evidently the most favorable case, this is the same as the power $|I_L|^2R_L$ which reaches the line. We therefore have

$$\left|\frac{I_L}{I}\right| = \sqrt{\frac{R}{R_L}}. \tag{16–2}$$

With the help of the principle of reciprocity it is easily shown that the voltage step-up in the input circuit is given by the precisely similar expression

$$\left|\frac{E}{E_L}\right| = \sqrt{\frac{R}{R_L}}. \tag{16–3}$$

If we let e^α represent either the current ratio $|I_L/I|$ or the voltage ratio $|E/E_L|$ and introduce the limitation on R given by (16–1) this leads immediately to the general formula

$$\int_0^\infty e^{2\alpha} d\omega = \frac{\pi}{2CR_L}. \tag{16–4}$$

As (16–4) is written, the response characteristic extends over the complete frequency spectrum. Since R cannot be negative, however, it is clear from (16–1) that the maximum response over a finite range will be obtained if $e^{2\alpha}$ is zero outside that range. This allows us to replace the limits of integration in (16–4) by ω_1 and ω_2, if these quantities represent the edges of the useful band. If a flat transmission characteristic is demanded, for example, it leads to

$$\alpha \leq \tfrac{1}{2} \log \frac{\pi}{2} \frac{1}{(\omega_2 - \omega_1)CR_L}, \tag{16–5}$$

where the equality sign holds in the limiting case when the transmission outside the useful band is zero. The difference $(\omega_2 - \omega_1)$ is evidently an illustration of the principle of conservation of band width discussed earlier. We observe that the best obtainable response is the same as that which would be secured if the network, including C, were replaced by an ideal transformer whose high side impedance when terminated in the line is equal to $\pi/2$ times the absolute value of the impedance of C for the given band width.*

The same formula can evidently be extended to include the case when the desired response characteristic varies with frequency. Such a problem might be encountered, for example, if we wished to adjust the input or output circuit to compensate for the characteristics of an associated transmission line. Let it be supposed that the transmission α is written as $\alpha = \alpha_0 + \alpha_1$ where α_1 represents the desired variation in the characteristic and α_0 fixes the general level of response. We then readily find

$$\alpha_0 \leq \tfrac{1}{2} \log \left[\frac{\pi}{2CR_L} \frac{1}{\int_{\omega_1}^{\omega_2} e^{2\alpha_1} d\omega} \right], \tag{16–6}$$

and since α_1 is known as a function of frequency, α_0 can be computed. The results in both cases can be summarized as the

Theorem: The average effective impedance ratio, over a given band, of an input or output circuit terminated in a prescribed capacity C is not greater than that of an ideal transformer whose high side impedance, when terminated in the line, is $\pi/2$ times the absolute value of the impedance of C for the prescribed band.

Examples of the use of this theorem in input and output circuit design are given later.

16.3. *Input and Output Circuits for Finite Terminations*

The second theorem deals with input and output circuits terminated at one end by a finite resistance and capacity in parallel. This is illustrated by Fig. 16.3, the terminating elements being indicated by R_1 and C. A situation of this sort might arise, for example, if the output pentode in Fig. 16.1 were replaced by a triode having appreciable plate conductance. Since the networks of Figs. 16.1 and 16.2 are pure reactances and thus present a very poor impedance to the line, we might also imagine R_1 to be

* The phrase " the impedance of C for the given band width " is used here and in later discussion for the quantity $1/(\omega_2 - \omega_1)C$. In accordance with the principle of conservation of band width, it represents the impedance of C at the edge of the band in an equivalent low-pass problem.

an element deliberately added to the circuit to secure an improved amplifier impedance. An analytic situation which is similar to that presented by Fig. 16.3 may also appear in other physical contexts. For example, in certain long-distance telephone systems the power supply to the repeaters is fed over the line. The shunt inductances and series capacities required to separate power and signal currents at each end of the repeater in such a system play a role which is somewhat analogous to that of the shunt capacity in Fig. 16.3.

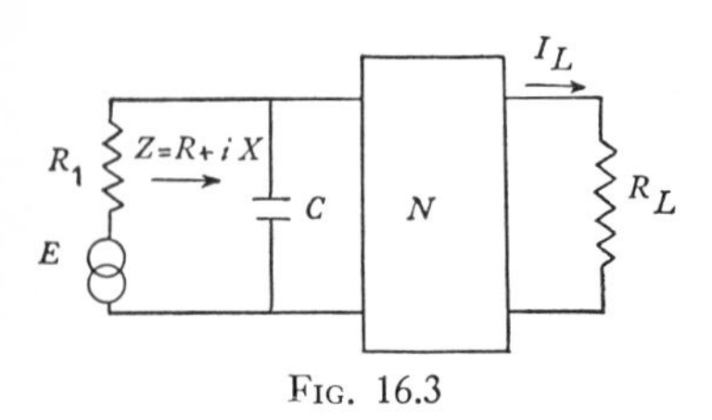

FIG. 16.3

The theorem to be established depends upon a study of the reflection coefficient, ρ, between R_1 and the impedance it faces. If we write $Z = R + iX$ for the impedance looking away from R_1, as indicated by Fig. 16.3, the formula for ρ appears as

$$\rho = \frac{R_1 - Z}{R_1 + Z}. \tag{16-7}$$

Although ρ itself is not of direct interest it is easily related either to the impedance which the amplifier presents to the line or to the transmission through the network. For example, if the network is non-dissipative and Z_a and Z_b represent the impedances looking in each direction from any junction, as illustrated by Fig. 16.4, it is easily shown that

$$|\rho| = \left| \frac{Z_a - \overline{Z}_b}{Z_a + Z_b} \right|, \tag{16-8}$$

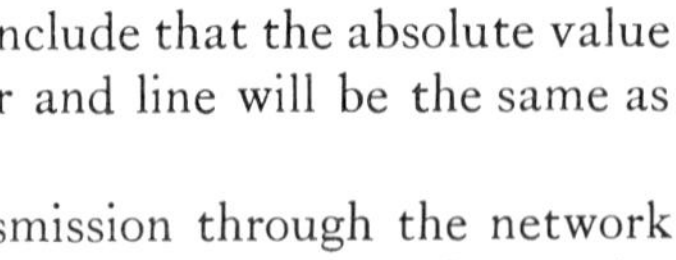

FIG. 16.4

where $\overline{Z}_b$ is the conjugate of Z_b. Thus in particular, if we take the junction as the line terminals, and assume the line impedance to be a pure resistance, we can conclude that the absolute value of the reflection coefficient between amplifier and line will be the same as the absolute value of ρ.

The relationship between ρ and the transmission through the network can be established by writing the power which a generator E in series with R_1 will deliver to the network as

$$\text{Power} = \frac{E^2 R}{(R + R_1)^2 + X^2}. \tag{16-9}$$

If the network is non-dissipative this must, of course, also be the power which flows into the line. The maximum power which the generator E in series with R_1 can deliver to any external load, however, is $E^2/4R_1$. If we let α represent the transmission loss with respect to this optimum, therefore, we have

$$e^{-2\alpha} = \frac{4RR_1}{(R + R_1)^2 + X^2}$$
$$= 1 - | \rho |^2. \tag{16–10}$$

The limitation on ρ which follows from the fact that Z must include the parasitic capacity C can be studied most easily by integrating log $(1/\rho)$ around the usual semicircular path. The real component, log $| 1/\rho |$, of this expression will be recognized as the quantity which is usually spoken of as the "return loss" (in nepers) in reflection coefficient theory. In performing the integration, however, allowance must be made for the fact that log $(1/\rho)$, or log $[(R_1 + Z)/(R_1 - Z)]$, is not necessarily analytic in the right half-plane. No trouble is to be expected from the factor $R_1 + Z$ in the numerator, since if R_1 and Z are both passive impedances their sum $R_1 + Z$ must also be a passive impedance and can have neither zeros nor poles in the right half-plane. This argument, however, does not apply to the roots of $R_1 - Z$. It is consequently necessary to suppose that, like a non-minimum transfer impedance, $1/\rho$ may have poles in the right half-plane.

Let the possible poles in the right half-plane be represented by $a_1 \cdots a_n$. They will be replaced by corresponding poles in the left half-plane if we multiply $1/\rho$ by factors of the form $(p - a_j)/(p + a_j)$. This procedure is essentially similar to the method which was followed in reducing a non-minimum phase shift transfer impedance to a minimum phase expression. Since the function is now analytic in the right half-plane it evidently allows us to write

$$\oint \log \left[\frac{R_1 + Z}{R_1 - Z} \frac{(p - a_1) \cdots (p - a_n)}{(p + a_1) \cdots (p + a_n)} \right] d\omega = 0. \tag{16–11}$$

As in all the previous analysis, only the real component of the integrand in (16–11) need be considered in evaluating the integral along the real frequency axis. At real frequencies, however, it is evident that the absolute value of the product of all the factors involving the a's is unity. In this range the integrand thus reduces effectively to log $| 1/\rho |$. When ω is very great, on the other hand, Z becomes $1/i\omega C$ and log $[(R_1 + Z)/(R_1 - Z)]$ is approximately $2/i\omega CR_1$. If we deal with any pair of factors of the form $(p - a_j)/(p + a_j)$ we find similarly that their contribution reduces to $-2a_j/i\omega$. These are evidently the expressions which it is appropriate to use in the integration around the large semicircular portion of the contour. The complete integral therefore reduces to

$$2\int_0^\infty \log\left|\frac{1}{\rho}\right| d\omega + \oint\left[\frac{2}{CR_1} - 2\sum a_j\right]\frac{d\omega}{i\omega} = 0, \qquad (16\text{–}12)$$

which is readily transformed into

$$\int_0^\infty \log\left|\frac{1}{\rho}\right| d\omega = \frac{\pi}{CR_1} - \pi\sum a_j. \qquad (16\text{–}13)$$

The a's in (16–13) are evidently real or conjugate complex quantities and in either case they must have positive real components, since they represent poles of the function $(R_1 + Z)/(R_1 - Z)$ lying in the right half-plane. Thus $\sum a_j$ must be a positive real quantity and serves to reduce the limit on the integral in (16–13) which would appear if we considered C and R_1 alone. The reason why such a term must appear in a general analysis is obvious if it is recalled, from (16–8), that the absolute value of the reflection coefficient must be the same whether it is measured at the terminals of R_1 or of R_L in Fig. 16.3. An equation of the type given by (16–13) can be developed equally well for either pair of terminals. If C in Fig. 16.3 is the controlling capacity in the circuit, however, the quantity which would correspond to $1/CR_1$ if we conducted the analysis at the line terminals must, in general, be smaller than $1/CR_1$ itself. Thus the line terminal result, at least, must include a term of the type represented by $-\sum a_j$ if the equality of the reflection coefficients is to be realized.

In special circumstances the additional term may appear at the R_1 terminals also. Suppose, for example, that the structure of Fig. 16.3 takes the special form shown by Fig. 16.5, in which R_0 represents R_L as seen through a transformer. If the elements are correctly chosen the network represents a simple filter and we can expect that R_1 and Z will be reasonably well matched, so that $\log|1/\rho|$ will be correspondingly large, over at least a limited range. If R_0 is made very small, on the other hand, the network approximates an anti-resonant circuit with small damping and gives a very poor match to R_1 at all frequencies. For purposes of practical design, however, such an unnecessary loss in performance need not be taken seriously, since it is usually a comparatively simple matter to secure a design in which no term of the form $-\sum a_j$ appears in the equation for the reflection coefficient at the terminals of the controlling parasitic element. The conditions which the network must satisfy in order to secure this result are described in a later section.

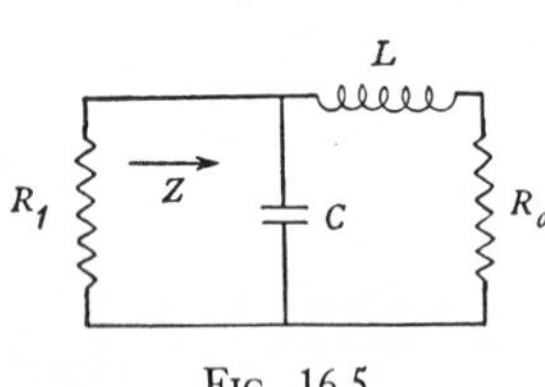

FIG. 16.5

Like the corresponding earlier expression (16–4), equation (16–13) as it stands involves the reflection coefficient over the complete frequency spectrum. The response can, however, be restricted to a finite range by noticing that $\log |1/\rho|$ can be written as

$$\log\left|\frac{1}{\rho}\right| = \log\left|\frac{R_1 + Z}{R_1 - Z}\right| = \tfrac{1}{2}\log\frac{(R_1 + R)^2 + X^2}{(R_1 - R)^2 + X^2}. \qquad (16\text{–}14)$$

It is apparent that the right-hand side of (16–14) will be zero when $R = 0$ and will be greater than zero for any positive value of R. As in the preceding theorem, therefore, we can conclude that the maximum value of $\log |1/\rho|$ in any prescribed interval will be obtained if R vanishes outside that interval. If ω_1 and ω_2 represent the edges of the prescribed band, this allows (16–13) to be written as

$$\int_{\omega_1}^{\omega_2} \log\left|\frac{1}{\rho}\right| d\omega \leq \frac{\pi}{CR_1}, \qquad (16\text{–}15)$$

where the equality sign obtains in the limiting case when $\sum a_j = 0$ and R is negligible below ω_1 and above ω_2.

The simplest example of (16–15) is found, of course, when the reflection coefficient is constant in the prescribed range. We then have

$$\log\left|\frac{1}{\rho}\right| \leq \frac{\pi}{(\omega_2 - \omega_1)CR_1}, \qquad (16\text{–}16)$$

which can also be written as

$$|\rho| \geq e^{-\pi/Q} \qquad (16\text{–}17)$$

where Q represents the reactance-resistance ratio $(\omega_2 - \omega_1)CR_1$. If we make an obvious extension to include circuits in which $|\rho|$ varies with frequency this general result can be summed up as the

Theorem: If a circuit including a final shunt capacity is connected to a terminating resistance, the average value of the return loss, in nepers, between the resistance and the circuit impedance is not greater than π divided by the reactance-resistance ratio of the prescribed resistance and capacity in parallel for the band width over which the average is taken.

A plot of $|\rho|$ against Q, as determined from (16–17) is shown by Fig. 16.6. The broken line gives, for comparison purposes, the value which $|\rho|$ would assume if the network N in Fig. 16.3 presented the fixed resistance R_1 to the terminating elements R_1 and C in parallel. It will be seen that when Q is less than about 0.7 or 0.8 a suitable design for N allows the presence of C to be compensated for almost completely and even if $Q = 1$

the reflection coefficient can be reduced from 45 per cent to about one-tenth this amount. For higher Q's, however, the smallest obtainable ρ increases rapidly and depends less and less on what can be done in the design of N.

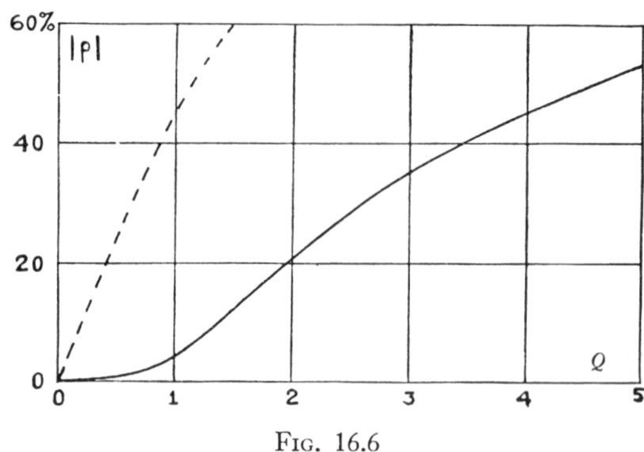

FIG. 16.6

In virtue of the relation between reflection coefficient and transmission loss given by (16–10), the same data can also be plotted in terms of the transmission efficiency of the circuit. This is shown by Fig. 16.7. Since $|\rho|$ appears only as the square in (16–10) the losses are extremely small for moderate Q's but they increase rapidly as Q grows larger. When Q is indefinitely great the physical situation is, of course, the same as that described by the first theorem.

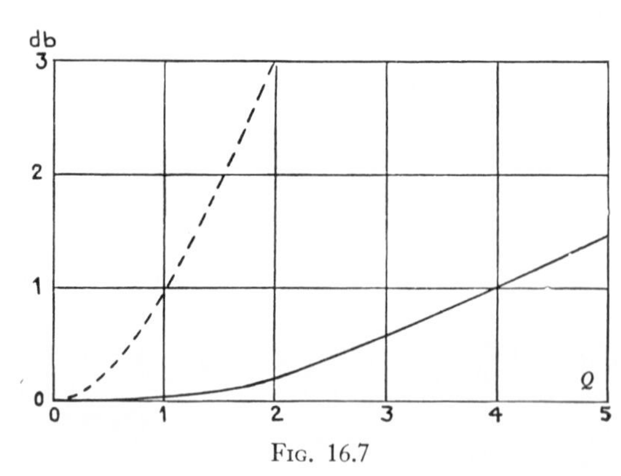

FIG. 16.7

16.4. *Implications of Input and Output Circuit Theorems for Practical Design*

The two theorems just established have been presented in the first instance as general theoretical measures of the maximum performance possibilities of input and output circuits incorporating prescribed parasitic elements. It is perhaps equally important to notice, however, that the theorems also suggest how the general framework of a practical design approximating the theoretical limits can appropriately be obtained. These implications do not provide, of themselves, a complete design technique, but they may be useful as accessories to other methods.

The most obvious suggestion of this type arises from the fact that the input or output circuit reaches the theoretical limit of performance only when the resistance component of the impedance seen at the terminal of the parasitic element is negligibly small at frequencies outside the useful band. Since the resistance is a measure of the power which can be absorbed by the network and transmitted to the line this means that the ideal solution must be obtained from an infinitely selective structure, or, in other words, a perfect filter. The tuned transformers of ordinary design practice are, of course, somewhat like simple filters in their properties. The analysis thus suggests that closer approximations to the limiting response, if required, should be obtainable by adding more elements to bolster up the selectivity of the circuit. The same considerations also apply to interstage network design, since it is shown in the next chapter that maximum interstage gain in a prescribed band likewise calls for a negligible resistance component outside the useful band.

If the circuit is regarded as a filter, it should differ from conventional filters in one important respect. Since R is a measure of power, the degree of approximation to the ideal depends upon the loss of the filter expressed as a power ratio. In these terms an attenuation of the order of 15 to 25 db, which would be regarded as quite low in ordinary filter design, is evidently substantial. On the other hand, the same considerations point to the importance of minimizing the breadth of the "transition region" just beyond the useful band, in which the loss is extremely low. Thus a design giving a reasonably close approximation to the maximum performance may have a low general level of attenuation outside the useful band* but its selectivity should be relatively sharp. Aside from considerations of simplicity and economy, the amount of filtering which it is desirable to add is limited by the effects which parasitic dissipation in the circuit elements may be expected to have. If the approximation to the theoretical limit is already reasonably good a further increase in the selectivity of the circuit may evidently lose more by increased dissipative losses than remains to be gained by a closer approach to the nominally ideal characteristic.

* These remarks apply to regions not more than a moderate distance from the useful band, where design control is both possible and important. Since the integrations are carried to infinite frequency the resistance at more remote frequencies must be indefinitely small if the result is not to be infinite. This, however, is cared for automatically by the parasitic elements in the circuit.

A question which frequently arises is that of the relation between the number of elements which are used in the design and the degree of approximation to the theoretical limit which may be expected as a result. A rough answer here can be obtained from known relationships in filter theory between the number of sections in a filter and the amount of discrimination which can be obtained from it over any given band. The filter relationship is best expressed by the formula*

$$\alpha_a = [10 \log_{10} (e^{2\alpha_p} - 1) - 10\ (2\eta + 1) \log_{10} q - 12], \quad (16\text{–}18)$$

where α_a is the minimum attenuation in db over the prescribed attenuation range, α_p measures the allowable distortion in the pass band, η is the number of sections in the filter, and q is a parameter measuring the frequency interval between the prescribed transmission and attenuation ranges. It is, of course, assumed that for any given η the individual sections are chosen to give the maximum possible α_a.

Since the input resistance in the attenuating band depends upon the power flowing through the structure we can represent it approximately by $e^{-2\alpha_a}$. But if α_p and q are taken as constants it is clear from (16–18) that the addition of one unit to η will change $e^{-2\alpha_a}$ by a constant factor, whatever η may be. Moreover, in the situation to which the preceding general theorems on input and output circuits apply, the difference between the theoretical limiting performance† of the circuit and the actual performance obtained by any particular network depends upon the resistance outside the useful band. If we generalize η to represent number of elements rather than number of sections this evidently allows us to conjecture the

Theorem: If a circuit is limited by a parasitic element in such a way that maximum performance over a prescribed band can be obtained only if the real component of a certain impedance is substantial within the band but vanishes outside it, the difference between the actual performance and the limiting performance tends to be reduced by a constant factor each time an element is added to the circuit, provided the design is readjusted at each stage to make the maximum possible use of the elements available.

This proposition is stated as a " theorem " only to make it conspicuous. Aside from the vagueness of its phraseology, which is intended to cover the

* Darlington, " Synthesis of Reactance 4-Poles," *Journal of Mathematics and Physics*, Sept., 1939, p. 332.

† The units in which " performance " is to be measured are not stated in this discussion because the issue is not usually important when the theoretical limit is approached very closely and in any event the discussion is only very roughly quantitative.

interstage networks of the next chapter as well as the input and output circuits now under discussion, the statement can be attacked on the ground that the reasoning on which it depends is inadequate. For example, (16–18) is only an approximate relation, based on the assumption that α_a is reasonably large. Moreover, in view of the relative importance of the region just outside the band in the total resistance integral, as discussed earlier, it is naturally to be expected that additional elements will be used to make the circuit more sharply selective as well as to increase the discrimination α_a. This does not necessarily upset the conclusion expressed by the theorem but it affects the quantitative relation given by (16–18).

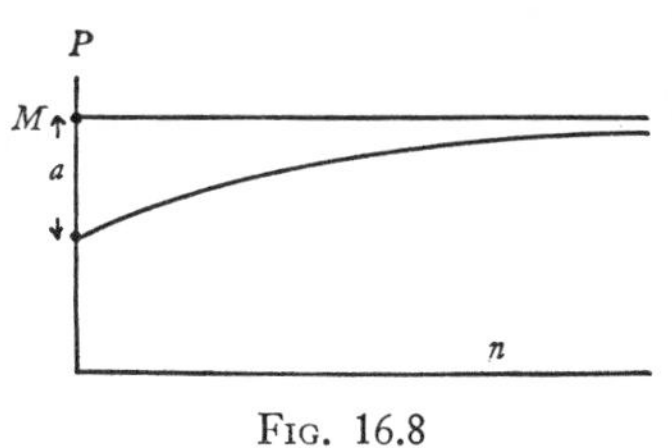

FIG. 16.8

If we nevertheless accept the statement of the theorem at face value it leads to the relation between performance and number of elements illustrated by Fig. 16.8. The curve corresponds to the equation

$$P = M - ae^{-bn}, \tag{16–19}$$

where a and b are constants, P is the actual performance, M is the maximum performance, and n is the number of elements used in the design. A study of the relation between (16–18) and (16–19) indicates that the constant a is analogous to α_p, in the sense that it can be regarded physically as an index of the accuracy with which the desired characteristic is to be realized in the useful band. If we disregard the difficulty that the theoretical justification for the equation extends at best only to situations in which the limiting performance is approximated fairly closely, it should be possible to determine a in most cases by an inspection of the circuit before any shaping elements are added to the design. If an open-circuited input or output circuit with flat response is required, for example, we might determine a by removing N in Figs. 16.1 and 16.2 and computing how large R_L may be before the distortion over the useful band caused by the parasitic capacity C exceeds a prescribed limit. The constant b is a scale factor which can best be determined by comparing the results obtained with two different networks. If (16–18) is followed, however, b depends principally upon the way in which q should be chosen to secure the best compromise between sharp selectivity and eventual loss, and is independent of the accuracy requirement α_p. Thus b should be roughly the same for all designs of a given type, without regard to changes in the constant a. If parasitic dissipation is considered it is, of course, necessary in interpreting (16–19) to assume that M may be somewhat smaller than the theoretical formulae based on non-dissipative networks indicate.

16.5. *Reconstruction of Imaginary Component as an Aid to Design*

The input and output circuit theorems can also be studied from another point of view, which can be used to aid design work whether the structure is regarded as a filter or is obtained by straight cut-and-try methods. The theorems as they stand appear as limitations on the values which the real component of some function related to the impedance of the structure can assume in the useful band. If the efficiency of the circuit is to be reasonably close to the theoretical limit, however, the real component must be quite small outside the useful band. We thus know the behavior of the real component with fair accuracy over the complete spectrum and it is consequently possible to use the methods described in the previous chapter to estimate what the associated imaginary component will be. This fixes the complete impedance seen at the terminals of the parasitic element, or, if we subtract the contribution of this element, the impedance of the network proper. Once the network impedance is known, however, it is generally an easy matter to find its structure.

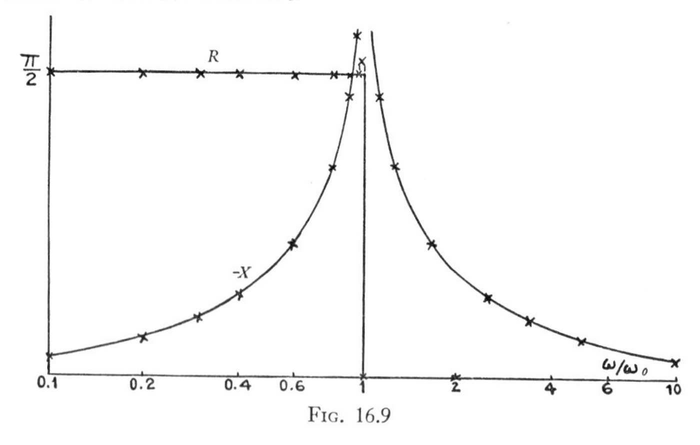

FIG. 16.9

As a simple example, let it be supposed that an open-circuited input transformer having a flat characteristic equal to the theoretical limit is to be designed. In terms of the low-pass equivalent, the high side resistance must be that shown by Fig. 16.9, where unit impedance is taken as the impedance of the capacity for the prescribed band width. This is a discontinuous real characteristic for which the corresponding imaginary characteristic is readily found from the charts in the preceding chapter and takes the form shown by the curve $-X$ in Fig. 16.9.

If we subtract the parallel impedance of the capacity, the resistance and reactance of the network proper appear as shown by the curves in Fig. 16.10. Let the reactance component be ignored for the moment. The resistance characteristic can be matched with sufficient accuracy for practi-

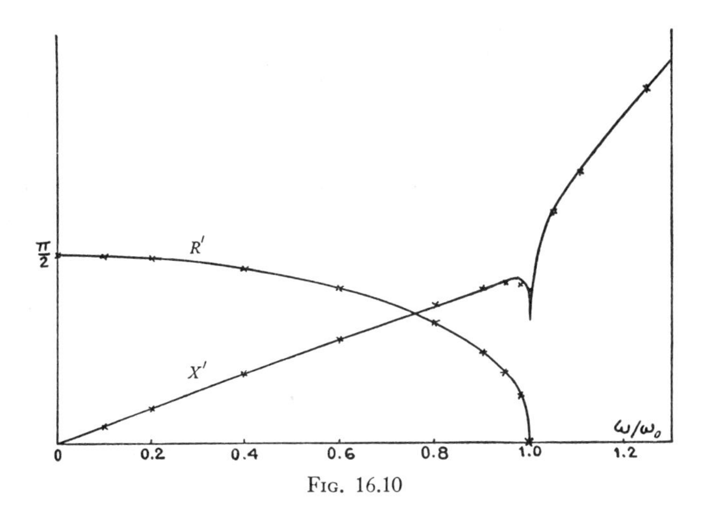

FIG. 16.10

cal purposes by an ordinary mid-series image impedance of the constant k type.* In order to illustrate the theoretical basis of the method, however, we will use the more complicated function

$$Z_I = \frac{\pi}{2} \frac{\sqrt{1 - \frac{\omega^2}{\omega_0^2}\left(1 - 0.91 \frac{\omega^2}{\omega_0^2}\right)}}{1 - 0.938 \frac{\omega^2}{\omega_0^2}}, \tag{16–20}$$

which matches the required characteristic to the accuracy indicated by the crosses in Fig. 16.10. The image impedance given by (16–20) can be obtained from a number of different networks. If we choose in particular a double m derived section the circuit takes the general form shown by Fig. 16.11. The parasitic capacity is indicated by C_0. The box represents

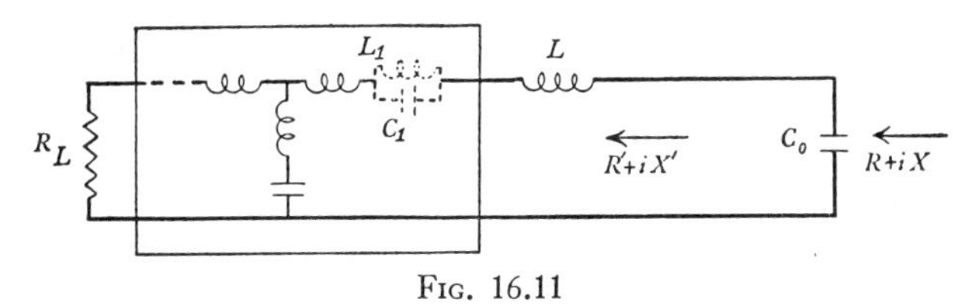

FIG. 16.11

the filter, the elements shown explicitly in the box being the double m derived termination. It is, of course, assumed that the filter is terminated at the other end in a section which matches the line impedance R_L with sufficient accuracy over the transmitted band.

* For references on standard filter theory, see the footnote in Chapter XIV, p. 326.

We now consider the reactance component in Fig. 16.10. It is obvious that it can be supplied approximately by the simple series inductance L in Fig. 16.11. An improved match can, however, be obtained by viewing the problem more generally. Broadly speaking, the analysis begins with an impedance, that shown by Fig. 16.9, which is appropriately chosen to include the parallel capacity C_0 and whose real and imaginary parts satisfy the relations necessary to permit the function as a whole to be represented by a physical network. It consequently follows that the impedance which remains when C_0 is removed must also be physically realizable. Any physically realizable impedance, however, can be regarded as a combination of a minimum reactance network and a purely reactive structure. If the resistance component is matched with sufficient accuracy with a minimum reactance circuit, consequently, we may expect that it will always be possible to find a physical pure reactance network to complete the design.

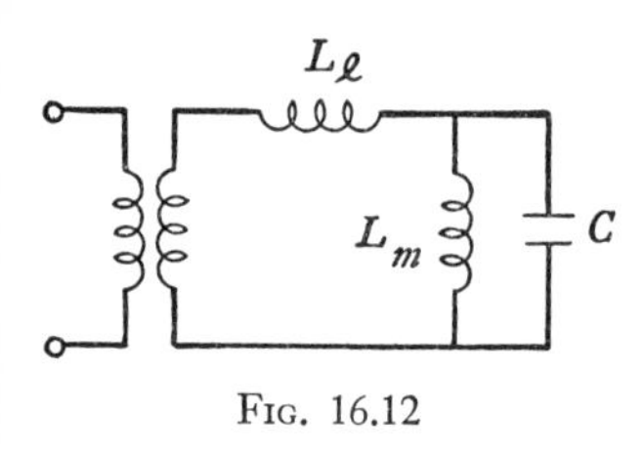

FIG. 16.12

In the present instance the difficulty with the reactance match evidently arises from the fact that the impedance presented by the filter is not of minimum reactance type. It has a pole on the real frequency axis both at infinity and at the anti-resonance of the elements L_1 and C_1 indicated by the broken lines in Fig. 16.11. The pole at infinity is not troublesome, since a series inductance must be added in any case, but the finite pole is objectionable and should be removed by deleting the corresponding elements from the network.* With this modification, the addition of the coil L in Fig. 16.11 allows the required reactance to be matched to the accuracy indicated by the crosses in Fig. 16.10. The final characteristics, including the parasitic capacity, are shown by the crosses in Fig. 16.9.

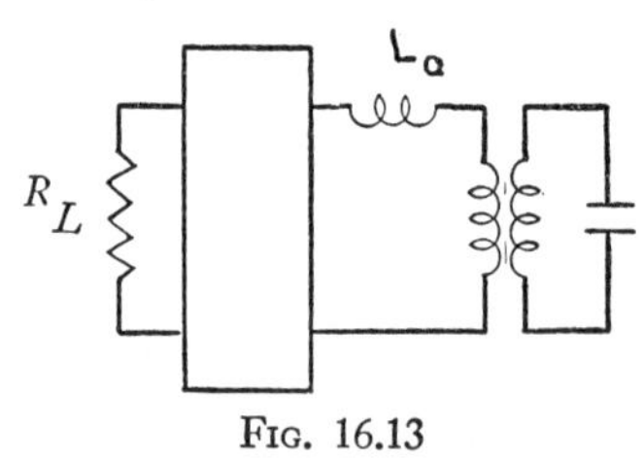

FIG. 16.13

The design can be converted to a practical form with the help of the familiar representation of a physical transformer shown by Fig. 16.12. The transformer in the drawing is supposed to be ideal, while the leakage inductance, mutual inductance, and parasitic capacity which would appear in an

* A similar reduction can be made for an image impedance of any complexity. The method is given in the author's U. S. Patent No. 2,249,415. It is also possible to remove the pole at infinity. Although this does not improve the reactance match in this circuit, it might have the practical advantage that it increases the inductance which can be identified with the leakage inductance of the final transformer.

actual structure are represented respectively by L_l, L_m, and C. If the useful band covers several octaves we can neglect L_m, on the assumption that Fig. 16.11 refers only to the high frequency behavior of the system. This evidently leads to the circuit shown by Fig. 16.13, where the box represents the original filter elements of Fig. 16.11 translated to the low side of the transformer and L_a is an inductance which may be added, if necessary, to facilitate the adjustment of the transformer leakage. If the useful band is relatively narrow, on the other hand, or if the coefficient of coupling in the transformer is low, it is more satisfactory to regard Fig. 16.11 as merely the low-pass equivalent of the actual circuit. In this event, the coils and condensers in Fig. 16.11 represent, respectively, resonant and anti-resonant branches in the physical structure. This gives a circuit of the form shown by Fig. 16.14. The box is now the band-pass equivalent of

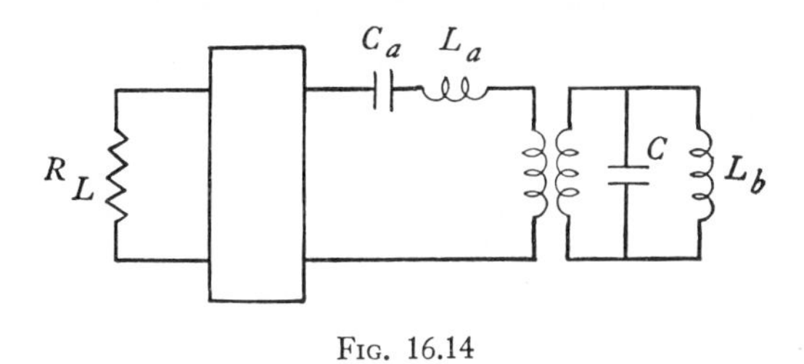

Fig. 16.14

the original low-pass filter. L_a and C_a are adjusting and tuning elements to convert the leakage to an appropriate resonant circuit. The inductance L_b is added to produce the correct anti-resonance in the final branch of the circuit, on the assumption that C rather than L_m is the limiting element in the branch as it stands. If the mutual inductance is the limiting factor the added element must, of course, be a capacity.

For practical purposes, the design procedure just described may be modified in two fairly obvious ways. In the first place, instead of simulating the resistance component by a filter image impedance, with all the network complexity which that implies, we may represent it directly by a suitable resistance-reactance combination. For example, the resistance characteristic in Fig. 16.10 is very nearly the characteristic we would expect to secure from a resistance in parallel with a tuned circuit resonating just outside the band. With the addition of a series inductance to furnish the necessary reactance this leads to the structure shown by Fig. 16.15. In spite of its simplicity the network gives an ade-

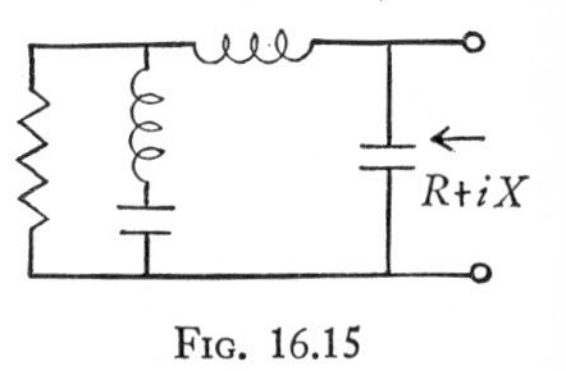

Fig. 16.15

quate practical match to the final theoretical characteristic, as Fig. 16.16 indicates.

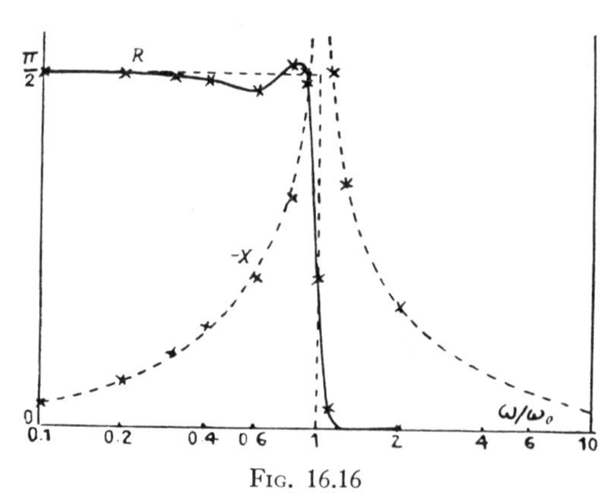

FIG. 16.16

If a more elaborate resistance characteristic is called for, use may also be made of the fact that an n element line of alternating series inductances and shunt capacities terminated in a resistance R_L, as indicated by Fig. 16.17, has an input resistance given by*

$$R = \frac{R_L}{1 + A_1\omega^2 + A_2\omega^4 + \cdots + A_n\omega^{2n}}, \tag{16–21}$$

where the n constants $A_1 \cdots A_n$ are related to, and can be used to determine, the n elements in the network. In this formulation, the ratio of R_L to the desired R fixes the curve which the polynomial $1 + \cdots + A_n\omega^{2n}$ should follow and the design process reduces to the choice of suitable values for the A's by known methods of polynomial approximation.

We may also modify the procedure by changing our conception of the final performance which the complete network will exhibit. For example, with the assumption made thus far, that the gain of the transformer is to be the maximum theoretically possible, all the area corresponding to the integral of the resistance looking into the high side terminals of the transformer must be found in the useful band. This may be spoken of as a "resistance efficiency" of 100 per cent. On the other hand, if the gain of the transformer can be 1 db less than the theoretical limit the resistance efficiency

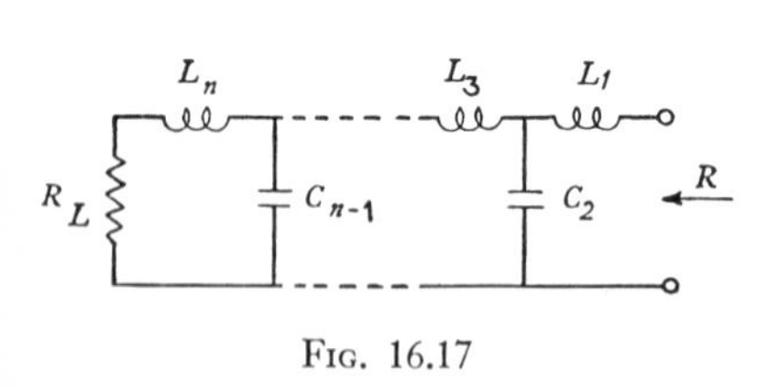

FIG. 16.17

* H. W. Bode, "A Method of Impedance Correction," *B.S.T.J.*, Oct., 1930.

need be only 80 per cent, and 20 per cent of the area can be used to cushion the sharpness of transition between the transmitted and attenuated regions. This is illustrated by Fig. 16.18, where the resistance is shown as a single straight line slope outside the band and the accompanying reactance is determined by the charts given in the preceding chapter. The resistance variation outside the band can be chosen in any way which appears realistic, as long as the total area is kept constant, but the simple slope characteristic given in the figure should be adequate for most purposes.

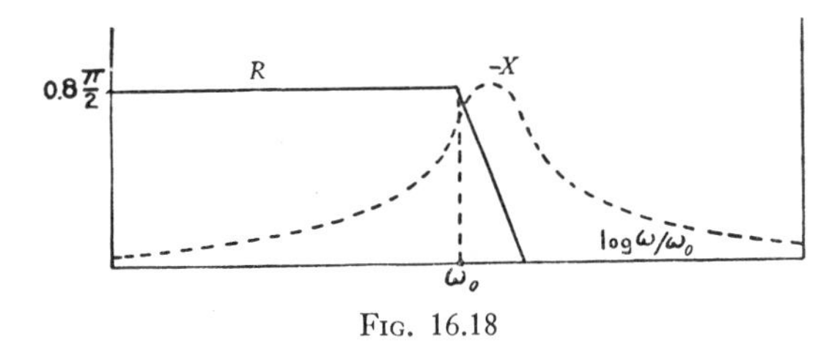

FIG. 16.18

The advantage of making this modification is, of course, that it leads to a residual impedance, after the parasitic capacity is subtracted, which is more easily matched by a simple network. The reduction in the sharpness of selectivity in the circuit as a whole is also helpful in minimizing the effects of parasitic dissipation in the network. An estimate of the quantitative importance of these changes can be made from the design examples given in the next sections.

The design procedure just described for input and output circuits has been given in great detail, in spite of its elementary nature, because the possibility of applying the contour integral relations to expedite design work in similar ways arises in many other network problems. For example, the interstage network design technique described in the next chapter follows a similar pattern. We begin with a relationship between the gain available from the interstage and its parasitic capacity. After the gain characteristic is thus determined the corresponding phase characteristic is computed. If the contribution of the parasitic capacity is allowed for, this fixes the resistance and reactance required from the interstage network proper. The design problem reduces, in effect, to the discovery of a minimum reactance network which will simulate the required resistance with sufficient precision. For the reasons described earlier, the additional reactance required to complete the design can always be obtained from a physical network and in practice the necessary network is usually so simple that it can be determined without effort. The same general attack can be used in many other situations. In principle, the procedure rests merely upon a recognition of the fact that the contour integral formulae make it possible to develop a relatively precise and detailed picture of the properties which any physical network giving the desired final characteristic must have. Since design assumptions leading to non-physical networks are thus eliminated the amount of cut-and-try work in the design is correspondingly reduced.

16.6. *Illustrative Reflection Coefficient Design*

An example of the theorem on reflection coefficients is furnished by the design of a network coupling the output stage of a long wave radio transmitter to its antenna.* If the antenna is identified with the output line the situation is broadly similar to that shown by Fig. 16.3. In discussing Fig. 16.3, however, it was assumed that the controlling parasitic element was the capacity C, at the terminals of the output tube, and that the reflection coefficient of physical importance was that measured at the terminals of the line. The situation was analyzed in terms of the reflection coefficient at the terminals of the output tube, the results being transferred to the line terminals by making use of the fact that if the network is non-dissipative the absolute value of the reflection coefficients at the two points must be the same.

In the present problem all these relations are reversed. Over a narrow band the capacity of the output stage can be tuned out or otherwise disposed of and is not limiting. On the other hand, the antenna is physically large to radiate effectively at the long wave lengths employed by the transmitter, and has an enormous capacity to ground. When this is tuned by suitable inductances in the antenna lead-in and down leads the net antenna impedance appears approximately as a constant resistance in series with a rapidly varying resonant circuit whose resonance frequency occurs in the center of the band to be transmitted.

Conversely, the impedance which is of direct engineering interest is that which the antenna and coupling network jointly present to the output tubes. At the 100 kw power level at which the transmitter operates the

* The transmitter under discussion is the original one located at Rocky Point, Long Island, to furnish commercial telephone service to England. The system is described in an article "Transatlantic Telephony," by O. B. Blackwell, appearing in the *B.S.T.J.* for April, 1928. The transmitter operates on a wave length of about 5000 meters. The reader will, of course, understand that the high antenna-ground capacity in the circuit is a consequence of the large antenna structure necessary to support such a wave length and does not appear in more modern short-wave systems.

The original antenna coupling network was designed by the author's colleague, Mr. E. L. Norton. It was redesigned some years ago by Mr. R. B. Blackman to provide two-channel operation. Only the redesign actually made use of the reflection coefficient theorem given in the text, but for the sake of illustration the entire design has been described from the point of view of this theorem.

current and voltage at the plate terminals are at best extremely high by ordinary standards. If the coupling network impedance oscillates between very large and very small values, so that the tubes work almost into an open circuit for certain signal frequencies and almost into a short circuit for others, the danger that they will either flash over or burn out is serious. For practical purposes, this amounts to a limitation on the absolute value of the reflection coefficient which can exist between the coupling impedance and the plate impedance of the tubes. The situation is illustrated by Fig. 16.19. The elements R_a, L_a, and C_a represent the antenna impedance. The reflection coefficient between R_a and Z_1 is that to which direct design attention is paid, while the reflection coefficient of final interest is that between the plate impedance R_p and Z_2.

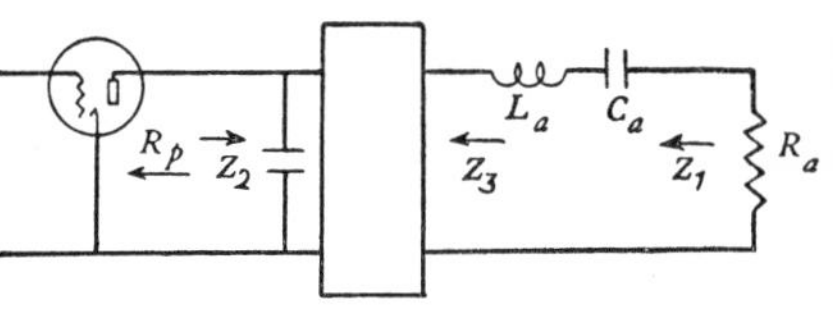

Fig. 16.19

The values of R_a, L_a, and C_a determined by measurement give an antenna reactance equal to about 2.5 times the antenna resistance at either edge of the band.* If the coupling network were merely a transformer matching the antenna and plate resistances this would give a reflection coefficient of 78 per cent. In accordance with (16–17) the minimum reflection coefficient obtainable with an ideal network is 28 per cent. Since it is not economically feasible to employ a large number of elements in a circuit operating at so high a power level, however, it must be expected that the final reflection coefficient will be somewhat worse than this limit.

To explore the situation, let it be supposed that networks are to be designed which are respectively 60 per cent and 80 per cent efficient. In other words, the networks are to be such that 60 per cent or 80 per cent of the total integral of $\log |1/\rho|$ in (16–15) falls within the useful band. This will give reflection coefficients in the useful range of 47 per cent and 36 per cent respectively. In terms of the relationship expressed by equation (16–19), the reduction of the original reflection coefficient of 78 per cent to 47 per cent is $\frac{31}{50}$ of the reduction, from 78 to 28 per cent, which could be obtained by using an infinite number of elements. Similarly, the reduction from 47 to 36 per cent wipes out $\frac{11}{19}$ of the amount remaining to be gained. Since the two ratios, $\frac{31}{50}$ and $\frac{11}{19}$, are approximately equal, the rule given by (16–19) would lead us to expect that the network with 80 per cent efficiency would require about twice as many elements as that with 60 per cent

* This assumes a rather narrow voice band. For a band of normal width the ratio is somewhat higher. A narrow band is used here for purposes of calculation since the final circuit is not very selective and effective transmission can be secured over a band somewhat greater than the nominal one.

efficiency.* It is interesting to notice that the rule is borne out in this particular case.

The actual design process begins with the construction of hypothetical complete characteristics for log $|1/\rho|$ and the computation of the imaginary components which must correspond to them, in accordance with the methods described in the preceding section. The results for the 60 per cent and 80 per cent cases are shown respectively by Figs. 16.20 and 16.21. All the curves are drawn for the low-pass equivalent circuit. The curves

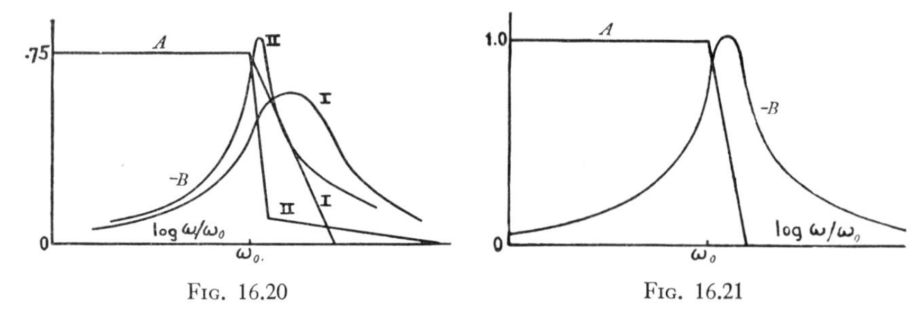

FIG. 16.20 FIG. 16.21

labelled A are drawn for log $|1/\rho|$ and those labelled B for the corresponding phase angle. In Fig. 16.21 the real component outside the band is drawn in the simplest possible way, as a single straight line segment. Figure 16.20 includes also an alternative characteristic which varies in a way more nearly in accordance with the characteristics one would intuitively expect from a physical circuit, in order to illustrate how different choices in this region may affect the solution. In any event, the area under the real characteristic outside the band must, of course, be the proper fraction, 20 or 40 per cent, of the total.

Since the curves in Figs. 16.20 and 16.21 specify the reflection coefficient between Z_1 and R_a in Fig. 16.19 completely we can readily determine from them what Z_1 must be in terms of R_a. If the parasitic reactances L_a and C_a are subtracted the computation also fixes the network impedance Z_3, which is the quantity with which we will deal directly. For the two cases illustrated by Figs. 16.20 and 16.21 the resulting Z_3 characteristics are those shown by Figs. 16.22 and 16.23, respectively.

* Roughly the same results are secured if the performance is measured in terms of log $|1/\rho|$ rather than in terms of $|\rho|$ itself, although the two measures would evidently depart seriously from one another if the limiting reflection coefficient were very much smaller than 28 per cent. In view of the uncertain logical foundation for (16–19), especially in the region of small values of n, it is scarcely feasible to decide which measure should be chosen. When n is large and the approximation to the limit is very close, it is of course permissible to use either measure since departures from the ideal measured in arithmetic and logarithmic terms become proportional to one another.

It is next necessary to determine suitable configurations for the coupling circuit by inspection, using the characteristics in Figs. 16.22 and 16.23 as guides in the process. For the characteristics of Fig. 16.22 this is a simple matter. An appropriate circuit is obviously the resistance and capacity in

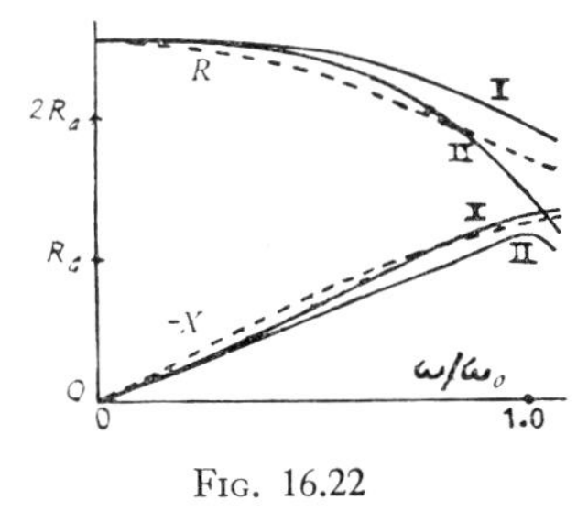

Fig. 16.22

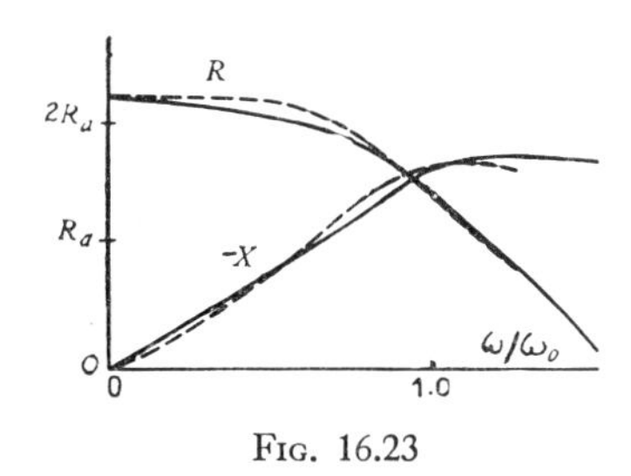

Fig. 16.23

parallel shown by Fig. 16.24. This gives the result indicated by the broken lines in Fig. 16.22. The simulation of the characteristics in Fig. 16.23 requires a more complicated network. Advantage may, however, be taken of the fact that since the characteristics must obviously represent a physical structure of minimum reactance type it is necessary to give explicit consideration only to the resistance component. The reactance will be supplied automatically. If the resistance is simulated by the method described in connection with equation (16–21) the resulting configuration is that shown by Fig. 16.25. It leads to the characteristics shown

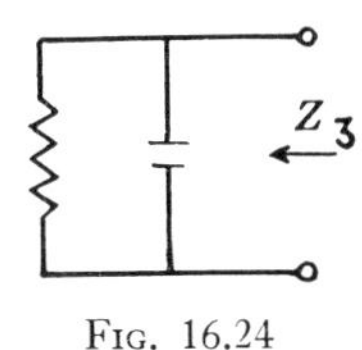

Fig. 16.24

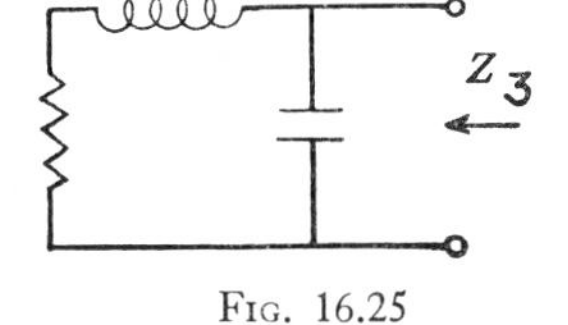

Fig. 16.25

by the broken lines in Fig. 16.23. The characteristics of Fig. 16.23 can also be simulated by first converting them to an admittance. Regarded in this form they must, of course, still specify a physical network, although not necessarily one of minimum susceptance type. With this procedure the resistance and inductance in Fig. 16.25 are determined from the conductance requirement and the capacity is supplied as a final step to give the required susceptance.

This design procedure has been described in great detail, in spite of its almost childish simplicity, chiefly to illustrate the advantages which accrue when the contour integral relations are used to provide a complete initial picture, including both real and imaginary components at all frequencies, of the network function to be realized in the design. The further steps in the design, however, are of less interest and need only be summarized. Briefly, the structure of Fig. 16.24 was chosen as giving an adequate result in the simplest possible manner. In band-pass terms it represents, directly, a resistance in parallel with an anti-resonant circuit. Unfortunately, however, the resistance does not have the right value to be identified with the plate resistance of the tubes. To avoid this difficulty the circuit was actually constructed in the form shown by Fig. 16.26. The theoretical justification for making this change can be understood if it is recalled from the discussion at the end of Chapter X that the locus of the impedance of a

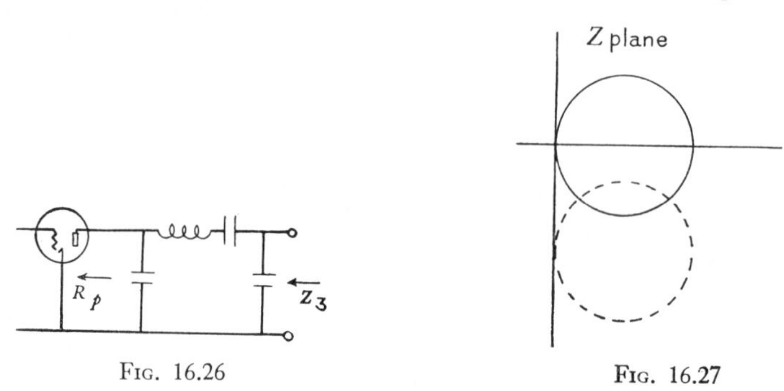

FIG. 16.26 FIG. 16.27

resistance and anti-resonant circuit in parallel must be a circle, as shown by the solid line in Fig. 16.27. If we regard the condensers in Fig. 16.26 as fixed reactances over a narrow band, however, the argument in Chapter X shows that the impedance locus in Fig. 16.26 will be a circle also. It is shown by the broken line in Fig. 16.27. The diameter of the new circle can be adjusted to the proper value, for a given R_p, by a suitable choice of the shunt capacities and it can be moved vertically into coincidence with the old circle by the addition of a final reactance, which can be incorporated with the antenna tuning. The shunt condensers, since their kva requirement is small, do not add greatly to the cost of the network.

Although the analysis has envisaged single-band transmission, in the actual network it was necessary to provide for the transmission of two bands, one centered at 60 kc and the other at 68 kc. This was accomplished by replacing each resonant circuit by two resonant circuits in parallel and making minor readjustments to compensate for changes in the resistance of the antenna and the reactance of the shunt condensers in Fig. 16.26 in going from one band to the other. In virtue of the conservation of band width principle, double tuning the antenna doubles the Q which the antenna will exhibit over a single band. To avoid this, a fixed resistance, producing 3 db loss, was added in series with the antenna.

The final result is shown by Fig. 16.28. The diagram represents the plot of the impedance Z_2 of Fig. 16.19. The point P represents the plate resistance of the output tubes and the heavy circle the locus of impedances whose reflection coefficient against this resistance is 45 per cent. It will be seen that the plot of Z_2 encircles the point P. This is because the reflection coefficient at this point is necessarily not a " minimum phase " function, for

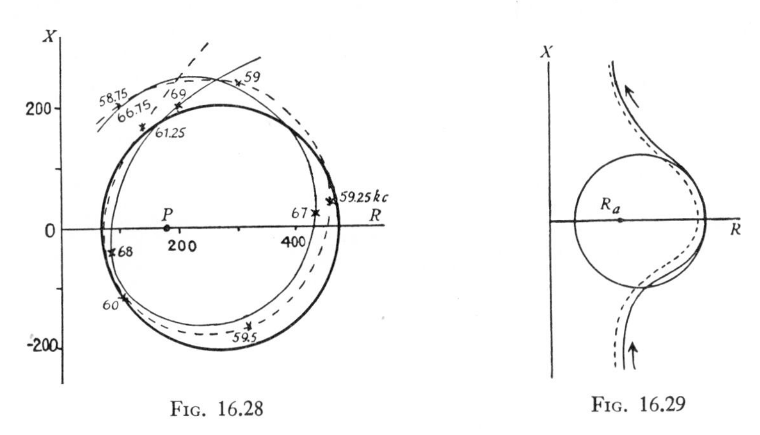

Fig. 16.28

Fig. 16.29

the reasons described in connection with the proof of the reflection coefficient theorem. The corresponding plot of the Z_1 impedance of Fig. 16.19, on the other hand, gives the same absolute value of the reflection coefficient but it does not encircle the reference point. This is illustrated by the small scale plot of Fig. 16.29.

16.7. *General Consideration in the Design of Input and Output Circuits for Feedback Amplifiers*

If we are to apply the theorems on the characteristics obtainable from input and output circuits terminated in various ways, it is obviously necessary to know, first of all, what elements of the amplifier are to be regarded as furnishing the termination. There is, of course, no difficulty with this question if the amplifier is of non-feedback type, like the structure which was used in illustrating the reflection coefficient theorem. In a feedback structure, however, the elements with which the input or output circuit is effectively terminated under operating conditions are not necessarily those which would be important if we opened the loop and analyzed the structure as a straightforward non-feedback device. An indication of how these changes may come about is furnished by the various theorems in Chapter V, which showed that the actual or active impedance presented by the amplifier proper to the input or output circuit, or through the input or output circuit to the line, may be quite different from the impedance which would be computed in the absence of feedback. Unfortunately for the simplicity of the situation, however, these modifications hold only for certain characteristics of the input and output circuits. In studying other aspects of their performance, apparent changes in impedance caused by feedback do not appear. If the example given later of the design of an input circuit for a feedback amplifier is to be intelligible it is first necessary to review this ground.

It is simplest to begin by listing the characteristics of the input or output circuit which are most commonly of engineering interest. In a non-feedback amplifier we are ordinarily interested in one or both of the following considerations:

1. The impedance which the input or output circuit presents to the line.*
2. The contribution of the circuit to the total amplifier gain. This is, of course, the transmission from the input line to the input grid, in the case of an input circuit, or the transmission from the output plate to the output line, in the case of an output circuit.

The use of feedback affects this situation in two respects. In the first place, it makes it necessary to evaluate both characteristics just mentioned in terms of the active rather than the passive state of the system. The fact that the active impedance of a feedback amplifier may differ from its passive impedance has already been mentioned. As later discussion shows, a similar correction may be necessary in evaluating the contribution of the input and output circuits to the overall amplifier gain. The use of feedback also makes it desirable to study the characteristics of the input or output circuit from two additional points of view. These are

3. The contribution of the input or output circuit to the transmission around the feedback loop.
4. The efficiency of the circuit in delivering power from the output tube to the line, in the case of an output circuit, or in providing a high signal-to-tube-noise ratio at the grid of the input tube, in the case of an input circuit.

The first of these is self-explanatory. The second would be indistinguishable from the straightforward transmission characteristic of the circuit, as

* In practical amplifiers the impedance which the circuit presents to the tubes may also be of direct importance. For example, if the output tube is of screen grid type, the impedance to which it is connected should be kept below some limiting value, irrespective of other considerations, in order to minimize non-linear distortion. Questions of this sort are not considered here, however, since in the situations at which the discussion is directed the impedance levels attainable in the circuit are limited much more severely by parasitic capacities.

given by (2) above, if we were dealing with a non-feedback amplifier. In a feedback structure, however, the characteristics defined by paragraphs (2) and (4) are not necessarily identical. In many applications the distinction between them is, in fact, the crux of the problem.

The situation can be studied most easily by recalling from Fig. 3.3 of Chapter III that the input or output circuit of an ordinary feedback amplifier must actually be regarded as a network having three pairs of terminals. One pair leads to the line, one pair to the μ circuit proper, and one pair to the β circuit proper. For the purposes of this discussion the diagram can conveniently be represented in the form shown by Fig. 16.30. The mean-

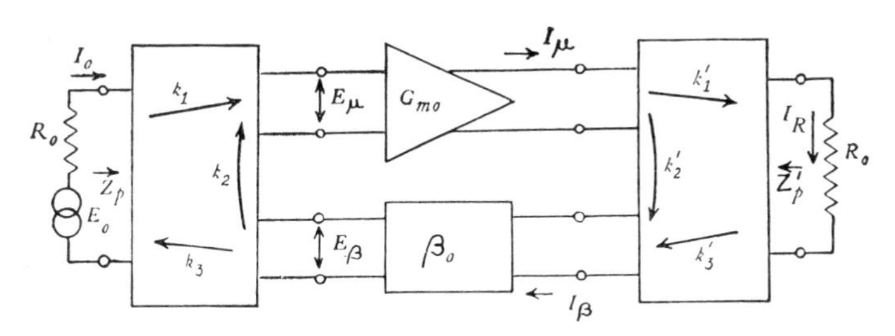

FIG. 16.30

ings of the various symbols should be easily understood from the drawing. For example, k_1 represents the path from the input line to the input grid and is so chosen, as a numeric, that if the line voltage is E_0, the input grid voltage E_μ is k_1E_0. Similarly, G_{m0} represents the circuit from the input grid to the output plate and corresponds to the output plate current $I_\mu = G_{m0}E_\mu$. In the same way the current delivered to the β circuit on account of the flow of plate current is given by $I_\beta = k'_2I_\mu$ and this produces a corresponding voltage $E_\beta = \beta_0I_\beta$ at the terminals connecting the other end of the β circuit to the input circuit.* With the exception of G_{m0}, which represents the ordinary forward circuit gain, all these quantities are to be evaluated with the tubes dead. It is convenient to suppose that the tube admittances are incorporated as part of the input and output circuits, so that the box G_{m0} exhibits an infinite impedance at each end.

The input and output circuits in Fig. 16.30 are defined by the passive impedances Z_p and Z'_p and the sets of parameters k_1, k_2, and k_3, or k'_1, k'_2,

* The β circuit is supposed here to be driven by a current and to produce a voltage in response under the assumption that its impedance is much smaller than that of the rest of the circuit, as it is, for example, in the series feedback amplifier to be examined later. Other assumptions, which may be more convenient for other types of feedback, are, however, obviously equally legitimate and affect the final results only in self-evident ways.

and k_3', representing various possible transmission paths through the circuit. The passive impedances and the parameters k_3 and k_3' specifying the transmission between the β circuit and the input or output lines are, however, of interest only in determining the actual impedance of the amplifier at input or output and can be dismissed briefly. If we assume that the feedback is very large, for example, it can be shown that the current flowing in the input line, with the tubes active, in response to the generator E_0, is

$$I_0 = E_0 \left[\frac{1}{Z_p + R_0} - \frac{k_3 k_1}{k_2} \right]. \tag{16–22}$$

Thus the active admittance of the circuit, including the line impedance, is equal to the passive admittance, $1/(Z_p + R_0)$, of the input circuit in series with the line diminished by k_3k_1/k_2. Equation (16–22) is included here merely for the sake of completeness, since this discussion will not deal with amplifier impedances. For practical purposes, moreover, it is not very useful, except perhaps as a convenient expression of the fact that the active impedance of the amplifier can be equal to its passive impedance only if we set $k_3 = 0$, or, in other words, only if we choose a circuit having zero transmission, on a passive basis, between the β circuit and the line. In ordinary circuits the rules established in Chapter V should be more convenient.

The input and output circuit parameters which remain to be investigated are k_1 or k_1' and k_2 or k_2'. In view of their obvious role the second of these pairs can be immediately identified and named as the *loop transmission characteristics* of the input and output circuits. The first pair, of course, represent the transmission from input line to input grid, or from output plate to output line, when the amplifier is passive, but since we may expect the active and passive characteristics of the network to be somewhat different it is not immediately clear what physical significance they may have for the final amplifier. We observe, however, that k_1' determines the ratio of the final output current to the current I_μ whether the circuit is supposed to be active or passive. Since the tube admittance is supposed to be part of the output circuit, I_μ must be the actual plate current flowing in the plate circuit of the last tube and is fixed by the power handling capacity of the tube, without regard to the fact that the tube is part of a feedback circuit. Thus the parameter k_1' determines the efficiency of the output circuit in providing a large power output from the final amplifier. Similarly, the parameter k_1 measures the efficiency of the input circuit in providing a high ratio of signal to tube noise in the first tube. This can be seen most easily by recalling from Chapter V that the final signal output for a unit generator in the input line is equal to the fractionated gain of the amplifier, taken with respect to the first tube, divided by the return difference for that tube. The formulae of Chapter V, however, show that the current flowing in the output in response to a noise generator in the first tube is equal to the current which would flow if the first tube were dead, divided, again, by the return difference for the tube. When the signal-to-noise ratio is computed, the two F's cancel out and the result reduces, in effect, to that which would be secured from the non-feedback amplifier obtained by opening the feedback path in the actual structure. The parameters k_1 and k_1' will be called the *passive transmission* or *volume performance* characteristics of the input and output circuits on this account.

The contributions of the input and output circuits to the final gain characteristics of the operating amplifier are still to be considered. They can be evaluated most easily by studying the expression for the final gain directly. The fractionated gain with respect to any one of the tubes in the forward circuit is evidently $k_1k_1'G_{m0}$, and the return ratio for any tube is $-k_2k_2'G_{m0}\beta_0$. If the direct transmission can be neglected, the current flowing in the output line in response to the generator E_0 is given by (5–28) of Chapter V as the ratio of the fractionated gain to the return difference. The reference from which the net gain is computed can be taken as the current $E_0/2R_0$ which would flow in the output line if the amplifier were removed and the input and output lines connected directly together. This gives the final gain expression as

$$e^\theta = \frac{2k_1k_1'G_{m0}R_0}{1 - k_2k_2'G_{m0}\beta_0}. \qquad (16\text{–}23)$$

When the loop gain is high, equation (16–23) reduces to

$$e^\theta = -\frac{k_1}{k_2}\frac{k_1'}{k_2'}\frac{2R_0}{\beta_0}. \qquad (16\text{–}24)$$

In this expression $2R_0/\beta_0$ evidently represents the gain characteristic which can be ascribed to the β circuit proper, while the ratios k_1/k_2 and k_1'/k_2' are the contributions of the input and output circuits. These last will be called the *external gain* or *active transmission* characteristics of the input and output circuits. In view of the significance which has already been assigned to the separate k's we can evidently state the

Theorem: The external gain characteristic of an input or output circuit is equal, in logarithmic units, to the difference between the volume performance and loop transmission characteristics of the circuit.

Although this relation is direct enough analytically, its implications for actual network design are somewhat less binding than they may appear to be. This is because we are usually interested in the gain and volume characteristics only in the useful band, while the problem of stabilizing the feedback loop, which involves the loop transmission characteristic, is most acute beyond the useful band. For practical purposes, consequently, it is often possible to regard the three transmission characteristics as independent, within modest limits.

In an actual amplifier, the distinction between the gain characteristics of the input and output circuits and their efficiency in transferring energy into and out of the amplifier is usually dependent principally upon the admittances at the input and output ends of the μ circuit proper. As noted previously, these admittances are incorporated as part of the input and output circuits for purposes of analysis. It is evident that if they are greatly increased both the volume and loop characteristics will be correspondingly degraded. The changes in these characteristics must, however, be the same, by Thévenin's theorem, and the external gain characteristic will consequently be unaffected. Thus in a low-frequency amplifier the distinction between the gain and volume characteristics is generally insignificant, unless the plate conductance of the output tube represents an effect worth considering. At higher frequencies, on the other hand, where the parasitic tube capacities lead to large tube admittances, the distinction becomes more important.

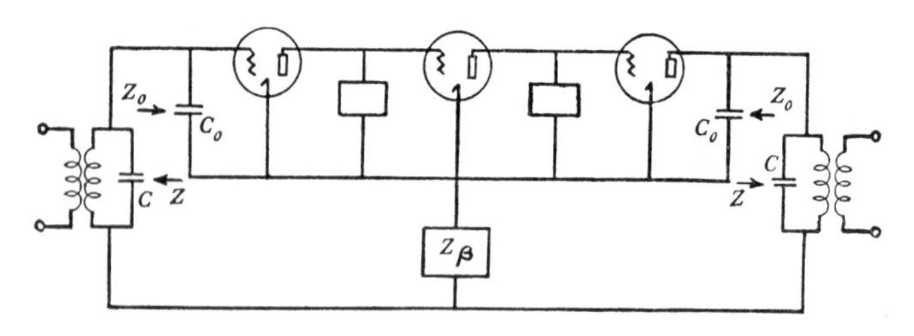

FIG. 16.31

16.8. *Volume Performance and External Gain Characteristics of Input and Output Circuits for Coaxial Repeaters*

An illustration of the analysis just concluded is furnished by the input and output circuits in certain of the repeaters used in the coaxial system.* The feedback connections in the repeaters are of series or cathode type. If we consider the series connection for simplicity the general repeater schematic takes the form shown by Fig. 16.31. The input and output circuits are identical. The controlling parasitic elements in the structure are the capacities C and C_0. The tube capacities, C_0, furnish the reference impedance in terms of which the impedance level of the rest of the circuit

* See footnote, p. 285.

is determined.* They should be as small as possible. The capacity C is a prescribed multiple of C_0, determined by methods described later, and is furnished physically by the high-side capacity of the transformers plus, usually, an additional padding condenser. The feedback impedance Z_β is evidently equal to the voltage-current ratio which was symbolized by β_0 in the preceding discussion. In accordance with (16–24) it can be fixed as a multiple of the line impedance as soon as the required final gain and the gain of the input and output circuits are determined. It is ordinarily very small in comparison with the other impedances in the feedback loop.

The volume characteristic, k_1, of these circuits is easily identified. If we neglect the small impedance Z_β it is evidently the transmission between high side and line when the high-side termination of the circuit is taken as the total capacity $C + C_0$. The loop characteristic, k_2, can be obtained if it is recognized that the feedback voltage is, broadly, the voltage drop across Z_β caused by the flow of plate current from the output tube. Because of the presence of C_0, however, only a fraction of the plate current actually reaches Z_β. If we neglect Z_β again in comparison with the other impedances of the circuit this fraction, in the notation of Fig. 16.31, is obviously $Z_0/(Z + Z_0)$. Similarly, at the input end the impedances Z and Z_0 in series form a potentiometer which imposes the fraction $Z_0/(Z + Z_0)$ of the total voltage across Z_β on the input grid. In either case, the fraction $Z_0/(Z + Z_0)$ is obviously k_2. This quantity is frequently called the *transformer potentiometer term* in practical design.

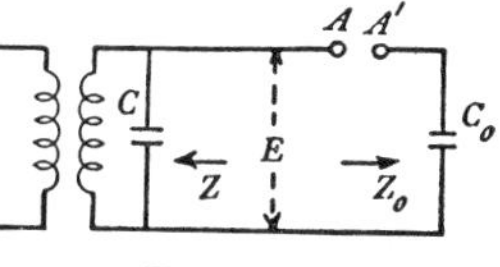

Fig. 16.32

The relation among the loop transmission, volume performance and external gain gives the external gain characteristic as $(Z + Z_0)/Z_0$ times the volume performance for either the input or output circuit. This can be given a simple physical interpretation. With the input† circuit redrawn in the form shown by Fig. 16.32, let E represent the high-side voltage when the terminals AA' are open-circuited. It follows from Thévenin's theorem that the voltage existing across C_0 when the terminals AA' are closed will be $Z_0E/(Z + Z_0)$, and this must, of course, be the volume performance voltage. The external gain voltage is therefore E itself. In other words, the external gain characteristic is the same as the open-circuit characteristic of the input or output circuit proper, when no allowance is made for the para-

* This assumes a high frequency broad-band structure of the type used in the coaxial system. In a low frequency amplifier the limiting impedance levels might be found from other considerations, the tube admittances themselves being negligibly small.

† The principle of reciprocity shows that the same result follows for the output circuit.

sitic admittances of the forward circuit. This may be verified by recalling from Chapter V that the active impedance which terminates the input or output circuit proper in a series feedback amplifier is substantially an open circuit.

The principal result established by this analysis is the conclusion that the parasitic capacity which limits the input or output circuit response is either C or $C + C_0$, depending upon whether we are examining the external gain or the volume characteristic. In practical design the choice of C in terms of C_0 depends upon a compromise between considerations of volume performance and feedback. The volume performance obtainable is maximized if C is very small in comparison with C_0. On the other hand, the loop transmission characteristic of the circuit reduces at very high frequencies to $C/(C + C_0)$. It is shown in a later chapter that maximum feedback in the useful band will be realized, other things being equal, if C is very large, so that the asymptotic loss represented by the factor $C/(C + C_0)$ is correspondingly small. For practical purposes we can suppose that a suitable compromise between these considerations is found when C is chosen in the general range $1.2C_0$ to $2C_0$.* The exact value of C is not very critical and is used as a design parameter in the discussion given later.

The physical significance of the conceptions of external gain and volume performance can be illustrated by a consideration of the requirements on these characteristics which would be imposed in a somewhat simplified and idealized coaxial system. In the idealized system the external gain and volume performance are the same for any input or output circuit† and each is equal, as a function of frequency, to one-half the characteristic required to equalize the attenuation of the line connecting successive repeaters. The reason for setting these requirements can be understood from Fig. 16.33. The sketch represents the output stage of one repeater, the first stage of the succeeding repeater, and the intervening line.

The external gain requirement on the input and output circuits is specified in order to allow the complete system to have a flat transmission

* The lower limit is a theoretical value, based upon the assumption that feedback is of interest chiefly in reducing modulation distortion and that the volume performance is of interest in determining signal-to-noise ratio according to the analysis made in the following paragraphs. Modulation and signal-to-noise ratio are related by the fact that one can be improved at the expense of the other by changing the signal level at which the system operates. The optimum compromise under these conditions is obtained for $C = 1.2C_0$. The use of a larger C is suggested because feedback is frequently of interest for other reasons than modulation reduction.

† It is assumed, as in the previous discussion, that the input and output circuits are identical.

characteristic without the use of equalization in the line.* This is desirable for reasons which will appear later. In Fig. 16.33 it leads to a flat transmission characteristic between points B and C and the overall transmission characteristic of the system will be flat if the repeaters are so designed that the β_0 of (16–23) is a constant. In general, we might, of course, avoid the necessity of introducing equalization in the line without specifying the external gain of the input and output circuits, by supposing that β_0 is an appropriately varying function of frequency. In the actual coaxial repeaters, however, the β circuit design must include regulation in any case. If the configuration is to be one permitting a maximum amount of feedback this makes it difficult to incorporate also any very substantial amount of β circuit equalization.

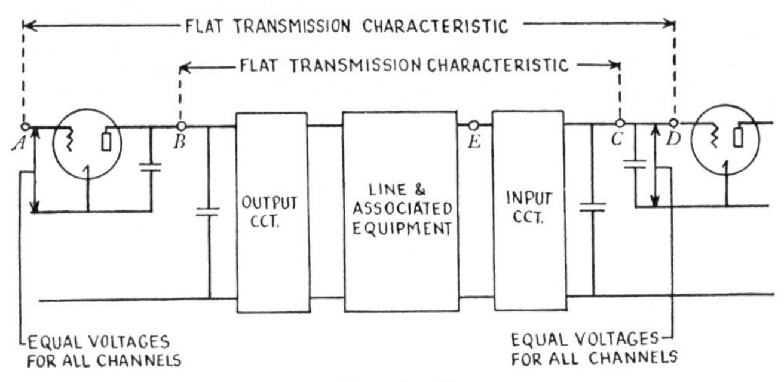

Fig. 16.33

The volume performance requirement depends upon a consideration of the signal-to-noise ratio in the system. The signal level at which the system operates is determined broadly by the power capacity of the repeater output tube and we can suppose that the tube will work at maximum efficiency if the signal level at its grid, point A in Fig. 16.33, is the same for all channels. Since the self-shielding properties of the coaxial line allow external interference to be neglected, the sources of noise to be considered are resistance noise and tube noise in the first stage of the repeater. These two can be represented as voltages appearing, respectively, at the points E and D in Fig. 16.33 and will, likewise, be constant with frequency.

It is assumed in setting the requirements that tube noise is more important than resistance noise. The signal-to-noise ratio of the system then

* In practice the equalization method described here is carried out only partially so that residual equalization does actually appear in the line at low frequencies. This is desirable in any event since, with the unterminated transformers described here, the repeater impedances give a very poor match to the line and it is necessary to maintain a certain minimum loss in the line to suppress interaction effects between successive line-repeater junctions.

depends upon the transmission from A to D in Fig. 16.33. This transmission may be called the *volume performance per repeater link*.* We will evidently secure the best repeater link volume performance, on the whole, if the line contains no unnecessary loss. This is the reason for equalizing the system by means of the external gain characteristics of the transformers in the manner just described. If the volume characteristic of the transformers themselves were flat this would give a repeater link performance which would be poorest for the top channel of the system, where the loss of the line is greatest, and would become increasingly better at lower frequencies. When the transformer volume characteristic assumes the prescribed shape, however, the response of the upper channels is improved at the expense of the others until the complete repeater link characteristic from A to D becomes constant at all frequencies in the useful band. This is evidently the optimum condition if the merit of the system is evaluated in terms of the signal-to-noise ratio in its weakest channel. It may be noticed in passing that if we assume that resistance noise rather than tube noise is controlling, the analysis follows the same lines except that now the transmission from A to E in Fig. 16.33 should be flat, so that the volume characteristic of the output circuit alone should equalize the complete line. That of the input circuit should be flat if there is residual tube noise to be overridden, and is otherwise unimportant.

16.9. *Illustrative Design of an Unterminated Input or Output Circuit*

As the final topic in this chapter we will consider the design of a network to illustrate the theorem on open-circuited input or output circuits which was developed at the beginning of the chapter. It will be assumed that the circuit is intended for a series feedback amplifier of the type described in the preceding section and that its external gain and volume performance characteristics are to satisfy approximately the idealized requirements developed there. In accordance with that discussion the external gain and volume characteristics depend respectively upon the real components, R_1 and R_2, of the impedances Z_1 and Z_2 in Fig. 16.34. The two resistances must evidently be equal throughout the useful band since it is physically obvious that they will be equal at low frequencies and the equalization requirement is the same for the external gain and volume characteristics.

* A more complete discussion of this and other aspects of volume performance is given in the author's U. S. Patent No. 2,242,878. It is also possible to extend the volume performance conception still further, as has been done principally by the author's colleague Mr. J. M. West, to make it apply to transmission through a complete communication system including intermediate repeaters, or to make it cover such situations as the transmission of television signals, where noise interference in different parts of the band is of varying relative importance.

Outside the useful band, however, the two resistance characteristics must be different since they correspond to different limiting capacities and therefore to different resistance integrals. Since the R_2 characteristic is the one which determines the final signal-to-noise ratio we can suppose that this design will be quite efficient, with a relatively small surplus resistance beyond the band. The surplus in the R_1 characteristic, which corresponds to a smaller limiting capacity, must, however, be fairly substantial.

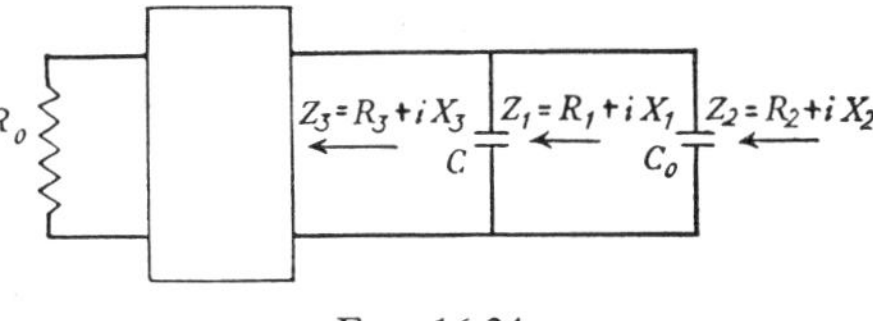

Fig. 16.34

The design begins with the computation of the desired characteristic for R_1 or R_2. In order to equalize half the power loss between repeaters these characteristics should vary as e^{α}, where α represents the complete line loss per repeater link. If we suppose that α is 40 db at the top frequency and varies as $\sqrt{f}$, which is the correct assumption for the attenuation corresponding to about 5 miles of ordinary coaxial cable with a top frequency of 2 mc, this leads to the resistance characteristic shown by Curve I of Fig. 16.35. The scale of the plot and the portion of it which lies beyond

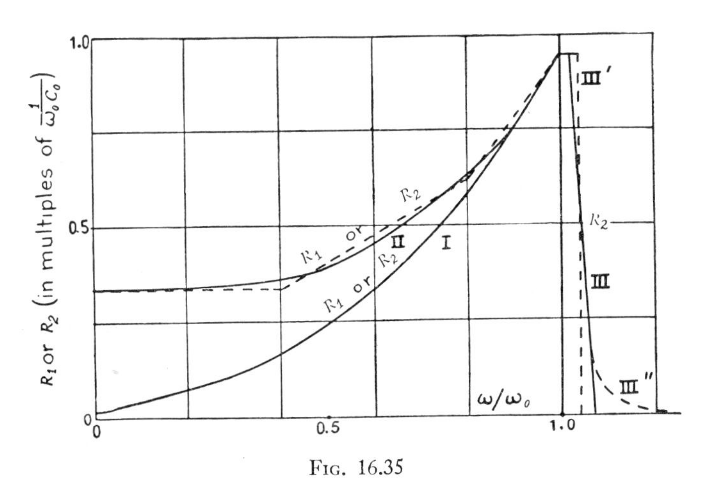

Fig. 16.35

the edge of the useful band, at $\omega = \omega_0$, can be ignored for the moment. In a practical design, of course, we cannot expect to control the transformer characteristics at low frequencies in the manner indicated by this curve. If we assume only a conservative amount of tuning the actual resistance characteristic, for design purposes, may be supposed to take some such shape as that shown by Curve II. Since the final limit on the performance of the circuit depends upon the resistance integral condition, it is evident that even as conservative a choice as this allows us to realize a large fraction of the advantage which can theoretically be obtained by using a sloped rather than a flat characteristic.

We have next to consider what condition must be met if the two resistances R_1 and R_2 are to be equal to each other and to the characteristic specified by Fig. 16.35 when account is taken of the fact that the corresponding impedances, Z_1 and Z_2 in Fig. 16.34, differ only by the parallel capacity C_0. It is readily shown that the requisite condition is one which applies to the accompanying reactance characteristics X_1 and X_2 and is given by

$$X_1 = -X_2 = \frac{1}{\omega C_0}\left[1 - \sqrt{1 - \omega^2 C_0^2 R^2}\right], \qquad (16\text{–}25)$$

where R, as in Fig. 16.35, represents either R_1 or R_2. The reactance specified by this equation tends to be small when $\omega C_0 R$ is small but it increases

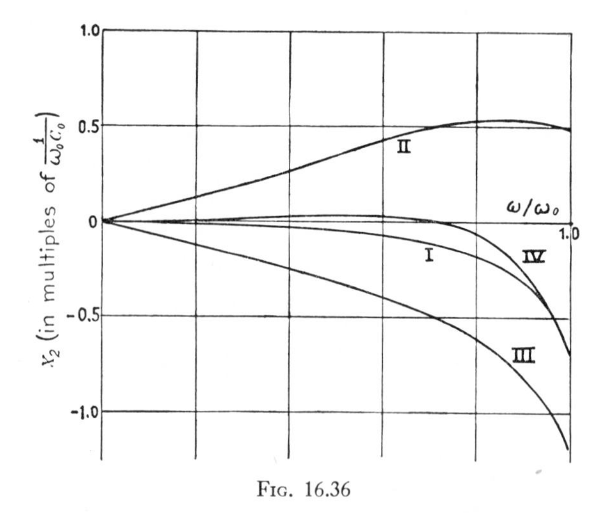

FIG. 16.36

rapidly when $\omega C_0 R$ approaches unity, while beyond unity a solution is no longer possible. In Fig. 16.35 the resistance scale has been so chosen that the maximum value of $\omega C_0 R$ is 0.95. This approximates the maximum possible value but leaves a slight margin to avoid the sharp changes which occur when the limit is approached extremely closely. If we deal in particular with Curve II of Fig. 16.35 the resulting X_2 characteristic is that shown by Curve I of Fig. 16.36.

The determination of a desirable reactance characteristic from equation (16–25) is unfortunately not enough to allow us to proceed with the design. If the final network is to be realizable we must also make certain that the reactance is physically consistent with the prescribed resistance. This question is most easily settled for a low-frequency region extending over perhaps one-half or two-thirds of the total band. It is easily shown that the reactance characteristic in this region will be almost zero whether it is specified by (16–25) or by the general relations between the real and imaginary components of network functions developed in preceding chapters. In any event, an accurate reactance characteristic is not necessary in order to provide substantial equality between R_1 and R_2 at these frequencies.

Near the top of the band advantage may be taken of the fact that the reactance which must correspond physically to the required resistance will depend largely upon the way in which the resistance behaves just beyond the useful band. Since this part of the resistance characteristic is not specified it can be employed to secure the reactance required by (16–25). The procedure is especially simple if we deal with R_2 and X_2 rather than with R_1 and X_1 since, as the previous discussion pointed out, the surplus of R_2 beyond the band is much less than that of R_1. Thus the R_2 characteristic outside the band can be basically nothing more than a relatively rapid diminution to zero in any event, and to secure the proper reactance we need merely make slight adjustments in the speed at which it decreases.

In order to make these adjustments we begin by computing the reactance which corresponds to the prescribed resistance characteristic within the useful band. If we use the straight line approximation to Curve II of Fig. 16.35 shown by the broken lines in the figure, together with the charts of Chapter XV, this gives the reactance shown by Curve II in Fig. 16.36. At $\omega = \omega_0$ the reactance is $+0.5$ while the required reactance given by Curve I is -0.7. The necessary difference, -1.2, must be supplied by the resistance characteristic outside the useful band. As a preliminary assumption, we may suppose that the resistance characteristic outside the band is merely a discontinuous drop, as indicated by the broken line III′ in Fig. 16.35. With the help of the charts again, we find that the necessary reactance at ω_0 will be supplied if the drop occurs at $\omega = 1.04\omega_0$. In order to make the solution more realistic the drop may be replaced by a slanting line of the type shown by III in Fig. 16.35. This makes a minor quantitative change in the result which is included in this example although it is scarcely large enough to be important in a practical design. The complete reactance characteristic corresponding to the slanting line is shown by Curve III of Fig. 16.36. When added to Curve II it gives the match to the required reactance indicated by Curve IV. The simulation of the required reactance is not perfect in an intermediate range between $\omega = 0.5\omega_0$ and $\omega = 0.8\omega_0$ but in a practical design, where relatively large tolerances may be permitted in volume performance if the external gain is precise, the difference between R_1 and R_2 to which the error corresponds may be regarded as insignificant.

If more equalization is demanded from the input and output circuits the analysis follows the same general pattern. The reactance shown by Curve II in Fig. 16.36 will, however, tend to increase, since it reflects the slope of the resistance in the useful band. This makes it necessary to allow the resistance characteristic to drop off more sharply beyond the band in order to secure the correct reactance at the band edge and it also tends to open the gap between Curves I and IV in Fig. 16.36. Conversely, as the circuits are assigned flatter characteristics they may be made less selective and their external gain and volume performance may be made more nearly identical.

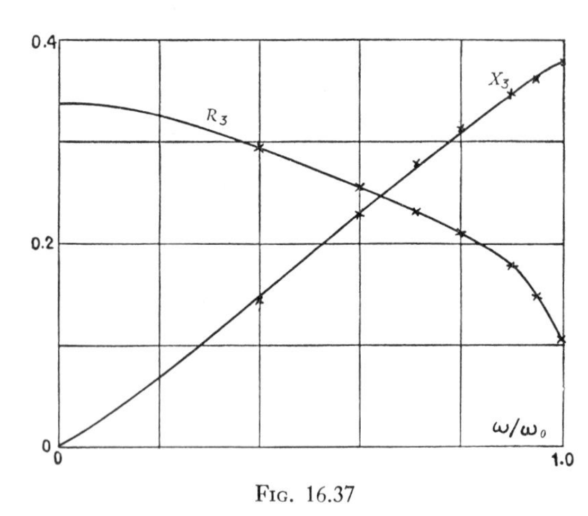

FIG. 16.37

The rest of the design procedure follows the routine described earlier in the chapter and need not be described in detail. Briefly, the next step in the design consists in the calculation of the area bounded by the lines II and III in Fig. 16.35. If we make an allowance for a slight high-frequency tail on the resistance characteristic, as indicated by the broken line III″ in Fig. 16.35, the area amounts to 0.53, in the units in which the figure is drawn. Since we are dealing with the R_2 characteristic, whose limiting capacity is $C + C_0$, however, it also follows from the resistance integral theorem (16–1) that the area in these units is $(\pi/2)[C_0/(C + C_0)]$. We can consequently determine that $C = 1.96C_0$.

To continue the design we next compute the impedance Z_3 in Fig. 16.34 by subtracting the parallel capacity $C + C_0$ from the Z_2 specified by Figs. 16.35 and 16.36. In making this computation the reactive component of Z_2 should, of course, be taken as Curve IV rather than the desired Curve I in Fig. 16.36, since it is a waste of effort to attempt to go beyond the limit of what is physically possible. The impedance obtained from the computation is shown by Fig. 16.37. We next match the real component of this new impedance by a suitable structure of minimum reactance type. This must be done by cut-and-try methods. In the present situation a suitable structure is found in the combination shown by Fig. 16.38. The element values are given on the assumption that the frequency and impedance units are taken as ω_0 and $1/\omega_0 C_0$ respectively. The design is easily obtained by observing that the resistance R_3 to which it leads satisfies the formula

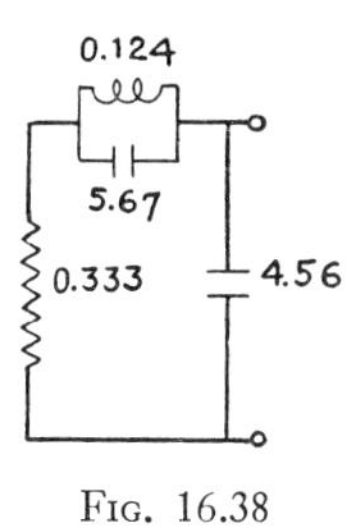

Fig. 16.38

$$R_3 = \frac{R_L X_2^2}{R_L^2 + (X_1 + X_2)^2}, \tag{16–26}$$

where X_1 and X_2 are respectively the reactances of the anti-resonant circuit and of the capacity. The maximum value of R_3/X_2^2 obviously occurs when $X_1 + X_2 = 0$. But since X_2 must vary as ω^{-1} we need merely plot $\omega^2 R_3$ in order to locate the maximum, and with this much established the rest of the design follows readily. It leads to the match to the desired R_3 characteristic shown by the crosses in Fig. 16.37.

As the final step the reactance furnished by the resistance matching network is computed and subtracted from X_3 in Fig. 16.37. The difference is then simulated by a series inductance. The crosses in Fig. 16.37 show the accuracy of simulation obtained when the inductance is chosen as 0.660, in the units used previously. If we include also the parasitic capacities the complete network takes the form shown by Fig. 16.39. It can be converted into a physical circuit including a transformer by identifying the series inductance with the leakage of the transformer, in the manner already described in connection with Fig. 16.13. The final characteristics for R_1 and R_2 are given by Fig. 16.40. The crosses are points introduced from the original characteristic of Fig. 16.35 for the sake of comparison.

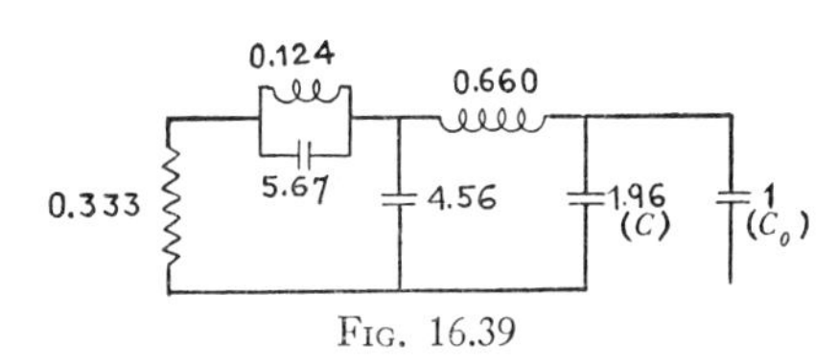

Fig. 16.39

The series inductance which is obtained as the final element in the design process deserves a further word of comment. It follows from the discussion given earlier in the chapter that the reactance characteristic which must be simulated at the final stage in the design is always that of a physical reactive network, but it may appear to be only a lucky accident that the required network is a coil, and so can be identified with the leakage inductance of a transformer. In fact, however, this is a result which is reasonably to be expected if the other parts of the design process, and in particular the estimation of C from the resistance integral theorem, are accurately

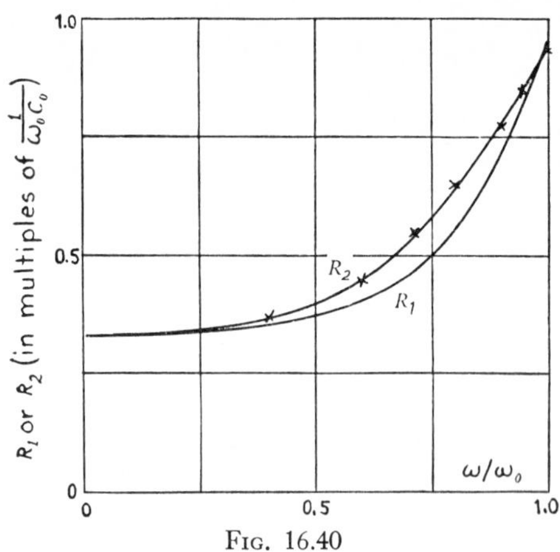

FIG. 16.40

carried out. To illustrate this, the design has been repeated on the assumption that C has been chosen through some mistake as $1.75C_0$ rather than as the correct value $1.96C_0$. This change leads to new charac-

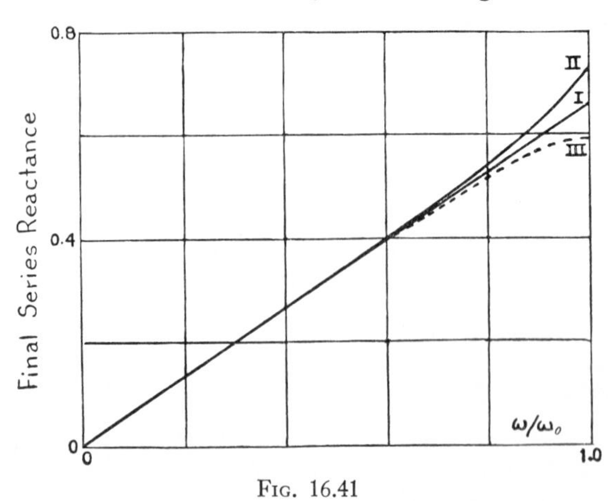

FIG. 16.41

teristics for R_3 and X_3 differing slightly from those shown by Fig. 16.37. The new R_3 can, however, be simulated by a configuration of the same type as that employed previously, and to about the same accuracy.

The major effect is encountered when we attempt to choose the final series reactance. This is illustrated by Fig. 16.41. Curve I is the reactance which must be supplied in the earlier design and Curve II the reactance required in the new design. The first curve is quite accurately a straight line but the second bends slightly upward and would require an anti-resonant circuit, with a rather remote anti-resonance, to represent it to the same standard of precision as has been employed in the rest of the design. If we introduce such a circuit the configuration of Fig. 16.39 is replaced by that shown in Fig. 16.42. In addition to the original parasitic capacities C and C_0 there is a new capacity path, composed of C_1 and C_3 in series, through the network at high frequencies and the new path is exactly sufficient to compensate for the difference, $1.96C_0 - 1.75C_0$, between the values assumed for C in the two cases. Conversely, if too large a C is assumed we may expect the required reactance to be that which would be obtained from an inductance in parallel with a negative condenser, with a downward curvature as illustrated by the broken line Curve III in Fig. 16.41. If either of these reactance characteristics is encountered the obvious remedy is to repeat the design with a corrected value of C. An irregular characteristic, falling into none of these three categories, is symptomatic of inaccuracy in one of the earlier stages of the design.

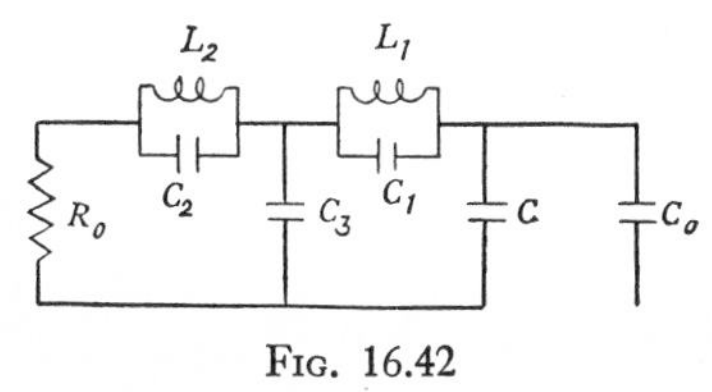

Fig. 16.42

16.10. *Practical Modifications in the Design*

The illustrative design just discussed has been intended primarily as an example of the application of the methods developed in previous chapters rather than as a model for practical design. For practical purposes the chief objections which may be directed at it appear to be the unnecessary accuracy with which the volume performance characteristic is controlled and the sharp selectivity of the circuit. The two are related by the fact that the sharp selectivity is introduced to provide a reactance component which will make the volume performance and external gain characteristics identical near the edge of the band. It can be reduced by relaxing this requirement and by accepting a somewhat less efficient design, including a resistance maximum which approaches the limit $1/\omega_0 C_0$ set by (16–25) less closely.

Examples of practical circuits with somewhat reduced selectivity are shown by Figs. 16.43 and 16.44. They are intended for amplifiers with useful bands of the order of 2 or 3 mc. In Fig. 16.43 the place of the shunt capacity and anti-resonant network of Fig. 16.39 in controlling R_3 is taken by the simple capacity C_1, the other elements retaining their previous functions. In Fig. 16.44, R_3 is controlled by the three elements C_1, L_1, and C_2, using the technique described in connection with equation (16–21).* The leakage inductance is identified, in this circuit, with L_1. The control of X_3 is exercised by the separate electrical coil L_2 with parasitic capacity represented by C_3. The proper parasitic capacity appears automatically in the simulation of X_3 if it is allowed for in advance as part of the total high-frequency path through the network, in accordance with the discussion given in connection with Figs. 16.41 and 16.42. The physical significance to be ascribed to C_0 and C is also changed in this circuit. In the series feedback amplifiers previously discussed they were identified respectively with the tube capacity and the transformer high-side capacity, plus padding. The amplifier with which Fig. 16.44 is used is, however, of the cathode feedback type shown originally by Fig. 3.12 of Chapter III. Since the substitution of cathode for series feedback places the cathodes of the input and output tubes off ground, a distinction must be made between the capacity of the input grid or output plate to its cathode and the capacity of the grid or plate to ground. These capacities can evi-

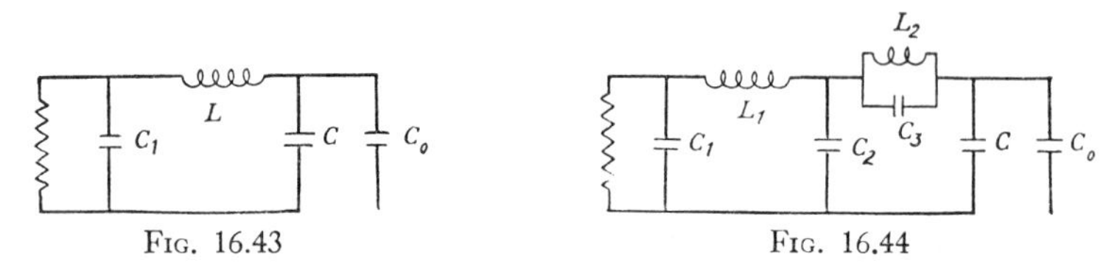

FIG. 16.43

FIG. 16.44

dently be identified respectively with C_0 and C in Fig. 16.44. It is to be observed that in the cathode connection the volume performance capacity $C + C_0$ is the same, except for slight padding adjustments, as the total tube capacity, while in a series feedback amplifier the tube capacity is identified with C_0 alone and the sum $C + C_0$ is necessarily much greater. This economy of capacity with the improved performance which it makes possible is one of the principal advantages of cathode feedback in a high-frequency design.

The suggestion that a practical input or output circuit design should be less selective than the illustrative circuit described in the preceding section is made in part to take account of the effects of dissipation, which were previously ignored. In view of the low value to which R_3 drops in Fig. 16.37, it is clear that any substantial resistance associated with the final inductance in the circuit will consume a large fraction of the power which is

* In this particular amplifier the volume performance requirement extends only to 2 mc, but an extremely accurate external gain characteristic is called for throughout a high frequency region extending to 3 mc. The use of as many as three elements in this part of the network is dictated by the necessity of making the external gain at high frequencies very accurate rather than by the shaping required below 2 mc, where volume performance and external gain considerations are jointly effective.

nominally transmitted through the structure. This is particularly important in Fig. 16.43 where the inductance represents the transformer leakage and has a relatively low Q. It is less serious in a circuit of the type shown by Fig. 16.44, in which the final inductance is a separate coil and can be assigned a much higher Q.

The other reason for attempting to secure a design without too great selectivity has to do with the loop transmission characteristic of the circuit. Within the useful band the loop transmission characteristic is completely fixed by the external gain and volume performance requirements since it depends only upon the impedances Z_1 and Z_2 of Fig. 16.34, both of which are fixed by these requirements. Moreover, the loop transmission changes from zero loss at zero frequency to a loss represented by the fraction $1/(C + C_0)$ at infinite frequency.

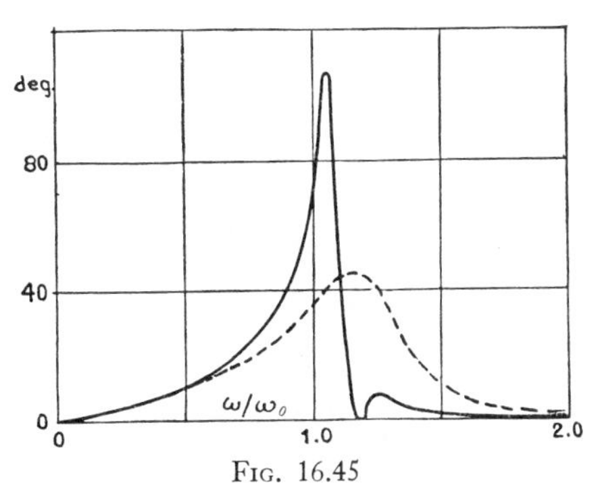

Fig. 16.45

If the ratio of C to C_0 is fixed this must correspond, in accordance with (13–19) of Chapter XIII, to a certain definite phase area. Since the phase characteristic within the useful band is fixed the phase area outside the useful band is also fixed. For practical purposes, however, it makes a great difference how this area occurs. The solid line in Fig. 16.45, for example, shows the loop phase shift exhibited by the illustrative design of the preceding section. The corresponding gain characteristic is shown by Fig. 16.46. In this instance the circuit is so selective that the resistance component of the high-side impedance of the transformer becomes negligible and both impedances in the loop potentiometer reduce to capacity reactances at frequencies slightly beyond the useful band. Since a capacity potentiometer cannot physically produce a phase shift this means that the phase area is packed into a narrow region just beyond the useful band and the characteristic must rise to a high peak. It is theoretically possible to compensate for the presence of such a peak in the design of one of the other parts of the feedback loop, such as an interstage network, so that

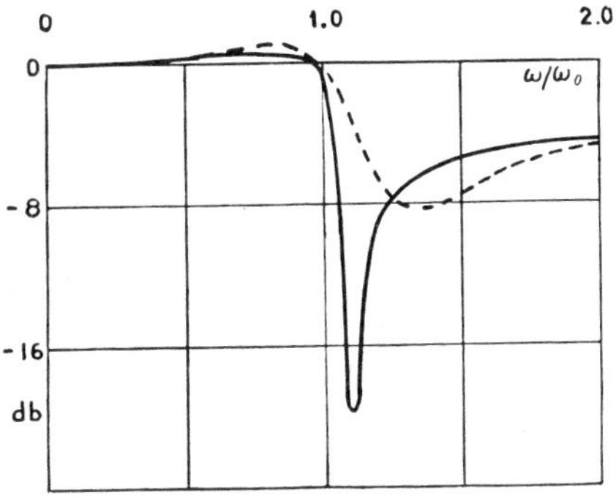

Fig. 16.46

the overall loop characteristic will reduce to one of the smoothly varying curves described in a later chapter. It is evident, however, that such a compensation must at least be exceedingly awkward, especially when account is taken of the fact that both input and output circuits must be considered. The overall loop design is much simplified if the circuits are made less selective so that the phase area can be spread over a broader region, as illustrated roughly by the broken line in Fig. 16.45.

CHAPTER XVII

Application of General Theorems to Interstage Network Design

17.1. *Introduction*

This chapter continues the discussion of the design of particular parts of a complete amplifier which was begun in the preceding chapter. The particular circuits treated here are interstage networks. As in the preceding chapter the material is actually intended merely as an illustration of the uses of the contour integral formulae and does not pretend to be comprehensive.

In a feedback amplifier the most satisfactory interstage networks are ordinarily two-terminal structures, that is, simple shunt impedances. A four-terminal interstage, containing a series impedance interpolated between the plate capacity of one tube and the grid capacity of the following tube usually produces a phase shift which is intolerably great in a feedback loop unless the series impedance is so small that the circuit does not differ materially from a two-terminal network. Most of the analysis is directed at the examination of two-terminal interstages in terms of one principal theorem which relates the gain of the interstage* in the useful band and its phase shift beyond the band to the parasitic capacity in the circuit. After the development of the theorem, the cases in which we are interested only in the gain characteristic, the phase characteristic being immaterial, and those in which requirements must be placed on both gain and phase, are taken up in order. The chapter closes with a brief and rather incomplete account of the corresponding limitations which may be expected to exist in four-terminal interstages, the gain characteristic alone being considered.

17.2. *General Theorems on Two-Terminal Interstages*

The two-terminal interstage is shown by Fig. 17.1. The plate is represented as a current source, in accordance with the nodal analysis method

* Strictly speaking, of course, the word " gain " should apply to a complete amplifier stage including both tube and interstage. Thus, in the notation of Fig. 17.1 the stage gain and phase are given by $\log E_1/E_0 = \log G_m Z$, where $G_m = I_1/E_0$ is the transconductance of the first tube. Since G_m is merely a prescribed constant, however, calculations will normally be based on $\log Z$ alone, as a matter of brevity.

described in Chapter I. This places the plate resistance R_p effectively in parallel with the rest of the interstage, just as Y_3 appears in parallel with Y_5 in Fig. 1.9. The grid resistance is represented by R_g in Fig. 17.1 and the total parasitic capacity by C. The elements introduced into the interstage by the design, exclusive of such elements as blocking condensers, effective only at very low frequencies, are represented by Z'. Together with R_p, R_g and C they form the total effective interstage impedance Z.

The grid and plate resistances are included here for the sake of completeness, but they will ordinarily be omitted in the interstage configurations shown later, since in most broad-band circuits the tubes are pentodes, in which both R_p and R_g are very high impedances in comparison with the rest of the interstage. The general theorems in the chapter remain valid even when R_p and R_g are significant, but the calculations on maximum gain possibilities of interstages should be modified, since they depend upon the assumption that the interstage can be assigned a purely reactive characteristic outside the frequency range of interest.

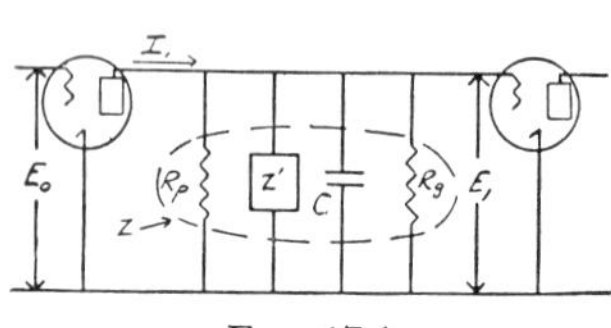

FIG. 17.1

The simplest result which can be established for circuits of the type shown by Fig. 17.1 is one relating the gain obtained from the actual interstage to that which would be obtained if we removed Z' entirely, except perhaps for infinite inductance choke coils to supply battery power to the tubes. It is given by the

Theorem: The average gain of a physical interstage network including a prescribed parasitic capacity C over the complete frequency spectrum is not greater than that which would be obtained if the network were composed of the capacity C alone.

To prove the theorem it is merely necessary to set $\theta = \log i\omega CZ$. Near infinite frequency we can write

$$Z = \frac{1}{i\omega C} + \frac{k_1}{\omega^2} + \frac{ik_2}{\omega^3} + \cdots \tag{17–1}$$

from which θ is given to a first approximation as

$$\theta \doteq \log\left[1 + i\frac{k_1 C}{\omega}\right] \doteq i\frac{k_1 C}{\omega}. \tag{17–2}$$

If we identify this θ with the θ which appears in equation (13–6) of Chapter XIII, therefore, we have $A_\infty = 0$; $B_\infty = k_1 C$. The result in Chapter XIII thus gives

$$\int_0^\infty \log |\, i\omega CZ \,|\, d\omega = -\frac{\pi}{2} k_1 C. \tag{17-3}$$

But the integrand in the left-hand side is obviously the difference between the gain obtained from the actual interstage impedance Z and that which would be obtained if we were dealing with C alone. On the right-hand side k_1 cannot be negative since we can readily show from (17–1) that it is $1/C^2$ times the conductance of the network at infinite frequency. Thus the average gain of the actual interstage cannot be greater than the gain obtained from C alone and will be equal to the gain obtained from C only if the infinite frequency conductance is zero.

As an example of the theorem let it be supposed that the interstage takes the form shown by Fig. 17.2. The corresponding gain characteristic is shown by the solid line Curve I of Fig. 17.3, the gain which would be

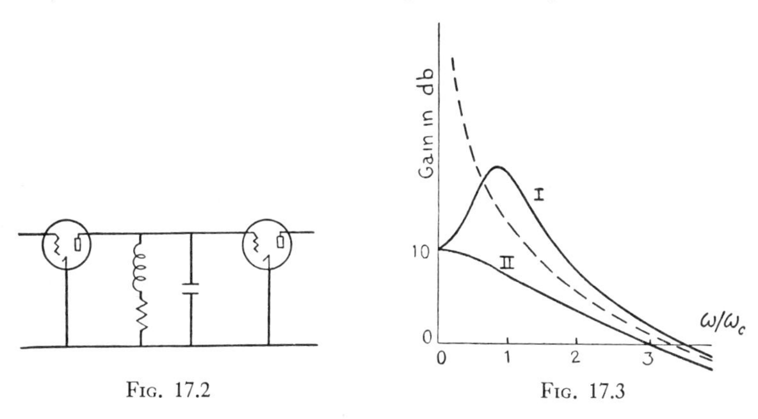

Fig. 17.2 Fig. 17.3

obtained from the capacity alone being represented by the broken line. In this instance the infinite frequency conductance is zero and the average height of the two curves is the same. If we remove the coil from the network, however, the gain drops to the position shown by Curve II, below the capacity gain.

The weakness of this result is, of course, the fact that it involves the interstage gain over the complete frequency spectrum. In a practical situation we are ordinarily interested in the gain over a prescribed finite band, which we can suppose, for the sake of definiteness, to extend from zero to ω_0. This problem can be studied by using equation (13–36) rather than (13–6) in Chapter XIII. It is also convenient, although not necessary, to suppose that the expression $\log i\omega CZ$, which has previously been used for θ, is replaced by $\log \frac{1}{2}(\sqrt{\omega_0^2 - \omega^2} + i\omega)CZ$. Since it will be shown later that the admittance of the interstage giving the maximum possible flat gain between zero and ω_0 is $\frac{1}{2}(\sqrt{\omega_0^2 - \omega^2} + i\omega)C$ this change is equivalent to using this interstage rather than the bare capacity C as the standard against which Z is measured. So far as their behavior at infinite frequency is concerned the two θ's are evidently identical.

If we use the new θ and substitute directly in (13–36) of Chapter XIII we secure

$$\int_0^{\omega_0} \frac{\log \frac{1}{2} \left| (\sqrt{\omega_0^2 - \omega^2} + i\omega)CZ \right|}{\sqrt{1 - \omega^2/\omega_0^2}} d\omega = -\int_{\omega_0}^{\infty} \frac{B}{\sqrt{\omega^2/\omega_0^2 - 1}} d\omega, \qquad (17\text{–}4)$$

where B in the right-hand side is retained, for brevity, as the imaginary component of θ. The expression can be somewhat simplified by writing $\log Z = \alpha + i\beta$. This allows us to replace B by $\pi/2 + \beta$. On the left-hand side of the equation the numerator of the integrand becomes $\alpha + \log \frac{1}{2} \left| \sqrt{\omega_0^2 - \omega^2} + i\omega \right| C$, which can also be written as $\alpha + \log (\omega_0 C/2)$, since the absolute value of $\sqrt{\omega_0^2 - \omega^2} + i\omega$ in the range of integration is ω_0. This allows (17–4) to be written as

$$\int_0^{\omega_0} \frac{\alpha}{\sqrt{1 - \omega^2/\omega_0^2}} d\omega + \int^{\omega_0} \frac{\log (\omega_0 C/2)}{\sqrt{1 - \omega^2/\omega_0^2}} d\omega = -\int_{\omega_0}^{\infty} \frac{\pi/2 + \beta}{\sqrt{\omega^2/\omega_0^2 - 1}} d\omega \qquad (17\text{–}5)$$

or, if we integrate the second term explicitly, as

$$\int_0^1 \frac{\alpha}{\sqrt{1 - \omega^2/\omega_0^2}} d\left(\frac{\omega}{\omega_0}\right) + \int_1^{\infty} \frac{\pi/2 + \beta}{\sqrt{\omega^2/\omega_0^2 - 1}} d\left(\frac{\omega}{\omega_0}\right) = \frac{\pi}{2} \log \frac{2}{\omega_0 C}. \qquad (17\text{–}6)$$

Equation (17–6) is the principal result of the chapter. Its physical significance can be understood most easily if we suppose for the moment that the second integral is ignored. Then the equation expresses a relation between the gain α in the useful band and the parasitic capacity C. If the relative gains at various frequencies in the useful band are prescribed we can readily determine from the equation what the absolute level of gain may be.

If we consider now the second integral we notice that β, since it represents the phase angle of Z, can be expected to approach $-\pi/2$ at high frequencies as Z degenerates into the parasitic capacity C. We cannot, however, assign β a larger negative value than $-\pi/2$ since Z cannot have a negative resistance component. Thus the second integral in (17–6) is always positive or zero and the assumption made previously, that it can be ignored in evaluating the gain, represents the optimum case. We may also notice that the optimum can be realized only if the resistance component of Z is zero outside the band, so that the interstage network giving maximum absolute gain is always an ideally selective filter of some description, no matter how the relative gains at various points in the useful band are prescribed.* In a non-feedback amplifier the complexity of the network required to give a reasonable approximation to an ideal filter is the most important design consideration. The situation here is broadly similar to that described for input and output circuits in the previous chapter. In a feedback amplifier, on the other hand, it may be necessary to impose a definite requirement on the phase angle of the interstage impedance over at least part of the range beyond the useful band in order to secure a stable circuit. In this event the second integral can be used to determine how much the gain in the useful band must be reduced in order to provide any given margin between the actual phase angle of the network and the pure capacitance phase which would be exhibited by a maximum gain structure. These calculations are described in more detail in succeeding sections.

This discussion implies one further corollary, which is of some incidental interest in connection with the theorem first developed. Since an interstage giving maximum gain in the useful band has a phase angle of $-\pi/2$ outside the band, it can have no appreciable conductance component in this region. With the help of the earlier analysis we can consequently state the

Theorem: The average gain of a two-terminal interstage network including a prescribed parasitic capacity C over the complete frequency spectrum is always the same if the network is of the type giving the maximum absolute level of gain in a prescribed finite band, without regard to the variation of the gain characteristic over the prescribed band, and is equal to the average gain which would be obtained if the network were composed of C alone.

In other words if we are dealing with an interstage network of maximum gain type we have at our disposal a fixed fund of what may be called gain area between zero frequency and some arbitrarily chosen high-frequency point at which the network may be regarded as degenerating into the parasitic capacity. Shaping the characteristic in various ways in the useful band redistributes this area without changing its amount.†

* This, of course, assumes also that the grid and plate conductances are negligible. Cf. the discussion in connection with Fig. 17.1.

† Allowance must, however, be made for the fact that area changes may occur just outside the useful band as well as within it. See the discussion of this point given later.

17.3. *Two-Terminal Interstages with Maximum Constant Gain*

As an illustration of the theorem just established we will consider the design of an interstage network having the largest possible constant gain over the range between zero and ω_0. The solution has been known empirically for many years* but the analysis is nevertheless presented in detail because of the theoretical interest of the subject.

If we neglect the second integral in (17–6) and replace α in the first integral by the constant α_0 the equation becomes

$$\int_0^1 \frac{\alpha_0}{\sqrt{1 - \omega^2/\omega_0^2}}\, d\left(\frac{\omega}{\omega_0}\right) = \frac{\pi}{2} \log \frac{2}{\omega_0 C}. \tag{17–7}$$

But since the left-hand side can be integrated directly to give $(\pi/2)\alpha_0$ the obtainable gain can be written as

$$\alpha_0 = \log \frac{2}{\omega_0 C}. \tag{17–8}$$

We notice that if the capacity were alone in the circuit the gain at the edge of the band would be $\log 1/\omega_0 C$. The maximum constant gain is therefore just 6 db higher than the gain represented by the capacity impedance at the limiting frequency.

The phase angle of the interstage impedance must, of course, be $-\pi/2$ at frequencies outside the useful band if the maximum gain within the band is to be realized. With the gain characteristic inside the band and the phase characteristic beyond the band thus determined the rest of the complete interstage characteristic can be found by the formula which appears as equation (14–33) of Chapter XIV. The computation is simplified if we notice that the prescribed gain, $\log 2/\omega_0 C$, in the useful band can serve physically only as a reference which determines the absolute level of gain in the final characteristic. We can suppose it to be zero instead if we make a corresponding correction in the gain computed for the region outside the useful band. This modification allows the first integral in the equation to

* A published account is given by H. A. Wheeler (*Proc. of the I.R.E.*, July, 1939). The potentialities of the full-shunt terminated filter as a two-terminal interstage were, however, familiar to filter specialists, although they were apparently not widely known to amplifier designers in general, at a much earlier date. To the best of the author's knowledge, the original discovery is due to his colleague Mr. E. L. Norton and was made some time prior to 1930.

Wheeler's paper also includes a discussion of the application of the filter structure to four-terminal interstages. This is described later in Section 17.8.

Filter-type interstages have also been described by W. S. Percival (Brit. Pat. Nos. 460,562 and 475,490, filed July 24, 1935, and Feb. 21, 1936).

be omitted. If we substitute $\beta = -\pi/2$ in the second integral the resulting formulae for α and β in the portions of the spectrum in which they are not directly specified appear as

$$-\int_{\omega_0}^{\infty} \frac{\omega_c}{\sqrt{\omega^2/\omega_0^2 - 1}} \frac{d\omega}{\omega^2 - \omega_c^2} = \frac{\beta(\omega_c)}{\sqrt{1 - \omega_c^2/\omega_0^2}}, \qquad \omega_c < \omega_0$$

$$= \frac{-[\alpha(\omega_c) - \log(2/\omega_0 C)]}{\sqrt{\omega_c^2/\omega_0^2 - 1}}, \qquad \omega_c > \omega_0. \tag{17-9}$$

Equation (17–9) is easily integrated by means of the substitution $\omega^2/\omega_0^2 = 1/(1 - x^2)$. If we consider in particular the formula for β this gives

$$\beta(\omega_c) = -\frac{\omega_c}{\sqrt{\omega_0^2 - \omega_c^2}} \int_0^1 \left[1 + \frac{\omega_c^2}{\omega_0^2 - \omega_c^2} x^2\right]^{-1} dx, \quad \omega_c < \omega_0, \tag{17-10}$$

which can be evaluated by standard methods as

$$\beta(\omega_c) = -\tan^{-1} \frac{\omega_c}{\sqrt{\omega_0^2 - \omega_c^2}} = -\sin^{-1} \frac{\omega_c}{\omega_0}. \tag{17-11}$$

Similarly,* the result for α appears as

$$\alpha(\omega_c) = \log \frac{2}{\omega_0 C} - \coth^{-1} \frac{\omega_c}{\sqrt{\omega_c^2 - \omega_0^2}}$$

$$= \log \frac{\dfrac{2}{\omega_0 C}}{\sqrt{\dfrac{\omega_c^2}{\omega_0^2} - 1} + \dfrac{\omega_c}{\omega_0}}. \tag{17-12}$$

The complete gain and phase† characteristics of the interstage, as determined by these equations, are shown by the solid lines in Figs. 17.4 and

* Although the integrals for β and for α are formally identical, account must be taken of the fact that ω_c is less than ω_0 in the first case and greater than ω_0 in the second. The pole at $\omega = \omega_c$ in the integrand of (17–9) consequently falls outside the range of integration when we are studying β but not when we are studying α. In accordance with the discussion in Chapter XIV the "principal value" of the integral must be taken in the second case. In other words, in evaluating α the integral from ω_0 to ∞ in (17–9) must be understood as signifying the sum of two integrals, one running from ω_0 to $\omega_c - \varepsilon$ and the other from $\omega_c + \varepsilon$ to ∞. The result (17–12) follows readily with this understanding.

† The negative of the phase characteristic in (17–11) is plotted to correspond with the usual convention that a shunt capacity phase is positive.

17.5. The broken line in Fig. 17.4 gives the gain characteristic which would be obtained from the capacity alone. With the logarithmic frequency scale employed in the figures this gain characteristic is a straight line and has a slope of 6 db per octave. The actual gain characteristic merges with this line at high frequencies, as we can see by noticing that (17–12) reduces to log $1/\omega_c C$ when ω_c is large, but it rises more rapidly near

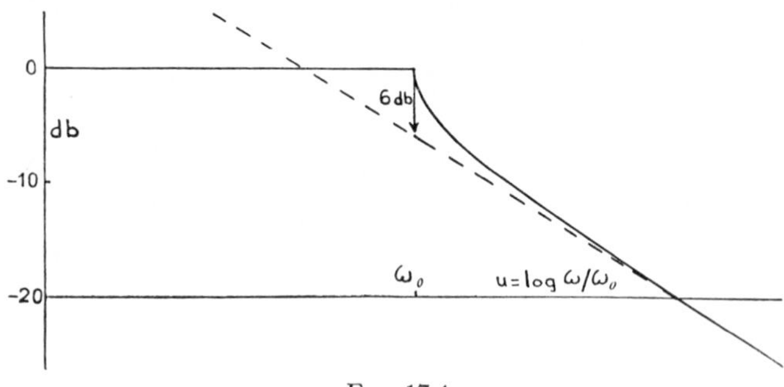

FIG. 17.4

the edge of the band to give the 6 db gain advantage at the band edge required by (17–8). In terms of the general relationship between phase shift and attenuation slope given by (14–11) of Chapter XIV the increased slope of the actual characteristic in comparison with the capacity characteristic just beyond the useful band and the decreased slope within the useful band can be looked upon as compensatory adjustments which together

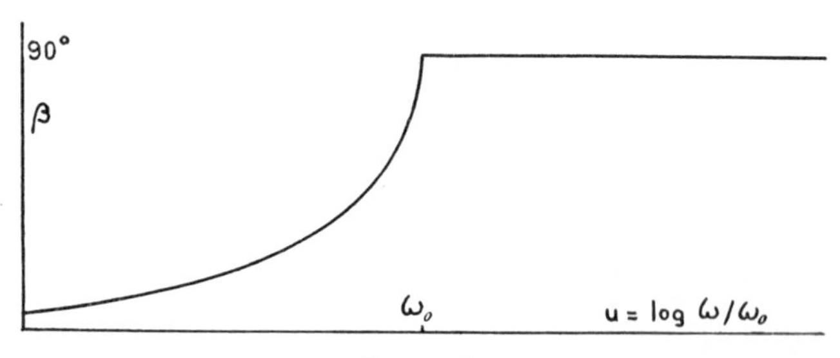

FIG. 17.5

maintain the phase characteristic at its original value throughout the range in which the interstage is cutting off. The characteristics shown by Figs. 17.4 and 17.5 should be examined with some care since they will also be used, except for a change in scale, as the basis of the general method of overall feedback loop design described in the next chapter.

A physical circuit which will represent these characteristics can be obtained most easily if it is noticed that the parts of α and β which were specified originally can be combined with the results in (17–11) and (17–12) to give the complete interstage gain and phase shift by the single formula

$$\alpha + i\beta = \log \frac{\dfrac{2}{\omega_0 C}}{\sqrt{1 - \dfrac{\omega^2}{\omega_0^2}} + i\dfrac{\omega}{\omega_0}}. \tag{17–13}$$

The corresponding interstage impedance or admittance is

$$Z = \frac{1}{Y} = \frac{2}{\omega_0 C}\left[\sqrt{1 - \frac{\omega^2}{\omega_0^2}} - i\frac{\omega}{\omega_0}\right] = \frac{1}{\dfrac{\omega_0 C}{2}\sqrt{1 - \dfrac{\omega^2}{\omega_0^2}} + i\dfrac{\omega C}{2}}. \tag{17–14}$$

If we deal in particular with the admittance

$$Y = \frac{\omega_0 C}{2}\sqrt{1 - \frac{\omega^2}{\omega_0^2}} + i\frac{\omega C}{2}$$

this expression can readily be identified with a full-shunt terminated low-pass filter in which the parasitic capacity C forms the final shunt branch. The structure is illustrated by Fig. 17.6. The network in the box represents an ideal low-pass structure of constant k type terminated at the orthodox mid-shunt junction and with cut-off at $\omega = \omega_0$. It supplies the admittance $\frac{1}{2}\omega_0 C\sqrt{1 - \omega^2/\omega_0^2}$. The final shunt branch is equal to half the parasitic capacity. The remaining half of the capacity appears outside the box and serves to build out the termination from mid-shunt to full-shunt. The fact that half the capacity is incorporated as part of the filter proper, whose admittance disappears at the cut-off is, of course, the reason why the gain of the interstage is 6 db greater than the gain which would be obtained from C alone at this frequency.

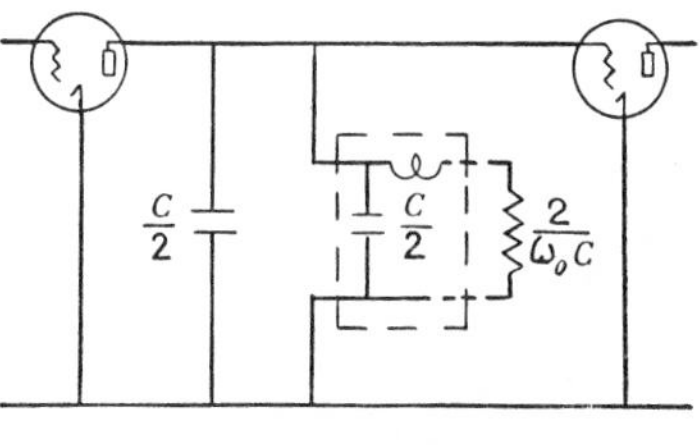

Fig. 17.6

For practical purposes the impedance of the ideal structure of Fig. 17.6 can be approximated by a finite network giving a reasonably accurate match to the terminating resistance $2/\omega_0 C$. Methods of constructing such networks are described in filter theory and need not be dealt with here. As a matter of completeness, however, a list of some special structures, graded in order of complexity, is shown by Fig. 17.7. In each circuit the element values are stated in terms of the frequency and impedance units ω_0 and $2/\omega_0 C$. The two final capacities, each equal to 1 in these units, are, of course, to be identified with the capacities $C/2$ in Fig. 17.6. The structure specified by the first set of element values in Fig. 17.7*C* and the structures of Fig. 17.7*B* and 17.7*E* are conventional filter networks in which the match

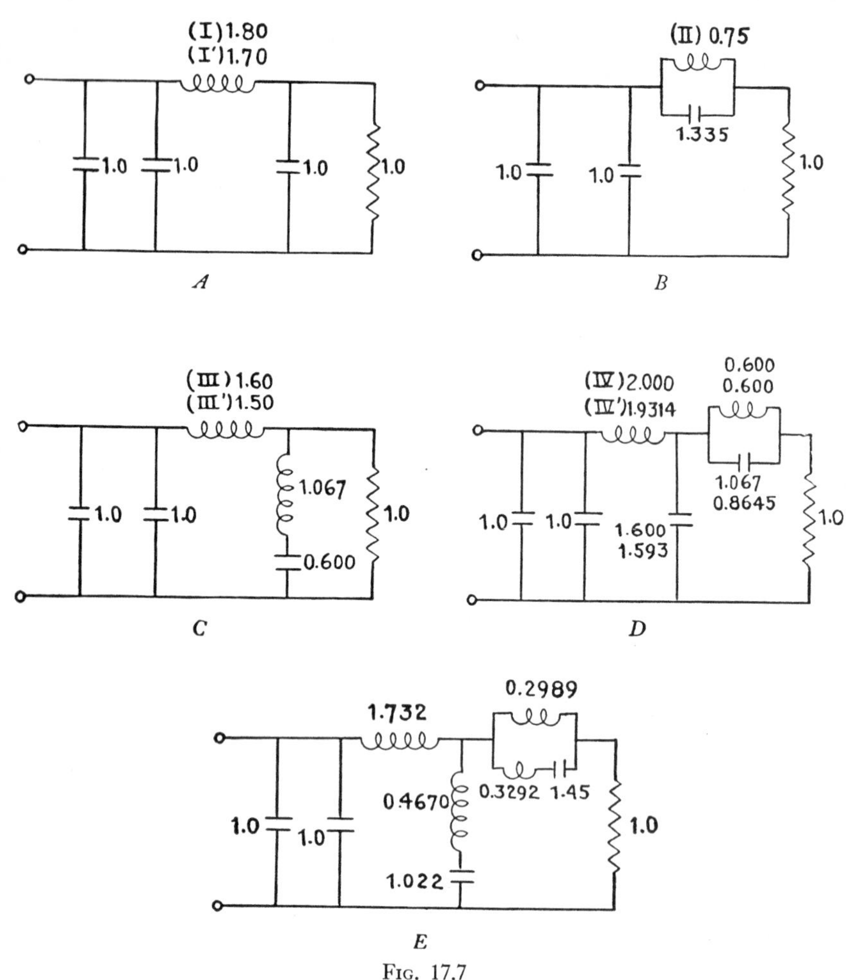

FIG. 17.7

to the final terminating resistance is obtained by terminations respectively of the single *m*-derived and double *m*-derived* types. The other structures were obtained by more or less unorthodox cut-and-try methods.

The gain and phase curves for the structures of Figs. 17.7*A* and 17.7*B* are shown by Fig. 17.8. Curves I and I′ refer to the successive sets of ele-

* See O. J. Zobel, "Extensions to the Theory and Design of Wave Filters," *B.S.T.J.*, April, 1931.

ment values in Fig. 17.7*A* and Curve II, to Fig. 17.7*B*. The gain and phase curves for the remaining structures are shown in Fig. 17.9. Curves

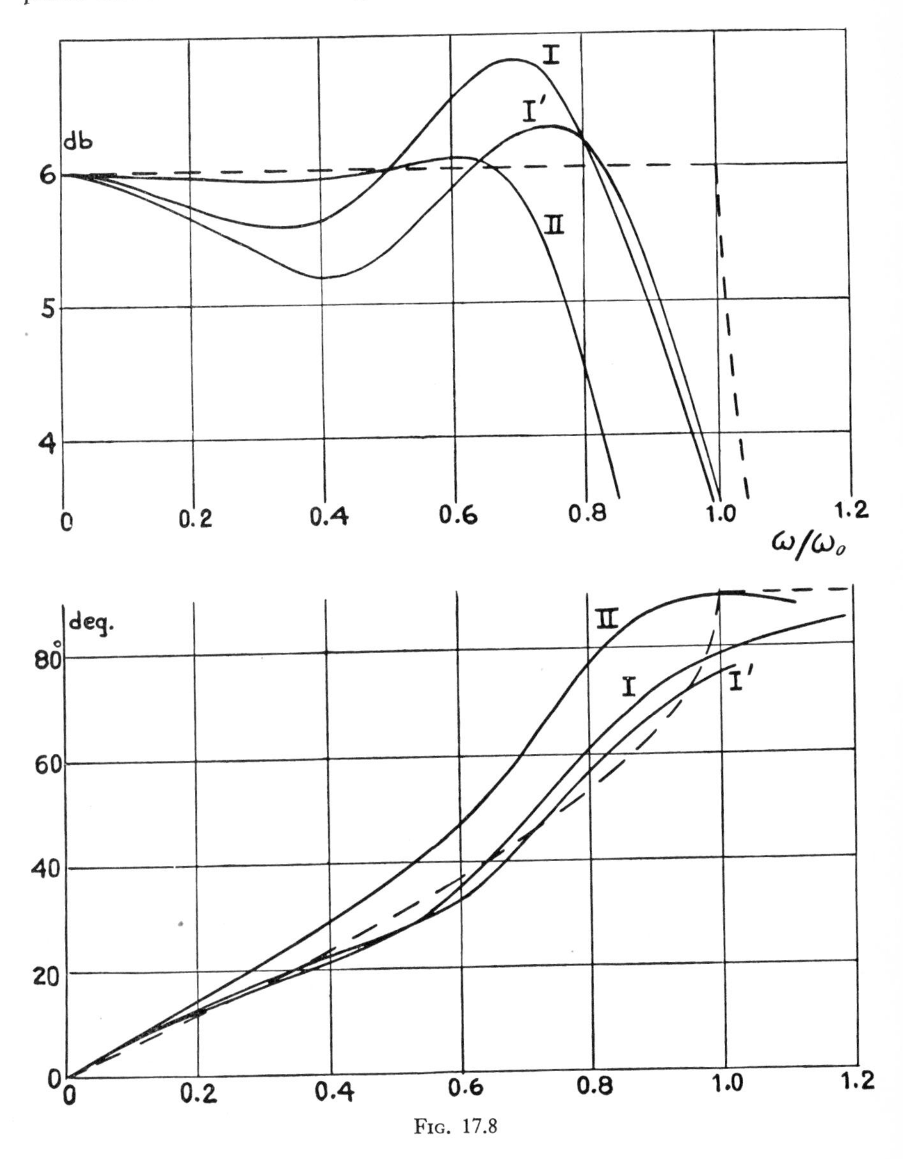

Fig. 17.8

III and IV refer respectively to the structures of Figs. 17.7*C* and 17.7*D*. The performance of the structure of Fig. 17.7*E*, which matches the ideal too closely to be shown by a separate curve, is indicated by the crosses.

The structures can also be used to represent a mid-series image impedance by removing the parasitic capacity and one unit of the final series

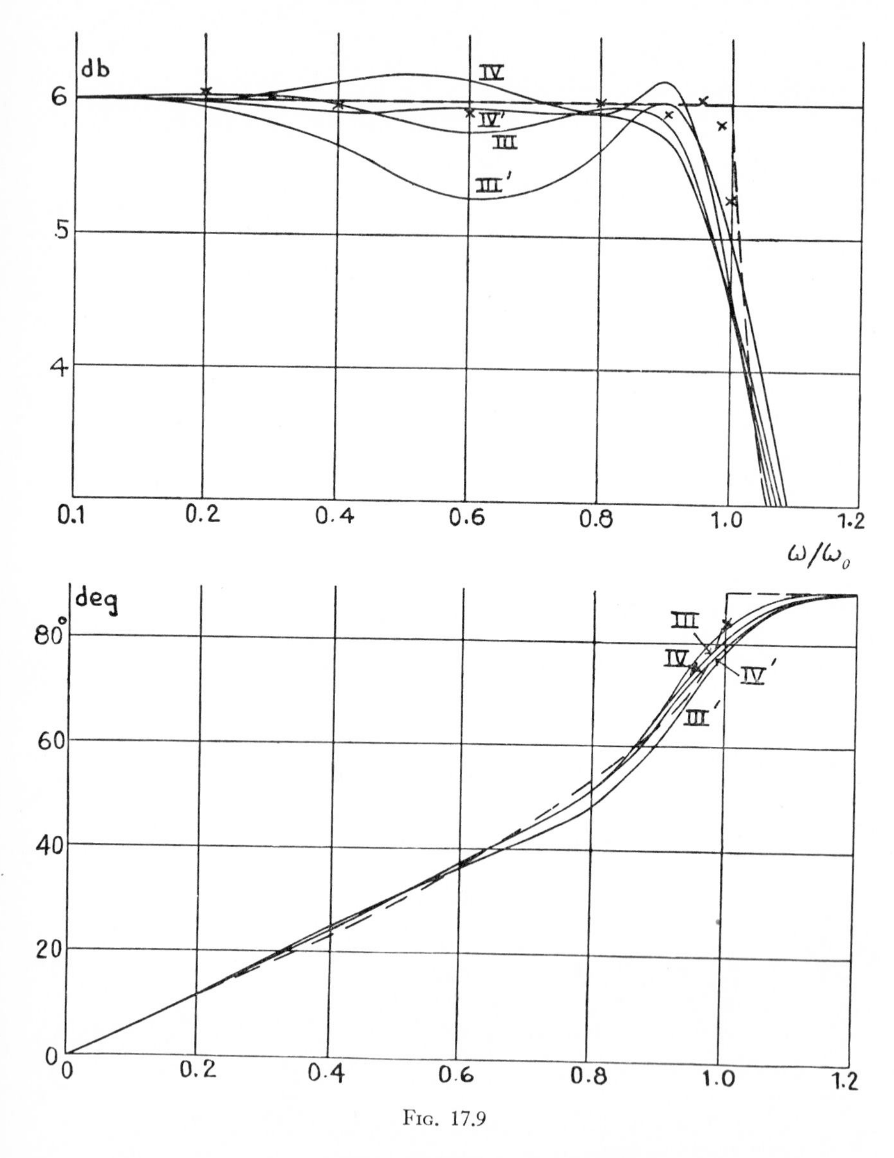

FIG. 17.9

inductance. This is occasionally useful in other design situations. Examples are found in the preceding chapter and will appear again later in the present chapter. The reason that filter impedances appear so frequently in a theoretical discussion like the present one is, of course, the fact that theoretical problems are frequently specified discontinuously in different ranges and require impedances whose character changes abruptly at some given point for their solution. For practical purposes the theoretically abrupt transition is to be regarded as the limit of a series of continuous but increasingly rapid transitions of the type illustrated by Figs. 17.8 and 17.9.

17.4. *Two-Terminal Interstages with Maximum Variable Gain*

If the gain in the useful band must be a function of frequency rather than a constant the analysis is naturally somewhat more complicated but it follows the same general pattern. For practical purposes the most important question is that of determining how high the varying gain characteristic can be placed, in comparison with a corresponding constant gain characteristic, when the parasitic capacity is fixed. This can be examined by replacing the variable of integration ω/ω_0 in the first integral of (17–6) by $\sin \phi$. Upon omitting the second integral, to give the maximum gain condition, the result is

$$\int_0^{\pi/2} \alpha \, d\phi = \frac{\pi}{2} \log \frac{2}{\omega_0 C}, \tag{17–15}$$

which is obviously equivalent to the

Theorem: If a two-terminal interstage including a prescribed parasitic capacity has the maximum absolute level of gain between zero and some fixed point ω_0 the area under its gain characteristic when plotted against $\phi = \sin^{-1} \omega/\omega_0$ is a constant, whatever the relative gains at various points in the prescribed band may be.

The application of this relation is illustrated by Fig. 17.10. Zero gain is taken for convenience as $\log 1/\omega_0 C$. The rectangle labelled I represents the plot of gain against ϕ when the interstage is of the maximum constant gain type described in the preceding section. Curves II and III represent two extreme cases of interstages with tilted characteristics. In the first the interstage is merely the parasitic capacity and this characteristic if drawn on log frequency paper would consequently have a constant downward slope of 6 db per octave. Curve III represents the inverse situation, in which the gain has a constant upward slope of 6 db

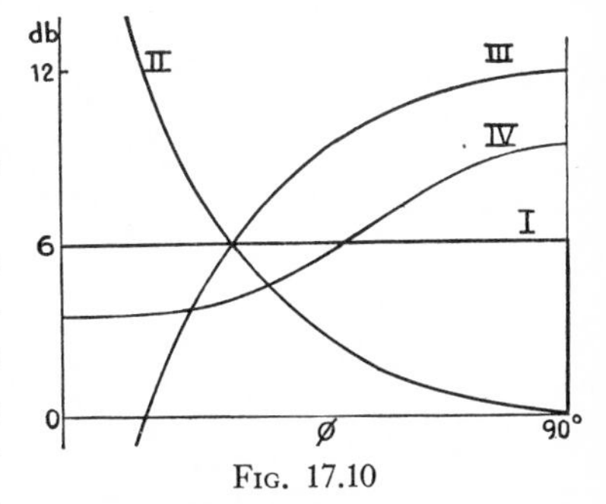

Fig. 17.10

per octave. This characteristic corresponds to the expression

$$\alpha + i\beta = \log \frac{1}{\dfrac{\omega_0 C}{2}\sqrt{1 - \dfrac{\omega^2}{\omega_0^2}} + i\dfrac{\omega C}{2} - i\dfrac{\omega_0^2 C}{4\omega}}. \tag{17–16}$$

We notice that the quantity $(\omega_0 C/2)\sqrt{1 - \omega^2/\omega_0^2} + i(\omega C/2) - i(\omega_0^2 C/4\omega)$, which is evidently the interstage admittance, is the same as the denominator of the final expression in (17–14) except for the additional term $-i(\omega_0^2 C/4\omega)$. The interstage can therefore be obtained by adding a parallel inductance to a " constant gain " interstage, as illustrated by Fig. 17.11. It is worth noticing also that an amplifier containing two " constant gain " interstages can be replaced by one containing one interstage each of the types represented by Curves II and III, with an economy of elements, provided the changes in impedance and signal level within the amplifier can be tolerated. The final curve, labelled IV in Fig. 17.10, represents a tilted interstage of the type commonly encountered in practice. Its gain characteristic on an arithmetic frequency scale is shown by Fig. 17.12.

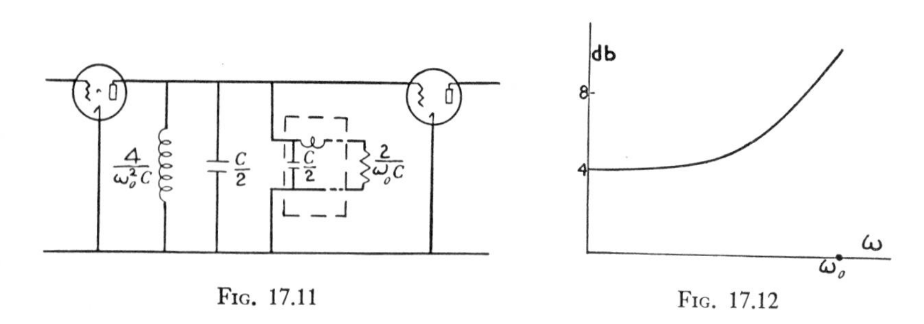

FIG. 17.11 FIG. 17.12

In accordance with the theorem developed earlier in this section the areas under all the curves in Fig. 17.10 must be the same. If a tilted interstage is to be physically realizable it must in addition meet the requirement that its phase angle in the useful band will not exceed the limits $\pm\pi/2$. Otherwise, of course, it cannot be constructed without the use of a negative resistance. No difficulty is to be anticipated here if the gain characteristic varies only moderately, like that represented by Curve IV in Fig. 17.10, but the phase characteristic may become too great if very large variations are attempted. Curves II and III were described as " extreme " when they were first introduced because their associated phase shifts just reach the limit. They can thus be taken as representing roughly the limit of what can be attained if we consider the variation of the gain characteristic over the complete band, but sharper variations over a small portion of the band are of course permissible.

The transformation from an arithmetic frequency scale to the ϕ scale has as its chief effect a spreading out or accentuation of the region near the edge of the useful band. The reason for emphasizing this portion of the gain characteristic can be understood most easily if it is recalled from one of the earlier theorems in the chapter that when the gain characteristic is plotted on an arithmetic frequency scale the total gain area over the complete frequency spectrum is the same for any maximum gain structure. As long as we are dealing with the characteristic only at frequencies well below the edge of the band this principle allows us to rearrange the gain area as we see fit, without penalty. Changes in the characteristic near the edge of the band, on the other hand, imply concomitant changes in gain area just beyond the useful band which must be allowed for even though they are not directly part of the useful characteristic. This is illustrated by Fig. 17.13, which represents the capacity gain and constant gain characteristic of Fig. 17.4 redrawn on an arithmetic frequency scale. In accordance with the gain area theorem, area I is equal to the sum of areas II and III. Area III is not directly useful but it cannot be dispensed with if area II is to exist because the gain characteristic cannot drop off beyond the band more rapidly than it does in the figure without producing a phase shift greater than $\pi/2$. The additional weighting of the gain characteristic just below ω_0 which the transformation to the ϕ scale produces is evidently an expression of the existence of this necessary surplus area beyond ω_0.

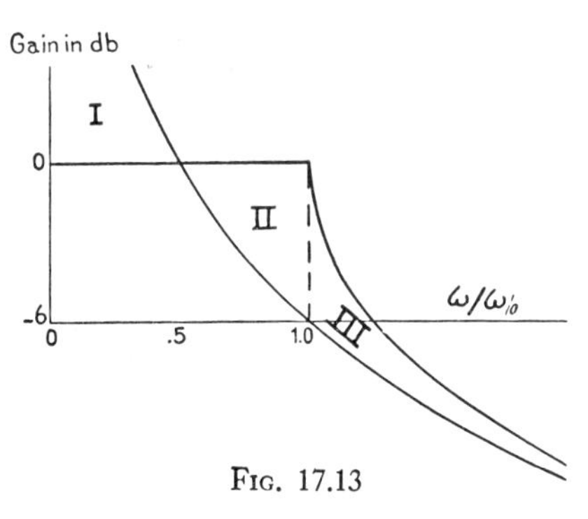

FIG. 17.13

The design of a tilted interstage of maximum gain type may be obtained by following broadly the procedure described previously. With α determined inside the useful band and β beyond it, it is first necessary to compute the rest of the characteristic from (14–33) of Chapter XIV, much as was done in connection with (17–9) of the present chapter except that both integrals of the general formula must be considered. A rough computation may be sufficient at this step. The parasitic capacity is next subtracted from the complete interstage admittance and the remainder simulated by cut-and-try methods. The basic constituent of the simulating network will, of course, be a filter image impedance. Analogous problems were discussed in connection with Fig. 14.19 of Chapter XIV and Fig. 16.11 of Chapter XVI.

17.5. *Explicit Formula for Band-Pass Interstages*

In confining the discussion to interstages of " low-pass " type, it is, of course, assumed that the solution advanced will be applied to broad-band and to symmetrical narrow-band problems by means of the transformations described in Chapter X. As a matter of completeness, however, the general formula which applies explicitly to both symmetrical and unsymmetrical band-pass structures will also be included. It appears as

$$K_1 + K_2 + K_3 = \frac{\pi}{2} \log \frac{2}{(\omega_2 - \omega_1)C},$$

where

$$\begin{aligned} K_1 &= \int_{\omega_1}^{\omega_2} \frac{\omega}{\omega_1\omega_2} \frac{\alpha \, d\omega}{\sqrt{\omega^2/\omega_1^2 - 1}\,\sqrt{1 - \omega^2/\omega_2^2}} \\ K_2 &= \int_{0}^{\omega_1} \frac{\omega}{\omega_1\omega_2} \frac{(\pi/2 - \beta) \, d\omega}{\sqrt{1 - \omega^2/\omega_1^2}\,\sqrt{1 - \omega^2/\omega_2^2}} \\ K_3 &= \int_{\omega_2}^{\infty} \frac{\omega}{\omega_1\omega_2} \frac{(\beta + \pi/2) \, d\omega}{\sqrt{\omega^2/\omega_1^2 - 1}\,\sqrt{\omega^2/\omega_2^2 - 1}} \end{aligned} \tag{17–17}$$

where ω_1 and ω_2 are the edges of the useful band and the general significance of the terms is the same as that of those appearing in the corresponding expression in (17–6). To study the maximum gain condition we omit the second and third integrals on the assumption that the interstage phase angle is $+\pi/2$, representing an inductive reactance, below the band, and $-\pi/2$, representing a capacitative reactance, above it. The remaining integral is exactly similar to the gain integral in the low-pass case except that the weighting function $1/\sqrt{1 - \omega^2/\omega_0^2}$, which accentuates the importance of the gain characteristic near ω_0, is replaced by $\omega/\omega_1\omega_2\sqrt{\omega^2/\omega_1^2 - 1}\sqrt{1 - \omega^2/\omega_2^2}$, which emphasizes both edges of the band.

17.6. *Two-Terminal Interstages with Specified Phase Margins*

We have still to examine the situation in which the phase angle of the interstage network cannot be as great as 90° everywhere beyond the edge of the useful band, so that it is not possible to ignore the second integral in (17–6). The difference, $\beta + \pi/2$ in (17–6), between the actual interstage phase shift and its limiting value will be called the interstage phase margin. Problems of this sort are particularly likely to arise in feedback amplifier design, where it may be necessary to restrict the phase angles of the interstage networks in certain frequency ranges in order to insure a stable circuit. The circumstances in which phase control of the interstage networks, rather than the feedback circuit, is necessary are described in the next chapter. They relate broadly to the amount of final gain required from the amplifier. For our present purposes we may imagine, as the design situation, that the input and output circuits and the feedback circuit have already been designed, that their contributions to the transmission around the overall feedback loop are known, that we have established what the final loop phase characteristic should be to secure a stable amplifier with a specified margin against singing, and that the relative feedbacks at various frequencies in the useful band have been specified. The reasons for supposing that the design situation takes this form and the details of the construction of the phase requirement will be better understood from the discussion in the next chapter. With the data as assumed, the phase characteristic of the interstage networks beyond the useful band and their relative gains within the useful band can be computed. What remains is the determination of networks meeting these requirements with as high an absolute level of gain in the useful band as is permissible with the given interstage capacities.*

This design problem can be attacked most directly if we begin by using (17–6) to determine how much gain must be sacrificed to permit the interstage to have the prescribed phase characteristic. As we have already noticed, the sacrifice depends upon the fact that the second integral in (17–6) must be positive unless $\beta = -\pi/2$ at every frequency outside the useful band and serves, with a given C, to reduce the value which can be assigned to the first integral. To evaluate it, let the variable ω/ω_0 in the second integral be replaced by $\phi' = \sin^{-1} \omega_0/\omega$. If we retain the earlier substitution $\phi = \sin^{-1} \omega/\omega_0$ for the first integral this allows the complete equation to be rewritten as

$$\int_0^{\pi/2} \alpha \, d\phi + \int_0^{\pi/2} \left[\frac{\omega}{\omega_0}\left(\frac{\pi}{2} + \beta\right)\right] d\phi' = \frac{\pi}{2} \log \frac{2}{\omega_0 C}. \qquad (17\text{–}18)$$

Thus the reduction in gain can be obtained by plotting the function $(\omega/\omega_0)(\pi/2 + \beta)$ against ϕ'. In view of the similarity between the two

* If the design method in the next chapter is followed the absolute level of gain in the final interstage can also be determined directly from the preliminary computations which govern the general choice of circuit arrangements and phase characteristics. The independent determination described here is nevertheless useful since it can usually be made much more accurately than the preliminary computations, for which the data may be approximations or estimates based on scattered measurements.

angle scales the result can be conveniently expressed as the

Theorem: If a two-terminal interstage including a specified shunt capacity has a specified phase angle β above a certain point ω_0 the reduction of the absolute level of gain, in nepers, below ω_0 from the theoretical maximum is equal to the average height, in radians, of the plot of $(\omega/\omega_0)(\pi/2 + \beta)$ against $\phi' = \sin^{-1} \omega_0/\omega$.

If a complete multi-stage μ circuit, rather than a single interstage, is under consideration, we can evidently make a single computation for the whole circuit and allocate the total gain reduction among the individual interstages in any way which appears likely to give a convenient design.

It will be noticed that the transformation to the ϕ' scale tends to accentuate the importance of the phase characteristic just beyond ω_0. This phenomenon is similar to that which was found for the transformation to the ϕ scale in the gain analysis and occurs for the same general reason. It will be recalled that in the gain analysis the gain area law applied to the response over the complete frequency spectrum, but that in dealing with the response over a limited region it was necessary to allow for the fact that a change in the gain characteristic near the edge of the band produced area changes outside as well as inside the band. In the present situation the response over the complete spectrum is governed in a similar way by the phase area law developed originally as equation (13–19) of Chapter XIII. When ω is large the second integral in (17–6) reduces to

$$\int \left(\frac{\pi}{2} + \beta\right) \frac{d\omega}{\omega} = \int \left(\frac{\pi}{2} + \beta\right) du,$$

where $u = \log \omega$, and expresses this law explicitly. It may be remembered that Chapter XIII also included a discussion, based on the phase area law, of the use of trap circuits to control interstage phase characteristics at frequencies remote from the band. If the phase control is exerted near the band the phase area law in a broad sense still applies, but a portion of the total area change occurs within the useful band and cannot be included directly in an integration which begins at the band edge. Exactly as in the gain analysis the transformation to the ϕ' scale expresses this effect indirectly by a relative increase in the importance assigned to the phase characteristic just beyond the useful band.

When the absolute level of gain in the useful band has been established the rest of the design can be obtained by following a routine somewhat similar to that used in several previous problems. It is simplest to describe the procedure in terms of an example. Since phase control at high frequencies through the use of a trap circuit has already been described in

Chapter XIII it will be assumed here that the phase control is to extend over a range bordering on the useful band. For illustrative purposes it will be supposed that the phase shift is to be 60° for one octave beyond the useful band and a slanting line between 60° and 90° for an additional octave, as shown by Fig. 17.14. It will also be supposed that the gain in the useful band is to be flat.

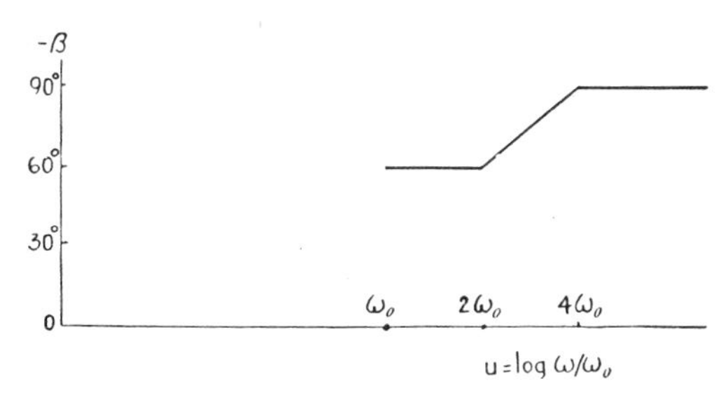

Fig. 17.14

The design begins with the plot of $(\omega/\omega_0)(\pi/2+\beta)$ against ϕ'. Using the β of Fig. 17.14, this leads to the result shown by Fig. 17.15. The average height of the curve is about 32°, or 0.56 radians. It follows from (17–18) that the absolute level of gain in the useful band must be 0.56 nepers, or 4.9 db, less than that of a maximum gain interstage. For a flat characteristic, in other words, the gain in the useful band will be 1.1 db above log $1/\omega_0 C$.

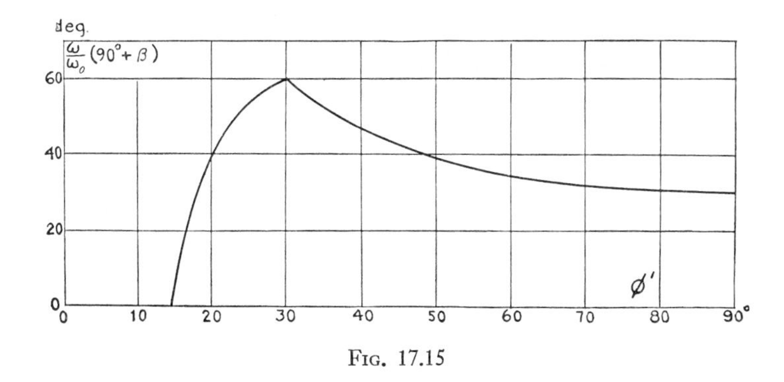

Fig. 17.15

We next compute the complete interstage characteristic from the known components of gain and phase. It is simplest to suppose initially that the phase characteristic is 60° at all frequencies above the useful band. With this assumption the situation is evidently the same as that treated by equations (17–9) through (17–13) except that the specified phase is 60° rather than 90° and the gain level in the useful band is somewhat different. We can consequently obtain the complete gain and phase characteristics by

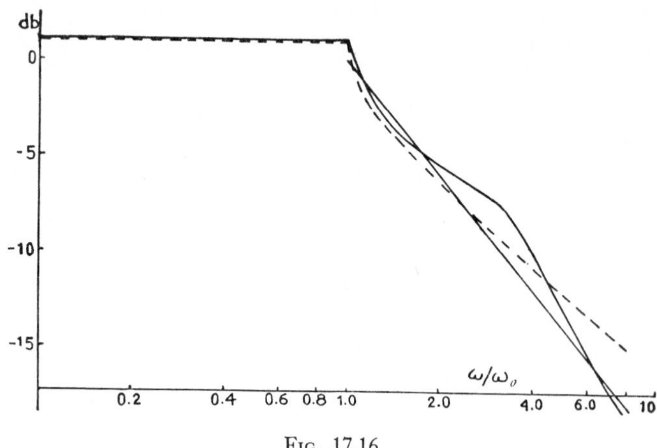

FIG. 17.16

multiplying (17–13) by $\frac{2}{3}$ and adding a constant to give the correct low-frequency gain. This leads to the results shown by the broken lines in Figs. 17.16 and 17.17. The reference gain in Fig. 17.16 is taken as

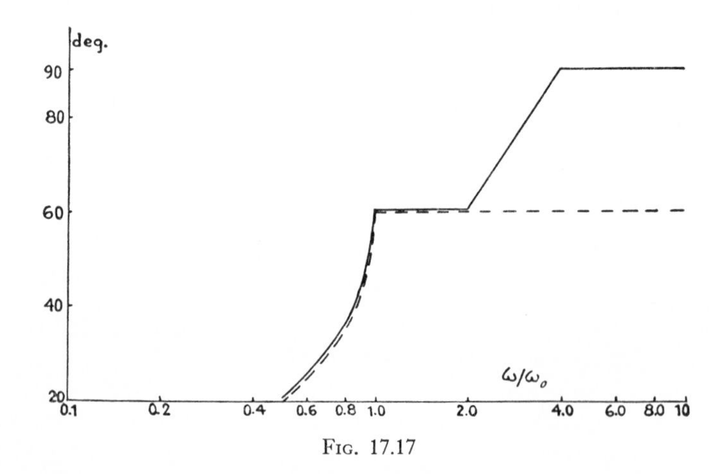

FIG. 17.17

log $1/\omega_0 C$ and the straight solid line represents the capacity gain, with which the actual characteristic must eventually merge.

The fact that the interstage phase angle is not actually equal to 60° at all frequencies above ω_0 can be most easily taken into account by introducing the error as B in equation (14–33) of Chapter XIV and evaluating the result by means of the charts in Chapter XV. It will be recalled that equation (14–33) is merely an expression of the standard relation between the real and imaginary components of network functions when the components have the special form indicated by (14–32). In this problem the " real component " with which we have to deal is evidently the difference between the actual interstage phase beyond ω_0 and 60°, divided by $\sqrt{\omega^2/\omega_0^2 - 1}$. This function is shown by Curve I in Fig. 17.18. With the

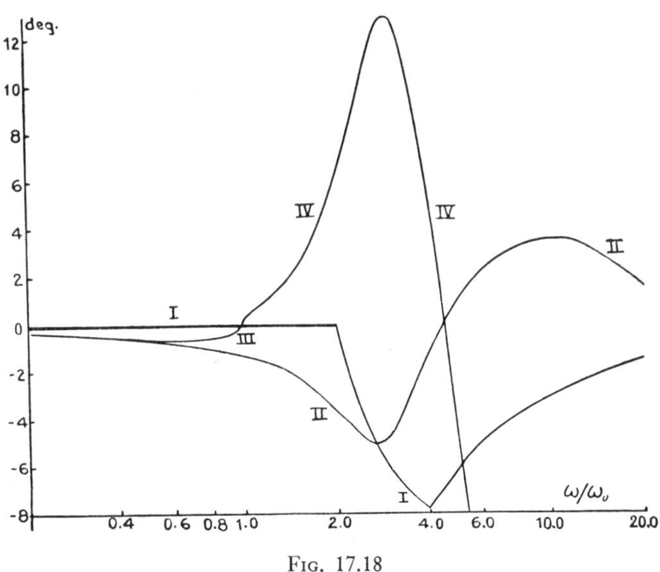

Fig. 17.18

help of the charts in Chapter XV the corresponding imaginary component is found and appears as Curve II in the figure. But the imaginary component is equal to $B/\sqrt{1 - \omega^2/\omega_0^2}$ for $\omega < \omega_0$ and to $-A/\sqrt{\omega^2/\omega_0^2 - 1}$ for $\omega > \omega_0$. Thus from Curve II we can secure Curves III and IV representing B and A themselves in these two ranges. These last curves are evidently the corrections which must be applied to the preliminary characteristics for the interstage gain and phase in order to take account of the departure of the required phase angle from 60° at high frequencies. When the corrections are made the complete interstage characteristics take the form shown by the solid lines in Figs. 17.16 and 17.17.

After this point is reached the design can be finished by following the routine described for a number of previous examples. We begin by computing from Figs. 17.16 and 17.17 what the impedance of the interstage, exclusive of the parasitic capacity, must be. The result is shown by Fig. 17.19, where the unit of impedance is taken as $1/\omega_0 C$. The resistance component is next matched with a minimum reactance network. In this example the principal portion of the resistance is furnished by a mid-shunt low-pass filter image impedance of the constant k type, with cut-off at $\omega/\omega_0 = 4$, plus a parallel capacity.* The structure is shown by network A

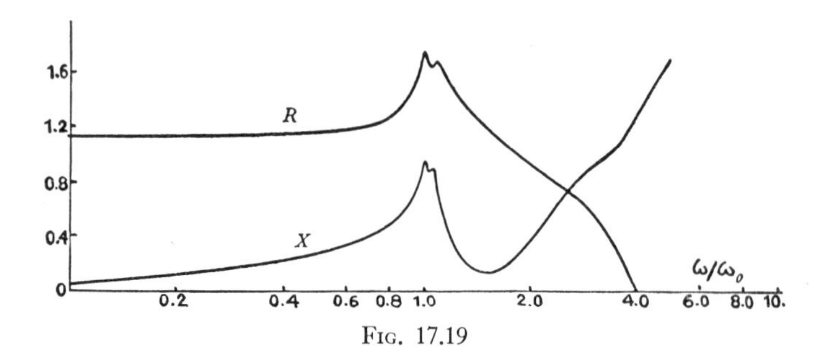

FIG. 17.19

in Fig. 17.20. The additional peak of resistance near ω_0 is provided by the damped anti-resonant network shown as network B in the figure. The filter impedance is used in the first network principally to provide a very accurate match to the assumed characteristics, for illustrative purposes. In a practical design a much simpler structure, such as a resistance in parallel with a capacity, should suffice.

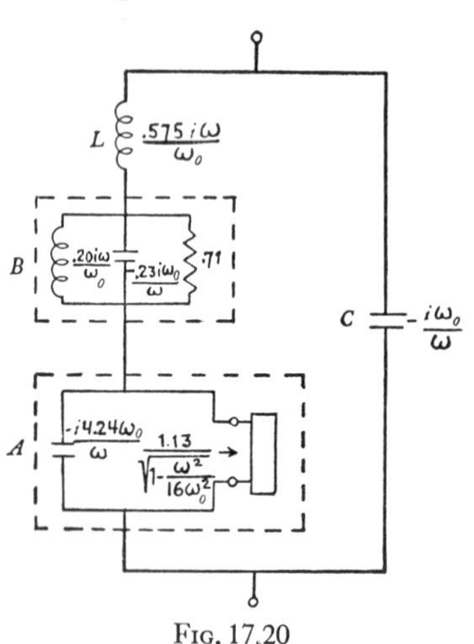

FIG. 17.20

The design is completed by adding the inductance L in Fig. 17.20 to make up the difference between the reactance furnished by networks A and B and the reactance specified in Fig. 17.19. The reasons for expecting that the reactance match can always be obtained and other general comments on the process were set forth in connection with the discussion of similar problems in the preceding chapter and need not be reviewed here. The final interstage gain and phase characteristics with the element values given in

* The additional capacity is almost the right value to change the termination from mid-shunt to full-shunt, so that the resistance component is nearly, although not exactly, the same as a mid-series constant k image impedance.

Fig. 17.20 are shown by Fig. 17.21. The characteristics of Figs. 17.16 and 17.17 are indicated by the broken lines.

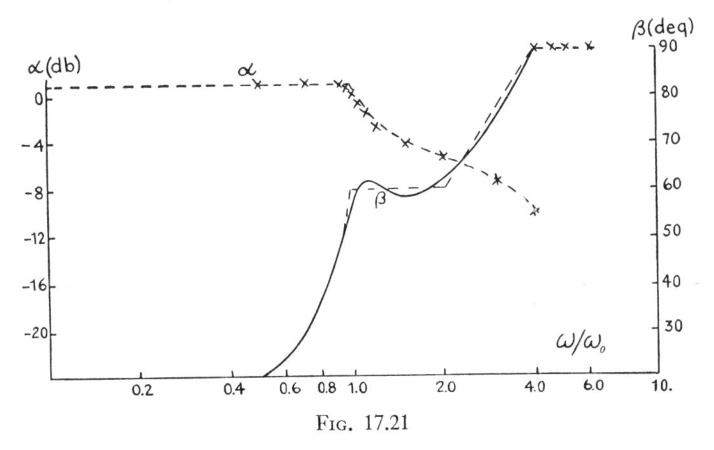

Fig. 17.21

17.7. *Interstage Networks of Simple Types*

The interstage design technique described thus far has been directed primarily at two extreme problems. In the first, a close approximation to maximum gain in the useful band was sought, while in the second a prescribed relative gain characteristic within the band was combined with a prescribed phase margin beyond it. In either case, the problem was conceived as a purely theoretical one, with no restriction on the number of elements employed, and the resulting structures turn out, in general, to be rather complicated.

In a practical design it is, of course, usually possible to rely upon much simpler networks. The extent of the permissible simplification depends, in general, both upon the amplifier requirements and upon the skill of the designer. The controlling relation is the fact that in any particular amplifier the integral of the sum of the interstage phase margins, plotted against ϕ', is a fixed quantity which can be determined from the general arrangement of the circuit and the required final gain. If the sum is zero the physical limit on the performance of the amplifier is one of available μ circuit gain. The interstages theoretically should be maximum gain structures and any departures from the maximum gain condition due to network simplifications are reflected directly in diminished feedback. If the integral is not zero, on the other hand, the situation is more flexible. For example, as long as the integral is fixed the frequency variation of the total μ circuit phase margin can usually be altered within wide limits by adjustments of the other parts of the circuit, while within the μ circuit itself the phase margin can, of course, be allocated arbitrarily to the several inter-

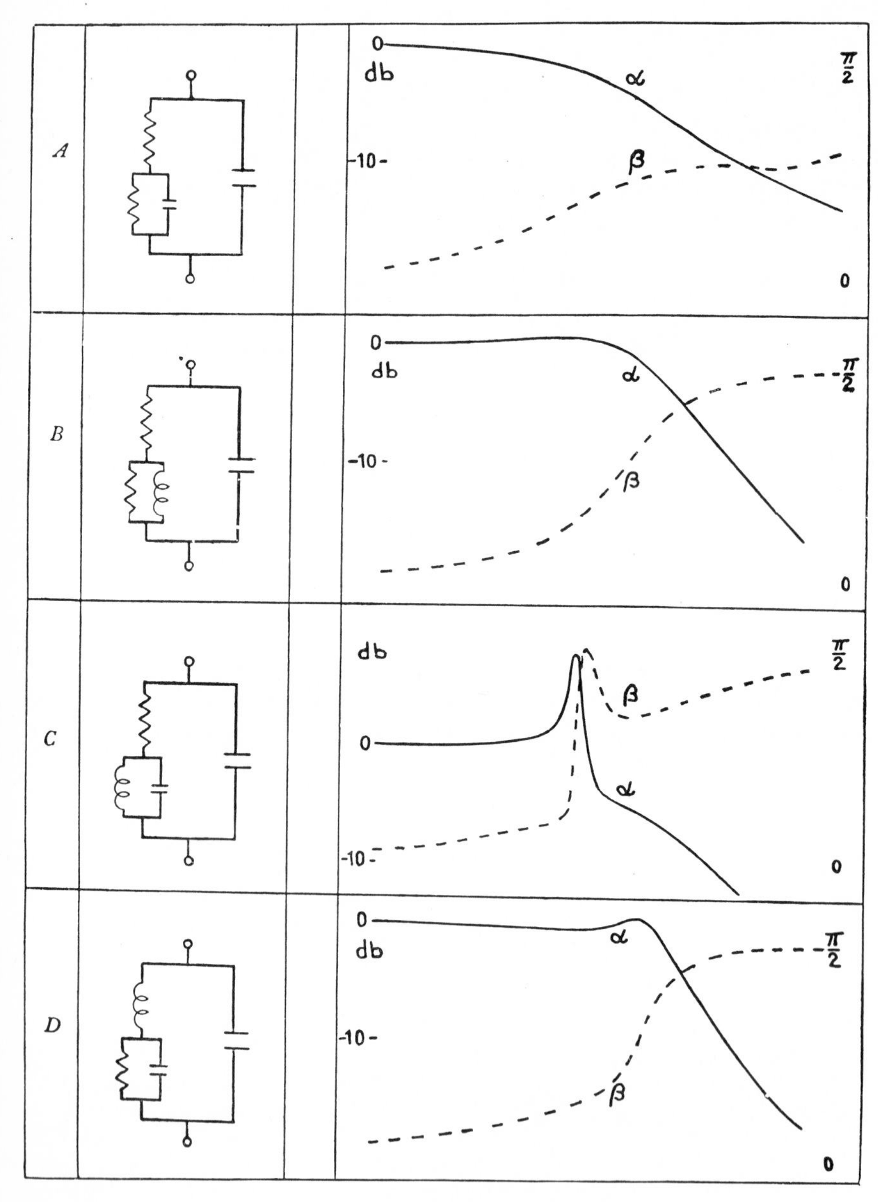

FIG. 17.22

stages. The design problem thus becomes one of splitting up the integral in such a way that the individual pieces correspond to especially simple structures. The technique described in the preceding section appears as a last resort when the splitting-up process is not completely successful. These relations are described in more detail in the next chapter and are merely summarized here.

When the interstages are very simple they are most easily designed directly by cut-and-try methods. As a guide to the process, however, a list of configurations is given in Fig. 17.22. The list gives all the structures of four elements, including the parasitic capacity, which can be expected to be appropriate for amplifier designs carried out on the low-pass equivalent basis.* The accompanying curves attempt to show the types of characteristics for which each structure is particularly suitable. For example, the first configuration is appropriate if the interstage must give a large and fairly uniform phase margin over a broad range beyond the useful band. The large phase margin is obtained, however, at the cost of a low and not very flat gain within the useful band. The second configuration allows the gain to be made higher and reasonably flat, or even upward tilting, but the phase margin becomes relatively less at high frequencies. The third configuration is convenient if the interstage should exhibit either a flat or a tilted gain characteristic within the useful band together with a modest phase margin over an extended high-frequency region.

The diversity of characteristics obtainable from these three networks is only that which may be estimated by physical inspection. The fourth configuration can be used only when a high-frequency phase margin is unimportant, but within this limitation it can exhibit a considerable variety of characteristics. A family of curves showing the characteristics secured with representative values of the network elements has therefore been prepared and is given in the charts at the end of the chapter. The charts also cover the two degenerate cases, in which the interstage exclusive of the parasitic capacity consists of a resistance alone or a resistance and inductance in series, obtainable by assigning extreme values to the elements in any of the configurations.

17.8. *Four-Terminal Interstage Networks — General Discussion*

In ordinary amplifier design the interstage networks are frequently four-terminal structures, such as tuned transformers and the like, rather than the simple shunt impedances which we have thus far considered. Four-terminal interstages are often convenient physically. For example, a transformer coupled amplifier, aside from being relatively simple of itself,

* That is, structures giving an infinite loss or gain at finite frequencies are omitted. For example, shunt inductance paths to ground are excluded on the assumption that in a design on the low-pass basis any such path, if present, will produce only a modification of the sort illustrated by the broken line in Fig. 10.14 of Chapter X and can be ignored in the high-frequency design.

affords a convenient method of introducing plate and grid voltages into the circuit. Four-terminal structures are also capable of giving more gain than can be obtained from two-terminal interstages. They have been ignored thus far principally because they usually exhibit excessively high phase shifts, which make them unsuitable in a feedback device. They will be considered here briefly, however, as a matter of general interest.

The reason why a four-terminal interstage can be expected to give more gain than a two-terminal structure can be seen most easily by means of the circuit* shown by Fig. 17.23. The network is a full-shunt terminated low-pass filter of the type described originally in connection with two-terminal maximum gain interstages. Instead of lumping plate and grid capacities together, however, they appear separately as the two capacities labelled $C/2$ in the drawing. The gain and phase characteristics are given by

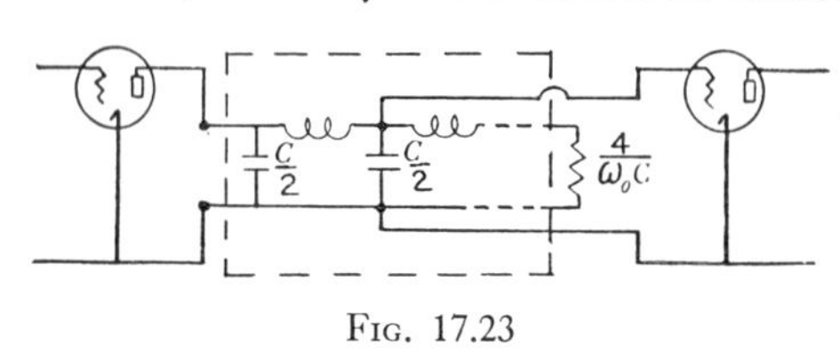

FIG. 17.23

$$\alpha + i\beta = \log \frac{4}{\omega_0 C} - 3 \log \left[\sqrt{1 - \frac{\omega^2}{\omega_0^2}} + i \frac{\omega}{\omega_0} \right]. \tag{17–19}$$

At high frequencies the gain of the circuit is much less than that of a two-terminal interstage and its phase shift is much greater, as we might expect from the fact that a filter section has been interpolated between grid and plate. Within the band, on the other hand, the filter is transparent and since it is of recurrent structure the absolute value of grid and plate voltages must be the same. At the plate terminals, however, the impedance is that of a full-shunt terminated constant k filter, and the flow of plate current therefore produces a voltage of constant absolute value throughout the useful band, just as it did in the case of the two-terminal interstage. The only difference lies in the absolute level of gain, which is 6 db higher in (17–19) than it is in the corresponding expression (17–13), in agreement with the fact that the final shunt branch of the filter can be identified with $C/2$ rather than with C. The separation of grid and plate capacities which makes this possible is evidently the general physical advantage of a four-terminal over a two-terminal interstage.

In preparing Fig. 17.23 it has, of course, been assumed that grid and plate capacities are equal. This is more or less approximately true with ordinary tubes. If the two capacities differ substantially the situation can be treated, for analytical purposes, by supposing that the network includes an

* Wheeler and Percival, *loc. cit.*

ideal transformer or the equivalent, as illustrated by Fig. 17.24. The voltage gain of such a circuit in comparison with a similar structure terminated in the capacities $(C_1 + C_2)/2$ at each end is $\frac{1}{2}\left(\sqrt{C_1/C_2} + \sqrt{C_2/C_1}\right)$. This is always greater than unity but the advantage amounts to only a few

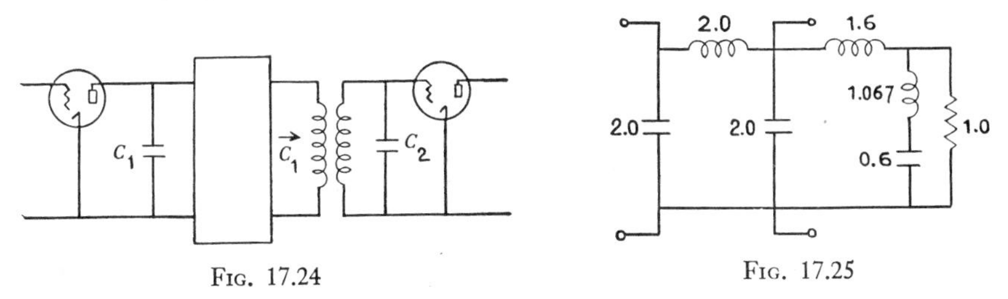

Fig. 17.24

Fig. 17.25

tenths of a db for ordinary ratios between C_1 and C_2 so that we need merely take the average of the grid and plate capacities in estimating performance. It may be noticed that except as a means of matching capacities there appears to be no general theoretical reason, on the basis of the analysis given in this section, for including a transformer in the network.*

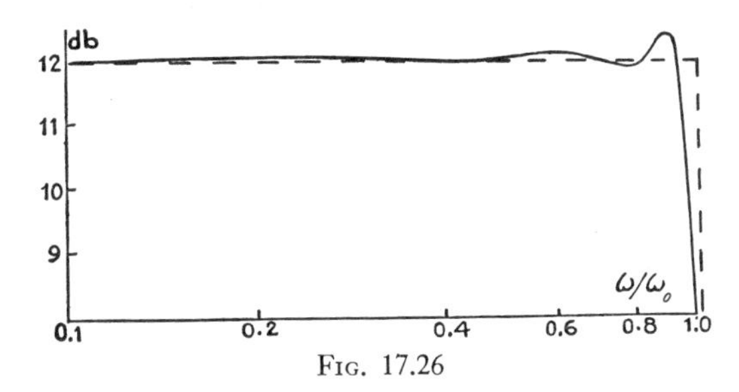

Fig. 17.26

For practical purposes the ideal filter structure of Fig. 17.23 can be approximated by a finite network in which the mid-shunt image impedance from grid to cathode is matched to the terminating resistance by a mid-series derived half section with $m = 0.6$ as shown on Fig. 17.25.† Fig-

* It must be remembered that this discussion is concerned only with the effect of capacity limitation on interstage design. In narrow band amplifiers the capacity limitation may permit higher impedance levels than can reasonably be constructed or than can be used with the tubes, especially in the plate circuit, and a transformer may be necessary on this account. Amplifiers with substantial grid or plate dissipation or with critical limits on tube loads must also be excluded.

† As in Fig. 17.7 the numbers refer to a filter with unit cut-off and unit impedance level, and the factors ω_0, for the unit of frequency, and $4/\omega_0 C$, for the unit of impedance, must be introduced to give actual element values, in ohms, henries, and farads. The same conventions apply to Fig. 17.28.

ures 17.26 and 17.27 show the gain and phase characteristics; the dotted lines are the theoretical characteristics.

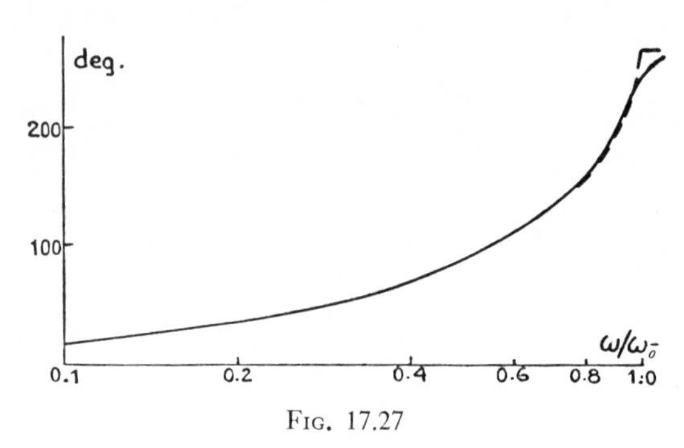

FIG. 17.27

Figure 17.28 illustrates a slightly different form of the structure* in which a mid-shunt derived half section is used to match the terminating resistance. This configuration is useful in permitting slightly unequal grid and plate capacities to be taken into account analytically, without the necessity of employing an ideal transformer as was assumed in Fig. 17.24. In terms of the parameter m of the final half section, the grid and plate capacities are $[2/(3+m)]C$ and $[(1+m)/(3+m)]C$, rather than $C/2$. In Fig. 17.28 it is assumed that $m = 0.6$ which corresponds to a capacity ratio of 5 : 4. With extreme capacity ratios the m becomes too small to provide an effective match to the terminating

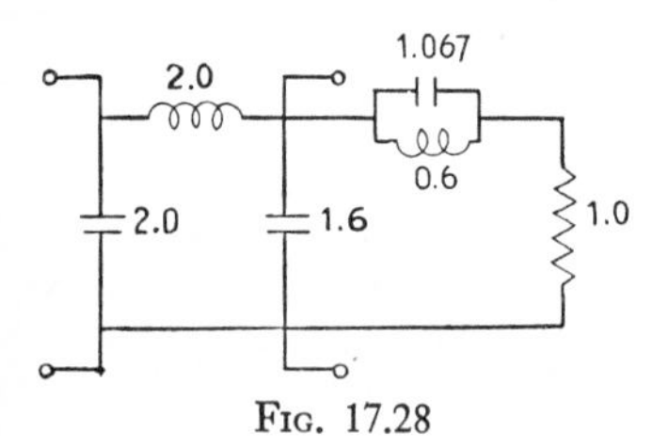

FIG. 17.28

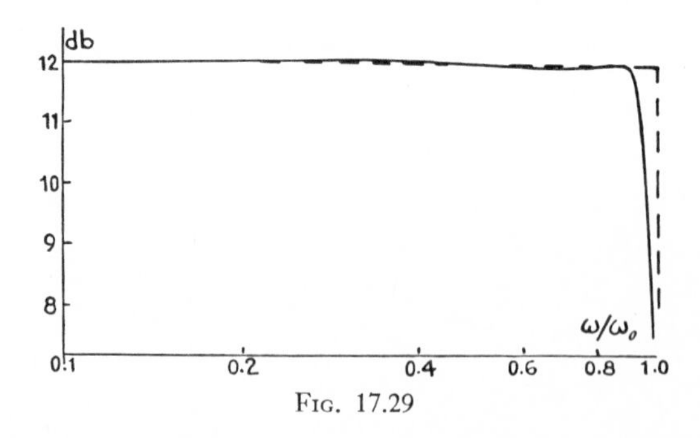

FIG. 17.29

resistance and it is simplest in practice to produce approximate equality between the two ends of the circuit by the addition of a certain amount

* This modification is due to the author's colleague, Mr. W. H. Boghosian.

of padding capacity. The particular choice illustrated by Fig. 17.28 leads to the approximations to the theoretical characteristics shown by the solid lines in Figs. 17.29 and 17.30.

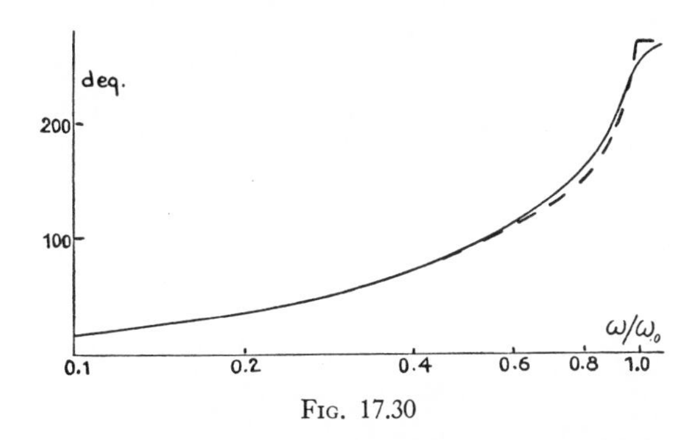

FIG. 17.30

17.9. *Equivalent Representation of a Four-Terminal Interstage*

The four-terminal interstage networks described in the preceding section are not necessarily those giving the maximum possible gain with prescribed capacities. A general theoretical examination of the problem, however, is unfortunately much more difficult for four-terminal interstages than it was for two-terminal structures. The chief reason for the added difficulty of the problem appears to be the fact that the absolute level of gain of a four-terminal interstage is not uniquely fixed by its parasitic capacities and the way in which its gain and phase characteristics vary with frequency. This is in contrast to the situation in the two-terminal case, where it was possible to set up a definite relation such as (17–6) among these quantities. Different physical four-terminal structures, on the other hand, may have identical parasitic elements, and gain and phase characteristics which vary in an identical manner as functions of frequency, and still exhibit different levels of absolute gain. Before the maximum gain can be calculated, therefore, it is necessary to find out why these differences in level can exist, and what further assumptions must be made concerning the network in order to secure the most favorable possible case. The discussion presented here gives only a general account of the problem and is not intended as either a rigorous or an exhaustive analysis.

The problem of establishing theoretical limits on the gain obtainable from a four-terminal interstage will be attacked by representing the interstage as a combination of a number of positive and negative impedances. Each impedance includes a parallel capacity, so that it is subject to the resistance integral condition (13–7). The gain limitations are established from a study of these conditions. It is convenient for purposes of analysis to suppose that the interstage is represented by its equivalent π of branches Z_1, Z_2, and Z_3, as shown by Fig. 17.31. Since Z_1 is not necessarily equal to Z_3 the interstage itself need not be symmetrical. The terminating capacities $C/2$ are, however, assumed to be the same at grid and plate terminals.

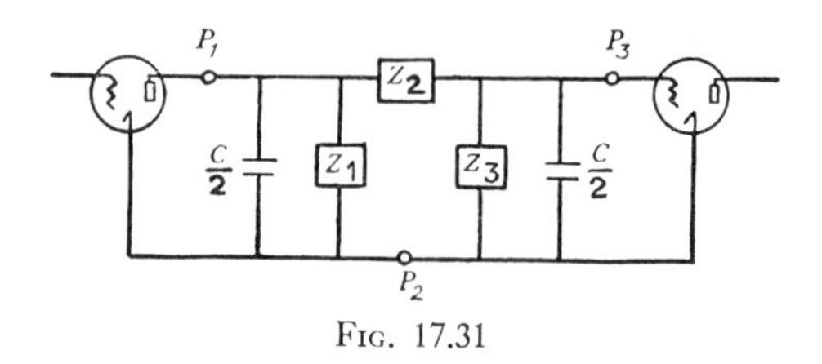

FIG. 17.31

It will be supposed that departures from this condition are treated by the methods described in connection with Fig. 17.24. Since the unsymmetrical π may include an ideal transformer of any ratio there is no loss of generality in making this assumption.

The gain can conveniently be expressed in terms of the transfer impedance, $Z_T = R_T + iX_T$, representing the voltage at the grid terminals per unit current in the plate circuit. We readily find

$$Z_T = \frac{Z_1'Z_3'}{Z_1' + Z_2 + Z_3'}, \tag{17–20}$$

where Z_1' and Z_3' are written for brevity to represent the parallel combination of Z_1 and Z_3, respectively, with the terminating capacities $C/2$. Equation (17–20) can be rewritten as

$$Z_T = \frac{1}{2}\left[\frac{Z_1'(Z_2 + Z_3')}{Z_1' + Z_2 + Z_3'} + \frac{Z_3'(Z_1' + Z_2)}{Z_1' + Z_2 + Z_3'} - \frac{Z_2(Z_1' + Z_3')}{Z_1' + Z_2 + Z_3'}\right]$$

$$= \frac{1}{2}[Z_A + Z_B - Z_C], \tag{17–21}$$

where Z_A, Z_B, and Z_C represent the corresponding terms in the first expression. We observe that these three quantities are all physical impedances which can be determined by external measurements on the network. For example, Z_A is the impedance which would be measured between terminals P_1 and P_2, and Z_C that which would be measured between P_1 and P_3 in Fig. 17.31. The transfer impedance can consequently be represented physically in the form shown by Fig. 17.32 where the successive impedances correspond to the successive terms in (17–21). It is to be noticed that each constituent impedance includes a parallel capacity and is therefore subject to the resistance integral limitation on its real component. In order to utilize these conditions, attention will be directed primarily at the real components so that (17–21) can be reduced to the simpler form

$$R_T = \tfrac{1}{2}(R_A + R_B - R_C). \tag{17–22}$$

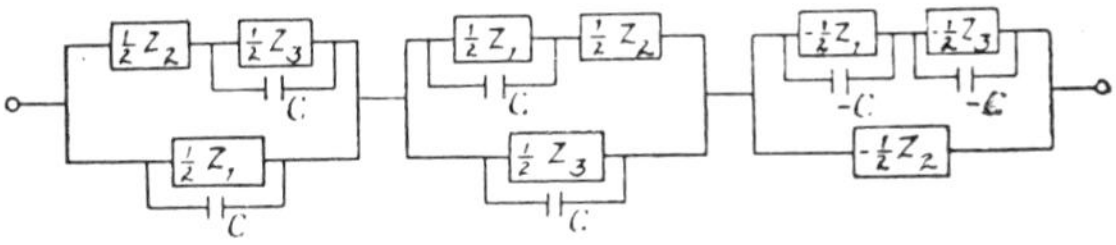

FIG. 17.32

17.10. *Four-Terminal Interstages with Restricted Phase Characteristics*

It is convenient to begin the analysis by showing that the gain advantage of the four-terminal over the two-terminal interstage can be realized only if the phase shift of the four-terminal structure is permitted to be more than 90°, or, in other words, more than the maximum obtainable from a two-terminal structure, over at least a portion of the frequency spectrum. Let it be supposed, on the contrary, that the maximum phase shift of the four-terminal network is limited to 90°. If we begin with any relative gain and phase curves for the interstage, subject to this restriction, we can immediately construct from them a curve of the corresponding R_T. With the given phase limitation the curve will, of course, always be positive while the scale upon which it is drawn will depend upon the assumed absolute level of gain. But if the phase shift is to be only 90° at high frequencies the gain must decrease at a rate of 6 db per octave or Z_T, in other words, must vary as $1/ik\omega$. The relation between the constant k and the area under the R_T characteristic in this situation is evidently exactly the same as the relation between the limiting capacity and the resistance integral in an actual two-terminal impedance. If we can find the minimum possible value for k, therefore, the area relation will show the scale upon which the R_T characteristic should be drawn, and from this the maximum permissible absolute level of gain can be deduced. Clearly, the absolute level of gain for the four-terminal structure will be greater than that of a two-terminal interstage having the same relative gain and phase characteristics only if we can assign k a value smaller than C.

If Z_A, Z_B, and Z_C in (17–21) include only the capacity paths shown explicitly in Fig. 17.32 the positive and negative resistance areas will cancel. In order to secure a net positive area under the R_T characteristic, therefore, it is necessary to assume that the interstage circuit proper will include capacity paths to supplement the paths furnished by the external parasitic capacities. This situation can be examined by supposing that the interstage proper can be represented at infinite frequency by an equivalent π of capacities C_1, C_2, and C_3 as shown by Fig. 17.33.* The corresponding expression for Z_T is

$$\lim_{\omega \doteq \infty} Z_T = \frac{1}{i\omega} \frac{4C_2}{C^2 + 2(C_1 + 2C_2 + C_3)C + 4(C_1C_2 + C_1C_3 + C_2C_3)}. \tag{17-23}$$

The fact that the actual interstage must be physically realizable does not necessarily mean that C_1, C_2, and C_3 in the equivalent π must all be positive. It is obvious, however, that the C's must be so related that a positive capacity will result from any external measurement on the circuit. Thus $C_1 + C_2$, $C_1 + C_3$, and $C_2 + C_3$ must all be positive since each is the capacity appearing between two of the external terminals when the odd terminal is short-circuited to one of these two. If, in addition, we make use of the fact that the measured capacity must also be positive when no connection is made to the odd terminal, it is a simple matter to show that the C's must satisfy the requirement

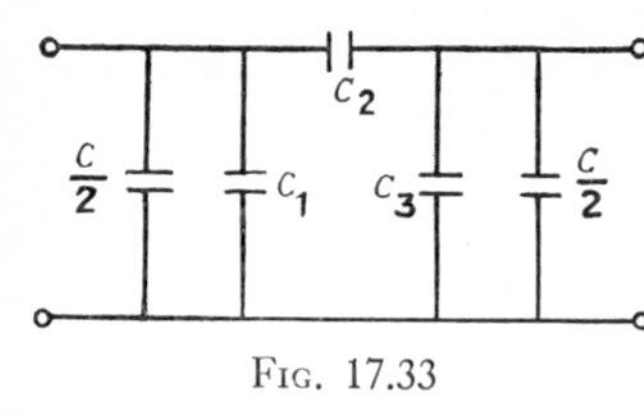

FIG. 17.33

$$C_1C_2 + C_1C_3 + C_2C_3 \geq 0. \tag{17-24}$$

It is easily demonstrated from these conditions that Z_T in (17–23) is not greater than $1/i\omega C$ and reaches this limit only when $C_2 = \infty$ and $C_1 = C_3 = 0$. We therefore have immediately the

Theorem: The absolute level of gain, over any given band, of a four-terminal interstage terminated in prescribed equal capacities at each end cannot be greater than that of a corresponding two-terminal interstage unless the phase shift of the four-terminal structure is greater than 90° over at least a part of the frequency spectrum.

* It is not inevitably true that the branches of the π must reduce to capacities at infinite frequency if a finite resistance area is to be secured, especially when account is taken of the possibilities afforded by interstages including ideal transformers. In general, we must assume that the branches may behave at infinite frequency as $A_1\omega^n$, $A_2\omega^n$, and $A_3\omega^n$, where, since the individual branches of the π need not themselves be physical impedances, n may be zero, one, or any negative integer. If the interstage as a whole is to be physically realizable, however, the branches of the equivalent structure must be so related that a physical impedance is obtained by any external measurement. This means that A_1, A_2, and A_3 must satisfy a relation of the form (17–24), where only the equality sign is permitted unless $n = 0$ or ± 1. With the help of these conditions it can be shown that the result established in the text for a capacity π holds also in the general case. The details of the analysis, however, are omitted for the sake of brevity.

The conditions $C_2 = \infty$ and $C_1 = C_3 = 0$ which give the maximum gain in the four-terminal case are evidently those which apply when the structure degenerates physically into a two-terminal network.

The restriction that the phase shift should not exceed 90° can be looked upon in either of two ways. At high frequencies it implies that the gain decreases at 6, rather than perhaps 12 or 18, db per octave. In a feedback amplifier, interstage phase shifts greater than 90° at high frequencies are usually fatal if any very large amount of feedback is to be obtained. A phase shift greater than 90° over a limited low-frequency region, on the other hand, may not be serious. It should be noticed, however, that if a two-terminal and a four-terminal interstage have the same gain and phase characteristics at high frequencies they must have the same total gain area at lower frequencies. Thus the absence of a low-frequency phase restriction on the four-terminal structure merely means that its gain can change more sharply, and therefore the given total gain area can be distributed more flexibly, than is possible with a two-terminal network. In a multistage amplifier, however, this additional flexibility should be important only in exceptional circumstances.

17.11. *General Limitations on the Gain of a Four-Terminal Interstage*

In view of these results it will be assumed hereafter that the four-terminal structure is to be designed to give the maximum possible gain, without regard to any limitation on its phase characteristic. This implies, of course, that the real component of Z_T will be positive in some frequency ranges and negative in others, as indicated by Fig. 17.34. Since the situation is now symmetrical, as between positive and negative resistances, we may expect that the optimum solution will be obtained if positive and negative areas are equal and are as large as possible. In other words, there will be no occasion, as there was in the previous discussion, to supplement the capacity paths shown explicitly in Fig. 17.32 by others in the interstage proper.

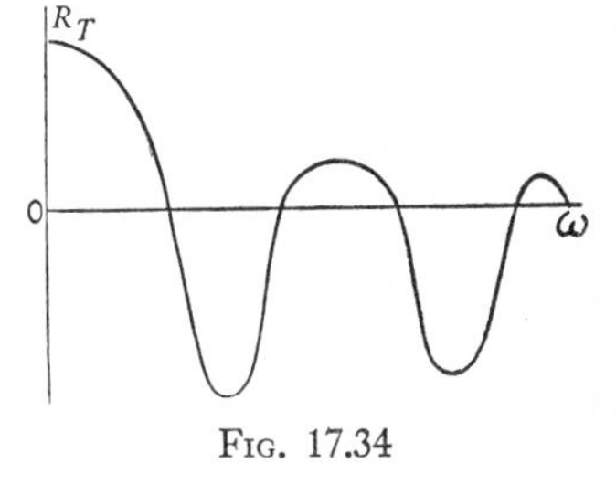

Fig. 17.34

Let it be assumed, as was done previously, that the shape of R_T in Fig. 17.34 has been determined from the relative gain and phase characteristics desired but that the scale of the characteristic remains to be fixed by the absolute level of gain. We cannot limit the absolute gain from a consideration of the resistance integral for R_T as a whole, since it follows from the statements made in the preceding paragraph that the net area under the characteristic can be expected to be zero in the optimum case. A limit can, however, be established from the resistance integral conditions applying separately to the positive and negative components $\frac{1}{2}(R_A + R_B)$ and $-\frac{1}{2}R_C$ of R_T in (17–22). For example, it is obviously not permissible to choose an absolute level of gain so high that the area under the positive parts of R_T exceeds the area under the curve for $\frac{1}{2}(R_A + R_B)$ alone.

In a network design chosen at random, it is to be expected that both $\frac{1}{2}(R_A + R_B)$ and $\frac{1}{2}R_C$ will be appreciable at most frequencies. Thus the two components will tend to cancel to some extent and the net area under the positive portions of the R_T characteristic alone, or under the negative portions, will be less than the integrals of $\frac{1}{2}(R_A + R_B)$ or $\frac{1}{2}R_C$ individually. This means, of course, that the absolute level of gain must be correspondingly reduced. For example, the broken line curves in Fig. 17.35

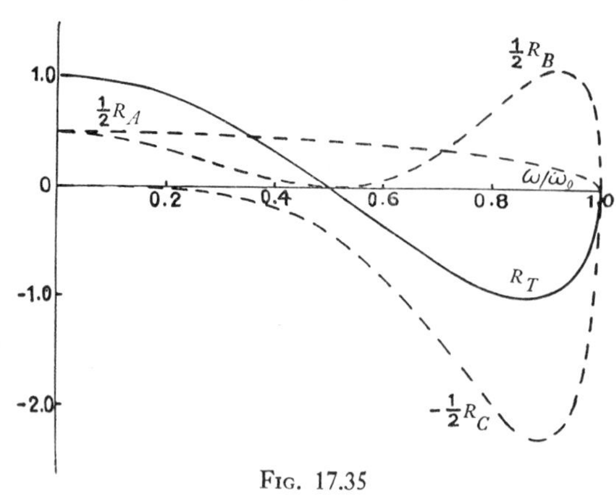

FIG. 17.35

show the several positive and negative resistance components for the particular network of Fig. 17.23 and the solid curve the net R_T which results.* This network meets the condition that it contains no high frequency paths to supplement those offered by the parasitic capacities, so that the area under the positive lobe of R_T, extending from $\omega = 0$ to $\omega = 0.5\omega_0$, is equal to the area under the negative lobe, extending from $\omega = 0.5\omega_0$ to $\omega = \omega_0$. We observe, however, that the component characteristics cancel out to such an extent that either area is only about 40 per cent of the areas associated with the characteristics for $\frac{1}{2}(R_A + R_B)$ and $\frac{1}{2}R_C$ individually. The fact that such cancellations may occur, and to a varying extent in different designs, explains why it is possible to have four-terminal interstages including the same parasitic capacities and with the same relative gain and phase characteristics but with different absolute levels of gain.

* The unit of impedance in Fig. 17.35, and in the corresponding Figs. 17.36, 17.38 and 17.39 given subsequently, is taken as $4/\omega_0 C$ ohms.

It is obvious that the maximum possible gain level would be obtained ideally if R_C were zero in frequency ranges for which R_T is positive and $R_A + R_B$ were zero when R_T is negative, so that no cancellations could occur. This relation, unfortunately, cannot be achieved if the interstage network is to be physically realizable. We can, however, determine what the minimum amount of cancellation must be. The condition that the interstage be physically realizable is*

$$R_A R_B - R_T^2 \geq 0 \tag{17–25}$$

or

$$\sqrt{R_A R_B} = |R_T| + \delta_1, \tag{17–26}$$

where δ_1 is positive or zero. This condition can be combined with (17–22), which is conveniently rewritten as

$$R_T = \sqrt{R_A R_B} - \tfrac{1}{2}R_C + \delta_2, \tag{17–27}$$

where $\delta_2 = \frac{1}{2}(\sqrt{R_A} - \sqrt{R_B})^2$ and is also either positive or zero. If R_T is negative the two equations give

$$2R_T = -\tfrac{1}{2}R_C + \delta_1 + \delta_2, \tag{17–28}$$

while if R_T is positive we have

$$\tfrac{1}{2}R_C = \delta_1 + \delta_2. \tag{17–29}$$

The optimum condition is readily determined from these expressions. It occurs when $\delta_1 = \delta_2 = 0$, which means that the network is symmetrical and just meets the requirement of physical realizability given by (17–26). With these δ's we have $R_C = 0$ when R_T is positive so that the complete integral for $\frac{1}{2}R_C$ is concentrated into frequency ranges in which R_T is negative. But R_T in these ranges is only half as great as $\frac{1}{2}R_C$, so that half of the integral for $\frac{1}{2}(R_A + R_B)$ must also be found here in order to supply the proper cancellation. The remaining half of the integral for $\frac{1}{2}(R_A + R_B)$, of course, supplies the R_T characteristic in the frequency ranges for which it is positive. These relations are illustrated by Fig. 17.36, which shows the positive and negative components which would correspond to the R_T characteristic of Fig. 17.35 in the ideal case. Only the total positive component, $\frac{1}{2}(R_A + R_B)$, is drawn, since if the network is to be symmetrical we must, of course, have $R_A = R_B$.

* Adapted from the conditions given by Gewertz, "Network Synthesis," Part III. The requirement is fundamentally similar to that established for a capacity network in (17–24). It can be deduced by studying under what conditions the input resistance of the network will remain positive when a pure reactance of arbitrary magnitude and sign is connected to the output terminals.

Since the capacities which limit Z_A, Z_B, and Z_C are known, these conclusions can be translated into quantitative terms. The general result appears as the

Theorem: The areas under either the positive or the negative portions of the real component of the transfer impedance of a four-terminal interstage network terminated in equal capacities at both ends cannot exceed the resistance integral associated with the sum of the terminating capacities. The limit is attained if and only if the network is externally symmetrical and its self and transfer resistances are in the limiting relation for physical realizability.

The fact that the optimum network must be symmetrical makes it possible to replace our preceding equation (17–21) for Z_T by a somewhat

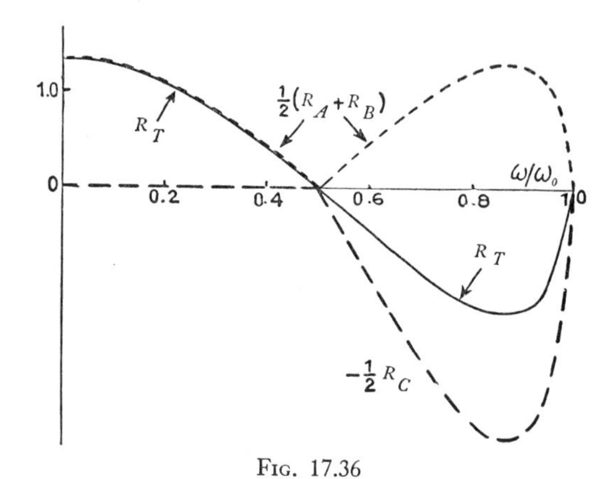

FIG. 17.36

simpler expression in which the necessary minimum of cancellation between positive and negative resistance areas is taken into account automatically. If we set $Z_1' = Z_3'$ in (17–20) we readily find that the equation can be rewritten as

$$Z_T = \frac{Z_1'^2}{2Z_1' + Z_2}$$

$$= \tfrac{1}{2}Z_1' - \tfrac{1}{2}\frac{Z_1'Z_2}{2Z_1' + Z_2}$$

$$= \tfrac{1}{2}Z_1' - \tfrac{1}{4}Z_C, \tag{17–30}$$

where the symbols have their previous significance. The expression represents the combination of positive and negative impedances shown by

Fig. 17.37. In comparison with the corresponding combination for the general case, shown earlier by Fig. 17.32, we notice that the limiting capacities for the positive and negative component impedances are just twice what they were before.

On the other hand, the positive and negative components can now be regarded as entirely independent impedances. It will be recalled that the positive and negative components in Fig. 17.32 could be determined by various external measurements on the network. In particular the negative component was a multiple of the impedance appearing between terminals P_1 and P_3 in the general circuit of Fig. 17.31. This measurement still applies in Fig. 17.37, since the negative component appearing there differs from the earlier one only by a constant factor. The two positive components $\frac{1}{2}Z_A$ and $\frac{1}{2}Z_B$ in Fig. 17.32 have, however, been replaced by the single impedance $\frac{1}{2}Z_1'$. To determine the new positive component we must

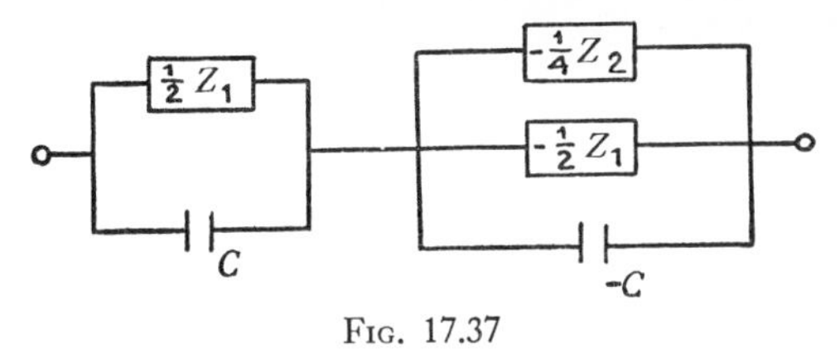

FIG. 17.37

substitute for the measurements used earlier a measurement between terminal P_2 in Fig. 17.31 and terminals P_1 and P_3 strapped together.

With this change the measurements which determine the positive and negative components become exactly the same as those used to find the branches of the equivalent lattice of a general unbalanced symmetrical structure in Fig. 12.18 of Chapter XII. The components are thus merely multiples of the branches of the equivalent lattice. We can suppose that they are chosen quite independently and that the various network relations described in Chapter XII will be used to go from them to a suitable physical configuration for the final interstage. This makes it unnecessary to suppose that there is any overlapping or cancellation of the positive and negative resistance characteristics. The optimum result is attained if we postulate that the positive parts of the R_T characteristic are due entirely to the positive component impedance and vice versa. The fact that a cancellation of at least 50 per cent was found to be necessary in the analysis of the general case is accounted for by the fact that the capacities limiting the component impedances are twice as large as they were previously, so that the resistance integrals are correspondingly reduced.

Since the absolute level of gain is finally limited by the positive and negative resistance integral conditions it is natural to suppose that maximum gain in any given region will be obtained if $R_T = 0$ outside that range so that, as in the two-terminal case, the resistance areas are concentrated entirely in the useful band. If we make this assumption the design procedure for a four-terminal interstage having any given relative gain characteristic in the useful range can be reduced to definite form. We begin by writing specific formulae for the gain and phase characteristics of the interstage. Such formulae can be constructed by multiplying the gain and phase characteristics of an appropriately chosen two-terminal interstage of maximum gain type by n, where n is any odd integer greater than one.* The R_T characteristic is next obtained and the scale of the drawing, which determines the absolute level of gain, is adjusted until the positive and negative parts of the characteristic by themselves satisfy the required integral conditions. The reactances which correspond to the positive and negative component resistances, taken separately, may then be determined. This fixes the branch impedances of the equivalent lattice of the final structure and a suitable actual configuration may be found by using the various equivalence relations described in Chapter XII. An example is given in the next section.

17.12. *Illustrative Design of a Four-Terminal Interstage*

The analysis just concluded will be illustrated by a discussion of the problem of designing a four-terminal interstage having the maximum possible constant gain over a prescribed band. We begin by constructing a formula for the gain and phase characteristics by multiplying the gain and phase of a constant gain two-terminal interstage by the odd integer n. This leads to

$$\alpha + i\beta = \log Z_T = \log K - n \log \left[\sqrt{1 - \frac{\omega^2}{\omega_0^2}} + i \frac{\omega}{\omega_0} \right] \cdot \qquad (17\text{–}31)$$

When $n = 3$ this is evidently the same, except perhaps for the absolute level of gain, as the expression given in (17–19).

The R_T characteristic defined by (17–31) follows a curve of the form shown by Fig. 17.38. The number of loops depends, of course, upon n but it is readily shown that the areas in the positive and negative loops will be equal for any permissible n. The problem to be solved is that of adjusting the factor K so that either the positive or negative areas will satisfy the resistance integral condition. If we substitute $\phi = \sin^{-1} \omega/\omega_0$ the curve in Fig. 17.38 becomes $R_T = K \cos n\phi$ and the equation for the integral of

* This choice of n is made because it leads to an R_T characteristic which has equal positive and negative areas and is zero outside the band.

the positive component, say, is

$$\int_0^{\pi/2} (+R) \cos\phi\, d\phi = K\left[\int_0^{\pi/2n} \cos n\phi \cos\phi\, d\phi + \int_{3\pi/2n}^{5\pi/2n} \cos n\phi \cos\phi\, d\phi + \cdots + \int_{(n-2)\pi/2n}^{\pi/2} \cos n\phi \cos\phi\, d\phi\right]$$

$$= \frac{\pi}{2\omega_0 C}. \tag{17–32}$$

The ω_0 in the right-hand side and the factor $\cos\phi$ in each integrand are introduced to take account of the fact that the resistance integral condition applies to an integration in terms of ω rather than ϕ.

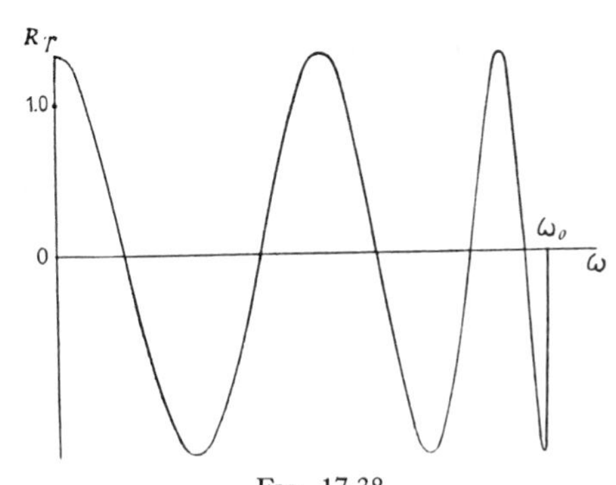

FIG. 17.38

Equation (17–32) can be integrated directly to give

$$\frac{nK}{n^2-1}\left[\cos\frac{\pi}{2n} + \cos\frac{3\pi}{2n} + \cos\frac{5\pi}{2n} + \cdots + \cos\frac{(n-2)\pi}{2n}\right] = \frac{\pi}{2\omega_0 C}. \tag{17–33}$$

But the trigonometric series is known* to be equal to $\frac{1}{2}\cot(\pi/2n)$. The formula for K consequently becomes

$$K = \left[2\frac{n^2-1}{n}\tan\frac{\pi}{2n}\right]\frac{\pi}{2\omega_0 C}. \tag{17–34}$$

The quantity in the brackets reaches its maximum value π when $n = \infty$. The limit on the maximum constant gain obtainable from the structure is

* Knopp, "Theorie und Anwendung der Unendlichen Reihen," p. 345.

therefore given by the

Theorem: The maximum transfer impedance which can be realized over a given band by a symmetrical four-terminal interstage network terminated at each end in the capacity $C/2$ is not greater than $\pi^2/2$ times the impedance of C for the given band.

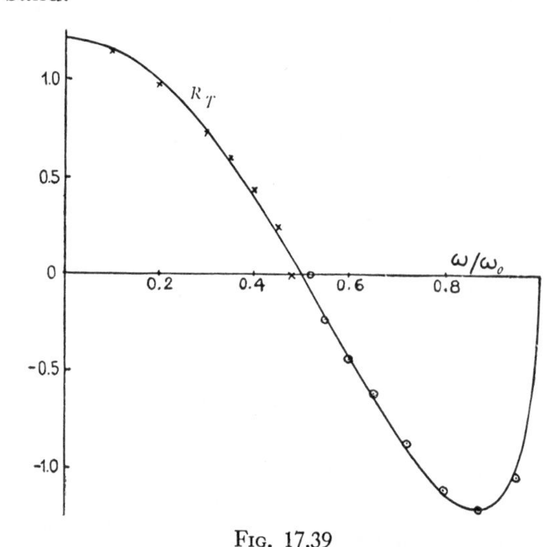

FIG. 17.39

This limit is about 8 db higher than the maximum gain obtainable from a two-terminal interstage, or about 2 db higher than the gain realized from the structure of Fig. 17.23.

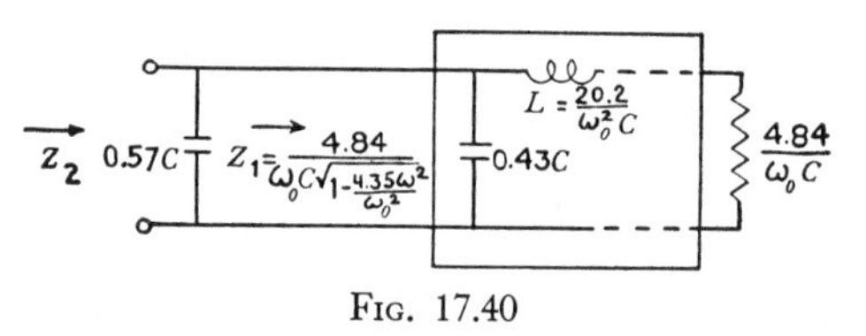

FIG. 17.40

If we approach the theoretical limit extremely closely, by making n very large, the positive and negative parts of the R_T characteristic will consist of a large number of disconnected segments and the corresponding networks must evidently be extraordinarily complicated. There is almost no penalty, however, in choosing $n = 3$, the smallest permissible value, since even with this n the bracketed quantity in (17–34) is 3.08, or only 0.2 db below the maximum. With this choice, the R_T characteristic takes the same form as that shown previously in Figs. 17.35 and 17.36. It is reproduced here to the proper scale in Fig. 17.39.

The positive resistance component is defined as the R_T characteristic from the origin to its intersection with the zero axis and as the zero axis thereafter. The curve is roughly filter-like in its characteristics and as an initial step in simulating it we may therefore construct the mid-shunt terminated low-pass filter, with cut-off near the point $\omega = 0.5\omega_0$ at which the positive characteristic reaches zero, shown by the box in Fig. 17.40. This

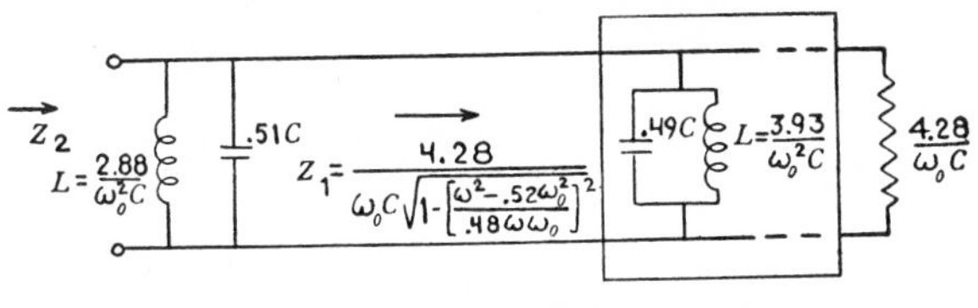

Fig. 17.41

structure includes the capacity $0.43C$ as its final shunt branch. Since the total parallel capacity for each component impedance in Fig. 17.37 is C, it is necessary to add an additional capacity $0.57C$ to the network. Without further modification this leads to the match to the positive resistance characteristic indicated by the crosses in Fig. 17.39.

The negative resistance component is equal to zero from the origin to $\omega = 0.5\omega_0$ and follows the R_T characteristic thereafter. It can be treated in much the same way. As the fundamental unit we take a mid-shunt terminated band-pass structure transmitting the band extending from roughly $\omega = 0.5\omega_0$ to $\omega = \omega_0$. This is shown by the box in Fig. 17.41.

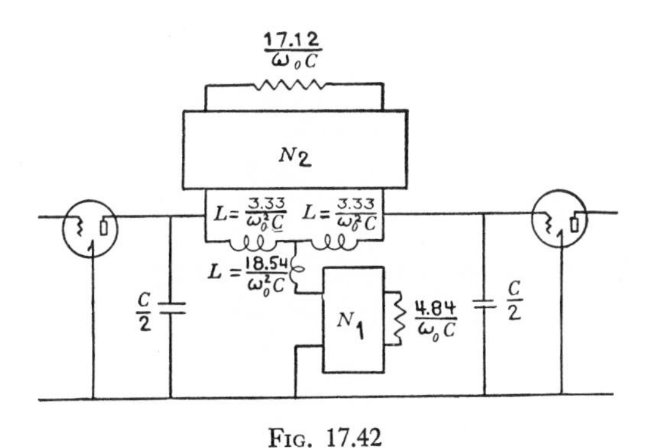

Fig. 17.42

The nominal image impedance is displaced slightly from the theoretical value, $4.84/\omega_0 C$, to make the actual image impedance correct at the peak of the negative resistance characteristic. The filter includes the capacity $0.49C$. To complete the network the required additional capacity, $0.51C$, is introduced and a tuning coil is added to place the resistance peak at the correct frequency. The match to the theoretical characteristic is indicated by the circles in Fig. 17.39.

In accordance with the discussion given in connection with equation (17–30), the networks of Figs. 17.40 and 17.41 have impedances which are half as great as those of the branches of the equivalent lattice of the complete circuit. To find the final structure we may begin by removing the parallel capacities, using the equivalence shown by Fig. 12.22 of Chapter XII. The remainder can be converted to a bridged-T by means of the equivalence described in connection with Fig. 12.26 of the same chapter. This leads to the circuit shown by Fig. 17.42. The network N_1 is equal to the structure of Fig. 17.40 after all the elements shown explicitly in Fig. 17.40 are removed and the network N_2 is equal to the structure of Fig. 17.41, but at a four times greater impedance level, under the same conditions. The final gain and phase characteristics, with the reference gain taken as $\log 1/\omega_0 C$, are shown in Fig. 17.43. The ripple

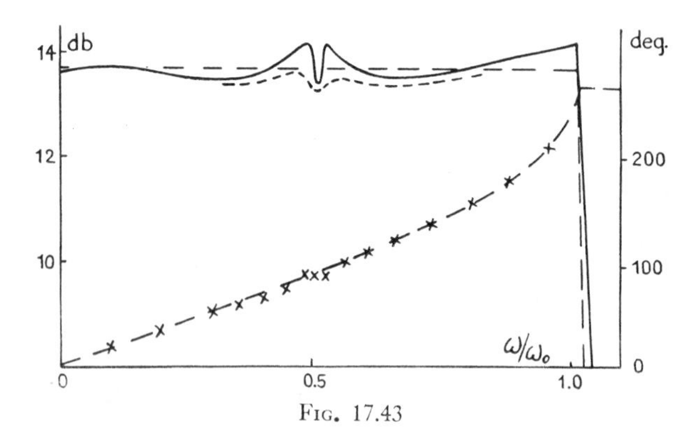

FIG. 17.43

in the center of the band is due to the fact that the filter circuits are too selective to follow the characteristics of Fig. 17.39 in this region. It can be reduced either by using simplified filters with imperfect selectivity or by adding traces of dissipation to the structures. The broken lines in Fig. 17.43 show the effect obtained if we suppose that the filters as they stand have a Q of 100.

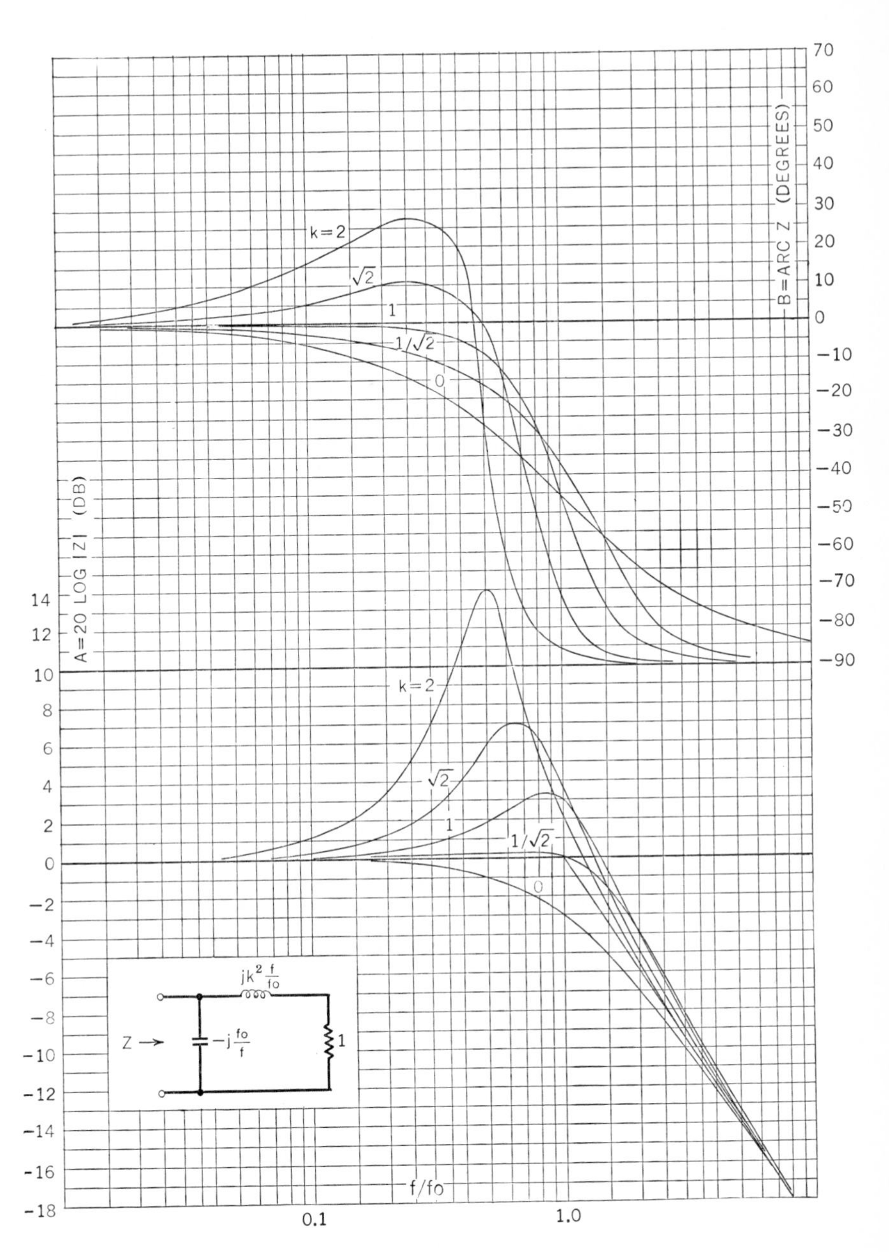

70
60
50
40
30
20
10
0
−10
−20
−30
−40
−50
−60
−70
−80
−90
B = ARC Z (DEGREES)
k=2
√2
1
1/√2
0
A = 20 LOG |Z| (DB)
14
12
10
8
6
4
2
0
−2
−4
−6
−8
−10
−12
−14
−16
−18
k=2
√2
1
1/√2
0
jk² f/fo
Z →
−j fo/f
1
f/fo
0.1
1.0

CHART 1

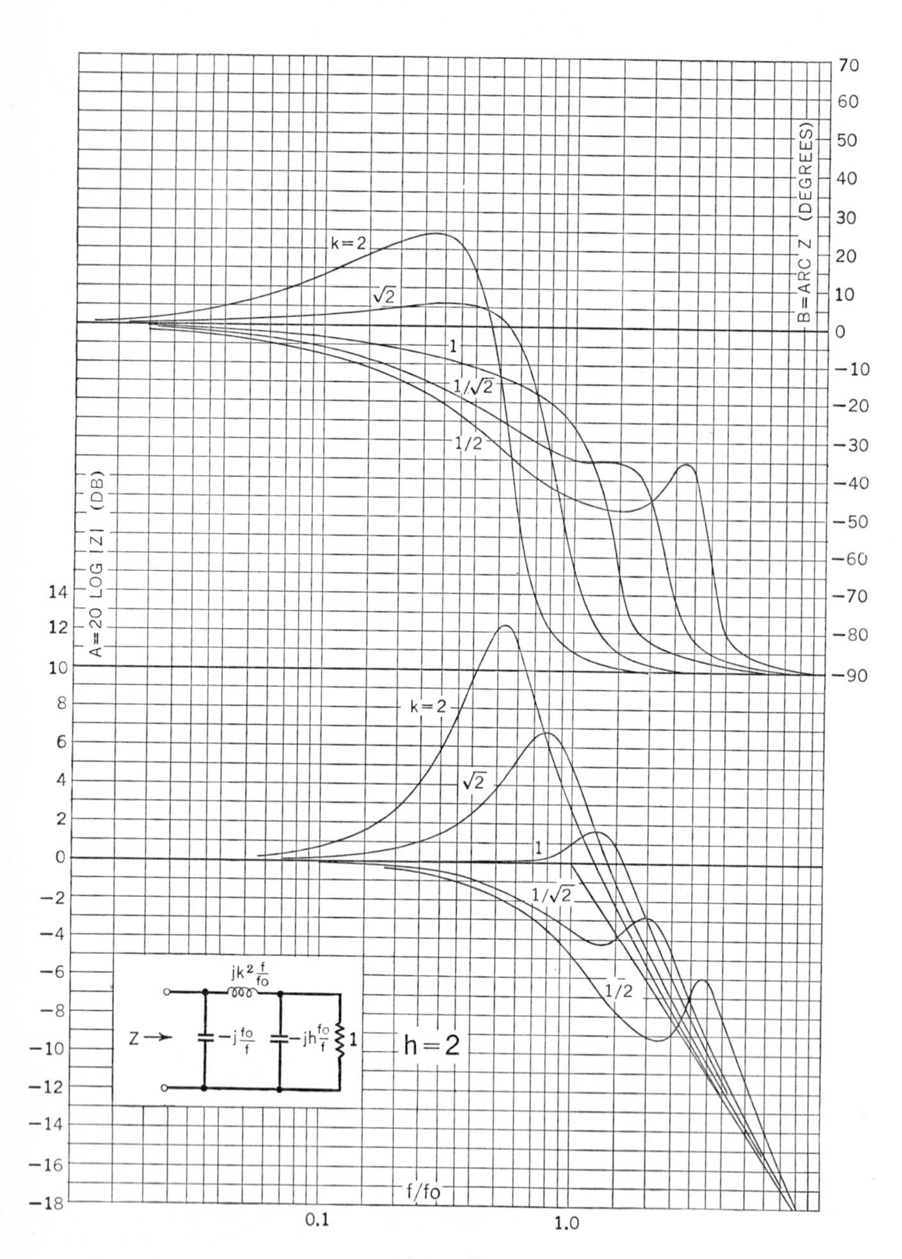
B = ARC Z (DEGREES)
A = 20 LOG |Z| (DB)
k=2
√2
1
1/√2
1/2
h=2
f/fo
0.1
1.0
70
60
50
40
30
20
10
0
−10
−20
−30
−40
−50
−60
−70
−80
−90
14
12
10
8
6
4
2
0
−2
−4
−6
−8
−10
−12
−14
−16
−18

Chart 2

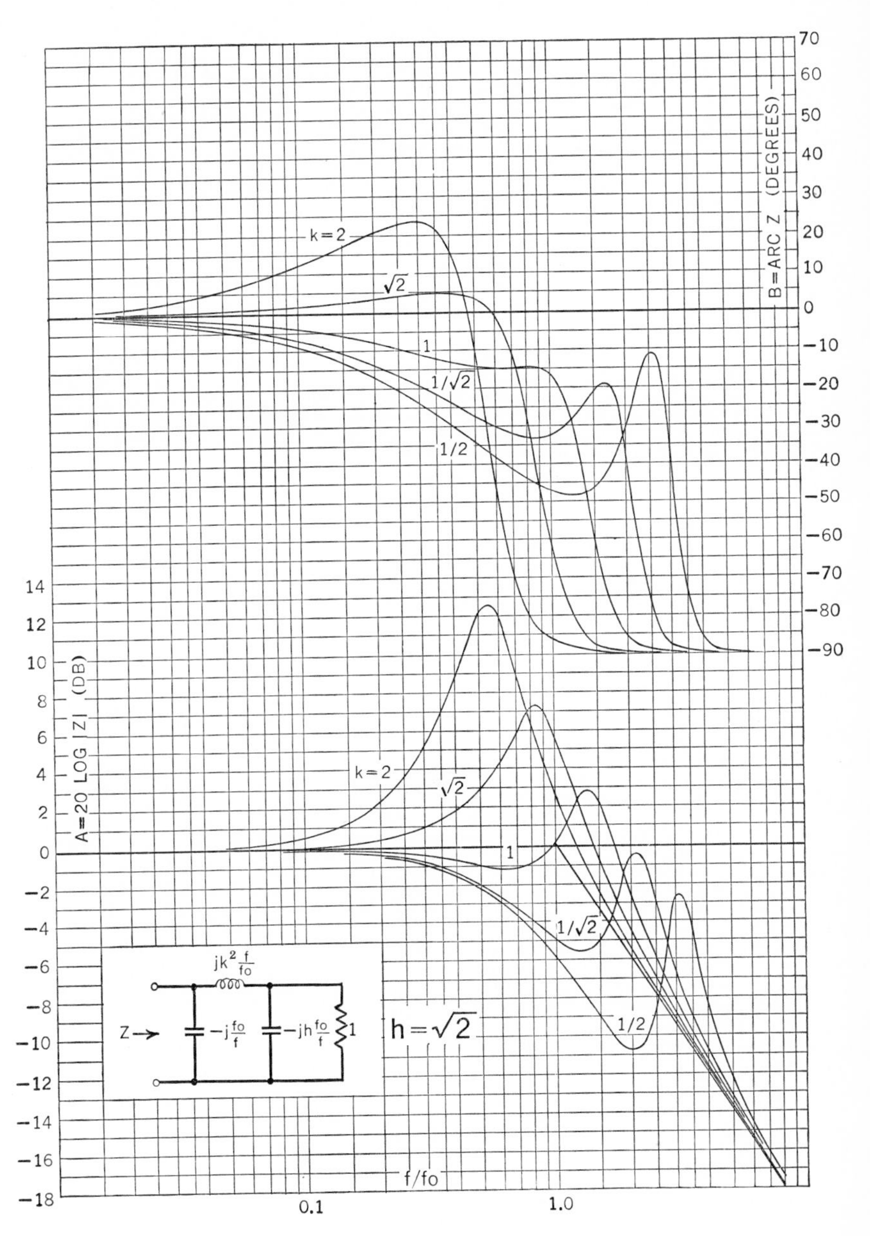

70
60
50
40
30
20
10
0
−10
−20
−30
−40
−50
−60
−70
−80
−90
B = ARC Z (DEGREES)
k = 2
√2
1
1/√2
1/2
14
12
10
8
6
4
2
0
−2
−4
−6
−8
−10
−12
−14
−16
−18
A = 20 LOG |Z| (DB)
k = 2
√2
1
1/√2
1/2
$jk^2\frac{f}{f_0}$
Z→
$-j\frac{f_0}{f}$
$-jh\frac{f_0}{f}$
1
h = √2
f/fo
0.1
1.0

CHART 3

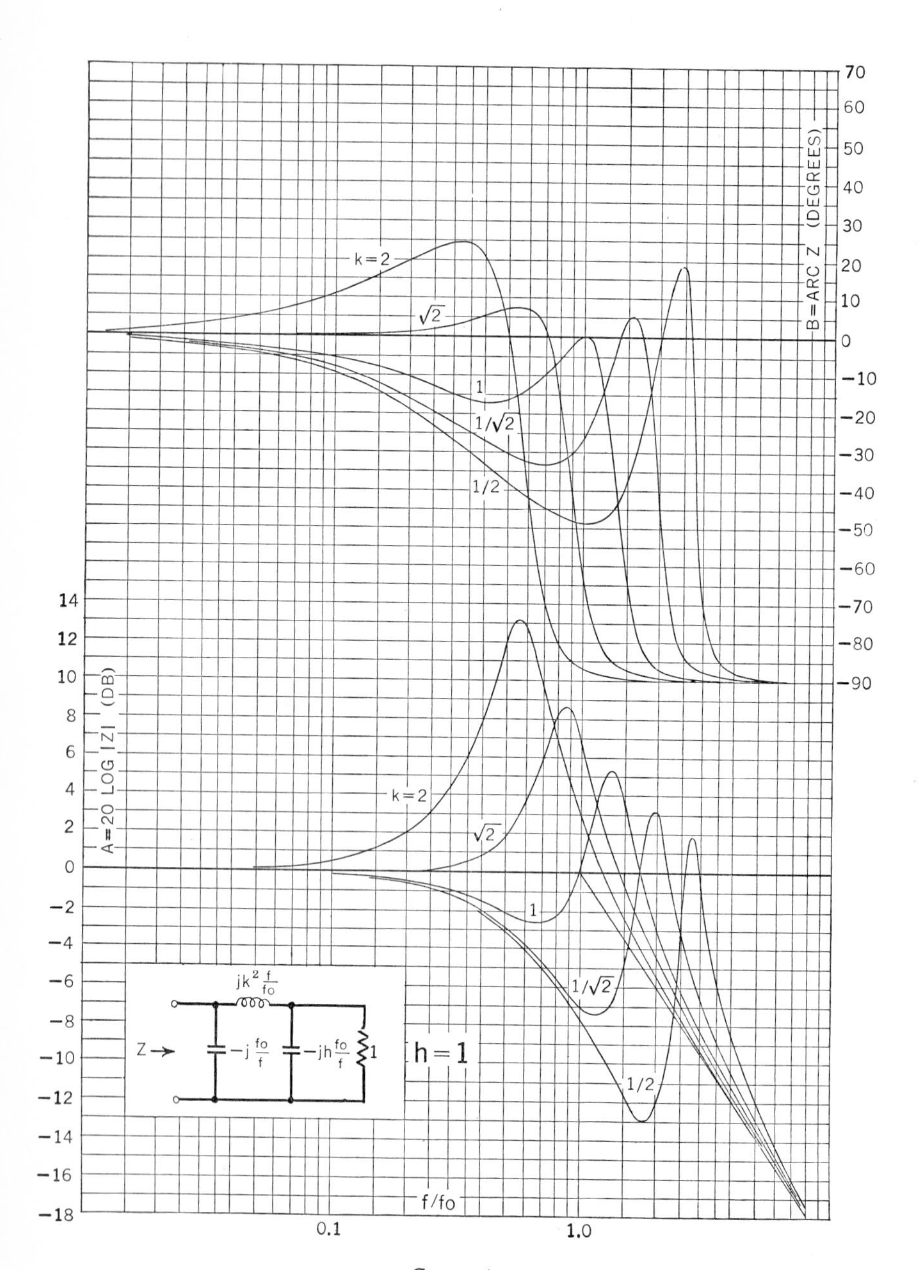
70
60
50
40
30
20
10
0
−10
−20
−30
−40
−50
−60
−70
−80
−90
B = ARC Z (DEGREES)
k=2
√2
1
1/√2
1/2
14
12
10
8
6
4
2
0
−2
−4
−6
−8
−10
−12
−14
−16
−18
A = 20 LOG |Z| (DB)
k=2
√2
1
1/√2
1/2
Z →
jk² f/fo
−j fo/f
−jh fo/f
1
h=1
f/fo
0.1
1.0

CHART 4

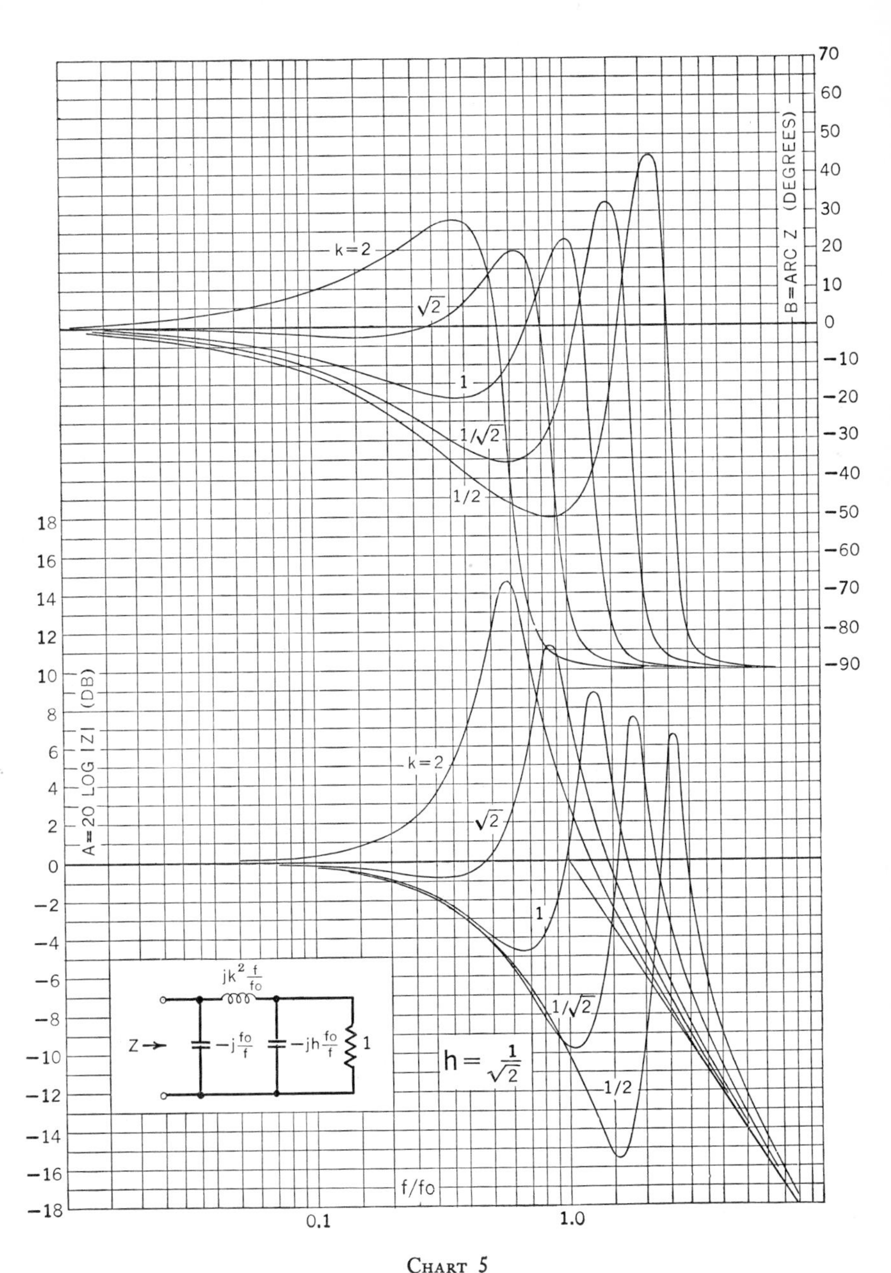
B = ARC Z (DEGREES)
70
60
50
40
30
20
10
0
−10
−20
−30
−40
−50
−60
−70
−80
−90
k=2
√2
1
1/√2
1/2
A = 20 LOG |Z| (DB)
18
16
14
12
10
8
6
4
2
0
−2
−4
−6
−8
−10
−12
−14
−16
−18
k=2
√2
1
1/√2
1/2
jk² f/fo
Z →
−j fo/f
−jh fo/f
1
h = 1/√2
f/fo
0.1
1.0

CHART 5

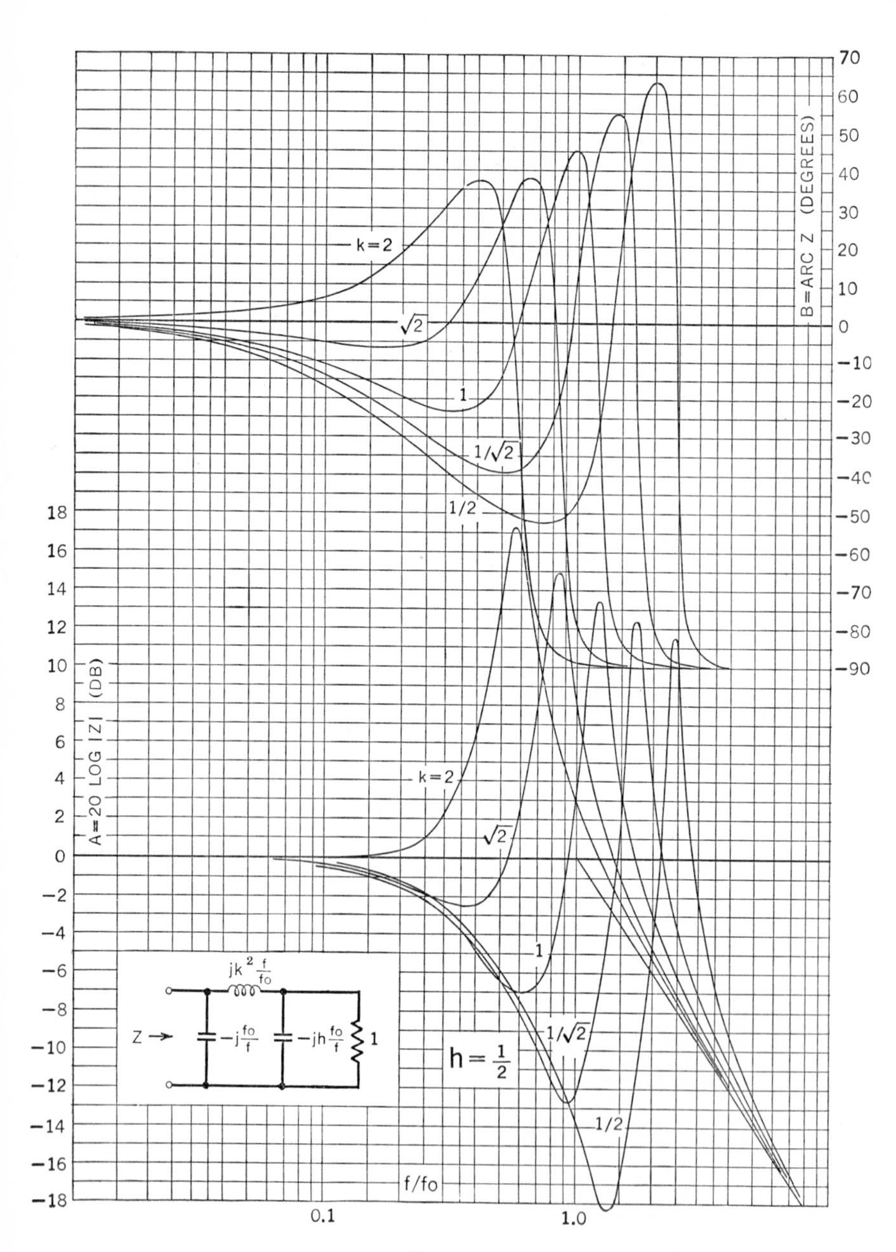
70
60
50
40
30
20
10
0
−10
−20
−30
−40
−50
−60
−70
−80
−90
B = ARC Z (DEGREES)
k = 2
√2
1
1/√2
1/2
18
16
14
12
10
8
6
4
2
0
−2
−4
−6
−8
−10
−12
−14
−16
−18
A = 20 LOG |Z| (DB)
k = 2
√2
1
1/√2
1/2
jk² f/fo
Z →
−j fo/f
−jh fo/f
1
h = 1/2
f/fo
0.1
1.0

CHART 6

CHAPTER XVIII

DESIGN OF SINGLE LOOP ABSOLUTELY STABLE AMPLIFIERS*

18.1. *Introduction*

IN the preceding two chapters attention has been centered on the design of particular parts of a feedback amplifier. From this point on, however, we will be concerned primarily with the overall design of the complete structure. Attention will be directed particularly to single loop, absolutely stable amplifiers, which are those most commonly encountered in contemporary design practice. Design examples for the theory developed in this chapter have been segregated and are presented in the chapter which follows. The chapter includes references, however, to permit the reader to turn to pertinent examples immediately if he so desires.

The restriction to single loop amplifiers means physically that the tubes are unilateral elements connected directly in tandem, as they are in the usual μ circuit. For the sake of later discussion, its precise meaning will be understood to be that given by the

Definition: A single loop amplifier is one in which the return difference of any tube is equal to unity if the gain of any other tube in the circuit vanishes.

This is evidently equivalent to saying that the transconductances of the various tubes can enter the circuit determinant only as the product $G_{m_1}G_{m_2}\cdots G_{m_n}$. It implies both that the tubes must be directly in tandem, as stated, and that the return differences for all tubes under operating conditions are the same.

It should be noticed that the definition excludes amplifiers in which there is local feedback on one or more of the tubes produced by an impedance in the cathode circuit, parasitic grid-plate capacity, or some similar instrumentality. For engineering purposes this restriction is somewhat too rigorous since many such circuits can be analyzed successfully as single loop structures merely by taking account of the modifications in the forward circuit gain which the local feedback produces. As a more comprehensive analysis would show, however, the stability of such a circuit is sometimes

* See also the author's paper in the *B. S. T. J.* for July, 1940, or U. S. Pat. No. 2,123,178.

much affected by the relative rates at which tube gains decay with age, or the relative rates at which they increase as the tubes warm up when power is first applied to the circuit, so that the assumption that the structure can be analyzed as a single loop amplifier, without qualification, is treacherous.

On the other hand, the definition includes as single loop amplifiers structures having any number of distinct paths for the return of voltage from the plate of the output tube to the grid of the input tube. An example is furnished by one of the illustrative designs described in the next chapter. The structure has one μ circuit and two β circuits as shown by Fig. 18.1. The distinction between the two β paths is of engineering importance, since only one is operative in the useful band and therefore has the external characteristics of the amplifier under its control. The other is added to improve the phase angle of the returned voltage at high frequencies. For the purposes of the present discussion, which is concerned primarily with the stability of the circuit, however, any number of such alternative paths can be combined and regarded as a single four-terminal network.

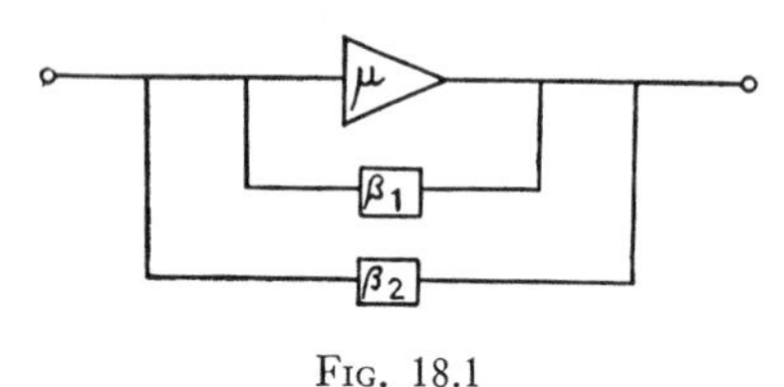

FIG. 18.1

The requirement that the structure be absolutely stable refers to the analysis developed in Chapter VIII. It will be recalled that the T plot of a typical amplifier fell into one of the three categories illustrated by Fig. 18.2.

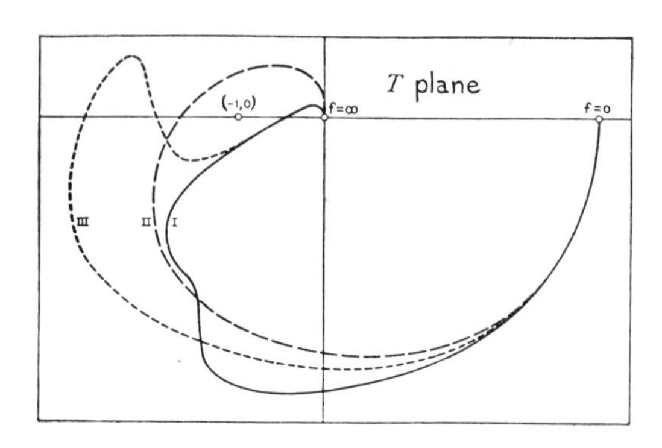

FIG. 18.2

If the path is like Curve II, which encircles the point $-1, 0$, the circuit is unstable. A stable amplifier is obtained if the path resembles either Curve I or Curve III, neither of which encircles $-1, 0$. The stability represented by Curve III, however, is only conditional since the path will enclose the critical point if it is merely reduced in scale. Thus the circuit may sing when the tubes begin to lose their gain because of age, and it may also sing, instead of behaving as it should, when the μ gain increases from zero as power is first applied to the circuit. In this chapter it will consequently be assumed that the amplifier is of the absolutely stable type represented by Curve I, and remains stable for any reduction in μ circuit gain.

The condition that the amplifier be absolutely stable is evidently that the loop phase shift should not exceed 180° until the gain around the loop has been reduced to zero or less. A theoretical characteristic which just met this requirement, however, would be unsatisfactory, since it is inevitable

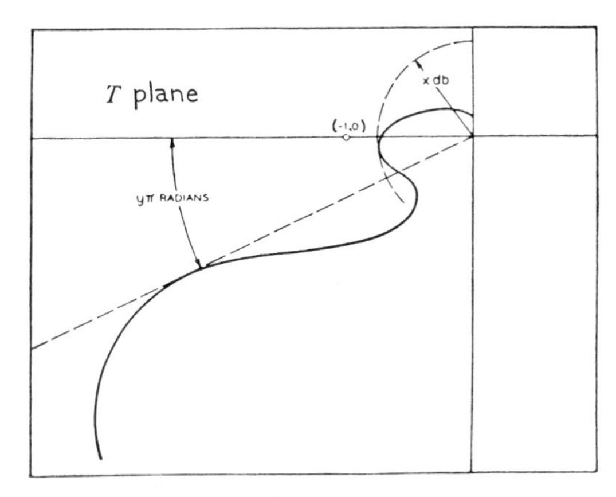

Fig. 18.3

that the limiting phase would be exceeded in fact by minor deviations introduced either in the detailed design of the amplifier or in its construction. It will therefore be assumed that the limiting phase is taken as 180° less some definite margin. This is illustrated by Fig. 18.3, the phase margin being indicated as $y\pi$ radians. At frequencies remote from the band it is physically impossible, in most circuits, to restrict the phase within these limits. As a supplement, therefore, it will be assumed that larger phase shifts are permissible if the loop gain is x db below zero. This is illustrated by the broken circular arc in Fig. 18.3. It is, of course, contemplated that the gain and phase margins x and y will be chosen arbitrarily in advance. If we choose large values we can permit correspondingly large tolerances in the detailed design and construction of the apparatus without risk of instability. It turns out, however, that with a prescribed width of cut-off interval the amount of feedback which can be realized in the useful range is decreased as the assumed margins are increased, so that it is generally desirable to choose as small margins as is safe.

It will be assumed throughout the chapter that the amplifier is of the low-pass type. The various transformations described in Chapter X, including in particular the theorem on conservation of band width, may be used to fit the results obtained to other situations. Examples requiring some of these modifications are given in the next chapter.

18.2. *Ideal Cut-off Characteristics*

The essential feature in the situation just discussed is the requirement that the gain around the feedback loop be reduced from the large value which it has in the useful band to zero or less at some higher frequency without producing an accompanying phase shift greater than some prescribed amount. It is evident from the general relations described in Chapter XIV that this requirement amounts basically to a condition upon the rate at which the gain outside the useful band is reduced. If it were not for the phase restriction it would be desirable on engineering grounds to reduce the gain very rapidly. The more rapidly the feedback vanishes, for example, the narrower we need make the region in which active design attention is required to prevent singing. Moreover, it is evidently desirable to secure a loop cut-off as soon as possible in order to avoid the difficulties and uncertainties of design which parasitic elements in the circuit introduce at high frequencies. But the analysis of Chapter XIV shows that the phase shift is broadly proportional to the rate at which the gain changes. If the phase shift is not to be greater than a prescribed amount, therefore, the rate at which the amplifier cuts off, on the whole, must not exceed a fairly well defined limit. For example, if we assume a phase margin of 30° the allowable $\mu\beta$ phase shift is 150°, which corresponds broadly to a gain characteristic changing at the rate of 10 db per octave.

It is evidently desirable to have a phase characteristic which is as great as possible, within the prescribed limit, in order to secure the most rapid cut-off. The exact cut-off shape which best meets this condition can be obtained if we return to the analysis which underlies equation (17–13), for the maximum gain interstage, in the preceding chapter. It will be recalled that this equation was derived from the general formula (14–33) of Chapter XIV by specifying that the interstage gain should be constant in the useful band and that its phase angle should be constant and equal to $-\pi/2$ beyond it. An essentially similar analytic problem exists in the present situation if we suppose that a constant feedback in the useful band is desired. The requirement on the gain around the feedback loop merely takes the place of the interstage gain requirement, while beyond the band the requirement that the loop phase shift should not exceed a prescribed amount takes the place of the requirement on the phase angle of the interstage. The only noteworthy difference is the fact that the phase requirement has been changed from $\pi/2$ radians to $(1 - y)\pi$ radians. This change multiplies the variable part of the final expression proportionately. We can consequently rewrite the interstage gain and phase shift expression to suit the feedback loop problem in the form

$$A + iB = A_0 - 2(1 - y) \log \left[\sqrt{1 - \frac{\omega^2}{\omega_0^2}} + i\frac{\omega}{\omega_0} \right], \qquad (18\text{–}1)$$

where A and B are respectively the real and imaginary components of $\log T = \log(-\mu\beta)$ and A_0 represents the gain around the loop in the useful band. A plot of A and B for the choice $y = \frac{1}{6}$, corresponding to a 30° phase margin, is shown by Fig. 18.4. The constant gain A_0 is, of course, still to be added.

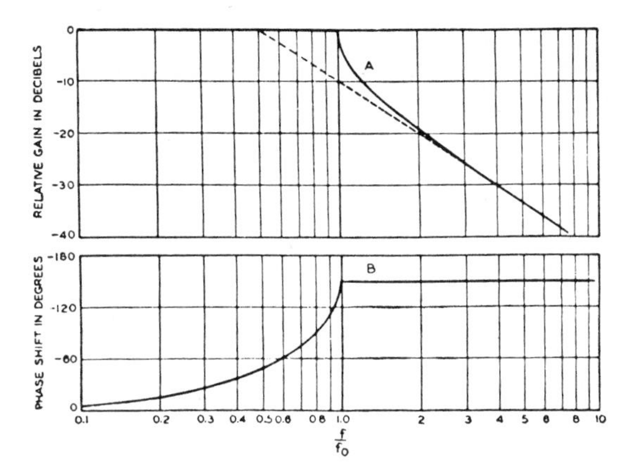

FIG. 18.4

In view of the exact analogy between the interstage problem and the feedback loop problem most of the detailed conclusions developed in the preceding chapter can be applied directly to the present situation. The results of principal interest are:

1. In the interstage analysis the plot of the gain characteristic against $\log \omega$ reduced, at high frequencies, to a straight line with a slope of 6 db per octave, representing the characteristic of the parasitic capacity alone. Here, similarly, equation (18–1) reduces at high frequencies to a straight line with a slope of $12(1 - y)$ db per octave. This is indicated by the broken line in Fig. 18.4. Near the edge of the band the actual characteristic varies more rapidly than the straight line, to take account of the fact that there is zero slope within the band, and at the band edge it lies $12(1 - y)$ db above the straight line. This corresponds to the 6 db advantage which a maximum flat gain interstage

has over the capacity gain at the band edge and permits us to save one octave of the cut-off interval which would be necessary if we relied upon a straight line characteristic alone.

2. If the phase margin and the loop gain at high frequencies are to be kept constant, but the loop gain in the useful band is to be variable with frequency, the absolute level of loop gain must meet the condition that the area under the gain characteristic when plotted against $\phi = \sin^{-1} \omega/\omega_0$ must be kept constant.
3. If the loop gain at high frequencies and the shape of the gain characteristic in the useful band are prescribed, but a variable rather than a constant phase margin is desired over a portion of the cut-off range, the absolute level of gain, in nepers, in the useful band should be changed by an amount equal to the average height, in radians, of the plot of $(\omega/\omega_0)[B - (1 - y)\pi]$ against $\phi' = \sin \omega_0/\omega$, where B and $(1 - y)\pi$ represent respectively the variable and constant margin phase characteristics.

In the interstage design the high frequency gain characteristic is used as a reference because it corresponds to the parasitic capacity. The reason for supposing that it is fixed in a feedback loop problem, as statements (2) and (3) assume, will appear later. It may also be noticed that although (2) and (3) are formulated for amplifiers in which a variable feedback in the useful band or a variable phase margin are desired, they can also be used in correcting a preliminary design in which the feedback and phase margin are variable when they should be constant. For example, if the preliminary design is satisfactory except that the feedback in the useful band is too irregular, statement (2) shows how much feedback we should attempt to get in adjusting the circuit to secure a flatter characteristic.

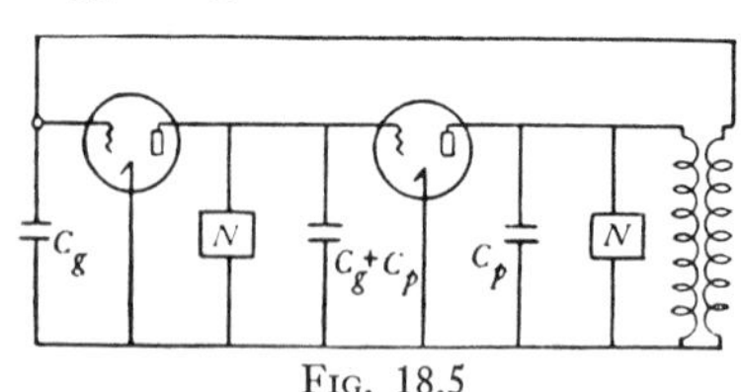

FIG. 18.5

The close analogy between the ideal cut-off defined by (1) and the characteristic of a maximum gain interstage makes it possible to exemplify (1) by an amplifier in which the transmission around the loop is determined entirely by interstages. The structure is shown by Fig. 18.5. It can be regarded as a degenerate shunt feedback amplifier in which the β connection is reduced to a short circuit and in which the input and output circuits are vestigial, and contribute only an infinitesimal admittance across the feedback path. The transformer shown in the drawing is supposed to be an ideal one, of unity ratio, and is introduced merely to secure the phase reversal necessary to permit feedback in the proper sign with an even number of tubes. We might dispense with it by converting the circuit to a push-pull structure with a pair of crossed terminals. The networks N in Fig. 18.5 are both maximum gain interstages of the type shown by Fig. 17.6 of the preceding chapter. The gain around the loop is evidently the sum of the gains of the two interstages and can be written as

$$A + iB = 2 \log \frac{2G_m}{\omega_0 C} - 2 \log \left[\sqrt{1 - \frac{\omega^2}{\omega_0^2}} + i \frac{\omega}{\omega_0} \right], \qquad (18\text{–}2)$$

where G_m is the transconductance and C the sum of the grid and plate capacities for either tube. The expression has the form assumed by (18–1) in the limiting case of zero phase margin.

Aside from serving as an example of (18–1) the structure of Fig. 18.5 is of considerable interest from another point of view. It represents the theoretical limiting form to which an amplifier reduces when every other design consideration is sacrificed to secure the maximum possible feedback. As the structure stands the feedback obtainable over any given band is, of course, given by the first term of (18–2) and depends only upon the ratio G_m/C and the band width ω_0. The ratio G_m/C is the so-called "*figure of merit*" of the tubes. It is equal to the frequency, in radians per second, at which the tubes working into their own parasitic capacities would have zero gain. Zero feedback is obtained when ω_0 is twice G_m/C, as we can see either from (18–2) or directly from the fact that the gain of a maximum gain interstage is 6 db greater than the capacity gain at the band edge. Since in some present-day tubes the figure of merit may represent a frequency of the order of 100 mc, this means that if a structure like Fig. 18.5 could be built it should be possible to realize some feedback (i.e., $|\mu\beta| \geq 1$) over bands as broad as 200 mc.* If we start with the 200 mc band as a basis, the feedback which the structure should furnish over narrower bands varies inversely as the square of the band width. Thus over a 10 mc band it is about 50 db, over a 1 mc band about 90 db, and over a 10 kc band about 170 db.

These are evidently much larger values of feedback than those to which we are accustomed in normal design practice. They are achieved, of course, only because of the artificial simplicity of the circuit. In a practical design it would be necessary, at least, to provide input and output circuits capable of transmitting a finite amount of signal power between the amplifier and the line and to include a β circuit having a finite loss, so that the amplifier might have some gain. We might also wish to give consideration to such factors as the transit angle of the tubes, the use of tubes with poorer figures of merit but better characteristics in other respects, or the provision of a definite phase margin to permit the circuit to be con-

* This ignores the tube transit time, discussed later in the chapter.

structed with reasonable standards of precision. These considerations inevitably reduce the amount of feedback which can be obtained in a practical design very substantially. In a broad sense, however, one of the most important problems in feedback amplifier design is that of planning the circuit in broad outline to prevent the sacrifice in feedback from becoming intolerably great. The structure of Fig. 18.5 is useful here, in spite of its artificiality, as a standard of comparison.

18.3. *Asymptotic Characteristic of the Feedback Loop*

The direct analogy between the interstage gain characteristic and equation (18–1) for the transmission around the feedback loop breaks down at only one important point. In dealing with the interstage the limit on the absolute level of gain is obviously set by the fact that the characteristic must reduce to that of the interstage capacity alone at sufficiently high frequencies. If we begin with too high a gain in the useful band it is impossible to reduce the gain fast enough beyond the band to reach the capacity characteristic without producing a phase shift which exceeds the 90° limit for a physical two-terminal structure.

In the loop transmission problem, the absolute level of loop gain which can be assumed to exist in the useful band is limited by similar, but more complicated, considerations. So far as a purely theoretical formula like (18–1) is concerned, there is clearly no limit to the feedback which can be postulated. As the constant A_0, representing the feedback in the useful band, is increased, however, the interval in which there is appreciable transmission around the loop extends to higher and higher frequencies. The process reaches a physical limit, broadly speaking, when the frequency becomes so high that parasitic effects are controlling and do not permit the transmission characteristic prescribed by (18–1) to be simulated with sufficient precision. For example, we are obviously in physical difficulties if (18–1) requires a net gain around the loop at a frequency so high that the tubes themselves working into their own parasitic capacities do not give a gain. This is the limit which is effective in the special circuit of Fig. 18.5, and is one of the reasons for regarding this structure as a reference in feedback computations. In a practical amplifier, limitations on the loop gain must be encountered more quickly because of the additional losses contributed to the loop transmission by the input and output circuits and the β circuit. In comparison with the interstage problem, the chief difference to be noticed is that the high-frequency transmission around the loop is controlled by a complex of elements rather than by a single specific parasitic capacity. The characteristic to which the loop transmission tends at sufficiently high frequencies under the influence of all the significant parasitic elements in the loop will be called the *asymptote* of the loop.

The calculation of the loop asymptote is easily understood from the illustrative circuit shown by Fig. 18.6. The structure is a shunt feedback amplifier. The β circuit is represented by the T composed of networks N_5, N_6 and N_7. The input and output circuits are represented by N_1 and N_4 and the interstage impedances by N_2 and N_3. The C's are parasitic capacities with the exception of C_5 and C_6, which may be regarded as design

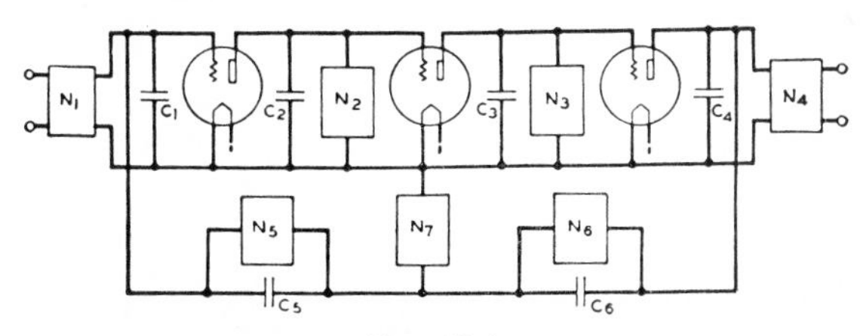

FIG. 18.6

elements added deliberately to N_5 and N_6 to obtain an efficient high-frequency transmission path from output to input. At sufficiently high frequencies the loop transmission will depend only upon these various capacities, without regard to the N's. Thus, if the transconductances of the tubes are represented by G_{m_1}, G_{m_2}, and G_{m_3}, the asymptotic gains of the first two tubes are $G_{m_1}/\omega C_2$ and $G_{m_2}/\omega C_3$. The rest of the loop includes the third tube and the potentiometer formed by the capacities C_1, C_4, C_5, and C_6. Its asymptotic gain can be written as $G_{m_3}/\omega C$, where

$$C = C_1 + C_4 + \frac{C_1 C_4}{C_5 C_6} (C_5 + C_6). \tag{18-3}$$

The complete asymptote is the product of these terms or, in other words, $G_{m_1} G_{m_2} G_{m_3}/\omega^3 C C_2 C_3$. It appears as a straight line with a slope of 18 db per octave, or 60 db per decade, when plotted on logarithmic paper. The fact that the asymptote can be expected to appear as a straight line on logarithmic paper in the general case is easily seen if we write the transfer impedance around the loop as

$$Z_T = \frac{A_0 + A_1(i\omega) + A_2(i\omega)^2 + \cdots + A_{m_1}(i\omega)^{m_1}}{B_0 + B_1(i\omega) + B_2(i\omega)^2 + \cdots + B_{m_2}(i\omega)^{m_2}}. \tag{18-4}$$

When ω approaches infinity the expression reduces to

$$Z_T = \frac{A_{m_1}}{B_{m_2}} (i\omega)^{-(m_2 - m_1)}, \tag{18-5}$$

which represents a straight line with slope $(m_2 - m_1)$ in units of 6 db per octave. The quantity $(m_2 - m_1)$ will be represented by n in future discussions. In Fig. 18.6, $n = 3$ and is the same as the number of tubes in the circuit. It is evidently not possible for n to be smaller than the number of tubes, since each tube must at least work into its own parasitic capacity, but it may be greater in some circuits. For example, if C_5 or C_6 were omitted in Fig. 18.6 and the associated network N_5 or N_6 were regarded as degenerating into a resistance, the asymptote would have a slope of 4 units and would lie below the present asymptote at any reasonably high frequency.

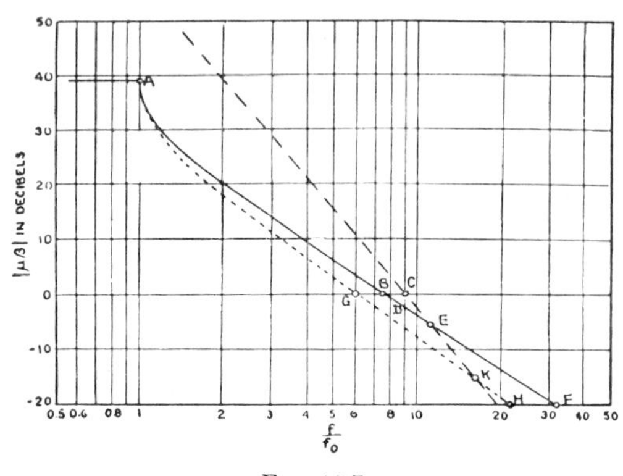

FIG. 18.7

The effect of the asymptote on the overall feedback characteristics is illustrated by Fig. 18.7. The curve *ABEF* is a reproduction of the ideal cut-off characteristic originally given in Fig. 18.4.* It will be recalled that the curve was drawn for the choice $y = \frac{1}{6}$, which corresponds to a phase margin of 30° and an almost constant slope, for the portion *DEF* of the characteristic, of about 10 db per octave. The straight line *CEK* represents an asymptote of the type just described, with a slope of 18 db per octave, and with a zero gain intercept at $\omega = 9\omega_0$. Since the asymptote may be assumed to represent the practical upper limit of gain in the high-frequency region, the effect of the parasitic elements can be obtained by replacing the theoretical cut-off by the broken line characteristic *ABDEK*. In an actual circuit the corner at E would, of course, be rounded off, but this is of negligible quantitative importance. Since *EF* and *EK* diverge by 8 db per octave the effect can be studied by adding a curve of the type shown by Fig. 14.8 of Chapter XIV to the original cut-off characteristic.

The phase shift in the ideal case is shown by Curve I of Fig. 18.8. The addition of the phase corresponding to the extra slope of 8 db per octave at

* Except, of course, for the constant A_0. In Fig. 18.7 and the succeeding Figs. 18.13, 18.15, and 18.18 the asymptote remains the same and A_0 is chosen, in each case, to suit the cut-off characteristic under investigation.

high frequencies produces the total phase characteristic shown by Curve I′. At the point B, where $|\mu\beta| = 1$, the additional phase shift amounts to 35°. Since this is greater than the original phase margin of 30° the amplifier is unstable when parasitic elements are considered. In the present instance stability can be regained by decreasing y to $\frac{1}{12}$, which leads to the broken line characteristic $AGKH$ in Fig. 18.7. This reduces the nominal phase margin to 15°, but the frequency interval between G and K is so much

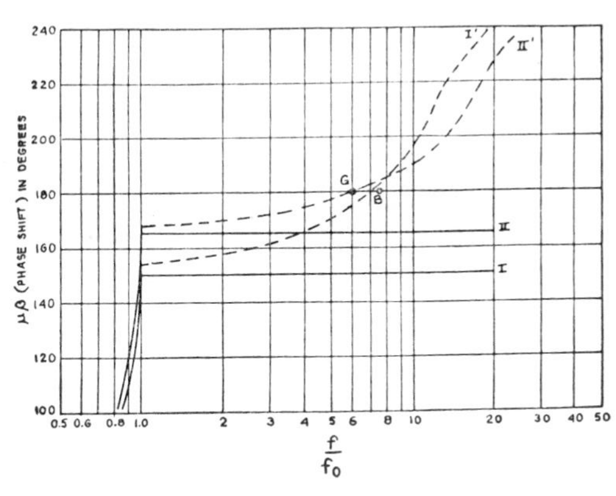

Fig. 18.8

greater than that between B and E that the added phase is reduced still more and is just less than 15° at the new crossover point G. This is illustrated by II and II′ in Fig. 18.8. On the other hand, if the zero gain intercept of the asymptote CEK had occurred at a slightly lower frequency, no change in y alone would have been sufficient. It would have been necessary to reduce the amount of feedback in the transmitted range in order to secure stability.

18.4. *Asymptotic Characteristics in Some Illustrative Circuits*

In later sections the discussion of the effect of the asymptote in limiting the amount of feedback available will be based upon a slightly more elaborate relation between the asymptote and the ideal cut-off than that indicated by Figs. 18.7 and 18.8. Even the simplified statement of the situation given by these figures, however, is sufficient to show the essential rôle which the asymptote plays in the design. It is evident that a large feedback cannot be obtained if the asymptote crosses the zero gain axis too close to the useful band or has too high a slope. Fortunately, the asymptotic characteristic can be obtained relatively easily, since it depends only upon the parasitic elements of the circuit and perhaps a few of the most significant design elements. It can thus be computed from a skeletonized version of the final structure. If waste of time in attempts to obtain unrealizable amounts of feedback is to be avoided such a computation should be made as early as possible, and certainly in advance of any detailed design.

Broadly speaking, the asymptotic characteristic depends in part upon the tubes and interstage capacities and in part upon the input and output circuits and the β circuit proper. This is the division suggested by the discussion in connection with Fig. 18.5. The particular circuit given there represents the extreme case in which the contributions of the input, output, and β circuits to the asymptotic characteristics are reduced to zero by reducing these structures themselves to vestigial appendages of the complete amplifier. If we regard the forward circuit as given, the design problem confronting the engineer is broadly that of introducing functional circuits in these positions without unduly degrading the asymptotic characteristic. The solution which is achieved will depend in part upon the type of feedback adopted and in part upon the balance which is struck between the desirability of a large feedback and other indices of the overall amplifier performance.

These considerations are most easily illustrated by reviewing briefly the asymptotic characteristics which we may expect to secure for the elementary structures listed in Figs. 3.5 to 3.8 of Chapter III. If we begin with a shunt feedback amplifier a typical circuit may be assumed to take the form already shown by Fig. 18.6 of the present chapter. The asymptotic path from the output plate to the input grid is shown by Fig. 18.9. The inclusion of input and output transformers in the circuit can be represented in the asymptotic path by adding their high side capacities to the shunt capacities C_1 and C_4. For maximum efficiency the added capacities should be small, but if we attempt to make them too small, as by reducing the transformers to a few widely spaced turns, for example, we may expect malfunctioning of the circuit for some other reason.

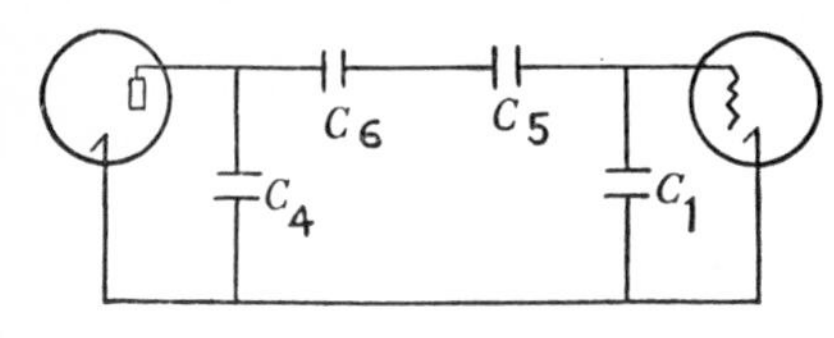

FIG. 18.9

The β circuit is represented in the asymptotic path by the series combination of C_5 and C_6. For maximum feedback these capacities should be very large. They can be made as large as we please, for any given β circuit loss, by scaling down the impedance levels of the series branches in the β circuit T of Fig. 18.6, provided the impedance of the shunt branch is also decreased by the proper amount. But if the impedance level of the β circuit is made very low it becomes an appreciable shunt on the input and output circuits within the useful band. This will degrade the volume performance characteristics of these circuits, as defined in Chapter XVI.

Thus the exact asymptote depends upon a compromise between volume performance and feedback considerations.

A simple series feedback amplifier is shown by Fig. 18.10. The asymptotic path from output plate to input grid is shown by Fig. 18.11. The central shunt capacity C_7 may be identified with the distributed capacity to ground of the β circuit and the input and output transformers. It should, of course, be kept as small as possible. The two series capacities, C_1 and C_6, represent the capacities across the high windings of the trans-

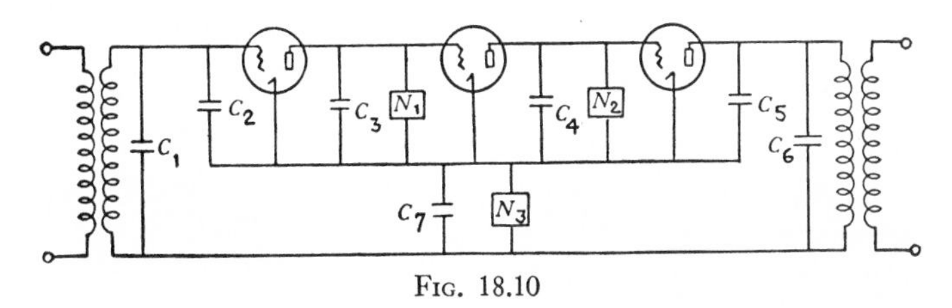

Fig. 18.10

formers. The best asymptotic transmission will be obtained if they are quite large. On the other hand, the relations of Chapter XVI show that the highest levels of volume performance and external gain can be obtained if the two capacities are made as small as possible. Thus the exact asymptote depends again upon a compromise between considerations of this sort and considerations of feedback, although the particular relationships involved are somewhat different from those appearing in the shunt type circuit.

In constructing Fig. 18.10 the β circuit was represented as a simple shunt impedance. As an alternative, we may suppose that the β circuit is constructed as a π. This change may be made either to secure additional

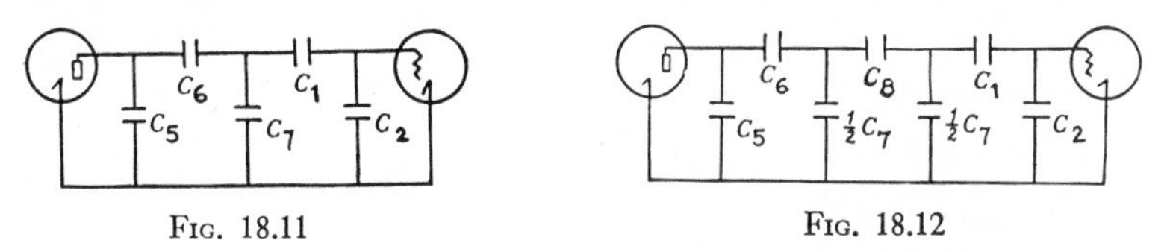

Fig. 18.11

Fig. 18.12

flexibility in design or to avoid the extremely low impedance levels which are sometimes encountered with single branch structures. If we suppose that the central branch of the π is paralleled by a capacity C_8 and that the capacity in shunt with the original β circuit is allocated equally to each end of the new structure, the new asymptotic path takes the form shown by Fig. 18.12. It is clear that the introduction of the capacity C_8 necessarily increases the asymptotic loss, so that the single branch β circuit represents the optimum choice. If the impedance level of the π circuit is low enough, however, it may be possible to make C_8 so large that the asymptotic penalty is unimportant.

The considerations affecting the asymptotic paths in the other principal types of feedback circuits are broadly similar. In the bridge type feedback illustrated by Fig. 3.6 of Chapter III, for example, the asymptotic path is roughly similar to that which might be found in a shunt or series type structure except that an additional loss due to the bridge is interpolated at each end. The amount of the added loss depends upon the bridge ratio. It is customary to use an unequal ratio structure to favor transmission between amplifier and line, or, in other words, volume performance. If the ratio is extreme, however, the loss introduced to transmission around the asymptotic loop becomes excessively great, so that here again it is necessary to compromise between volume performance and feedback considerations. It is also possible to control the asymptotic loss to some extent by introducing small series coils or shunt condensers into the various bridge arms in order to remove them, as far as possible, at high frequencies.

In hybrid coil circuits the asymptotic characteristic depends largely upon whether high side or low side feedback is used. If we use high side hybrid coil feedback, for example, the asymptotic transmission may be regarded as taking place through the capacities across the high side coil windings. This is similar to the situation found in a series feedback circuit and leads to the same general type of asymptote. In a low side feedback, on the other hand, the asymptotic path goes directly through the hybrid coils, so that their leakage inductances appear as series elements between the parasitic capacities furnished by the rest of the circuit. In many amplifiers this may increase the asymptotic loss so greatly that the amount of feedback available is seriously reduced. As a compensation, the fact that the feedback path passes through the hybrid coils in the low side case means that the external characteristics of the amplifier are stabilized against coil variations, which is not true in a high side circuit.

18.5. *Maximum Obtainable Feedback**

The analysis given in connection with Fig. 18.7 shows why the asymptote limits the amount of feedback which can be obtained, but it is not sufficient to show exactly what the maximum feedback with any given asymptote should be. As the situation was left, the final phase characteristic reaches the limiting 180° only at the crossover point, and there is a phase margin, of varying magnitude, at all lower frequencies. The relation between

* The formulae for maximum available feedback presented in this section are based upon loop cut-off characteristics of a type appropriate for practice. By using more elaborate characteristics, however, it is theoretically possible to obtain slightly more feedback. This is discussed at a later point.

phase margin and feedback given earlier in the chapter shows that a somewhat more efficient solution for the extreme case will be obtained if the limiting 180° is approximated throughout the cut-off interval.

The desired phase characteristic is attained if the original ideal cut-off is connected to the asymptote in a somewhat more complicated manner than was used previously. The new overall cut-off characteristic is shown by Fig. 18.13. It consists of the original theoretical characteristic, drawn for $y = 0$, from the edge of the useful band to its intercept, f_b, with the

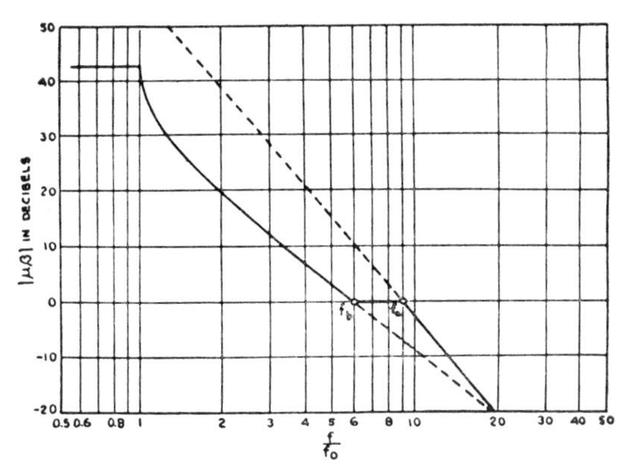

Fig. 18.13

zero gain axis, the zero gain axis from this frequency to the intercept, f_a, between the zero gain axis and the asymptote, and the asymptote thereafter. It can be regarded as a combination of the ideal cut-off characteristic, prolonged to infinity, and two semi-infinite slope characteristics. One of the added slopes starts at f_b and has a positive slope of 12 db per octave, since the ideal cut-off was drawn for the limiting value of y. The other starts at f_a and has a negative slope equal to that of the asymptote itself.

As equation (15–12) of Chapter XV shows, the phase characteristic corresponding to a semi-infinite slope is proportional to frequency at low frequencies. The phase shifts corresponding to the two additional slopes thus vary in the same way with frequency and since they are of opposite sign they can be made to cancel one another provided the constants determining the scales on which they are drawn are suitably chosen. The proper relation is evidently obtained if the frequencies at which the slopes begin are in the same ratio as the slopes themselves. If we represent the slope of the asymptote, in units of 6 db per octave, by n, this fixes f_b in terms of f_a by the equation

$$f_b = \frac{2}{n} f_a. \tag{18–6}$$

In Fig. 18.13, for example, where the asymptotic slope is 18 db per octave the frequency ratio is 18 : 12 or 3 : 2. At low frequencies, this leaves the complete phase characteristic equal to that which would be obtained from the unmodified ideal curve alone. At higher frequencies, where the linear approximation to the phase characteristics of the semi-infinite slopes is not quite accurate, some account of these constituents must, of course, also be taken. As Fig. 18.14 shows, however, the exact curve dips slightly below 180° at the point at which the gain characteristic reaches the zero axis, so that the circuit is in fact stable.

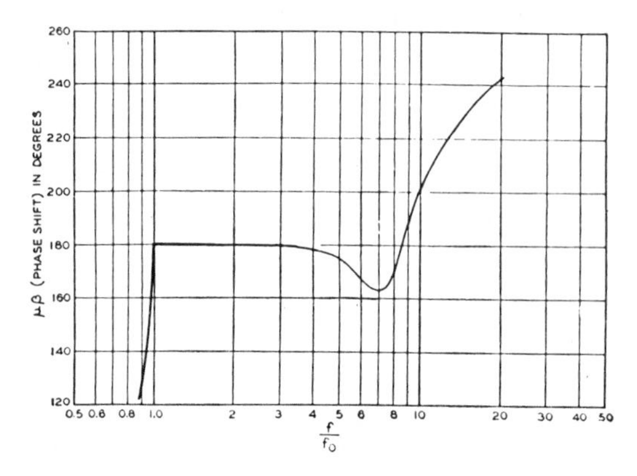

FIG. 18.14

Once f_b has been determined the proportions of the drawing make it an easy matter to determine how large a feedback can be obtained within the useful band. It is merely necessary to allow 12 db for each octave between the band edge and f_b, together with an additional 12 db to take account of the increased slope of the cut-off characteristic near the band edge. With the help of (18–6) the result can be written as

$$A_m = 40 \log_{10} \frac{4f_a}{nf_0} \tag{18–7}$$

where f_0 represents the band edge and A_m is the feedback in the useful band in db.

If the feedback indicated by (18–7) is more than is required in the final amplifier the surplus can be utilized to provide a cut-off characteristic having definite gain and phase margins against singing. This is illustrated by the characteristics of Figs. 18.15 and 18.16. The curves are drawn for the gain and phase margins $x = 9$ and $y = \frac{1}{6}$, in the notation of Fig. 18.3. The phase margin $y = \frac{1}{6}$, or 30°, is provided by drawing the ideal cut-off portion of the characteristic for a 10 db per octave, rather than a 12 db per octave, slope. The gain margin is provided by drawing the flat part of the characteristic, linking the ideal cut-off and the asymptote, a corresponding distance below the zero gain axis. As in the preceding analysis, the ratio

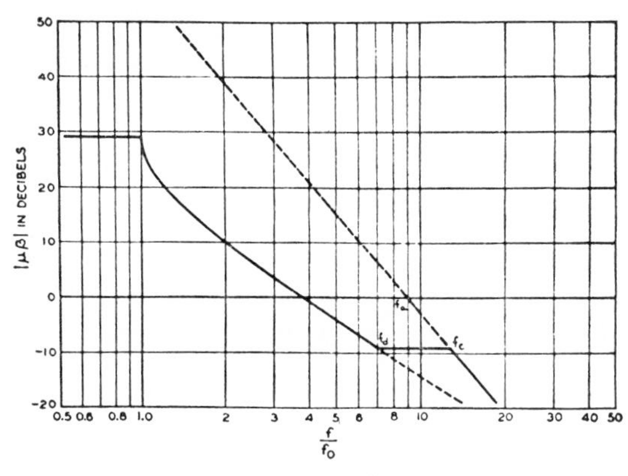

FIG. 18.15

of the frequencies terminating the flat portion is supposed to be the same as that of the slopes to which it is connected, so that the net phase characteristic in the cut-off range proper is substantially the same as that of the ideal characteristic.

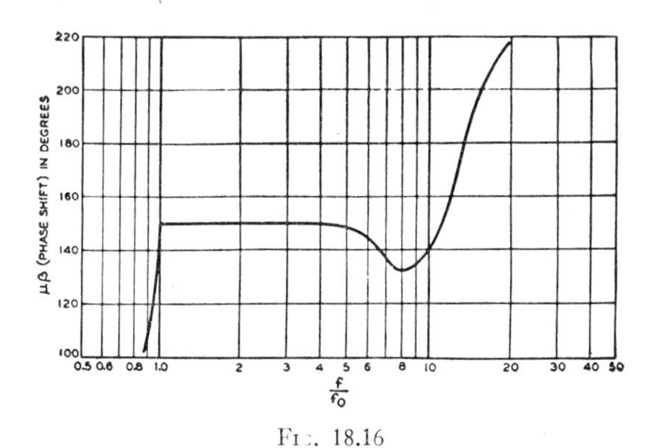

FIG. 18.16

The degradation in feedback in the useful band which must be accepted to provide prescribed phase and gain margins in this manner can be determined by a relatively simple calculation. To begin with, the frequency f_c in Fig. 18.15, at which the cut-off finally joins the asymptote, is fixed in terms of f_a by the asymptotic slope and the gain margin x. Since the asymptotic slope is $6n$ db per octave, or $20n$ db per decade, we evidently have $\log_{10} f_c/f_a = x/20n$, or, in other words, $f_c = 10^{x/20n} f_a$. But the ideal cut-off slope is $12(1 - y)$ db per octave, or $40(1 - y)$ db per decade. The relation between the slopes and the frequencies bounding the flat portion of the characteristic therefore gives $f_d = [2(1 - y)/n] f_c$. Finally, the known proportions of the ideal cut-off show that the feedback at the band edge, f_0, must exceed that at f_d by $40(1 - y) \log_{10} 2f_d/f_0$ db. But this difference is equal to $A + x$, where A is the feedback in the useful band. Upon collecting results, therefore, we have

$$A = 40(1 - y) \log_{10} \left[\frac{4(1 - y)}{n} 10^{x/20n} \frac{f_a}{f_0} \right] - x$$

$$= 40(1 - y) \log_{10} \frac{4f_a}{nf_0} + 40(1 - y) \log_{10} (1 - y) + \frac{2(1 - y)}{n} x - x. \tag{18-8}$$

Since y is small we may expand $\log_{10} (1 - y)$ in a power series and ignore powers of y higher than the first. This permits the term $40(1 - y) \log_{10} (1 - y)$ in (18–8) to be replaced by $-17.4y$. If we also replace $40 \log_{10} 4f_a/nf_0$ by A_m, from (18–7), we secure the final expression

$$A_m - A = (A_m + 17.4)y + \frac{n - 2}{n} x + \frac{2}{n} xy. \tag{18-9}$$

Since the xy term is usually small the total degradation in feedback appears substantially as the sum of separate degradations due to the phase and gain margins individually. An example of the relation is furnished by a comparison of Figs. 18.13 and 18.15. In both cases the asymptotic frequency f_a was chosen as $9f_0$. In accordance with (18–7) this permits a maximum feedback, A_m, of 43 db, which is the feedback realized in Fig. 18.13. The realized feedback in Fig. 18.15, however, is only 29 db. Of the 14 db difference, about 10 db is spent in the phase margin term of (18–9), about 3 db in the gain margin term, and about 1 db in the product term.

18.6. *Relation between Corrected and Uncorrected Loop Characteristics in Typical Cases*

The precise methods by which such a cut-off characteristic as that shown by Fig. 18.13 is to be achieved will naturally differ from amplifier to amplifier. The various possibilities are discussed at some length later in the chapter and will be suggested in greater detail by the illustrative designs in the chapter which follows. It is possible, however, to make one general physical observation which applies to the great majority of amplifier designs. In an amplifier designed in the simplest way, without regard to the shaping of the cut-off characteristic, it is generally true that some, at least, of the circuits which are responsible for a flat feedback characteristic in the useful band will tend to maintain their uniform response also for some distance beyond the useful band. At higher frequencies, however, their response characteristics begin to fail because of the parasitic elements which the circuits contain and as the frequency increases still further parasitic effects become more and more important until finally the overall

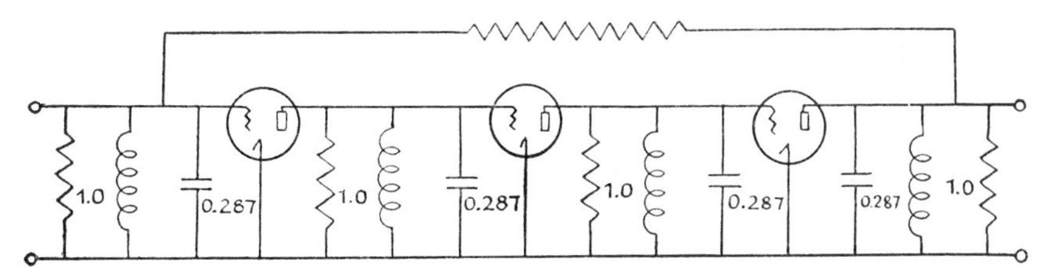

FIG. 18.17

loop characteristic merges smoothly into the asymptotic condition, in which the response of every circuit varies in a manner dictated essentially by the parasitic elements alone. Thus the overall loop gain characteristic tends to be concave downward at least at high frequencies, if not over the complete cut-off interval. The cut-off characteristic shown by Fig. 18.13, on the other hand, is concave upward. Thus the general design problem in most amplifiers is that of introducing such losses in the loop that the cut-off rate will be increased at frequencies moderately removed from the useful band and decreased at more remote frequencies. This is equivalent to discounting parasitic effects in advance, so that they do not control the loop characteristic until the cut-off finally meets the asymptote and design effort is abandoned.

As a somewhat extreme example of these relationships we may consider the circuit shown in Fig. 18.17. The structure is supposed to represent a simple band-pass amplifier in which the interstage and input and output coupling networks are damped tuned circuits. All the circuits will be supposed to have the same Q. In terms of the equivalent low-pass structure the loop characteristic may be written as $140/(1 + 0.287i\omega)^4$. The constants in the expression are chosen to permit easy comparison with Fig. 18.13. They give the same low frequency gain and the same* asymptote as were used in that figure. The loop gain characteristic of the struc-

* That is, the asymptotic slope n of Fig. 18.13 has been increased from 3 to 4 but the zero gain intercept f_a is changed in proportion to give the same effective condition at lower frequencies, in accordance with (18–6).

ture is shown by Curve I of Fig. 18.18, the theoretical cut-off of Fig. 18.13 being shown by Curve II. The difference indicated by the shaded area is therefore the loss characteristic which should be introduced into the loop, by an equalizer or some analogous means, in order to stabilize the circuit.

The effect of such a change may be studied by comparing the corresponding phase characteristics shown by Curves I and II of Fig. 18.19. The areas under the two curves are the same, but the insertion of the additional loss characteristic redistributes the total area so that the maximum phase shift remains less than 180° over a much broader interval. It will be seen that the unmodified phase characteristic crosses 180° at $f = 3.5\ f_0$. If the circuit were stabilized by a gain control which reduced the loop gain to zero at this point the resulting feedback in the useful band would be 12 db. This compares with the 43 db obtained with the theoretical cut-off. About half the 30 odd db of additional feedback would be obtained if Curve I of Fig. 18.18 were replaced merely by a straight line of appropriately chosen slope. The increased slope of the actual theoretical characteristic just beyond the edge of the useful band is responsible for an increment of about 12 db and the final flat portion just before the junction with the asymptote for an improvement of about 5 or 6 db. The first example of the next chapter shows a design problem of this sort in more detail.

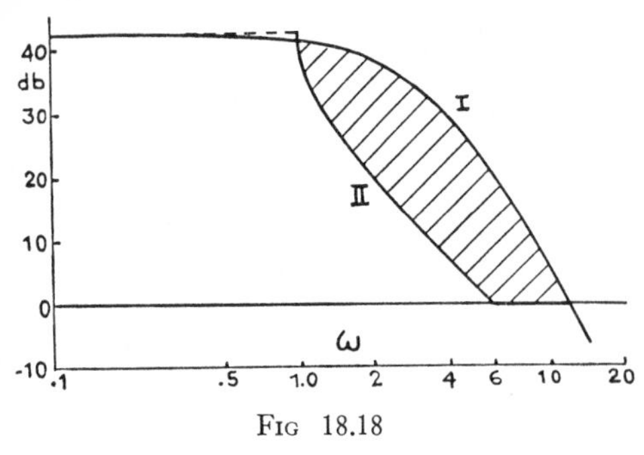

FIG 18.18

The analysis just concluded leads to one other conclusion of considerable general importance. This has to do with the effective band width, for design purposes, of a feedback amplifier.

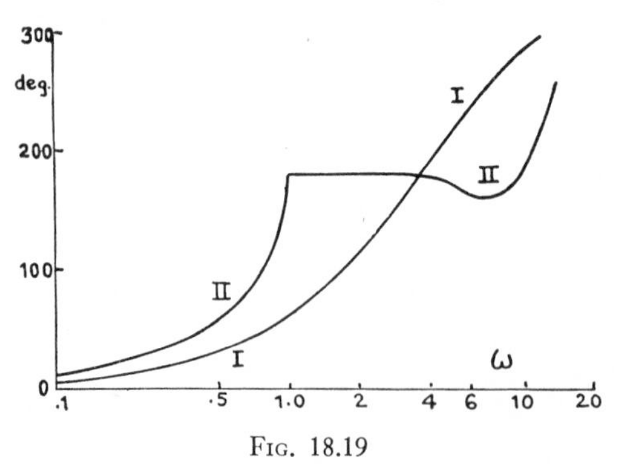

FIG. 18.19

If we accept the proportions in Fig. 18.15 as typical for a practical design, we notice that the interval, in octaves, between the edge of the useful band and the frequency at which the cut-off characteristic intersects the zero gain axis is one less than the feedback in the useful band, expressed as a multiple of 10 db. Between the zero gain intercept and the junction of the characteristic with the asymptote, where we can say that design control is finally relaxed, there is an additional interval of nearly two octaves. Thus the total effective design range is roughly one octave for each 10 db of feedback in the useful band, plus one additional octave.

Changes in the phase and gain margin assumed for the amplifier, or in its asymptotic slope, may affect this estimate somewhat, but not enough to alter the order of magnitude of the result. If we take the estimate at face value it indicates that an amplifier with a useful feedback of 30 db will have an effective band which is 4 octaves, or 16 times, broader than the useful band. If we raise the feedback to 60 db, the effective range must be more than a hundred times the useful range. If the useful band is itself large these factors may lead to enormous effective ranges. For example, in a 4 megacycle television amplifier they indicate an effective range of about 60 megacycles for 30 db feedback, or of more than 400 megacycles if the feedback is 60 db.

The general engineering implications of this result are obvious. It evidently makes even the paper design of a feedback amplifier a far more formidable undertaking than one might anticipate from a consideration of the useful band alone. The construction and testing of the apparatus to follow a prescribed characteristic over such wide bands is perhaps a still more difficult problem. Unfortunately, the situation, in unconditionally stable amplifiers, at least, appears to be an inevitable one. It merely reflects the fact that the cut-off rate is broadly proportional to the loop phase shift and must be held within comparatively modest limits if the phase shift is not to be excessive.

18.7. *Alternative High-Frequency Cut-off Characteristics*

It will be recalled that the determination of theoretical loop characteristics for a feedback amplifier was first attacked by constructing an ideal cut-off characteristic which extended from the edge of the useful band to infinity and produced a prescribed constant phase characteristic throughout this complete range. In order to fit the solution for practical application, however, it was necessary to allow for the fact that the loop characteristic of a physical amplifier at extremely high frequencies must follow the asymptotic line determined by its parasitic elements rather than the line representing the ideal characteristic. The adjustment was made in Figs. 18.13 and 18.15 by connecting the ideal characteristic and the asymptote by a horizontal straight line " step " of particular length.

This appears to be the simplest device. There are, however, other ways in which the two characteristics may be connected and some of the alternatives permit slightly more feedback than can be obtained with the simple step connection. Thus the statement that A_m in (18–7) is the maximum available feedback cannot be taken rigorously. For practical purposes the alternative solutions need not be regarded seriously, since they lead to at most only a few db more feedback in ordinary situations and they envisage a degree of design control which is scarcely feasible in a frequency region where, by definition, parasitic effects are substantially controlling. They are, however, of theoretical interest and they are of some practical importance, indirectly, as measures of the accuracy with which the step characteristic must be realized in order to secure a satisfactory result.

The reason why we may expect that the step type cut-off leaves something still to be gained can be understood from an inspection of the phase characteristic to which it leads. It follows from the phase integral theorem* that the difference between the loop gain at some extremely low frequency in the useful band and the loop gain at some extremely high frequency, where we can regard the asymptotic condition as thoroughly established,

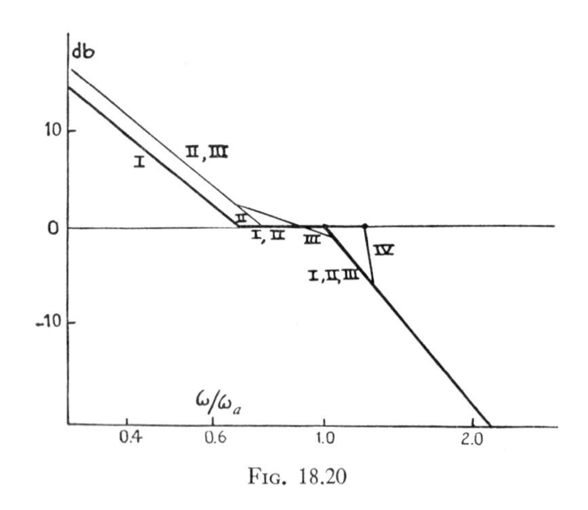

FIG. 18.20

is measured by the area under the phase characteristic between these two points. Thus a slight improvement on the step type cut-off should be obtained if the phase characteristic of Fig. 18.14 were replaced by one which followed the 180° line exactly below the loss crossover and rose more rapidly to its ultimate value thereafter.

This problem can be attacked either theoretically or by cut-and-try modifications of the step type characteristic. Examples of possible cut-and-try modifications are shown by the gain curves of Fig. 18.20 and the associated phase curves of Fig. 18.21. The figures cover only the region of transition from the ideal cut-off to the asymptote. In each figure the curves labeled I represent the original step type solution while the remaining curves correspond to the various modified characteristics. In prepar-

* Equation (13–19) of Chapter XIII.

ing the curves, it has been assumed as a matter of simplicity that the low-frequency feedback for all the modified characteristics is the same and is 2 db greater than the feedback obtained from the unmodified characteristic. This is, in fact, approximately the maximum improvement which the modifications permit for the case considered, in which the asymptote has a slope of 3 units. A slightly greater advantage can, however, be obtained with larger values of n.

The simplest possible modification is represented by Curves II. It consists in reducing slightly the length of the horizontal step in the original characteristic. The effect this has in improving the approximation of the phase characteristic to 180° in the region near the loss crossover can be understood from a study of the phase curves of Fig. 18.21. Strictly speaking, this modification is inadmissible in an absolutely stable amplifier, since it leads to a phase shift slightly greater than 180° at low frequencies. The overswing is very small, however, and can be neglected if it is assumed that the amplifier will actually be built with a definite phase margin, so that A_m is of interest only as one of the quantities entering equation (18–9).

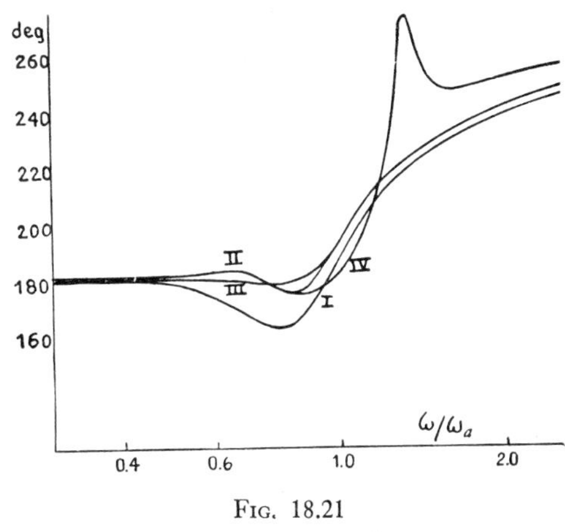

Fig. 18.21

The modification illustrated by Curves III consists in replacing the original horizontal step by a line having a slight slope. Except for the fact that the phase overswing at low frequencies is avoided, the results to which it leads are similar to those produced by the first modification. In view of the difficulty of controlling the loop characteristics in the asymptotic region with precision, however, these curves represent a more nearly attainable result than do either Curves I or Curves II.

Curves IV have been introduced to illustrate the effect of prolonging the flat step beyond its junction with the asymptote. We might imagine such a characteristic to be produced by anti-resonating a parasitic capacity in one of the low impedance portions of the loop in this general region. On paper, this method permits a large increase in available feedback if the prolongation is carried sufficiently far, to a frequency perhaps ten or more times the intersection between the asymptote and the zero gain axis. It is obvious, however, that these proportions require an impossible increase in loop gain at high frequencies. As a more direct limitation, we may notice that as the flat portion of the characteristic is extended to higher and higher frequencies the contribution of the steeply sloping line which is necessary to join it finally to the asymptote leads to a larger and larger maximum phase shift. But if the loop is regarded as consisting essentially of n reactive branches in series or shunt, corresponding to the n parasitic elements in the circuit, the maximum phase shift which is physically possible is $n(\pi/2)$ radians. It will be seen that this limit is slightly exceeded even with the proportions actually used in Figs. 18.20 and 18.21.

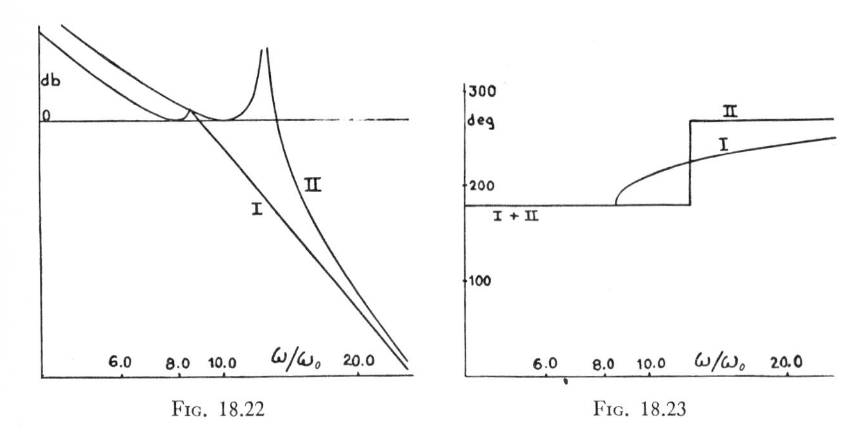

FIG. 18.22

FIG. 18.23

A somewhat more systematic approach to the general problem is obtained if we begin by specifying exactly the phase characteristic which is to be secured at all points above the useful band. The final asymptotic behavior of the loop is taken into account by specifying that the phase shift at very high frequencies shall be equal to $n(\pi/2)$ radians. The corresponding gain characteristic can then be determined either by inspection or by application of the general formulae of Chapter XIV. One example of the results to which this attack leads is furnished by the expression

$$A + iB = A_0 - 2\log\left[\sqrt{1 - \frac{\omega^2}{\omega_0^2}} + i\frac{\omega}{\omega_0}\right] - (n-2)\log\tfrac{1}{2}\left[1 + \sqrt{1 - \frac{\omega^2}{\omega_r^2}}\right], \tag{18–10}$$

where, as in (18–1), A and B represent the loop gain and phase and A_0 is the loop gain in the useful band. Sketches of the A and B characteristics to which the expression leads are shown by Curves I, Figs. 18.22 and 18.23.

A second example is furnished by the expression

$$A + iB = A_0 - 2\log\left[\sqrt{1 - \frac{\omega^2}{\omega_0^2}} + i\frac{\omega}{\omega_0}\right] - (n-2)\log\sqrt{1 - \frac{\omega^2}{\omega_r^2}}. \tag{18–11}$$

This corresponds to the A and B characteristics shown by Curves II in Figs. 18.22 and 18.23. It will be seen that the two expressions give qualitatively similar characteristics, but the distinctive features of the characteristics are greatly exaggerated in the second case.

The meaning of (18–10) and (18–11) can best be understood by comparing them with (18–1). It is evident that the first portion of either expression represents an ideal cut-off solution taken for the limiting case of zero phase margin. The final terms in the two expressions are transition factors which convert the ideal cut-off solution at high frequencies into the asymptotic characteristic. Thus neither term makes any appreciable contribution to the loop gain in the useful band* and both leave the loop phase shift unchanged below f_r. This frequency corresponds to the corner in Curve I of Fig. 18.22 or to the peak in Curve II. At frequencies well above f_r, on the other hand, the final terms contribute a phase shift of $(n - 2)(\pi/2)$ radians and a slope of $n - 2$ units. In combination with the phase and slope contributions of the ideal cut-off this leads to the n unit slope and corresponding $n(\pi/2)$ radian phase shift which are appropriate for the asymptote.

The expressions are made quantitative by choosing f_r and the feedback A_0 in the useful band to satisfy two conditions. The first condition, obviously, is that the equations must correspond to an asymptote which has the correct level of absolute gain as well as the correct slope. The second condition requires that the minimum occurring in each gain characteristic just below f_r should fall on the zero gain axis. This arrangement permits the maximum possible feedback in each case. It leads to stable circuits if we suppose that the two phase characteristics have a differentially small slope near the minimum point and cross 180° at the minimum. This permits the resulting Nyquist plots to skirt just around the critical point, as Figs. 18.24 and 18.25 show, so that the region of net loop gain and large phase shift near f_r does not indicate instability. The broken line arc in the second figure is intended to represent the circular arc of infinite radius which would correspond ideally to the gain peak and phase discontinuity at f_r in Curves II of Figs. 18.22 and 18.23.

The algebraic relations to which these conditions lead are somewhat complicated and will not be reproduced here. For the characteristics of equation (18–11) they indicate an increase in feedback over the maximum available with the step type cut-off of about 4 db when $n = 3$. The feed-

* The integral relations of Chapter XIV evidently make it possible to derive solutions in which the feedback in the useful band remains strictly constant. This possibility is ignored here, however, since it results in much more complicated formulae and the variation in feedback to which the actual expressions (18–10) and (18–11) lead is insignificant in practical cases.

back advantage rises gradually with n and reaches 8 db when $n = 6$. This is evidently a meager return for the design complexity which would be necessary to approximate such a cut-off. If the less extreme solution furnished by equation (18–10) is followed the improvement in feedback is about 1 or 2 db smaller. Neither solution can be used when $n > 6$, since with larger values of n the phase shift at frequencies above the gain minimum becomes so great that the Nyquist plot encloses the critical point on the second trip around the origin.

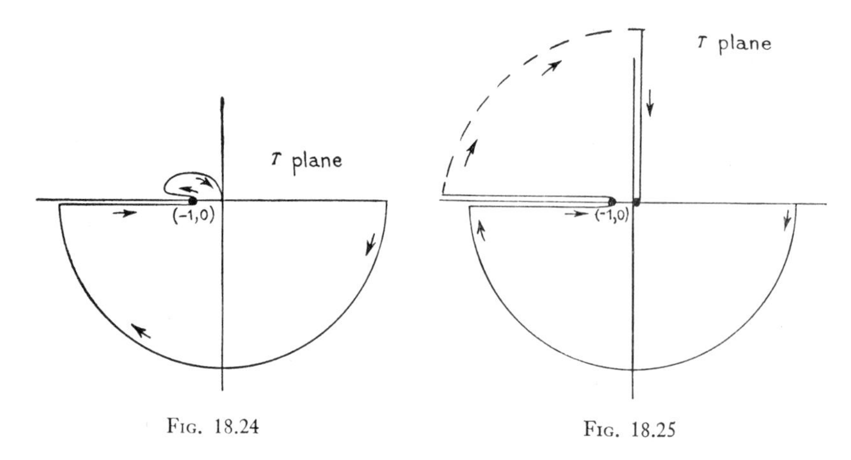

FIG. 18.24

FIG. 18.25

18.8. *Relative Importance of Tubes and Circuit in Limiting Feedback*

The discussion of the last few sections has shown how the feedback which can be obtained in any given amplifier depends upon the high-frequency asymptote of the feedback loop. It is a matter of some importance, then, to determine how the major portions of the amplifier contribute to the asymptote and what the effect of an improvement in any one of them may be on the total feedback available. In the earlier discussion the asymptotic loop was regarded as made up of two principal portions. One consisted of the forward circuit proper and the other of the return path provided by the input and output circuits and the feedback circuit proper. As we saw, the tubes furnish a positive upper limit on the asymptote, since we can scarcely improve upon the result secured when the return path is a direct short circuit from output plate to input grid, but within this limit a great deal depends upon the skill of the design engineer in providing functioning circuits in the return path without adding unduly to the asymptotic loss. It is convenient to continue this discussion by showing in more detail how the two factors affect the total feedback available.

The contributions of the forward circuit and the return path to the complete asymptote can be segregated most easily if we add a second asymptote, representing the gains of the tubes working into their own parasitic capacities, to the diagram of Fig. 18.13. This leads to the result illustrated by Fig. 18.26. The tube asymptote is shown by the broken line. It crosses the zero gain axis at the frequency $f_t = G_m/2\pi C$, where G_m and C are respectively the transconductance and capacity of a typical tube. Since the ratio G_m/C is the so-called " figure of merit " of a tube we may call f_t the "figure-of-merit frequency" for the forward circuit. The distance between the two asymptotes at f_t is indicated as the loss A_t. It is evidently equal to the contribution of the return path to the asymptotic loss at this frequency. In the simplest and, for feedback purposes, most favorable circuits, such as those shown in Figs. 18.6 and 18.10, the return path reduces at high frequencies to a capacity potentiometer and its asymptotic contribution is merely a constant potentiometer loss. This is illustrated in Fig. 18.26 by drawing the two asymptotes with the same slope but in more complicated circuits we may, of course, expect the slopes to be different.

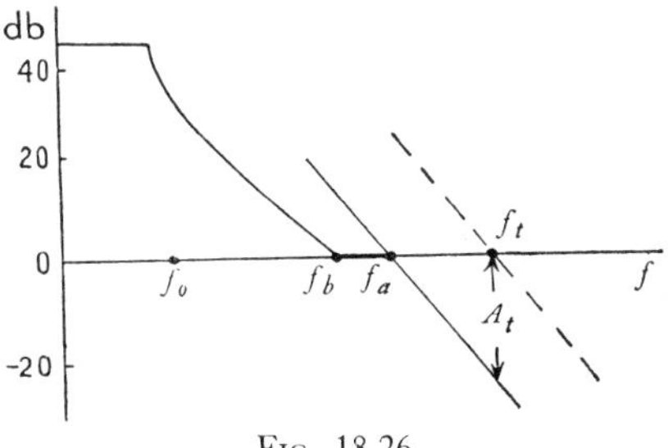

Fig. 18.26

The desired formula is obtained by expressing the asymptotic crossover frequency f_a in terms of f_t, A_t, and n. This allows us to replace (18–7) by

$$A_m = 40 \log_{10} \frac{4f_t}{nf_0} - \frac{2A_t}{n}. \qquad (18\text{–}12)$$

The first term of (18–12) shows how the available feedback depends upon the intrinsic band width of the available tubes. In low power tubes especially designed for the purpose it is possible to secure an f_t as high as 50 or 100 mc, but if f_0 is small the first term will be substantial even if tubes with much lower values of f_t are selected. The second term of (18–12) measures the sacrifice in feedback which can be ascribed to the rest of the circuit. If the amplifier is well planned and the other requirements on it are reasonably favorable it is possible for this term to be as small as 10 or 15 db. With present-day tubes the second term must necessarily be of this order of magnitude if the amplifier is to have a reasonably large feedback over a useful range of several megacycles. If the requirements on the input, output, and β circuits are particularly severe, on the other hand, or if the useful band is so narrow that adequate feedback can be obtained without careful planning, the second term may be very much greater.

18.9. *Optimum Number of Stages in a Feedback Amplifier*

In addition to f_t and A_t, equation (18–12) includes the asymptotic slope n. Since the tubes make no contribution to the asymptotic loss at $f = f_t$ we can vary n without affecting A_t by changing the number of tubes in the circuit. This makes it possible to compute the optimum number of tubes which should be used in any given situation in order to provide the maximum possible feedback. If A_t is small the first term of (18–12) will be the dominant one and it is evidently desirable to have a small number of

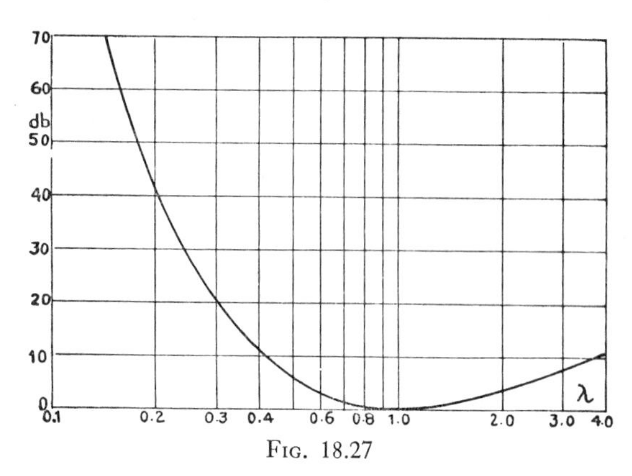

FIG. 18.27

stages. The limit may be taken as $n = 2$ since with only one stage the feedback is restricted by the available forward gain, which is not taken into account in this analysis. On the other hand since the second term varies more rapidly than the first with n, the optimum number of stages will increase as A_t is increased. It is given generally by

$$n = \frac{A_t}{8.68}, \tag{18–13}$$

or in other words the optimum n is equal to the asymptotic loss at the tube crossover in nepers.

The effect of choosing an n which is greater or less than the optimum can be studied by setting $n = \lambda(A_t/8.68)$. This permits (18–12) to be replaced by

$$A_m = 40 \log_{10} \frac{12.8}{A_t} \frac{f_t}{f_0} - \left[40 \log_{10} \lambda + \frac{17.4(1 - \lambda)}{\lambda} \right]. \tag{18–14}$$

The first term obviously represents the feedback obtained when the optimum number of stages is used and the second term the reduction in feedback which follows from the use of some number other than the optimum. A plot of the second term is shown by Fig. 18.27. We see that there is comparatively little penalty in using any number of stages between half and twice the optimum, but that larger departures are more serious.

Since feedback amplifiers are usually constructed with three stages in the forward circuit we can conveniently illustrate these relations by considering under what circumstances a three stage amplifier is likely to give the maximum amount of feedback. One extreme is represented by a very broad band amplifier, such as a television amplifier with a 4 mc useful band. With such a large f_0 a reasonable amount of feedback is obtainable only if f_t is as large and A_t as small as possible. Let it be supposed, for example, that the best obtainable values for these quantities are 80 mc and 18 db, respectively. If we assume that $n = 3$ the maximum available feedback, from (18–12), is 45 db. An appreciably smaller feedback is to be expected in practice, when allowance is made for reasonable phase and gain margins. With the assumed A_t the nearest integral n satisfying (18–13) is 2, but it is clear from Fig. 18.27 that the use of a three stage circuit instead makes only an insignificant difference in the result. A severe penalty will be incurred, on the other hand, if we either use many more than three stages with the same A_t or increase the optimum n by increasing A_t.

When the amplifier has a much narrower band it becomes relatively much easier to secure a large feedback. Let it be supposed, for example, that $f_t = 40$ mc and that $A_t = 3$ nepers, or 26 db, so that three stages is the optimum number. Then in the three stage circuit the maximum feedback is 68 db for a useful band of 400 kc, it is more than 90 db for a useful band of 100 kc, and more than 130 db for a useful band of 10 kc. Except perhaps for the first, these values lie beyond any range of normal practical interest. They are not readily approximated in actual amplifiers principally because the values of A_t which are usually encountered, in fact, are much greater than the value, 3 nepers, which was postulated in the computation. This, of course, implies that the optimum number of stages is correspondingly greater than 3. As a general rule of thumb, therefore, we can say that when present-day high gain tubes are used the most appropriate number of stages is likely to be two or three for amplifiers whose useful bands cover a few megacycles but that for narrow band structures, extending perhaps to a few hundred kilocycles, the available feedback can always be increased by increasing the number of stages beyond three unless the feedback available even with three stages is so great that there is no practical incentive to secure further improvement in any event.

This discussion obviously ignores the fact that in many amplifiers the number of stages which can be used is limited by economic considerations. In other circumstances, however, the addition of extra stages to compensate for a high A_t is frequently a comparatively simple means of increasing the available feedback. An example is furnished by high power circuits, such as radio transmitters, where circuit limitations are usually severe but the cost of additional tubes, at least in low power stages, is relatively unimportant. As an extreme example, we may consider the problem of providing envelope feedback around a transmitter. With the relatively sharp tuning ordinarily used in the high-frequency circuits of a transmitter the asymptotic characteristics of the feedback path will be comparatively unfavorable. For illustrative purposes we may assume that $f_a = 40$ kc and $n = 6$. In accordance with (18–7) this would provide a maximum available feedback over a 10 kc voice band of 17 db. It will also be assumed that the additional tubes for the low power portions of the circuit have an f_t of 10 mc.* The corresponding A_t is 33 nepers† so that equation (18–13) indicates that the feedback would be increased by the addition of as many as 27 tubes to the circuit. Naturally in such an extreme case this result can be looked upon only as a qualitative indication of the direction in which to proceed. If we add only 4 tubes, however, the available feedback becomes 46 db while if we add 10 tubes it reaches 60 db. The ultimate feedback, when all 27 tubes are added, is given by the first term of (18–14) as 66 db. It is to be observed that only a small part of the available gain of the added tubes is used in directly increasing the feedback. The remainder is consumed in compensating for the unfortunate phase shifts introduced by the rest of the circuit.

18.10. *Amplifiers with Excess Phase Shift*

Thus far it has been assumed that the loop phase shift of the amplifier is the minimum consistent with the loop gain characteristic. In occasional amplifiers, however, departures from the minimum phase shift laws are encountered. The departure can usually be represented by adding a phase characteristic which is proportional to frequency to the normal minimum characteristic, and only added characteristics of this type will be considered here. The additional phase shifts are usually trivial if we consider the useful band alone. They may be worth taking into account, however, when we give consideration to the fact that the effective band width of a feedback amplifier, for design purposes, is many times its useful band.

* In tubes operating at a high power level f_t may, of course, be quite low. It is evident, however, that only the tubes added to the circuit are significant in interpreting (18–13). The additional tubes may be inserted directly in the feedback path if they are made substantially linear in the voice range by subsidiary feedback of their own. This will not affect the essential result of the present analysis.

† It is, of course, not to be expected that the actual asymptotic slope will be constant from 40 kc to 10 mc. Since only the region extending a few octaves above 40 kc is of interest in the final design, however, the apparent A_t can be obtained by extrapolating the slope in this region.

Departures from the minimum phase shift laws in the feedback loop may occur for a variety of reasons. Some of the principal causes are given in the list below.

1. It is well known that the response of an electrical system can be studied exactly only by means of the electromagnetic field equations. The circuit laws are approximations which work well when the wavelength of the signal employed is very much larger than the geometrical dimensions of the apparatus, but which become erroneous when these distances are comparable. In the design of a feedback loop, this means that difficulties with additional phase shifts are to be expected whenever the distance around the loop is not small compared with the wavelength corresponding to the highest effective design frequency.

As an example, let it be supposed that the distance around the loop is one meter. This is the wavelength of a 300 mc wave. Since one full wave corresponds to a phase retardation of 360°, we can consequently say roughly* that the actual loop phase characteristic contains an added linear component having a slope of 1.2° per mc. In a narrow band amplifier this much excess phase is insignificant, but if the useful band is of television size, so that the effective design band extends over perhaps 50 or 100 mc, it constitutes an important problem. It can evidently be dealt with most directly by building the amplifier as compactly as possible, so that the distance around the loop becomes much less than the one meter originally postulated. Conversely, much more excess phase shift is to be expected when the feedback path is very long, as it might be, for example, if we attempted to feed back around a radio transmitter through pick-up from an antenna located at some distance from the transmitter proper.

2. A second general cause of excess phase is found in the transit times of vacuum tubes. The transit time of the tube is the time required for the passage of electrons from cathode to plate under the influence of the *B* battery voltage and depends broadly upon the battery voltage and the spacing between electrodes. It can be treated as the equivalent of a linear phase characteristic, just as we treat the " delay " of an ordinary electrical

* The reason why the computation may not lead to an accurate result can be understood from a consideration of the transmission down an ordinary transmission line. On the average, the phase characteristic is the straight line corresponding to the delay of the circuit. If the transmission line is badly mismatched at both ends, however, the actual phase characteristic ripples about the linear characteristic, intersecting it at the quarter wave points. Thus the actual characteristic may depart appreciably from the linear characteristic, especially in the region below the first quarter wave point. The various components of the feedback loop, when analyzed in terms of distributed constants, may obviously present a broadly analogous situation.

system. In present-day tubes adapted for high-frequency operation the corresponding phase angle may be as little as a few tenths of a degree per megacycle per tube. Even so, however, the total phase shift may be serious if we add the phase shifts of several tubes and consider effective bands of the order of 50 to 100 mc.

3. In occasional amplifiers excess phase shift may appear accidentally through the use of a non-minimum structure in some part of the loop. These difficulties are usually easy to avoid. An example is furnished by Fig. 18.28, which represents a shielded input transformer used as part of a series feedback amplifier. Ideally, the transformer enters the feedback loop only as a two-terminal impedance inserted in series between the β

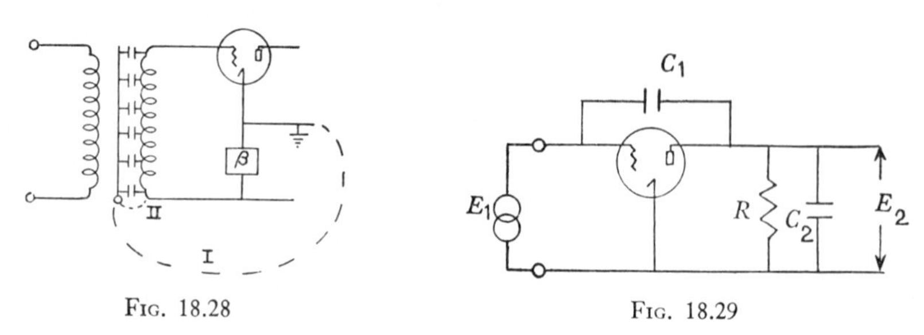

FIG. 18.28

FIG. 18.29

circuit and the input grid. As the drawing shows, however, there is distributed capacity between the transformer high winding and the shield. If the shield is connected to ground, as shown by broken line I, this capacity in association with the inductance of the high winding produces a non-minimum phase four-terminal network with properties very similar to those of a transmission line, and a large amount of excess phase will result. This difficulty is avoided by connecting the shield to one end of the high winding, as indicated by the broken line II.

4. Departures from the minimum phase characteristic may also be produced in some amplifiers by parasitic local feedback paths associated with the individual tubes in the forward circuit of the amplifier.* An example is furnished by the triode with parasitic grid-plate capacity C_1 shown by Fig. 18.29.† The circuit is supposed, for simplicity, to be energized by a generator of zero internal impedance and the following interstage is taken as an elementary capacity-resistance combination. We notice that the signal can pass to the following interstage by either of two paths. The

* Strictly speaking, amplifiers of this type are multiple loop structures and do not fall in the class of circuits considered in this chapter. They are included in the present list on the assumption that the local feedbacks are small enough to make the single loop analysis adequate.

† The author is indebted to his colleague, Dr. C. R. Burrows, for this analysis.

first is the normal path directly through the tube while the second is the path through C_1 which would exist even if the tube were dead. The first path is, of course, dominant at low frequencies but it becomes less efficient than the second when the frequency is made sufficiently great. Moreover, the outputs of the two paths are broadly of opposite sign, because of the phase reversal in the tube, and therefore tend to cancel. These, however, are the general conditions which were shown in Chapter XI to lead to transmission of the non-minimum type and we may therefore expect that the net phase characteristic will include an all-pass phase in excess of the minimum.

The situation illustrated by Fig. 18.29 can be treated analytically by writing the voltage gain E_2/E_1, as

$$\frac{E_2}{E_1} = -\frac{G_m R}{1 + i\omega(C_1 + C_2)R} + \frac{i\omega C_1 R}{1 + i\omega(C_1 + C_2)R}, \quad (18\text{–}15)$$

where G_m is the transconductance of the tube and the two terms on the right-hand side represent transmission through the two separate paths. The equation can be rewritten as

$$\frac{E_2}{E_1} = -R\frac{G_m + i\omega C_1}{1 + i\omega(C_1 + C_2)R}\,\frac{G_m - i\omega C_1}{G_m + i\omega C_1}. \quad (18\text{–}16)$$

In this form the second factor, which corresponds to an all-pass structure of the elementary type shown by Fig. 11.11 of Chapter XI, represents the excess phase. At moderate frequencies the excess appears as a linear characteristic with a slope of $7.2 \times 10^8 (C_1/G_m)$ degrees per mc.

5. The final source of excess phase is not due, strictly speaking, to a departure from minimum phase shift configurations, but it is convenient to include it in this list for purposes of discussion. It will be recalled that we have thus far assumed that the asymptotic characteristic of the amplifier would be fully established, so that it could be represented by a simple straight line on logarithmic paper, by the time design control of the feedback loop was finally relinquished. In exceptional amplifiers this may not be true and an excess phase term should be used to represent subsequent changes in the behavior of the asymptote. As an example, let it be supposed that N_5 and N_6 in Fig. 18.6 reduce to resistances at high frequencies and that the capacities C_5 and C_6 which parallel them are extremely small. If we neglect C_5 and C_6 entirely the loop gain characteristic takes the form shown by Fig. 18.30, where ABC is the asymptotic characteristic with the

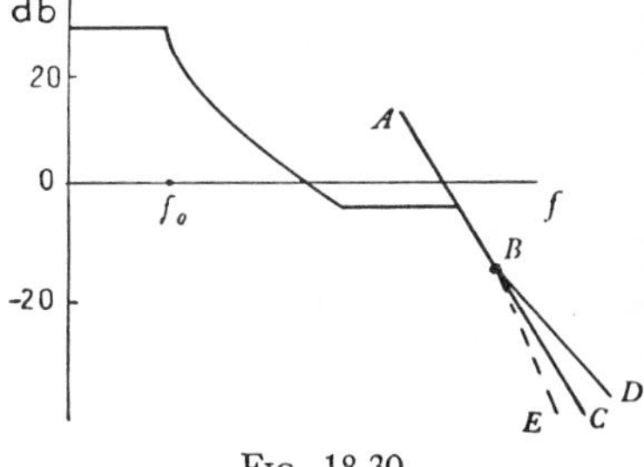

FIG. 18.30

two capacities absent. The actual high frequency behavior, with C_5 and C_6 included, follows the broken line path ABD. We can evidently represent this situation most simply by supposing that ABC is the asymptote, for purposes of analysis, and that the divergence between BC and BD will be treated by adding a corresponding linear phase shift to the loop characteristics at lower frequencies. The " excess " phase shift in this case will, of course, be negative. The broken line BE represents a modification leading to an increased loss at extremely high frequencies, and a corresponding positive excess phase.

18.11. *Adjustment of Overall Cut-off Characteristic to Compensate for Excess Phase*

It will be recalled that the sharp changes in slope at the ends of the horizontal step in the overall loop gain characteristic produce linear phase characteristics which can be made to cancel one another by choosing the correct ratio for the terminating frequencies of the step. Since the excess phase characteristic is also assumed to be linear we can evidently cancel it out also by making an appropriate change in the step length. In terms of the notation of Fig. 18.13, for example, the phase characteristics corresponding to the changes in slope at the ends of the step are respectively $-(4/\pi)(f/f_b)$ and $(2n/\pi)(f/f_a)$. If we specify the excess phase characteristic, from whatever source, by means of the frequency f_p at which it would equal $2n/\pi$ radians, if extrapolated, the required relation therefore becomes

$$-\frac{4}{\pi}\frac{f}{f_b}+\frac{2n}{\pi}\frac{f}{f_a}+\frac{2n}{\pi}\frac{f}{f_p}=0, \tag{18–17}$$

from which f_b is fixed in terms of f_a and f_p by the equation

$$f_b=\frac{2}{n}\frac{f_af_p}{f_a+f_p}. \tag{18–18}$$

Since the cut-off proportions below f_b are not affected by these changes, equation (18–18) evidently implies that formula (18–7) for the maximum available feedback should be rewritten in the general case as

$$A_m=40\log_{10}\frac{4}{nf_0}\frac{f_af_p}{f_a+f_p}. \tag{18–19}$$

Thus the effective asymptotic frequency in limiting feedback is the " parallel combination " of f_a and f_p. If we make the same changes in (18–12) we secure

$$A_m = 40 \log_{10} \frac{4}{nf_0} \frac{f_p f_t}{f_p + f_t\, 10^{-A/20n}} - \frac{2A_t}{n}. \tag{18–20}$$

This equation is of particular interest for extremely broad band amplifiers, where the fundamental physical limitations are found in the figures of merit and transit times of available tubes. We notice that when A_t is very small the figure of merit frequency f_t and the transit time frequency f_p are of equal importance in limiting the available feedback. As the circuit loss A_t grows, however, an improvement in f_t becomes more effective than an improvement in f_p.

If the amplifier is to be built with prescribed margins the procedure is the same, except that since a gain margin shifts the step of the cut-off to a slightly higher frequency it makes the importance of the excess phase characteristic somewhat greater. One modification should, however, be introduced when the amplifier is to transmit a geometrically narrow band. Here it is desirable to break down the total excess phase characteristic into a constant, representing the phase displacement at the center of the band, and a variable portion representing the phase variation over the effective design band on each side of the center. The constant is treated by crossing terminals, if necessary, and adding either a short length of line or some relatively unselective lumped constant structure, such as one of those shown by Fig. 18.31, to make the net phase displacement at the center of the band equal to an integral number of revolutions.* This leaves only the variable characteristic to be considered in converting the actual band-pass amplifier to an equivalent low-pass structure of the type described in this chapter. The principle of conservation of band width is maintained for this part of the total phase shift. In other words, an excess phase characteristic having a given slope in degrees per megacycle will be equally limiting for a band of a given breadth, in megacycles, whatever the absolute location of the band in the frequency spectrum may be. In extreme cases this arrangement may evidently lead to a Nyquist plot which encircles the origin many

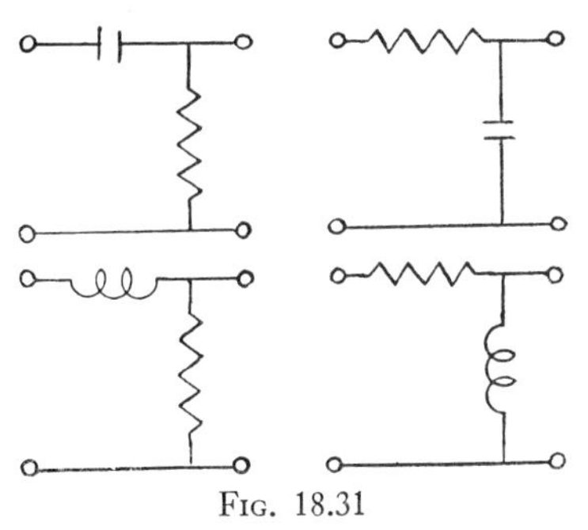

FIG. 18.31

* See R. C. Shaw, U. S. Pat. No. 2,210,503.

times above and below the effective design range, but if the amplifier is properly cut off within the effective range, the stability of the system is not jeopardized.

18.12. *Relation between the Loop Design and the External Gain of the Amplifier*

The discussion thus far has been concerned with the most desirable shape for the overall loop cut-off characteristic without regard to the portion of the loop in which the shaping is to be obtained. It is clear, however, that the loop characteristic can ordinarily be adjusted most easily by the interstage networks which, unlike the input and output circuits or the β circuit, are independent of any of the other characteristics of the amplifier. In the absence of any special reasons to the contrary, it is most logical to begin the overall amplifier design with the design of the input and output circuits, paying especial attention to impedance and volume performance requirements, for which these circuits are controlling. The contributions of the input and output circuits to the external gain can then be computed and a β circuit chosen to give the required final gain characteristic. The interstage networks are designed as a last step to furnish the difference between the overall loop characteristic and the loop characteristic supplied by the input, output, and β circuits.

This general procedure must be qualified in one respect to take account of the fact that the impedance, external gain and volume performance characteristics are normally specified only within the useful band. Thus there is, at least on paper, a certain element of arbitrariness in the way in which the various components of the feedback loop enter into the overall loop characteristic in the cut-off interval. On the other hand, as we approach higher and higher frequencies and parasitic elements become more and more significant, it is increasingly difficult to secure effective design control of any one of the components over a very wide range. Thus it is important to allocate the overall characteristic among the various components with reasonable care if difficult or impossible design problems are to be avoided.

The allocation of the loop cut-off characteristic among the various components beyond the band is governed, broadly speaking, by the external gain requirement within the useful band. In general, the cut-off will be shaped chiefly by the interstage networks when the gain is relatively low and chiefly by the β circuit when the gain is relatively high. An illustration is furnished by the series feedback amplifier shown previously in Fig. 18.10. If a low external gain is required in the useful band the impedance of the feedback network N_3 must be correspondingly high. This evidently implies that the feedback network will be governed in the cut-off interval principally by the prescribed parasitic capacity C_7 in shunt with it, and cannot be put under effective design control. On the other hand, the low β circuit loss requires only a low interstage gain to give the prescribed loop gain and since low gain interstages are comparatively flexible they can be used to control the loop characteristics in the cut-off interval as well as in the useful band. Conversely, if the required external gain is high the interstage networks must be approximately of the maximum gain type* and will have determinate characteristics outside the band. The β circuit, however, will be well under our control, since the high external gain corresponds to a feedback impedance so low that C_7 is no longer hampering. Since maximum gain interstages cut off rapidly outside the band the required feedback impedance will evidently be one which increases gradually through the cut-off interval, in order to bring the total loop cut-off rate within safe limits.

The situation can be studied quantitatively by means of equation (17–18) of the preceding chapter. It will be recalled that this equation was developed to show how much it was necessary to reduce the gain of an interstage below the maximum possible level within the useful band in order to provide any prescribed interstage phase shift less than 90° beyond the band. In the present situation the same relation can be used backward. If we begin by comparing the interstage gain necessary for the required feedback with the maximum possible interstage gain the formula gives the integrated phase margin which will be exhibited by the interstage networks and from this it is easy to determine the phase margin which must be derived from the rest of the circuit. For example, if a three-stage μ circuit is used, the phase angle of the two interstage circuits in the cut-off interval will be approximately 180°. Since the total loop phase shift is also about 180° the net phase shift of the return path from output plate to input grid must be roughly zero. The loop phase margin can be obtained either by using interstage circuits with phase angles slightly less than 90° or by using a return path with a negative phase angle. The reduction-in-gain integral gives the fraction of the total which must be obtained from the interstages.

* It is evident here that if the external gain is very high even maximum gain interstages may not be sufficient to supply it and also the feedback which would otherwise be obtainable with the given asymptotic conditions. This is an obvious physical limitation which applies to all the analyses of this chapter and requires no further discussion. It should also be noticed that in the particular circuit of Fig. 18.10 changes in external gain do not affect the asymptote, and therefore the available feedback. This tends to be true whenever pains are taken to choose configurations with favorable asymptotes, but it may not hold in other circumstances, as when the gain change is made by the addition of a simple loss pad in the β circuit.

Once this allocation has been made the areas under the phase margin plots can be distributed as functions of frequency in any way which seems likely to give simple network designs. In general, it is convenient to employ the interstage phase margin near the edge of the useful band, where use may be made of the shaping elements required within the band, and to rely upon the rest of the circuit at more remote frequencies, where adjustments can be made with considerable freedom without marring the precision of the external gain characteristic in the useful band. An illustrative design involving calculations of this sort is given in the next chapter.

CHAPTER XIX

Illustrative Designs for Single Loop Feedback Amplifiers*

19.1. *Introduction*

This chapter consists of a number of examples of the overall feedback loop design method advanced in the preceding chapter. An attempt has been made to choose designs which will illustrate, for a variety of situations, some of the detailed ways in which the theoretical overall cut-off characteristic can be realized. In view of the enormous range of possibilities, however, many other techniques can, of course, also be used. In each design example attention is focused primarily on the feedback loop problem. The other aspects of the amplifier design are described only briefly, and sometimes in an oversimplified fashion. Two of the designs include subsidiary feedback on individual tubes in addition to the principal loop feedback. These are treated, for simplicity, as single loop structures although they do not, of course, meet the strict requirements of the definition advanced in the last chapter.

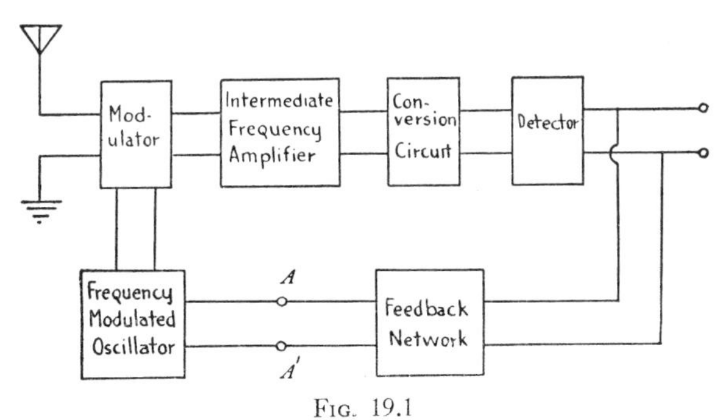

Fig. 19.1

19.2. *Feedback Design for a Frequency Modulation Receiver*

The first example is the feedback design for the frequency modulation receiver shown diagrammatically in Fig. 19.1.† If we suppose for the

* Most of the designs in this chapter are due to the author's colleagues R. L. Dietzold, H. G. Och, and W. H. Boghosian. The double feedback path design is due to J. G. Kreer and E. H. Perkins, the forward circuit of the radio transmitter with envelope feedback to C. R. Burrows and A. Decino, and some of the lower cut-off designs to J. M. West.

† This circuit is the invention of J. G. Chaffee — see *B. S. T. J.*, July, 1939.

moment that terminals AA' are open, the " frequency modulated oscillator " in the drawing becomes an ordinary fixed frequency local oscillator, and the circuit reduces to a conventional superheterodyne receiver for FM signals. The conversion circuit is the usual " slope " network which changes frequency modulated to amplitude modulated signals, and the detector is an ordinary rectifier which recovers the audio signal from this amplitude modulated wave. When the feedback loop is closed, the local oscillator frequency is varied in accordance with the audio signal and this frequency variation is superposed upon that of the incoming wave in transmission through the intermediate frequency stages.

A detailed exposition of the operation of this device is beyond the scope of this book. Briefly, however, it may be recalled that external interference in an FM signal can be resolved into two components, one representing frequency modulation and the other amplitude modulation of the incoming wave. The first of these cannot be separated from the frequency modulation representing the signal proper, but its interfering effect can be made very small by using a very large frequency swing to represent the signal. The amplitude modulation component is, however, more serious. Since the final detector is an amplitude modulation device, this component may evidently appear in the final audio output, and be large enough to be important in the signal-to-noise ratio for the system. In the orthodox Armstrong circuit, consequently, the amplitude modulation due to interference (or fading) is first eliminated by passing the incoming wave through a volume limiter which restricts it to a nearly constant amplitude.

The feedback circuit in Fig. 19.1 serves as an alternative to the volume limiter. Its operation can be understood most readily if we think of it as an ordinary feedback amplifier in which μ is the voice frequency output per unit frequency displacement at the modulator terminals and β is the frequency displacement of the local oscillator per unit voice frequency output. This is equivalent to measuring the signal by current or voltage in the voice frequency parts of the circuit and by frequency displacement from the carrier in the intermediate frequency stages. From these definitions, the product $\mu\beta$ is the voice frequency transmission from terminals AA' around the complete loop and back to AA' again. In the ordinary feedback amplifier, the signal intensity in the early stages of the forward circuit is reduced by feedback, and it is necessary to make a corresponding increase in the forward circuit gain if the input signal level and output power are to be kept constant. Here, similarly, the FM feedback reduces the frequency swing in the intermediate frequency stages. The " gain " of the forward circuit is increased correspondingly by increasing the slope of the conversion circuit to provide the same efficiency of conversion from frequency to amplitude modulation with the reduced frequency swing.

In these terms the reduction, by the feedback circuit, in the effects of amplitude modulation due to external sources can be treated exactly as the reduction, by feedback, in forward circuit noise in an ordinary amplifier was treated in Chapter III. Just as in that analysis, we find that if we regard

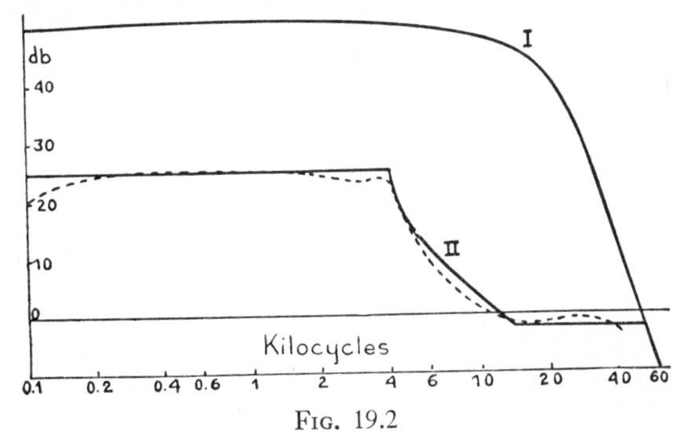

FIG. 19.2

the voltage appearing in the detector due to amplitude modulation of the incoming signal as an extraneous noise generator applied at that point, its effects are reduced through feedback in the ratio $(1 - \mu\beta):1$. As an alternative, we may notice that since the voice frequency output is proportional to the amplitude as well as the frequency displacement of the modulator out-

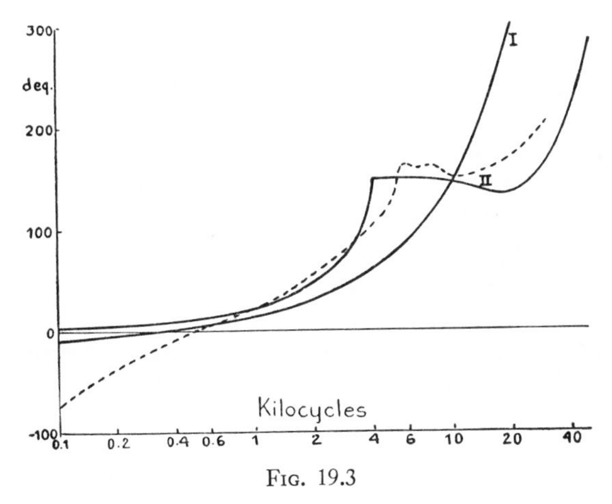

FIG. 19.3

put, amplitude changes in the incoming signal may also be regarded as changes in μ. These again are reduced by feedback in the ratio $(1 - \mu\beta):1$.

Fortunately, a detailed understanding of the operation of the high frequency portions of the circuit is not necessary for the feedback design problem. If we view the circuit from terminals AA', we are interested only in shaping the transmission characteristic around the loop at voice frequencies to conform with the ideal cut-off. Since the contribution of the high frequency portions of the structure can be determined by measurement, the problem reduces to that of finding a passive equalizer which can be inserted in the β path to give the required total characteristic. This is the simplest as well as one of the most common forms in which a feedback design problem may be presented.

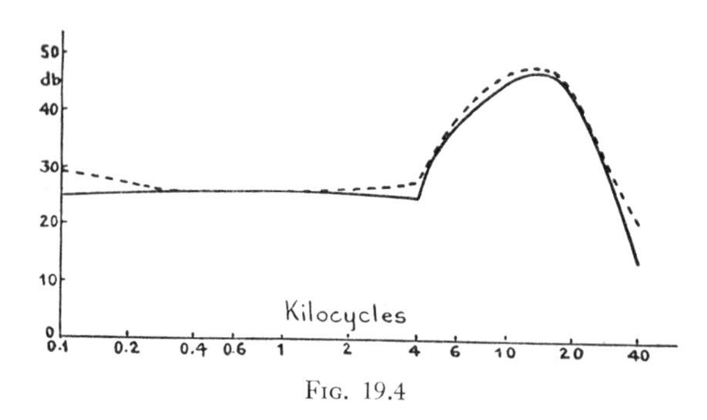

FIG. 19.4

The measured gain and phase characteristics between the input terminals of the local oscillator and the output terminals of the rectifier are shown by Curves I of Figs. 19.2 and 19.3. It will be seen that the gain becomes zero at about 50 kc and that the high frequency slope of the gain characteristic may be estimated at about 36 db per octave. These figures may be taken to represent the asymptotic performance of the complete loop if we suppose that the loss introduced by the equalizer at high frequencies will not be great. They indicate, from equation (18–7) of the preceding chapter, that the maximum available feedback will be about 36 db for the prescribed useful band of 4 kc. When allowances are made for phase and gain margin, the expected feedback may be taken as 25 db. The ideal cut-off characteristics for this feedback with a phase margin of 30° and a gain margin of 2 db* are shown by Curves II of Figs. 19.2 and 19.3.

The rest of the design consists in the simulation of the difference between the measured loop gain characteristic and the theoretical gain characteristic by an equalizer. This difference, expressed as a loss, is shown by the solid curve of Fig. 19.4 and the loss actually obtained from the equalizer by the broken curve of the same figure.† The equalizer structure itself is shown by

* A small gain margin is assumed in the design since the experimental circuit included a gain control by which the margin could be adjusted.

† The low-frequency behavior of the broken curve in this figure, or in Figs. 19.2 and 19.3, is explained by the presence of a blocking condenser in the feedback path. This element is not shown explicitly in Fig. 19.5 since only the high frequency characteristic is of immediate design interest.

Fig. 19.5.* The complete loop characteristic with the equalizer included is shown by the broken lines in Figs. 19.2 and 19.3.

The feedback of 25 db obtained by the design is adequate in this application. It is interesting to notice, however, that the assumed asymptotic characteristic for the loop corresponds to a very high " circuit loss " A_t. Thus it follows from equation (18–20) of the preceding chapter that it should be possible to secure much more feedback over the given band, or the same feedback over a wider band, if we add several stages of vacuum tube gain as well as a passive equalizer in the feedback circuit. A design including tubes can be obtained by following principles somewhat similar to those used here, although it will naturally be much more complicated.

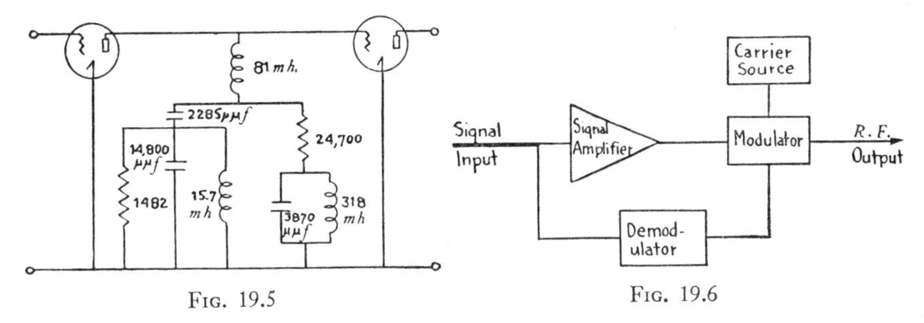

FIG. 19.5

FIG. 19.6

19.3. *Envelope Feedback for a Radio Frequency Transmitter*

The second example consists of the feedback design for a low-power radio transmitter transmitting multiplex signals on an ultra short wavelength. The circuit is of particular interest as an illustration of the principles developed in the preceding chapter on the optimum number of stages for a feedback amplifier.

The transmitter is shown diagrammatically in Fig. 19.6. The low-frequency signal is applied at the left. It consists actually of one group of 12 telephone channels. With the standard 4 kc channel spacing the signal occupies only 48 kc but the useful band is assumed for design purposes to extend to 100 kc to permit the transmitter to carry a second 12-channel group if desired. The signal is first stepped up to its final power level by means of the signal amplifier, and it is then applied to the antenna at radio frequencies by the modulator and local oscillator shown in the drawing. The carrier frequency is 141 mc. A portion of the output is passed through the demodulator and reapplied at the original signal frequency to the input.

* The tubes in Fig. 19.5 were part of the original circuit. The equalization is obtained by replacing the constant resistance interstage which connected them originally by the general impedance shown in the figure. The absolute level of gain depends upon a gain control elsewhere in the circuit.

This provides envelope feedback around the complete structure. The feedback is useful chiefly in suppressing distortion due to inter-channel modulation which would otherwise appear in a transmitter carrying so many channels. The desired value of feedback is 30 or more db.

All parts of the loop enter to some extent into the determination of the envelope feedback characteristic. The detailed shaping of the loop characteristic, however, is most conveniently obtained in the circuits of the signal amplifier. The circuits associated with the modulator are not very suit-

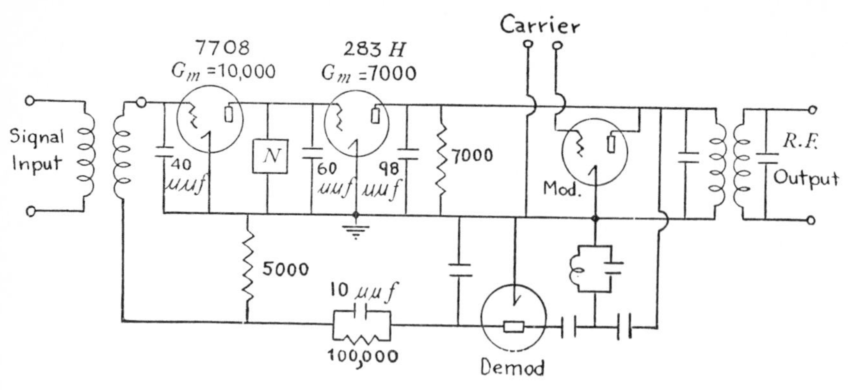

FIG. 19.7

able for this purpose because of the high frequency and power level at which they operate. Neither of these objections applies to the circuits associated with the demodulator. We must observe, however, that the demodulator is effectively part of the β circuit. Evidently, the reduction in interchannel modulation which is desired from the complete system will be realized only if the demodulator operates very accurately as a linear rectifier without introducing unwanted modulation products. The problem of providing a demodulator meeting these conditions is so difficult that it is undesirable to complicate it by introducing any other considerations in the design of this part of the structure.

A preliminary layout for the transmitter on this basis is shown by Fig. 19.7. A 283H tube has been chosen for the output power stage for the signal amplifier. The output impedance of the tube, consisting of 7000 ohms* in parallel with the plate capacity, is selected to secure the most efficient delivery of power from the tube, and should not be regarded as one of the circuits at our disposal in shaping the $\mu\beta$ characteristics. The output stage is preceded by a 7708 tube giving high gain but relatively low power

* This is not an inserted resistance; it represents the loading on the 283H tube due to the modulator stage.

to provide the rest of the forward gain for the circuit. The interstage network N is reserved in this tentative design for the solution of the loop shaping problem.

The networks associated with the modulator and demodulator need not be described in detail. They are represented in the drawing by much simplified versions of the actual structures. Broadly speaking, the modulator

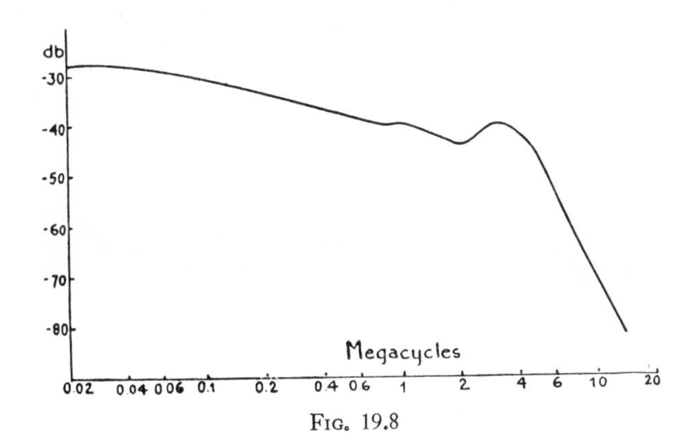

FIG. 19.8

networks consist of resonant circuits tuned to the carrier, the tuning being broad enough to prevent them from adding excessively to the asymptotic loss of the loop, as seen from the low-frequency parts of the circuit. The feedback path is assigned a loss of about 60 db from the modulator terminals to the input grid of the signal amplifier. About 30 db of this loss is furnished by the coupling circuit between modulator and demodulator. This places a very light load on the demodulator, which favors its operation as a linear rectifier. The remaining 30 db is furnished by the potentiometer of resistances and capacities connecting the demodulator to the input circuit. The potentiometer impedances are also chosen to provide maximum linearity of operation in the demodulator.

The loop transmission of the structure shown in Fig. 19.7 measured from the grid of the output tube to the grid of the input tube is given by Fig. 19.8. From this curve, and the known data for the transconductance and interstage capacity for the first tube in Fig. 19.7, we can easily estimate what the asymptotic performance of the complete loop will be. We find that the asymptote has a slope of 4 units, or 24 db per octave, and crosses the zero gain axis at about 1.5 mc. With the help of equation (18–7) of the preceding chapter and these figures the maximum available feedback over the nominal 100 kc signal band is found to be 47 db. This is more than the required feedback, but the excess is too small to provide large gain and phase margins.* It is consequently desirable to review the structure in an attempt to secure an improved asymptote before the detailed shaping of the $\mu\beta$ characteristic is undertaken.

Inspection of the circuits associated with the modulator and demodulator shows several ways in which an improved asymptotic performance might be obtained. For example, the high-frequency path in the present circuit includes as series elements the small capacity in parallel with the 100,000 ohm resistor in the demodulator output. If the resistor were replaced by a filter, exhibiting an impedance of 100,000 ohms at low frequencies but reducing to a capacity at high frequencies, the contribution to the asymptotic loss secured from this part of the circuit might evidently be decreased. We might also modify the coupling network between the modulator and demodulator to produce a decreasing loss at frequencies remote from the band. These are possibilities which might be exploited if no better alternative were available, but they evidently lead to circuit complications which it is desirable to avoid if possible.

A simpler method of improving the asymptotic characteristic in the structure under consideration is obtained by increasing the number of voltage stages in the signal amplifier. The 7708 tube already used for one stage of the amplifier has a " figure of merit " frequency f_t of about 50 mc.† From the known asymptote for the present loop the circuit loss A_t at this frequency is about 120 db, or 14 nepers. It follows from the discussion in the preceding chapter that if we add more 7708 tubes the available feedback will reach a maximum when enough tubes have been added to make the asymptotic slope equal to 14 units. Since the asymptotic slope in the circuit as it stands is 4 units, this would require the addition of 10 more voltage stages. The feedback obtained under these conditions is given by the first term of equation (18–14) of the preceding chapter and is equal to 69 db. The feedback obtained with any other number of stages in the forward circuit can be determined by subtracting the amounts indicated by the corresponding Fig. 18.27 in the preceding chapter from this limit. Thus, for example, in the circuit as it stands before any extra tubes are added, we have $\lambda = 0.286$ and the available feedback becomes $69 - 22 = 47$ db.

* In the structure of Fig. 19.7 the available feedback is, in fact, still more severely limited by the amount of gain which can be obtained from the first tube. This difficulty is ignored here, since in the final circuit the available forward gain is more than adequate for the feedback requirement.

† This figure refers to a number of 7708 tubes in tandem. A considerably lower f_t is realized in the single tube of Fig. 19.7 because of the large contribution of the interstage capacity furnished by the succeeding power tube and the decreased transconductance obtained from the tube when it delivers sufficient power to drive the final stage.

This agrees with the result obtained previously from a direct computation of the asymptotic performance of the structure. If we add two stages to the present circuit we find $\lambda = 0.43$ and the available feedback is 60 db. This choice was decided upon for the actual design, since the improvement in available feedback is quite adequate to give a convenient loop characteristic and the further advantage obtainable by adding more than two stages is comparatively small.

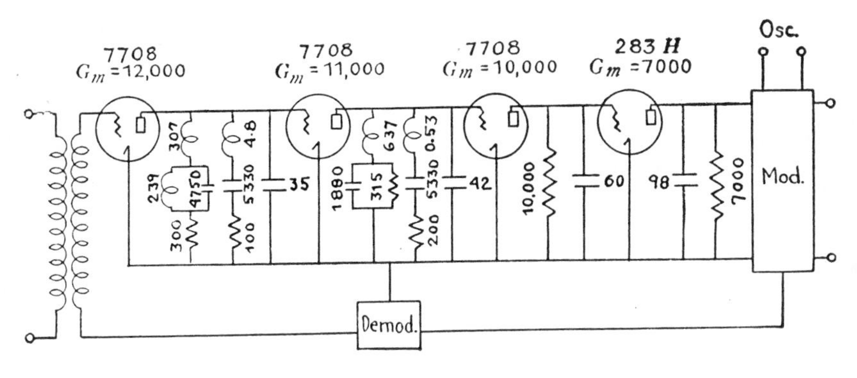

Fig. 19.9

With the figure of 60 db for the maximum available feedback at hand, the feedback which can be realized with any given phase and gain margins is readily determined from equation (18–9) of the preceding chapter. In this design, the margins were chosen as 30° and 12 db respectively and lead to a useful feedback of 38 db. The rest of the design consists merely in shaping networks which will provide the difference between the characteristic of Fig. 19.8 and an ideal cut-off characteristic corresponding to these values. With the two extra stages added to the amplifier, we now have, of course, three interstages among which the difference characteristic is to be allocated. The arrangement finally chosen is shown by Fig. 19.9. The last interstage, which has the highest power level, is made very simple, and it is also assigned most of the gain in order to make the power level in the earlier stages quite low. The first two interstages are essentially " trap circuit " designs of the type described in connection with Figs. 13.10 to 13.13 of Chapter XIII. The very low level of gain which these interstages are required to furnish permits the trap circuits to be designed at a very low impedance level so that they are effective in controlling the loop characteristics over a broad frequency range beyond the useful band.

The gain and phase characteristics obtained from the three interstages are shown by Fig. 19.10,* and the total loop gain and phase shift by Fig. 19.11. It will be seen that a feedback of about 35 db in the useful band is realized. This compares with the theoretical feedback of 38 db computed

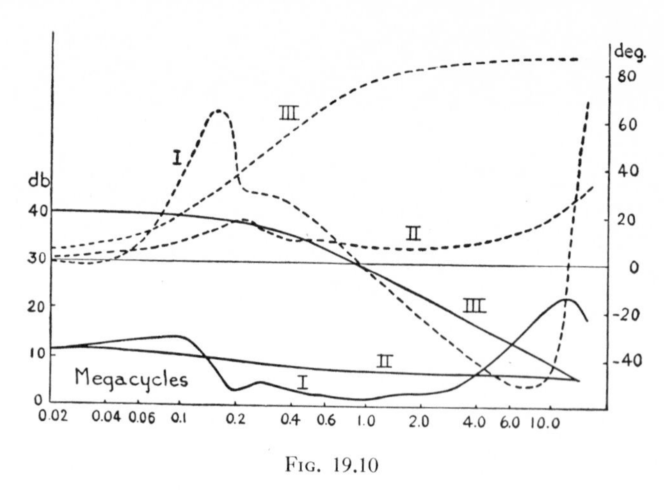

FIG. 19.10

earlier. The slight difference may be attributed to the fact that the design does not follow the sharp corner in the theoretical characteristic at the edge of the useful band accurately. No attempt was made to procure a precise match in this region, since adequate feedback was obtained without it.

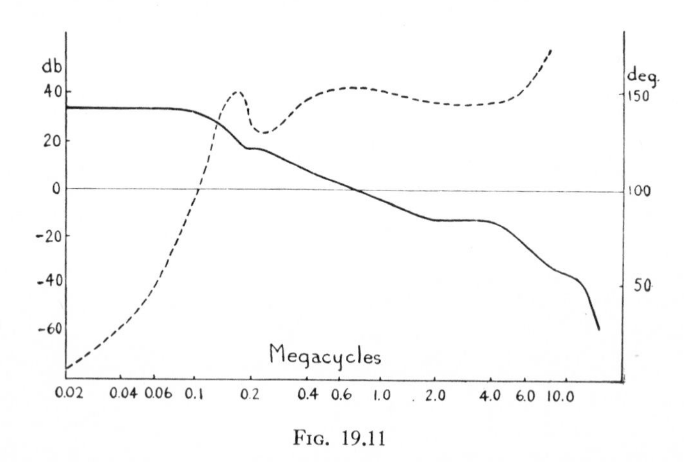

FIG. 19.11

* The relatively simple characteristics obtained from the second interstage, in spite of the complexity of the network, are explained by the fact that this structure was actually intended to be adjustable. The characteristics shown correspond to a reference setting for which the effect of the trap circuit is not prominent.

19.4. *Illustrative Design of an Amplifier with a Double Feedback Path*

The next example is an amplifier design for the type J system.* Since the circuit is relatively complicated it will not be described in detail. It does, however, afford a very interesting illustration of the salient role which the asymptote plays in determining the amount of feedback available and will be considered briefly from this point of view.

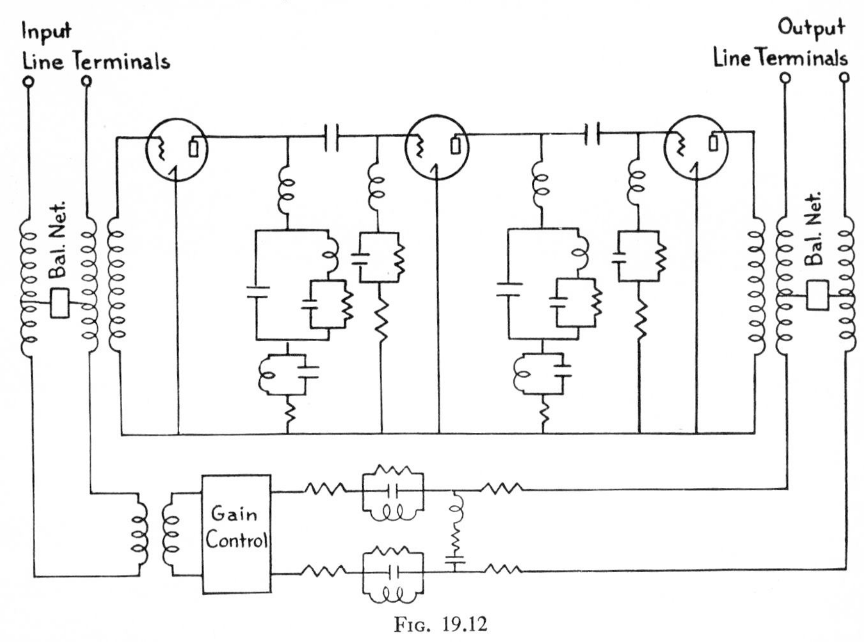

FIG. 19.12

The amplifier under consideration was intended to serve as a repeater in the type J open wire carrier system. It consists of three principal parts: the forward circuit, an outer or principal β path, and an inner β path. The general arrangement was shown schematically by Fig. 18.1 of the preceding chapter. If we ignore the inner β path for the moment, the structure is given in more detail in Fig. 19.12. The β circuit includes a gain control and an equalizer to compensate for variations in line attenuation. Otherwise the amplifier is characterized chiefly by the fact that the feedback is of the low side hybrid coil type at both ends. This feedback connection is particularly appropriate for the type J system, where one of the controlling problems is that of providing very good impedance matches everywhere in the system to avoid reflection crosstalk. As the discussion

* This is a reference to a carrier telephone system for open-wire lines, operating in the frequency range between 30 and 140 kc. For a more complete description see B. W. Kendall and H. A. Affel, *B.S.T.J.*, Jan., 1939.

of previous chapters showed, a hybrid coil feedback at input or output permits the active impedance of the amplifier to be controlled by the balancing network so that it can be matched very accurately to the characteristic impedance of the line. Low side rather than high side feedback is chosen

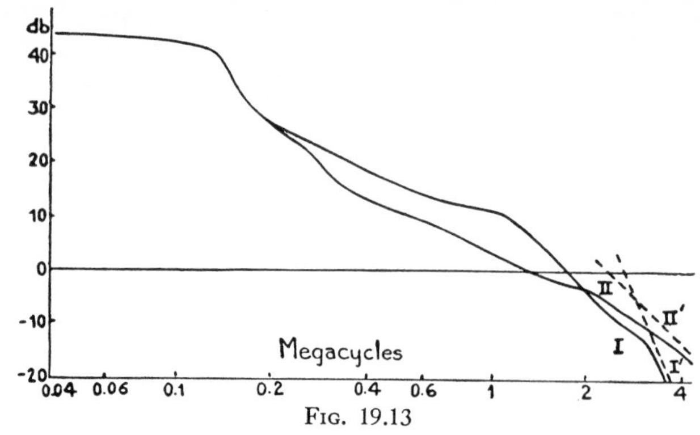

FIG. 19.13

for this application because with the low side connection most of the hybrid coil can be regarded effectively as part of the μ circuit and the impedance match to the line consequently remains good even if manufacturing variations in the coil are large.

Although the choice of the low side hybrid coil circuit is most satisfactory for the operating requirements on the amplifier, it carries with it one

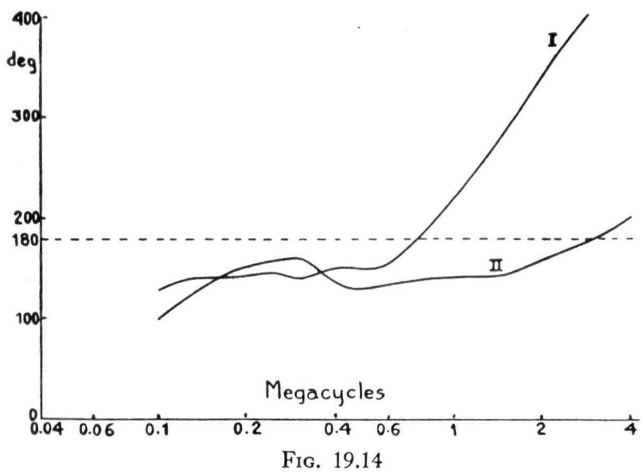

FIG. 19.14

unfortunate consequence. Since the feedback path goes through the coils, their leakage inductances appear as series elements in the asymptotic loop and the asymptotic characteristics of the circuit are consequently much less favorable than those obtained with most other types of feedback. This is illustrated by Curves I of Figs. 19.13 and 19.14, which represent the gain and phase characteristics for the loop composed of the forward circuit and the outer β circuit in Fig. 19.12 with the element values as they were established in the final design. The estimated asymptote for this loop is shown by the broken line I′ in Fig. 19.13. As the curves stand, they provide the desired feedback (45 db) in the useful band extending up to 150 kc. The circuit is, however, unstable, since the phase shift crosses 180° before the loop gain reaches zero. Stability might, of course, be retained by redesigning the circuit with a lower feedback. With an asymptote as unfavorable as the one indicated in the drawing, however, a sacrifice of at least 10 or 15 db in feedback would be necessary to secure a stable circuit.

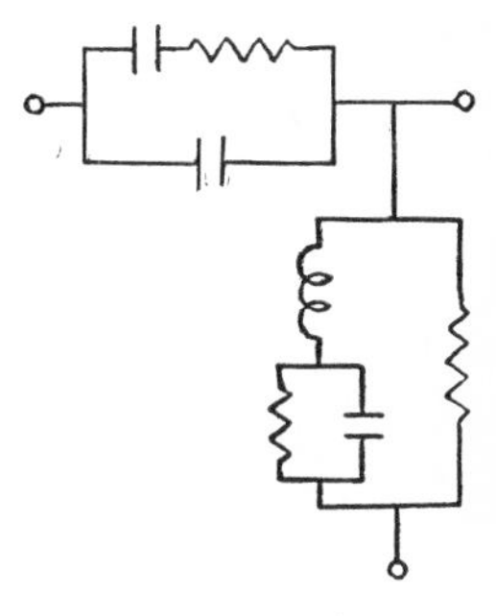

Fig. 19.15

This difficulty is overcome by the introduction of the inner feedback path. The structure used for the inner path is shown by Fig. 19.15. It is connected directly between the output plate and the input grid. The properties of the circuit are broadly similar to those of a high-pass filter. Within and near the useful band its attenuation is so great that the current fed through it can be neglected in comparison with the feedback through the outer β path. Thus computations of the gain and impedance character-

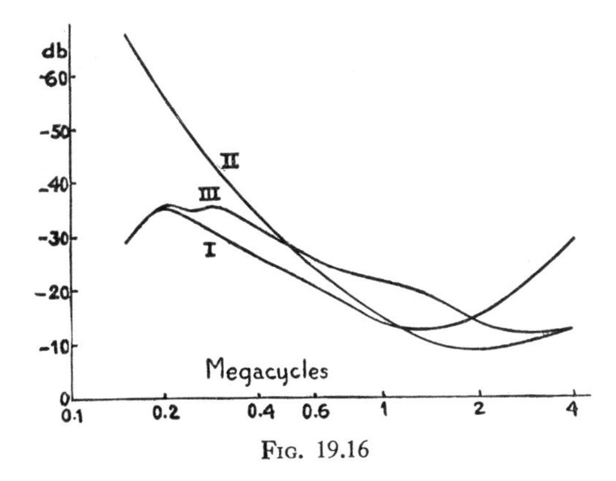

Fig. 19.16

istics of the amplifier based upon the outer circuit remain valid after the inner path is added. At higher frequencies, on the other hand, the inner path becomes more and more transparent until it constitutes an effective by-pass on the outer circuit at frequencies for which the asymptotic loss of the outer circuit is large.

These relations are shown in more detail in Figs. 19.16 and 19.17. The first curves in the two figures give the loss and phase corresponding to transmission from the output grid to the input grid through the outer β circuit. The second curves give the corresponding quantities for transmission through the inner circuit, while the third curves represent the net transmission from output grid to input grid through the two paths in parallel. The third curves are, of course, the ones of interest in a stability calculation, since from the point of view of the tubes all possible feedback paths

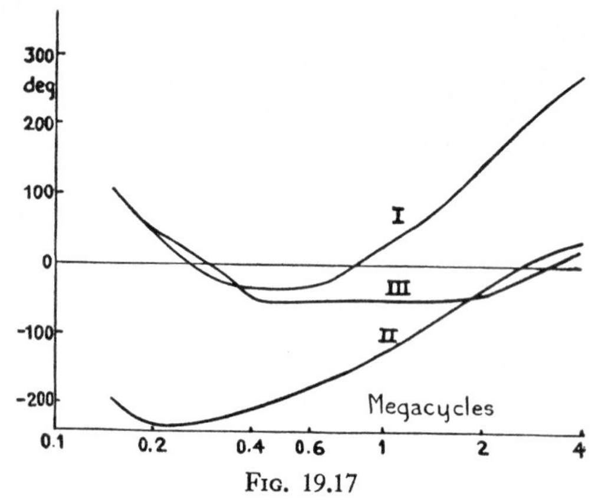

FIG. 19.17

can be lumped together as a single four-terminal network, without regard to their relations to the input and output lines. With the design elements as chosen, the transition from the region in which the outer path is dominant to the region in which the inner path is dominant occurs at about 1 mc. The total transmission characteristic of course depends upon the phase as well as the magnitude relations between the two paths. In this design the phase difference between the paths at the transition point is 140°, which increases the net transmission loss above that of either component. With a phase difference of 120° all three loss curves would cross at the transition point.

The effect of the addition of the inner β circuit on the overall $\mu\beta$ characteristic can be found by correcting the first curves in Figs. 19.13 and 19.14 for the difference between the outer β circuit transmission and the resultant transmission in Figs. 19.16 and 19.17. This leads to the results shown by Curves II in Figs. 19.13 and 19.14. It will be seen that the amplifier is now absolutely stable. The improved asymptote secured by the introduction of the inner circuit is shown by the second broken line in Fig. 19.13.

19.5. *Amplifiers with Band-Pass Transmission Characteristics*

The illustrative designs presented thus far in the chapter have been of the "low-pass" type. In other words, the useful band extended to such low frequencies that it could be regarded as including direct current, so far as the characteristics near or beyond the upper edge of the band were concerned. In accordance with the principles described several times previously, amplifiers transmitting relatively narrow bands may be treated as low-pass amplifiers by means of the low-pass to band-pass transformation described in Chapter X. It will be recalled that the band-pass amplifier and its low-pass equivalent have the same breadth of useful band in cycles per second. The band-pass structure can be obtained from the low-pass design by replacing coils and condensers, respectively, in the low-pass design by resonant and anti-resonant circuits tuned to the center of the design band. The coil in each resonant circuit and the condenser in each anti-resonant circuit are the same as the coil or condenser which is replaced. The resistances in the original circuit are not changed.

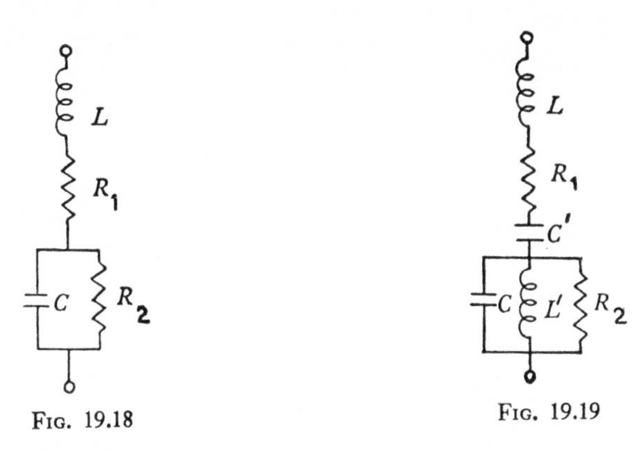

FIG. 19.18 FIG. 19.19

The low-pass to band-pass transformation is relatively easy to apply in most cases. When the band is extremely narrow, however, the use of the transformation may be hampered by two practical difficulties of a type familiar in the analogous problem of building a very narrow band-pass filter. One such difficulty has to do with the range of element values necessary in the transformed network and the other with the Q's required in the individual elements. This may be seen most easily from a consideration of the networks in Figs. 19.18 and 19.19. The first represents a tuned circuit in the low-pass equivalent structure. We may imagine that the circuit resonates near the edge of the useful band in the low-pass design and that the two reactive elements represent reasonable element sizes for this design region. Parasitic dissipation is allocated for convenience equally between the inductance and capacity and is represented by the two resistances in the circuit. The band-pass transform is shown by Fig. 19.19. The elements L and C remain the same, but elements C' and L' are added to resonate with them at f_r, the center of the final band. Thus, from the assumption made previously, we must have $L/L' = C/C' = f_r^2/f_0^2$, where f_0 is the edge of the useful band in the low-pass design. If f_r is much greater than f_0 this relation obviously indicates an extreme disparity in the element sizes of the network, so that some of the elements are almost certain to be inconveniently large while others are inconveniently small. We may also notice that since the resistances in the circuit remain the same the Q's required in the reactive elements will be larger in the band-pass design in the proportion f_r/f_0. The difficulty with element sizes can frequently be overcome, or at least ameliorated, by representing the network branches in other equivalent forms, but the problem of providing an adequate Q is not so easily avoided.

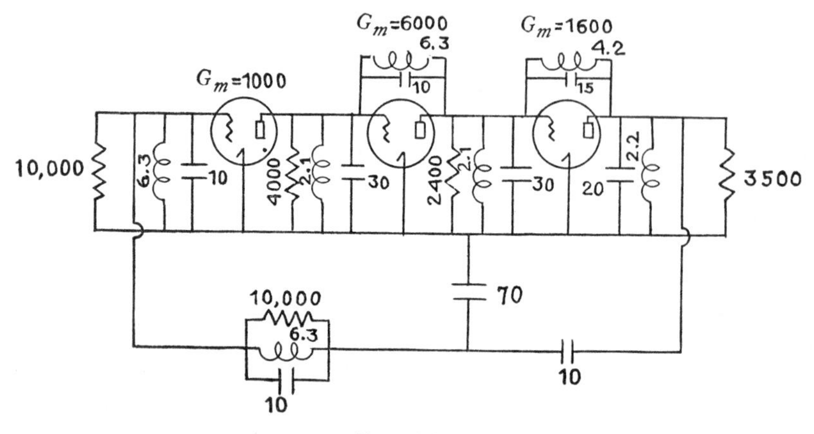

FIG. 19.20

A simple illustration of the low-pass to band-pass transformation is furnished by a set of preliminary designs for an intermediate power radio transmitter. The structure was intended to operate on a carrier frequency of 20 mc and to transmit 12 channels, occupying 50 kc on a single side band basis. The feedback was applied to suppress interchannel modulation. Thus the circuit is somewhat similar to the transmitter described previously, with the exceptions that radio frequency rather than envelope feedback is used, so that it contains no modulator or demodulator, and that it operates on a somewhat higher power level, which means that tubes with a lower figure of merit must be used.

A tentative design for the transmitter is shown by Fig. 19.20. Each coil resonates with the associated capacity reactance at the center of the band. The source and load impedances, the latter including the parallel plate resistance of the output tube, are represented by the 10,000 and 3500 ohm resistances at input and output. The feedback circuit is of shunt type. Its loss is controlled chiefly by the potentiometer formed by the L of capacities in the drawing. The additional series resistance is added to present a reasonably high impedance at the input and it is shunted by the anti-resonant network to diminish its effect on the asymptotic loop. In the forward circuit, the interstages are simple tuned circuits. The parallel resistances are introduced to represent the effects of coil dissipation and also the plate and grid dissipation of the adjacent tubes. The second and third tubes are power triodes having relatively large grid-plate capacities. They are coil neutralized, as the drawing indicates.

Since the tuned circuits are all anti-resonant networks, the low-pass equivalent is obtained merely by deleting all the coils in the structure.* This leads to the unfolded loop shown by Fig. 19.21. The computed gain and phase characteristics for the structure are shown by the solid line Curves I in Figs. 19.22 and 19.23. The asymptote, as determined graphically, crosses the zero gain axis at 2 mc and has a slope of 12 db per octave.† The loop characteristic depends largely upon the grid-plate coupling capacities in the last two tubes. To illustrate this, the broken lines in the two figures have been drawn to show the gain and phase characteristics which would be obtained if the coupling capacities were neglected. It is also important to recall, from the discussion in the previous chapter, that the presence of the coupling condensers changes the structure from a minimum to a non-minimum phase configuration. This is indicated by the dotted line in Fig. 19.23, which represents the minimum phase characteristic corresponding to the actual gain characteristic shown by Curve I in Fig. 19.22.

The ideal cut-off characteristics are shown by Curves II in Figs. 19.22 and 19.23. Phase and gain margins of 30° and 10 db, respectively, are shown. It may be noticed that the horizontal step in the gain characteristic is much broader than it would be in a normal design. With the usual proportions the limiting frequencies of the step would be in the same ratio,

* The elements in the capacity potentiometer introduce no difficulty because the coil in the output plate circuit is supposed to tune with the total capacity (about 29 $\mu\mu f$) which it faces. This permits the low-pass equivalent in Fig. 19.21 to be a valid representation of the actual circuit except for very low frequencies (of the order of 0.1 mc or below), where the impedance of the potentiometer shunt branch in Fig. 19.21 is so large in comparison with the impedances which follow it that the potentiometer can no longer be thought of as operating essentially as a voltage dividing circuit. Hence the curves of Figs. 19.22 to 19.24 do not correspond to Fig. 19.21 at the lowest frequencies.

† That is, this is the assumed slope for purposes of computation. The actual high-frequency characteristic depends largely upon the grid-plate coupling condensers and eventually reaches a slope of 6 db per octave, whereas the slope would be 18 db per octave if the coupling condensers were omitted. The effect of this subsequent slope change is lumped with the excess phase term described later.

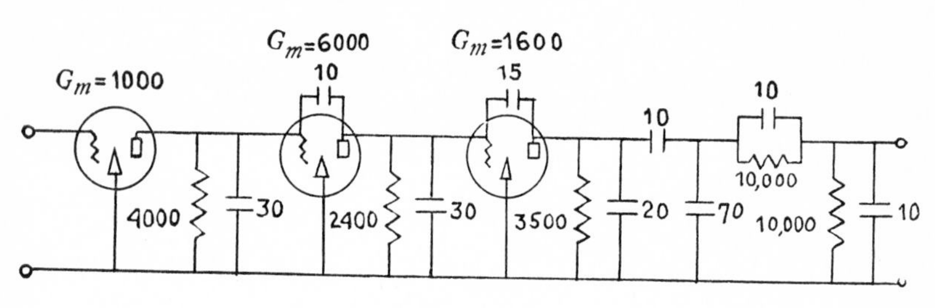

FIG. 19.21

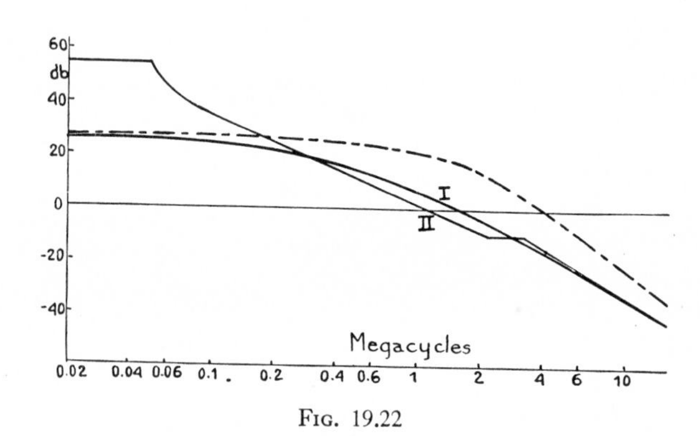

FIG. 19.22

FIG. 19.23

12 : 10, as the adjacent slopes. In accordance with the discussion near the end of the last chapter, however, the actual step is made nearly half an octave broader than this to compensate for the excess phase in the $\mu\beta$ loop.

The ideal cut-off can be simulated without trouble at frequencies more than a few hundred kilocycles from the band, but near the edge of the band the Q and element value limitations in the low-pass to band-pass transformation make it difficult to secure a sufficiently selective characteristic.

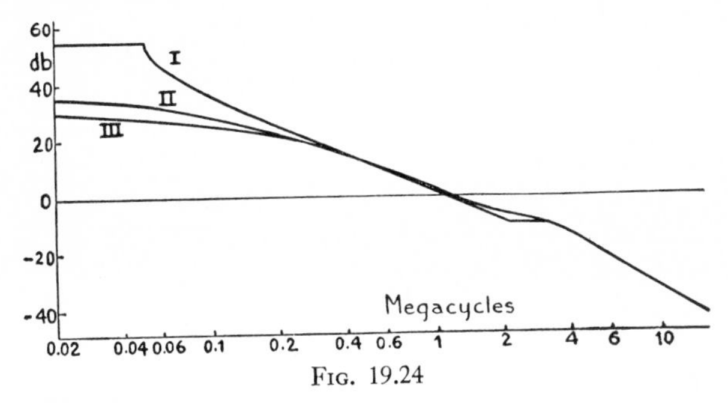

FIG. 19.24

This is illustrated by Curves II of Figs. 19.24 and 19.25, which represent the result secured when the original first interstage in Fig. 19.21 is replaced by the structure shown in Fig. 19.26*A*. It will be seen that the lack of adequate low-frequency selectivity leads to a feedback in the useful band which is nearly 20 db less than the amount promised by the theoretical cut-off, shown by Curves I in the two figures.

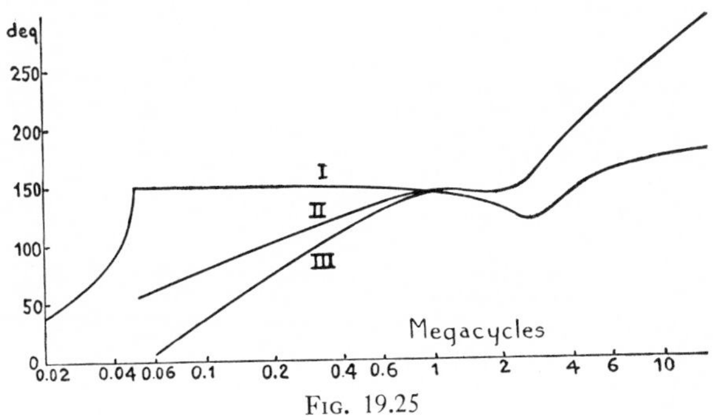

FIG. 19.25

The structure of Fig. 19.26*A* is a simple trap circuit design with a trap circuit resonance near 1 mc to fill in the difference in loss between Curves I and II of Fig. 19.22 in this general region. Figure 19.26*B* represents a slightly modified form of the network having a distribution of dissipation more suitable for the band-pass equivalent structure. As either structure stands we could evidently secure a considerably larger feedback in the use-

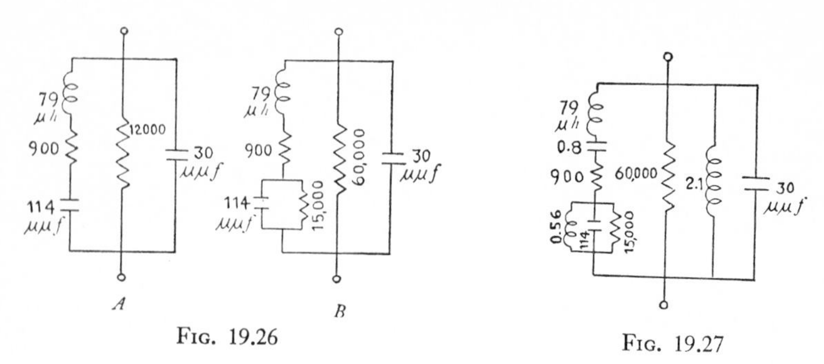

FIG. 19.26

FIG. 19.27

ful band without materially affecting the $\mu\beta$ characteristic at higher frequencies merely by decreasing the zero frequency conductance path through the network. If we transform the network of Fig. 19.26B to the band-pass equivalent shown by Fig. 19.27 however, we notice that even

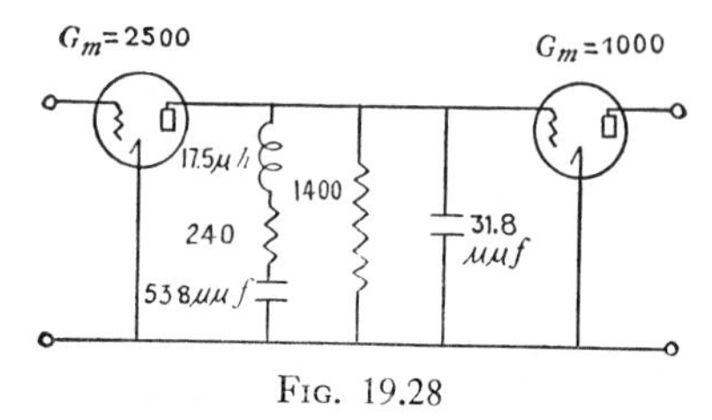

FIG. 19.28

with the present element values the coils in the two anti-resonant circuits must have Q's of more than 200 at the carrier frequency. If Q's this large are not available the feedback in the useful band will, of course, be still further diminished. Curves III of Figs. 19.24 and 19.25, for example, show the result secured if the maximum obtainable Q is 100.

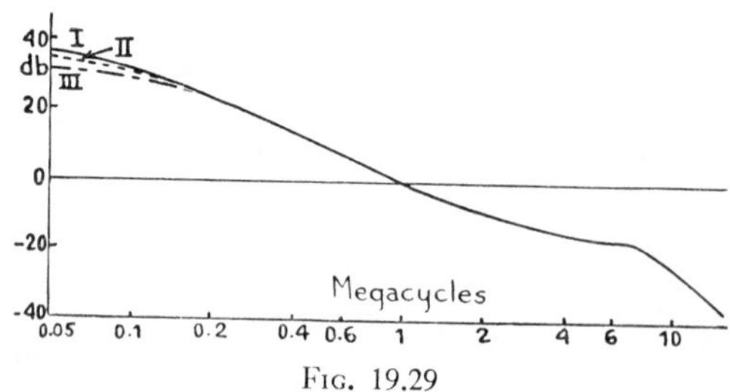

FIG. 19.29

In view of these limitations it appeared that adequate feedback could be obtained more simply by adding a fourth stage* to the existing structure of

* The phase reversal necessary for operation with an even number of stages is obtained merely by crossing terminals. The amplifier is actually a push-pull circuit, shown single sided in this discussion as a matter of simplicity.

Fig. 19.21. This leads to the same general advantages that an increased number of stages permitted in the transmitter described previously. The configuration chosen for the new interstage is again of the trap circuit type, as shown by Fig. 19.28. It leads to the overall loop gain and phase shown

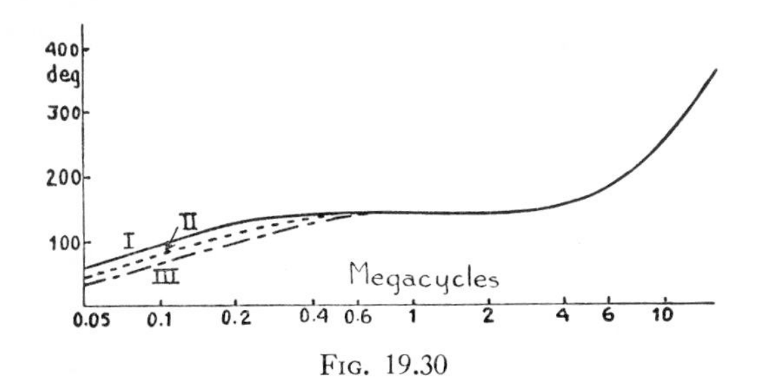

FIG. 19.30

by Curves I of Figs. 19.29 and 19.30. The Q required in the band-pass structure is in this case 100. Curves II and III show the results obtained with Q's respectively one-half and one-quarter as great.

19.6. *Lower Cut-Off Characteristics for Feedback Amplifiers*

The low-pass to band-pass transformation just described is appropriate for amplifiers in which the ratio of the upper to the lower edge of the useful band is not very great. When the lower frequency limit for the band is only a small fraction* of the upper, it is simpler to regard the cut-off characteristic below the useful band as an independent problem. An appropriate shape for the lower cut-off can evidently be obtained by plotting the upper cut-off characteristic on a reciprocal frequency scale. Figure 19.31, for example, shows, on an arithmetic frequency scale, a combination of upper

* Since the band-pass characteristic is always theoretically more efficient than a combination of low-pass and high-pass characteristics, the dividing line depends upon the amount of improvement in feedback which is regarded as worthwhile. The advantage of the band-pass characteristic is easily computed by identifying f_0 in equation (18–7) of the preceding chapter with, first, the upper edge of the useful band and, second, the difference between the upper and lower edges. For example, if the edges are in the ratio 5 : 1 the use of the band-pass characteristic allows an increase of about 4 db in available feedback, while if the edges are in the ratio 10 : 1 the improvement is about 2 db. It should be noticed, however, that the various power supply elements, such as grid leaks, blocking condensers, choke coils, etc., can be used as controlling elements in shaping the lower cut-off in the combination characteristic, while the band-pass characteristic is valid, strictly speaking, only when these elements are made so large that they do not enter into the characteristic in the cut-off range. This consideration usually limits the applicability of the band-pass characteristic to much narrower bands than the above figures might suggest.

and lower characteristics for an amplifier whose useful band in octaves is very broad.

If we use a combination characteristic of this type, the asymptote for the lower cut-off characteristic is furnished by the various elements controlling the direct current potentials in the amplifier. The chief of these are usually choke coils, blocking condensers, and grid-leak combinations in the interstages, filtering elements in the plate supply circuits, and condenser-resistance combinations in the cathode leads to provide self-bias on the tubes. The low-frequency cut-off is not usually so difficult a design prob-

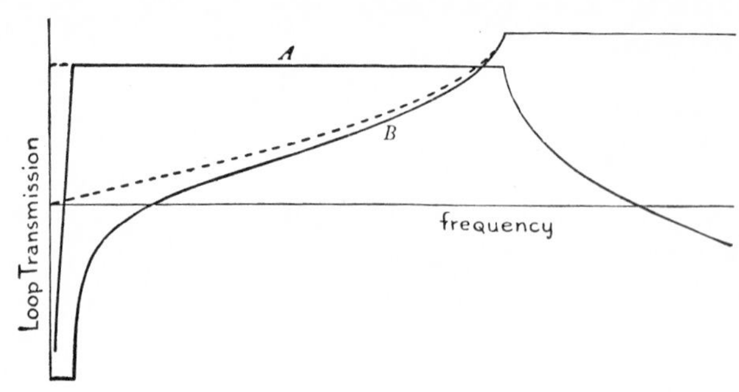

FIG. 19.31

lem as the high-frequency cut-off, since we can obtain as favorable an asymptote as we need by making the various blocking condensers and choke coils large enough. For this reason it is not usually necessary to provide a very efficient cut-off, having a low phase margin and a sharp corner at the band edge. It should be emphasized, however, that a necessary minimum of design effort in shaping the low-frequency cut-off must be expended. It is not enough merely to make the power supply elements very large. For example, if we double all the coils and condensers which are effective at low frequencies, the original frequency characteristics will be repeated one octave lower. If the amplifier is unstable on account of the original elements it will still be unstable. It can be stabilized only by altering the relative proportions of the low-frequency elements.

An example of a low-frequency cut-off characteristic is furnished by the low-frequency design of a preliminary version of the amplifier used as the concluding illustration in this chapter. The lower edge of the useful band occurs at 60 kc. A sketch of the amplifier to show the elements effective at low frequencies is given in Fig. 19.32.* The 4200 ohm, 2000 ohm, and

* The value assumed for the impedance of the first interstage corresponds to the configuration in Fig. 19.57 without the 5657 μh coil. In the final low-frequency design there were a number of changes which made the presence of this coil appropriate.

550 ohm resistances are the low frequency values for the impedances of the two interstage networks and the β circuit. The other elements will be recognized as self-biasing units in the cathodes,† blocking condensers, grid

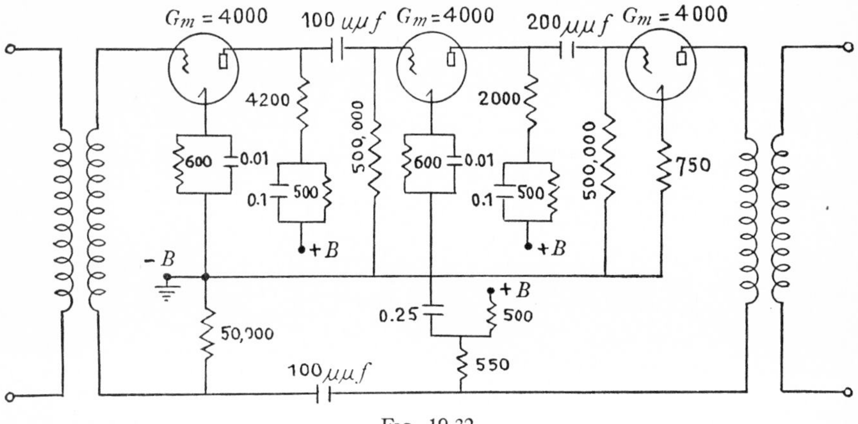

FIG. 19.32

leaks, and condenser-resistance filters in the plate supply leads. If we consider each blocking condenser and its associated grid leak as a unit, all these structures, as it happens, are simple capacity-resistance combinations. Thus they can be specified by their CR products, which fix the frequency at which the capacity and resistance exhibit impedances of equal absolute value. A table showing the CR products and the associated frequencies for the various units is given below.

Network	CR	f_r
First Cathode	6×10^{-6}	26.5 kc
Second Cathode	6×10^{-6}	26.5 kc
Blg. Cond. — Grid Leak in first interstage	50×10^{-6}	3.2 kc
in second interstage	100×10^{-6}	1.6 kc
in β circuit	5×10^{-6}	32.0 kc
CR filter in first plate cct.	50×10^{-6}	3.2 kc
in second plate cct.	50×10^{-6}	3.2 kc
in third plate cct.	125×10^{-6}	1.3 kc

The principle upon which the design is based can be understood from an inspection of the table. It consists, broadly speaking, in staggering the CR products so that the various networks are effective in different parts

† Self-bias on the power tube is provided by a simple resistance, without a shunting capacity, in order to provide additional local feedback on the tube within the useful band.

of the frequency range, and a fairly uniform cut-off rate can be established. For example, two of the three networks with the largest values of f_r are the cathode biasing units, each of which has an f_r occurring slightly more than one octave below the useful band. The two biasing units are of no

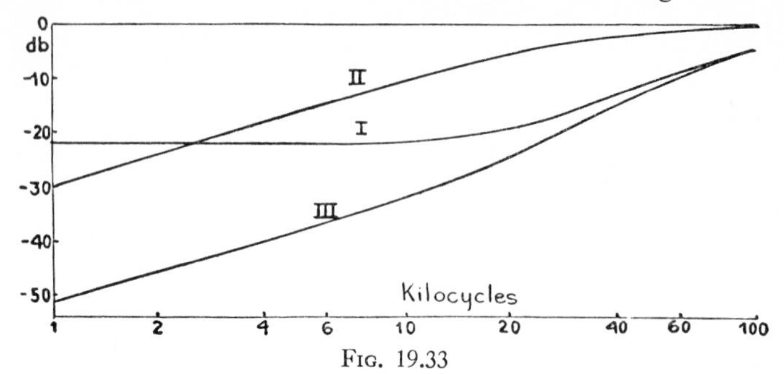

FIG. 19.33

effect at very high frequencies, while at very low frequencies they introduce local feedbacks which depress the gain of each stage by about 11 db. The CR product marks the approximate frequency below which the local feedback characteristic is fairly well established. Thus with the CR products as chosen for the biasing units, most of the 22 db total change in gain

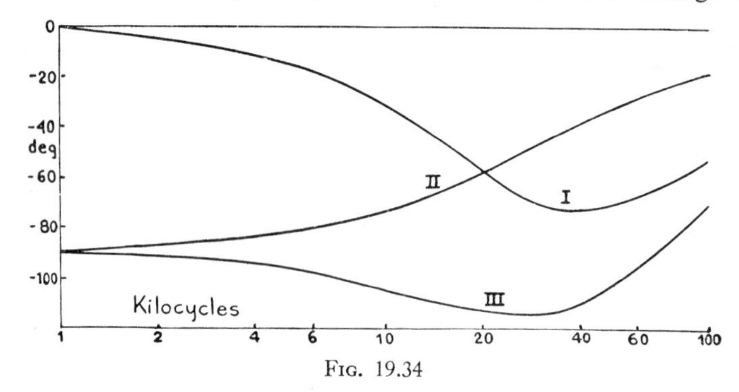

FIG. 19.34

which they produce occurs in the first octave and a half, roughly, below the useful band, and represents the chief constituent of the $\mu\beta$ characteristic in this region. The effect of the biasing units is shown in more detail by Curves I of Figs. 19.33 and 19.34.*

* As Fig. 19.33 is drawn, it appears that the local feedback characteristic extends sufficiently far into the useful band to produce an appreciable rounding of the $\mu\beta$ characteristic above 60 kc. In the actual design this was largely compensated for by the varying interstage and β circuit impedances, which had not yet reached the low-frequency condition indicated in Fig. 19.32. In the absence of such compensation, it would probably be desirable to choose f_r's another half octave or so lower.

The third network having a comparatively high f_r is the blocking condenser-grid leak combination associated with the grid of the first tube. The characteristics of this structure are shown by Curves II in Figs. 19.33 and 19.34. It introduces a 6 db per octave loss slope in the range below its f_r, i.e., at frequencies more than one octave below the useful band, and comparatively little effect above its f_r. Thus it comes into play as the slope introduced by the biasing units begins to fail. The combination, as shown by Curves III in the two figures, provides a fairly constant slope of about 9 db per octave for several octaves below the useful band.

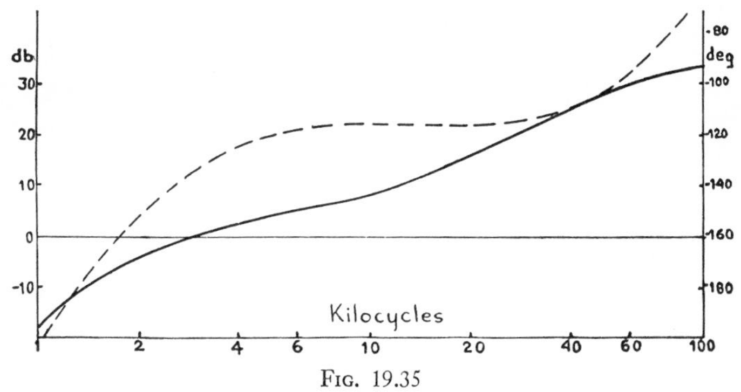

FIG. 19.35

The remaining elements in the loop become effective at much lower frequencies. The chief contributors are the blocking condenser — grid-leak combinations associated with the second and third grids. Together with the similar combination for the first grid, already considered, they produce a final asymptotic slope of 18 db per octave. The junction with the final asymptote is, however, slightly retarded by the elevation in loop gain due to the CR combinations used as plate supply filters in the leads to the two interstages and the β circuit. This produces a slight "step" in the cut-off. The final loop characteristics, including some slight effects not considered here and adjustment for the loop gain level in the useful band, are shown by Fig. 19.35.

In the method of design just described, the slope of the lower cut-off characteristic is controlled essentially by choosing constituent networks having a variety of CR products so that they will come into play in different parts of the cut-off interval. This is possible in an amplifier operating at moderate frequencies where reasonable element sizes are to be anticipated. When the useful band extends to extremely low frequencies, on the other hand, the limitations represented by permissible sizes of blocking condensers and grid leaks require consideration. Evidently the method of distributing the CR products is likely to fail in this case, since the largest product may be expected to correspond to an excessively large condenser or resistance.

An alternative way of controlling the characteristic at extremely low frequencies can be obtained if we suppose that the grid leaks in the conventional amplifier may be replaced by some more elaborate arrangement of condensers and resistances. The advantage of using the grid circuit to shape the characteristic is, of course, the fact that the impedance level represented by the usual grid leak is so great that the capacities required in the shaping networks are relatively small even at very low frequencies. A typical arrangement is shown by Fig. 19.36. The resistance R and condenser C in the drawing represent a conventional interstage impedance and blocking condenser, but the usual grid leak is replaced by the three-element network composed of R_0, R_1, and C_1.

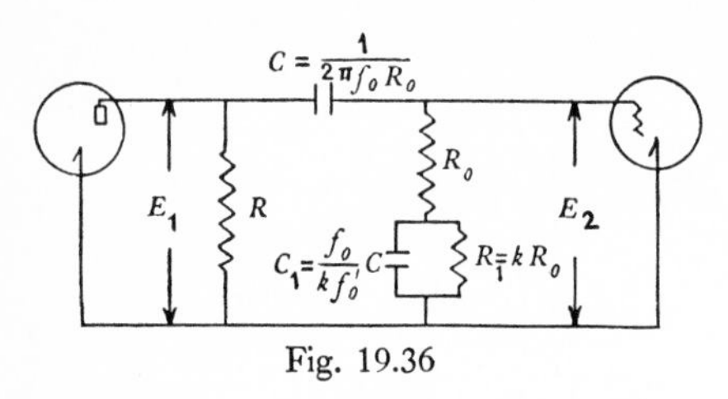

Fig. 19.36

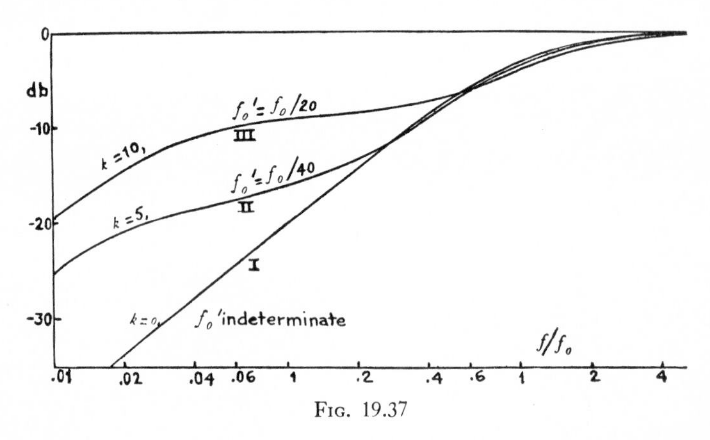

FIG. 19.37

If we suppose that the d-c grid resistance $R_0 + R_1$ is fixed, the shape of the characteristic obtained in the low-frequency region depends upon the ratios R_1/R_0 and C/C_1. These may be specified by the parameters k and f_0'/f_0 defined in the figure. In terms of k and the frequency ratio, a simple calculation shows that the voltage E_2 across the grid for a voltage E_1 across R is given by

$$E_2 = if \frac{(1 + k) f_0' + if}{f_0 f_0' + if [(1 + k) f_0' + f_0] - f^2} E_1. \tag{19–1}$$

Sample characteristics corresponding to two special choices of k and f_0/f_0' are shown by Curves II and III in Fig. 19.37. Curve I, which gives

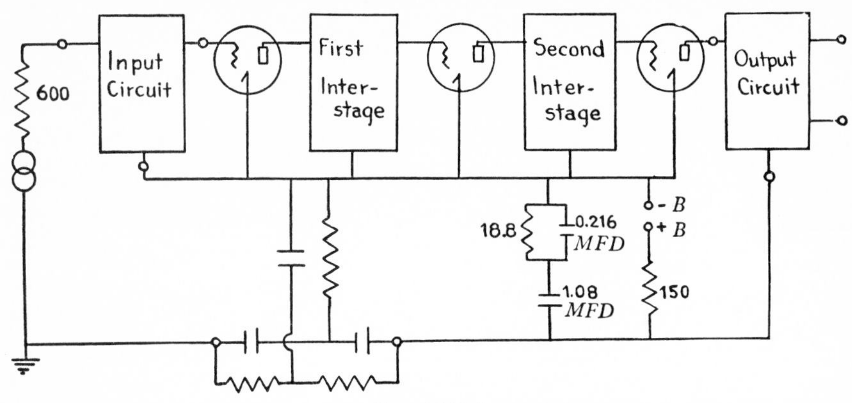

FIG. 19.38A

the result for a simple grid leak, is introduced for comparison. It will be seen from the curves that the networks have roughly the fundamental property necessary for a cut-off solution, that they permit a predetermined average cut-off slope and corresponding phase to be maintained over a considerable region. The degree of approximation can be improved by staggering the designs in the various grid circuits.

An example of the use of this technique is furnished by the design of a

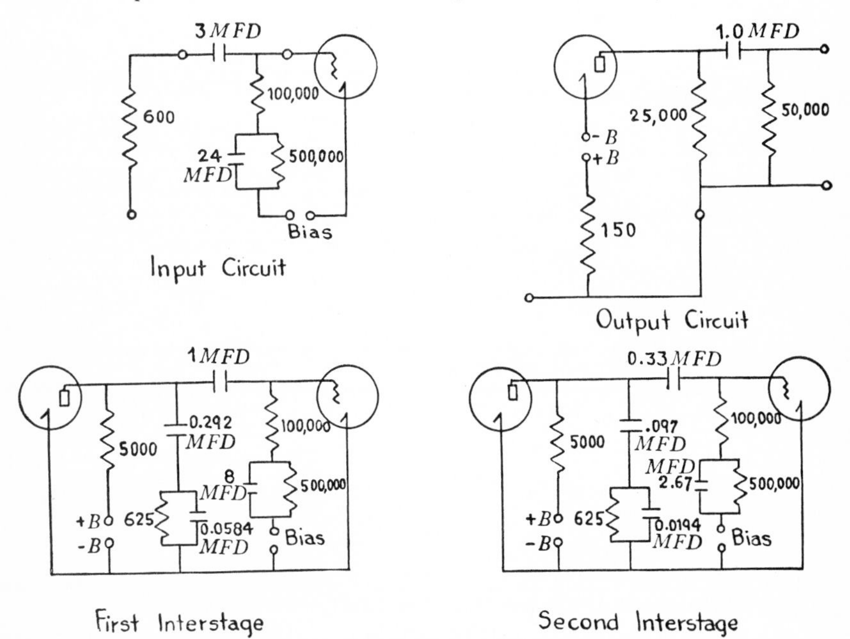

FIG. 19.38B

laboratory amplifier intended to give 60 db feedback in the frequency region from 5 to 25 cycles. A schematic of the amplifier is shown by Figs. 19.38*A* and 19.38*B*. The principal constituent of the β circuit is a condenser-resistance bridge intended to give a peak of loss at an ad-

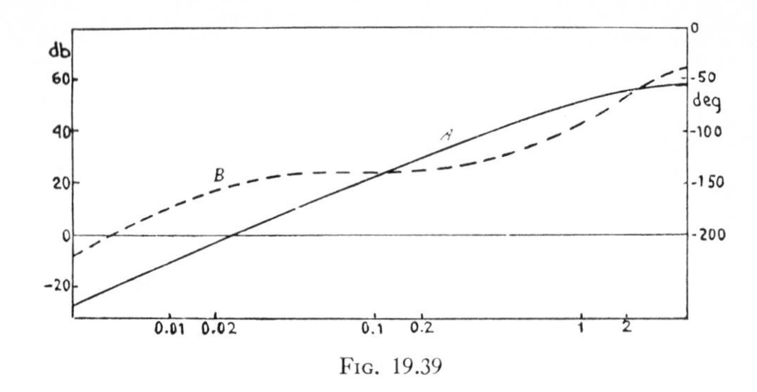

FIG. 19.39

justable frequency in the 5 to 25 cycle range. For design purposes it can be regarded as a flat high impedance pad. The grid circuit designs are of the type just described with $k = 5$ and $f_0/f_0' = 40$ in each case. These parameter values correspond to the characteristic shown by Curve II in Fig. 19.37. The designs are, however, staggered in frequency, the reference frequency f_0 being increased by a factor of three as we go from the first to the second or from the second to the third grid. The overall low-frequency gain and phase characteristics are shown by Fig. 19.39.* It will be seen that a cut-off slope of 9 db per octave is realized with great accuracy down to a frequency of one cycle per minute.

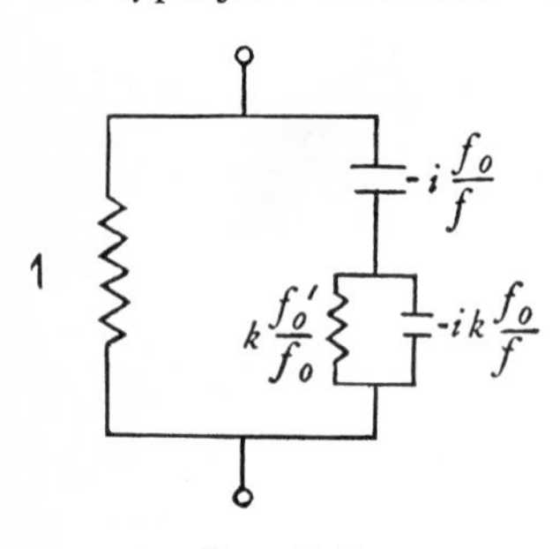

FIG. 19.40

In designing the low-frequency cut-off it was assumed, as Fig. 19.36 indicates, that the impedance in the plate circuit of each interstage is a rather low resistance. The high-frequency cut-off of the amplifier must be obtained by adding suitable shaping elements to these resistances. In the present instance advantage may be taken of the fact that if we replace if/f_0 by f_0/if the expression for E_2/E_1 given by (19–1) can also be interpreted as the impedance of the structure shown by Fig. 19.40.

* The absolute level of gain depends, of course, upon the tube transconductances and the loss assumed for the β circuit. This discussion is omitted here since the β circuit design involves a number of questions of no particular interest for the overall loop design.

Thus by suitable adjustments of the unit of impedance and frequency the lower cut-off design which has already been found provides a ready-made design for shaping networks which will furnish a precisely symmetrical upper cut-off characteristic. The remaining elements in the two inter-stage networks, Fig. 19.38, were determined by this means. The 150 ohm resistance and associated three element CR structure in the β circuit performs the same function for the circuit leading to the first grid. We observe that the complete $\mu\beta$ characteristic is obtained without the use of coils, which would evidently be undesirable in a circuit operating at such low frequencies.

19.7. *Illustrative Design of a Regulating Broad-Band Amplifier*

The final example consists of one of the repeaters designed for the co-axial system.* The useful band of the structure extends from 60 to 2000 kc. Since low-frequency cut-off designs have been described in the preceding section, only the high-frequency characteristic will be considered here. The spacing between repeaters is nominally 5 miles, which corresponds at 2000 kc to a line loss, which the repeater must overcome, of about 40 db. In order to compensate for irregularities in repeater spacing and for variations in line attenuation due to temperature, however, the amplifier is supposed to include a variable β circuit control which will introduce a positive or negative characteristic proportional to that of a small length of line. The maximum swing is ± 1.2 miles of line† or from about 30 to about 50 db in gain at 2000 kc. Feedback of the order of 25 to 30 db is desired.

With a useful band as great as the one specified, the problem of securing adequate feedback must be the controlling consideration in choosing the general arrangement of the amplifier. It appeared upon investigation that series feedback would give the most favorable asymptote.‡ A circuit of this type was therefore adopted. The general configuration is shown by Fig. 19.41. Aside from the use of the series feedback circuit, the asymptote was made as favorable as possible by reducing all parasitic

* See footnote, p. 285. The regulating network in the feedback path of the amplifier belongs to the general class of structures described in "Variable Equalizers" by H. W. Bode, *B.S.T.J.*, April, 1938.

† As a matter of simplicity the complete regulator range over which the amplifier was supposed to remain stable is given here. The useful range for normal service is somewhat smaller.

‡ The cathode feedback circuit, which is slightly more favorable, was not developed at the time this amplifier was designed. Comments of a similar sort apply to the numerical values given for the capacities and transconductances of the tubes in the circuit.

capacities to a minimum and by constructing the variable β circuit as a single shunt branch, so that a small series coil would remove it entirely from the high frequency path.

The physical origins of the various capacities shown in the drawing should be self-evident, with the possible exception of the capacity across the β circuit, which is due chiefly to the capacity to ground of the transformers. With the indicated transconductances and interstage capacities the " figure of merit " frequency f_t is about 50 mc. The asymptote has

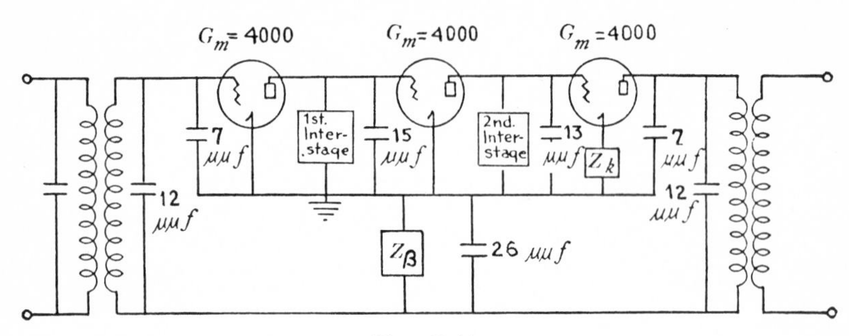

FIG. 19.41

a slope of 18 db per octave and the " circuit loss " A_t at 50 mc is 18 db. The resulting A_m over the useful band is obtained from equation (18–12) of the preceding chapter as 48 db. It is interesting to notice that the series feedback circuit used in the amplifier is quite close to the ideal. With tubes of the given figure of merit, the available feedback could be increased only 12 db even if we had a theoretically perfect circuit with $A_t = 0$.

The detailed amplifier design begins with the input and output circuits. These structures, however, are not of great interest here and will be dismissed briefly. Broadly speaking, the input and output circuits provide a varying gain characteristic which compensates (at normal line lengths and temperatures) for the varying attenuation of the line in the upper part of the useful band. Supplementary equalization at lower frequencies is supplied by an additional conventional equalizer inserted in front of the amplifier.* The general technique of design is the same as that described in Chapter XVI. For our present purposes the input and output circuit designs are of interest chiefly for their effect on the overall loop characteris-

* In general, of course, line equalization might also be provided by a variable loss in the β circuit. When the β circuit is required to be a regulator of the single branch type, however, it appears that its normal loss characteristic, for the mean regulator setting, must be almost constant. The characteristic of the actual β circuit is given later in Fig. 19.50.

tic through the so-called " transformer potentiometer terms " described in connection with Fig. 16.31 of that chapter. A plot of the sum of the potentiometer terms for the two circuits is shown by Fig. 19.42.

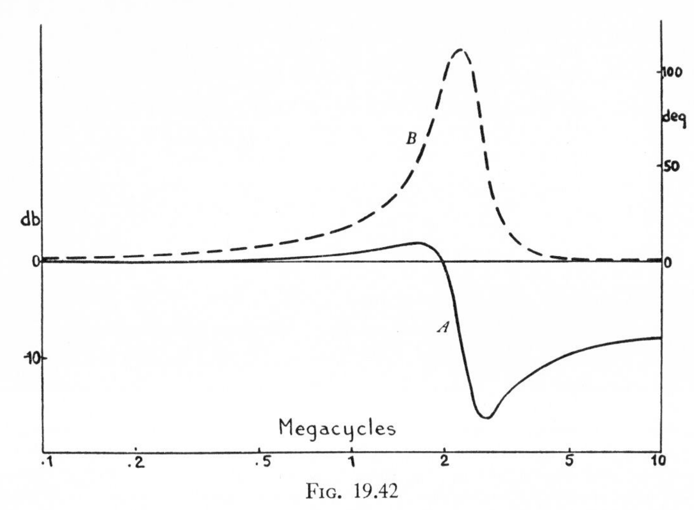

Fig. 19.42

We have next to consider the design of the forward circuit and feedback impedances to secure an appropriate loop characteristic. This problem is complicated by the fact that the loop characteristic must obviously vary as we vary the β circuit to compensate for different lengths of line. The

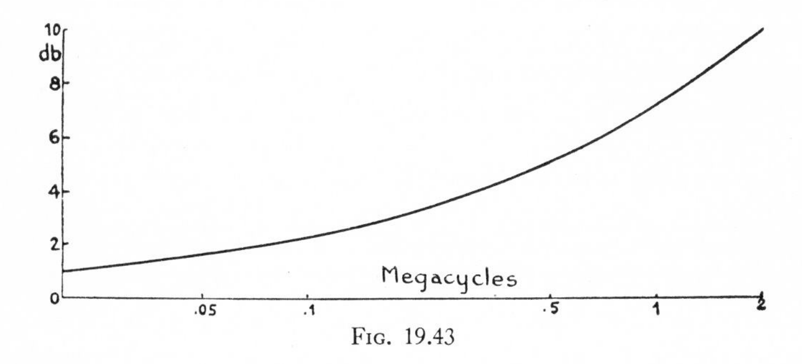

Fig. 19.43

situation can be examined by plotting the variable characteristic on the Φ scale described in Chapters XVII and XVIII. Thus Fig. 19.43 shows the required change in loss from the mean to one extreme regulator setting plotted on an ordinary log frequency scale, while Fig. 19.44 gives the same characteristic on the Φ scale. The average height of the plot on the Φ scale is about $7\frac{1}{2}$ db. The variable changes in loop transmission introduced by regulation are consequently equivalent at extreme settings to a constant change of $7\frac{1}{2}$ db in feedback in either direction from the mean.

Since the asymptote is fixed these changes in effective feedback must evidently imply corresponding changes in the gain or phase margins, or both, assigned to the loop cut-off. For design purposes it was assumed

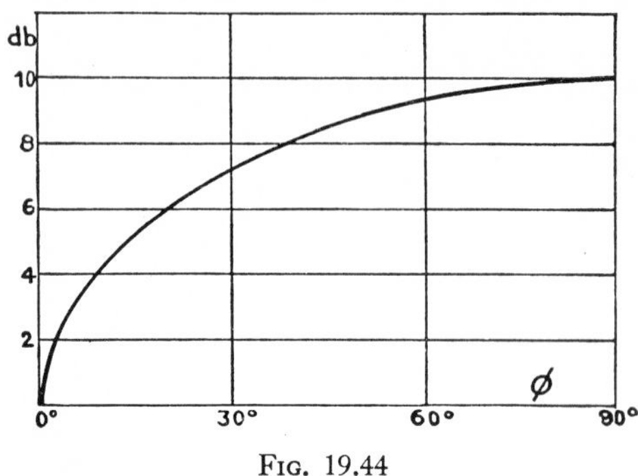

FIG. 19.44

that the gain margin would remain fixed and equal to 15 db for all settings of the regulator and that changes in effective feedback due to regulator operation would be taken up by varying the phase margin. Specifically, a constant feedback of $28\frac{1}{2}$ db in the useful band was assumed for the mean

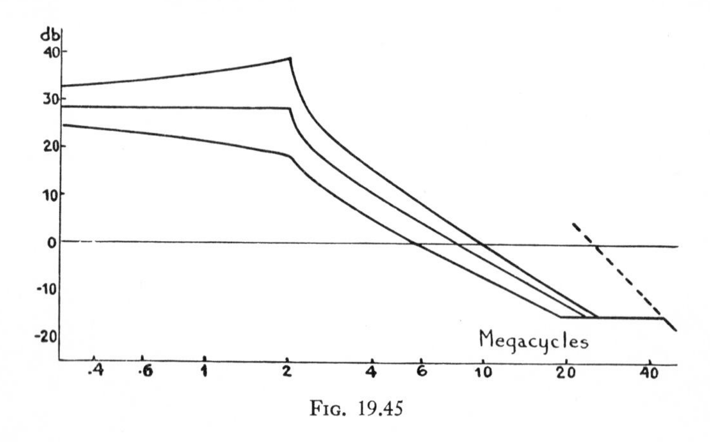

FIG. 19.45

regulator setting. The variable characteristics for the extreme settings, then, are equivalent to constant feedbacks of 21 and 36 db, respectively. Since A_m is known, equation (18–9) of the preceding chapter allows the corresponding phase margins to be determined. They turn out to be equal to 17°, 35°, and 53°, respectively, for the maximum, average, and minimum settings. Detailed cut-off characteristics computed from these data* are shown by Figs. 19.45 and 19.46.

Since the difference between the successive curves in Figs. 19.45 and 19.46 must be equal to the regulator characteristic this analysis leads to the complete specification of the regulator loss and phase characteristics at all frequencies, in spite of the fact that only the loss in the useful band is specified by the overall amplifier requirements. The loss and phase specification above the useful band need not be taken very literally since

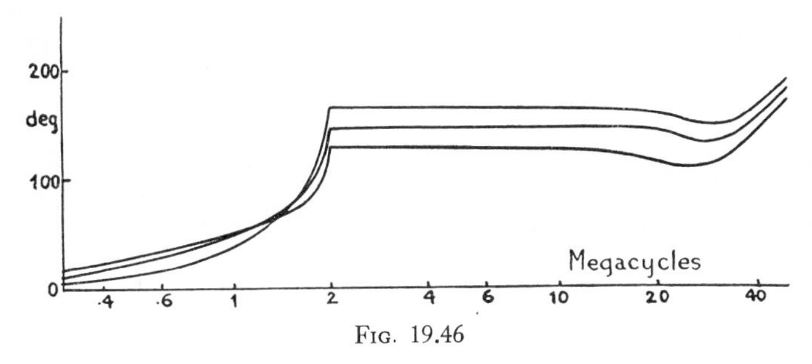

FIG. 19.46

reasonable departures from constancy of phase margin in the characteristics corresponding to the intermediate and lowest regulator settings are tolerable if the characteristic for the maximum setting is well designed, but they represent a useful general guide in choosing the regulator circuit. The characteristics actually obtained from the regulator are shown by solid lines in Figs. 19.47 and 19.48.† The "theoretical" characteristics, obtained as differences between the overall cut-off characteristics, are shown by the broken lines.

The details of the regulator design are beyond the scope of this treatment. The structure itself is shown by Fig. 19.49. The reference loss and phase at the average setting, from which the regulator characteristics are computed, are shown by Fig. 19.50.‡ The curves take account of parasitic capacities, as well as the elements shown explicitly in Fig. 19.49.

* An exact computation for the extreme settings, for which the feedback in the useful band varies with frequency, requires the application of some such formula as equation (14–33) of Chapter XIV but it is sufficiently accurate to estimate the characteristics from the known loop characteristic for a circuit having an equivalent constant feedback.

† Only one characteristic is shown in each figure, since positive and negative departures from the reference condition are symmetrical.

‡ The curves represent the gain and phase which would be obtained if the network were used as an interstage for one of the tubes in the forward circuit. Since the transconductance is 4000 micromhos this is equivalent to choosing 250 ohms as the unit of impedance.

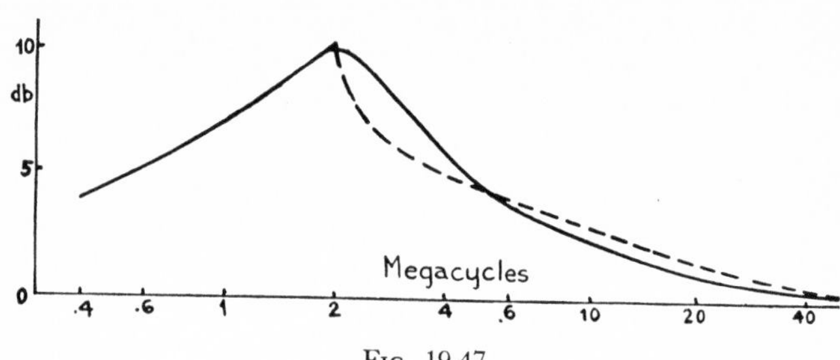

FIG. 19 47

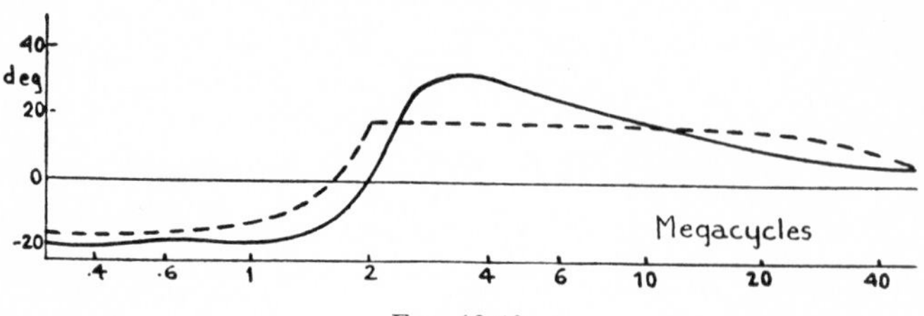

FIG. 19.48

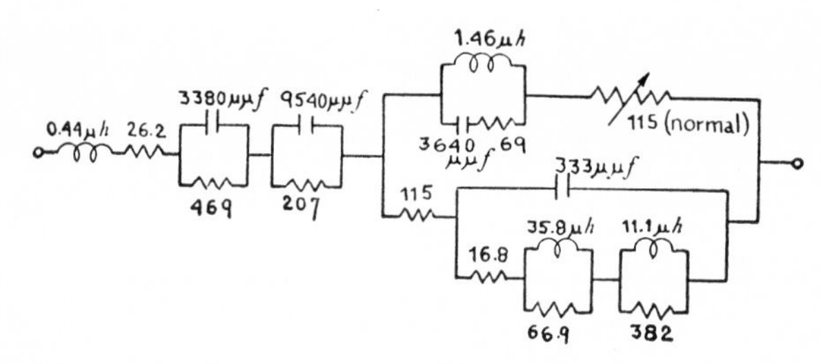

FIG. 19.49

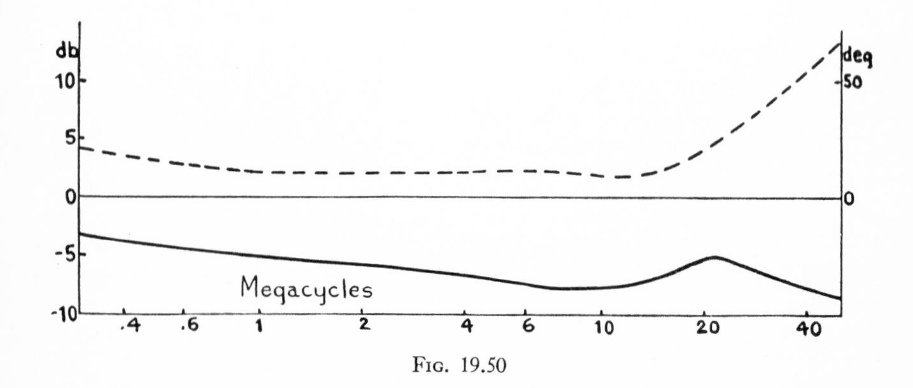

FIG. 19.50

The exact behavior of the circuit is, of course, quite complicated. In the high frequency range, however, it is roughly similar to that of the well damped anti-resonant circuit shown in Fig. 19.51. The condenser represents the 26 $\mu\mu$f transformer-to-ground capacity shown in Fig. 19.41, together with allowances for the shunting effect of the input and output circuits on the β circuit impedance and for the parasitic capacity of the β circuit elements themselves. The inductance is, of course, the same as the leading element in Fig. 19.49, while the 115 ohm resistance represents the rest of the network. Within rather broad limits the anti-resonant frequency can be placed arbitrarily by varying the inductance. The reason for setting it at the very high value which is found in the actual circuit will appear later.

The design is completed by supplying a μ circuit which, in cooperation with circuits already designed, will provide the requisite overall cut-off characteristics. In general, a large number of possible designs can be obtained both because the division of labor between the two interstages can be changed and because we can change the required forward circuit characteristic as a whole by varying the β circuit anti-resonance in Fig. 19.51. Since some of these combinations may be much simpler than others, it is worthwhile to survey the situation before a detailed design is attempted. One clue is afforded by the relations between excess gain and phase margin developed for interstages in Chapter XVII and for the feedback loop as a whole at the end of Chapter XVIII. Another attack is obtained if we attempt to correlate the various corners and slopes in the ideal cut-off characteristic with the separate physical parts of the amplifier which may be supposed to produce them.

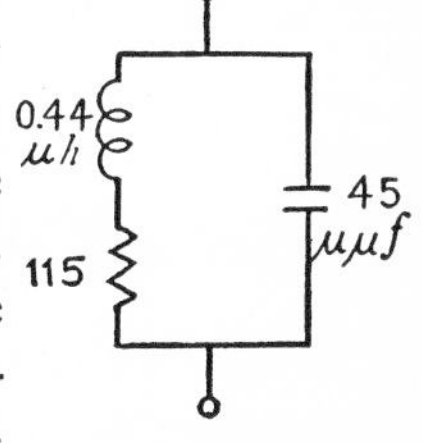

Fig. 19.51

The excess gain and phase margin computation is conveniently begun by the observation that if we begin with the gain characteristics shown by Figs. 19.42 and 19.50 the required $28\frac{1}{2}$ db feedback for the normal regulator setting is obtained with a nearly constant total interstage gain of about 35 db throughout the useful band. With the prescribed transconductances and interstage capacities, however, the maximum available gain from the two interstages over the useful band is 66 db. Thus there is an available surplus gain of 31 db, or 3.6 nepers. In accordance with equation (17–18) of Chapter XVII, this means that the average height of the interstage phase margin plot on the Φ' scale must be 3.6 radians. The relations are shown in more detail in Fig. 19.52. Curve I represents the plot of (ω/ω_0) $(180° - B_L)$ where B_L is the phase shift for the ideal cut-off characteristic at normal setting. Curves II and III are similar plots for $(\omega/\omega_0)B_T$ and $(\omega/\omega_0)B_\beta$, where B_T and B_β represent the transformer phase terms and the β circuit phase given by Figs. 19.42 and 19.50, respectively. Since with two interstages the limiting phase shift against which the interstage phase margins are computed is 180°, it is easy to see that the sum of all three curves represents the interstage phase margin function which appears in equation (17–18) of Chapter XVII.

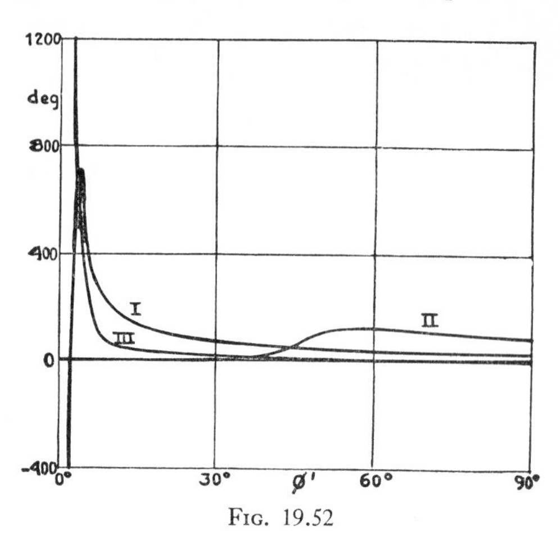

FIG. 19.52

The sum of the three curves in Fig. 19.52 has been plotted as the heavy curve of Fig. 19.53. The broad shoulder extending from about $\Phi' = 50°$ to $\Phi' = 90°$ is relatively easy to interpret. Since $\Phi' = \sin^{-1} \omega_0/\omega$, this

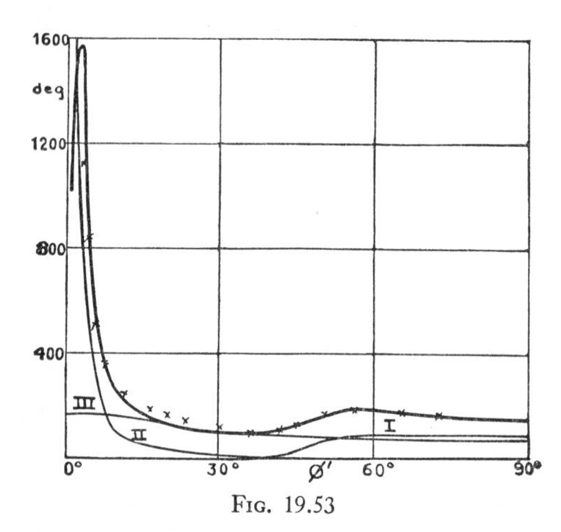

FIG. 19.53

interval on the Φ' scale corresponds to a relatively narrow interval just beyond the useful band on the true frequency scale. We would evidently expect to secure a phase margin characteristic which is relatively constant in this range, but drops off gradually as we approach lower values of Φ', from a well damped interstage of the simple type indicated by Fig. 19.54. We may consequently assume, tentatively, that the first interstage will be of this simple form and will introduce a phase margin contribution of the type indicated roughly by Curve I in Fig. 19.53.* In an ordinary amplifier it would be worthwhile to redesign the β circuit in an attempt to concentrate all the area under the phase margin curve into a

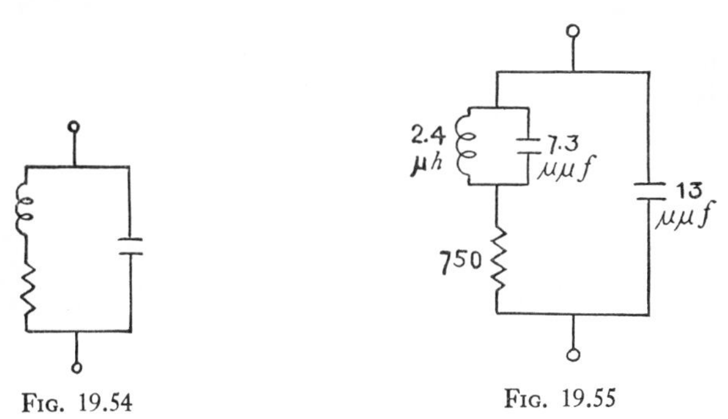

Fig. 19.54

Fig. 19.55

shoulder near the right-hand end of the plot. This would permit both interstages to be realized by relatively simple structures. In this amplifier, however, the regulation requirement on the β circuit permits no effective design control of its normal characteristics beyond the shifts introduced by varying the anti-resonance in Fig. 19.51. It is consequently necessary to elaborate the forward circuit design to obtain the required phase margin at low values of Φ'.

In the actual design the peak in the phase margin plot near $\Phi' = 5°$ was provided by inserting the network shown by Fig. 19.55 in the cathode of the third tube. The 13 $\mu\mu$f condenser represents the parasitic capacity from cathode to ground and is not a physical element. The structure provides local feedback on the third tube which depresses its gain by 12 db. In other words, it consumes 12 db of the total of 31 db surplus gain which is to be expended. The local feedback remains almost constant in the useful band and beyond it up to about 20 mc. At higher frequencies, however, it is eliminated by the filterlike action of the anti-resonant circuit and parallel capacity in Fig. 19.55. This leads to an increased gain in the third stage with the associated phase shift shown by Curve II in Fig. 19.53.

* That is, Curve I is roughly a plot, against Φ', of $(\omega/\omega_0)(90° - B_1)$, where B_1 is the phase characteristic to be expected from an interstage of the type shown by Fig. 19.54. Similarly, Curve III is a plot of $(\omega/\omega_0)(90° - B_2)$, where B_2 is the phase characteristic of the interstage in Fig. 19.56, while Curve II is a plot of $-(\omega/\omega_0)B_c$, where B_c is the phase shift introduced into the forward circuit by the cathode network of Fig. 19.55.

The loss and phase characteristics introduced by the local feedback circuit might also be obtained very nearly from an interstage trap circuit. The local feedback solution is preferred because of the additional advantage which it gives in reducing the effects of non-linear distortion in the output tube. One difficulty connected with its use, however, should be mentioned. Since the phase shift introduced by the local feedback term depends upon the transconductance of the last tube, the circuit may conceivably become unstable if the gain of this tube fails through age, even though the ideal cut-off characteristic for the principal loop is met exactly for normal tube gains. In the present amplifier this difficulty is avoided by concentrating the phase protection obtained from the local feedback circuit into the very high frequency range beyond the loop cut-off. In order to produce this result, however, it is necessary to limit the local feedback in the useful band to approximately the 12 db value which was actually assigned to it, since if we begin with a much larger cathode impedance the shunting effect of the parasitic cathode-ground capacity becomes conspicuous at too low a frequency.

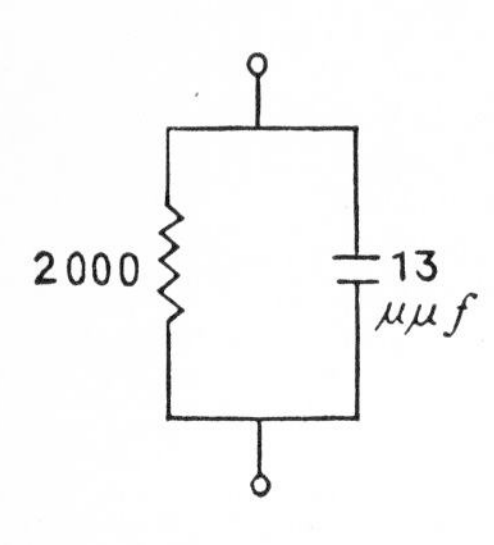

FIG. 19.56

The provision of the peak and shoulder in the phase margin curve leaves a nearly constant residue remaining. This was provided by the second interstage, whose structure is shown by Fig. 19.56. Its contribution to the total phase margin is represented by Curve III in Fig. 19.53. The physical interstage resistance is only about one-third as large as the capacity impedance at the top of the band, so that this interstage consumes about half the total 31 db of surplus gain. This proportioning between the resistance and capacity is, as it happens, well suited to the solution of the phase margin problem, but it is also chosen for another purpose. If the capacity reactance is represented by X, the interstage phase shift is evidently $B \backsimeq \tan^{-1} R/X = \tan^{-1} \omega RC$. From this we can write

$$\frac{dB}{dR} = \frac{\omega C}{1 + \omega^2 R^2 C^2} = \frac{1}{R}\left(\omega RC + \frac{1}{\omega RC}\right)^{-1}. \tag{19–2}$$

But it is well known that the function $(z + 1/z)$ is approximately stationary for values of z anywhere in the neighborhood of $z = 1$. With the proportions chosen ωRC becomes unity at 6 mc, which is at the geometrical center of the cut-off interval stretching from 2 to 15 or 20 megacycles. Thus a small change in R produces a more or less constant change in phase margin throughout the cut-off interval. Since a small change in R evidently produces a nearly constant change in gain in the useful band also, the structure thus provides a simple means of adjusting the balance between feedback and phase margin.

As the final step, the tentative configuration assumed for the first interstage was elaborated to produce a better match with the desired feedback characteristic in and near the useful band. The final configuration for this interstage is shown by Fig. 19.57. It gives the contribution to the overall phase margin curve shown by Curve I in Fig. 19.53, corresponding to the consumption of about 4 db of surplus gain. The crosses in Fig. 19.53 show the sum of the three constituent characteristics in relation to the heavy solid line, representing the ideal phase margin characteristic.

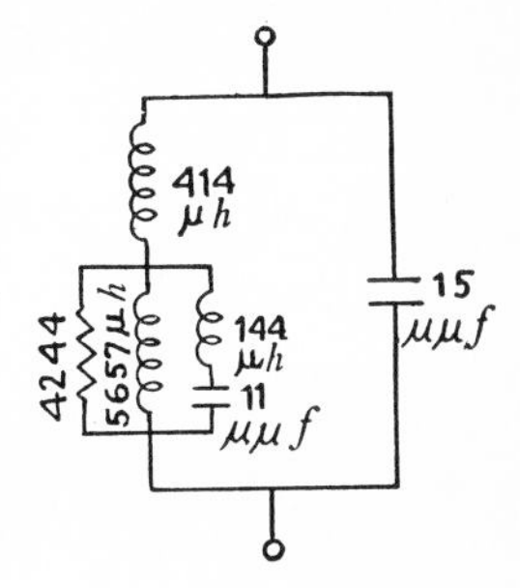

Fig. 19.57

This discussion has been conceived primarily in terms of the phase characteristics of the various networks in order to illustrate how the phase margin plot may be used as an aid in the selection of suitable configurations. In a practical design, of course, a study of the relation between the gains of the various components and the overall loop gain may be equally useful. In this particular circuit we may divide the loop characteristic roughly into a region of sharp slope just beyond the edge of

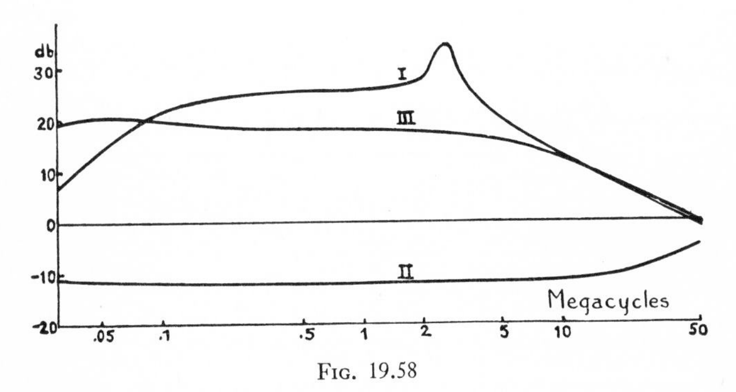

Fig. 19.58

the band, a region with nearly constant slope of about 9 to 10 db per octave extending from about 3 to about 25 megacycles, and the final horizontal step. With the networks as they have been chosen, the initial sharp slope is contributed principally by the transformer potentiometer term shown by Fig. 19.42. Since the transformer term is, however, somewhat more selective than it should be, a compensating characteristic is introduced by peaking the gain of the first interstage slightly above the useful band. At higher frequencies this interstage contributes a 6 db per

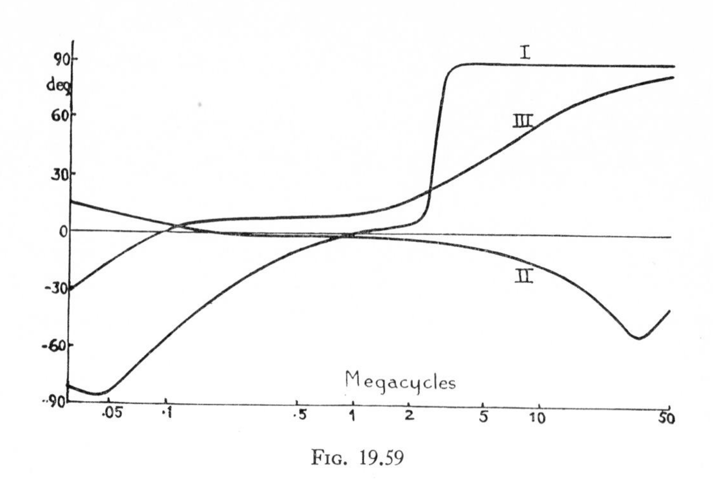

FIG. 19.59

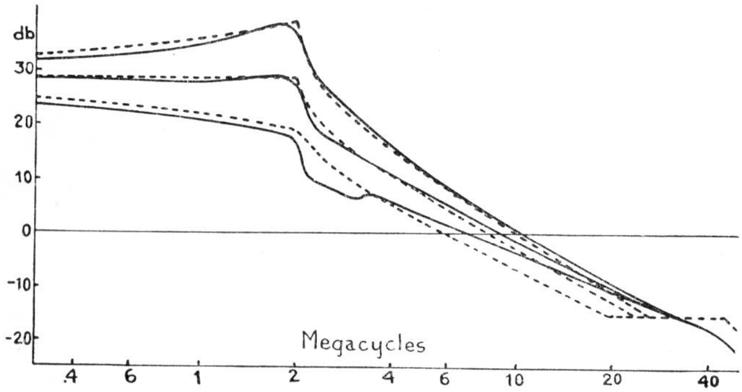

FIG. 19.60

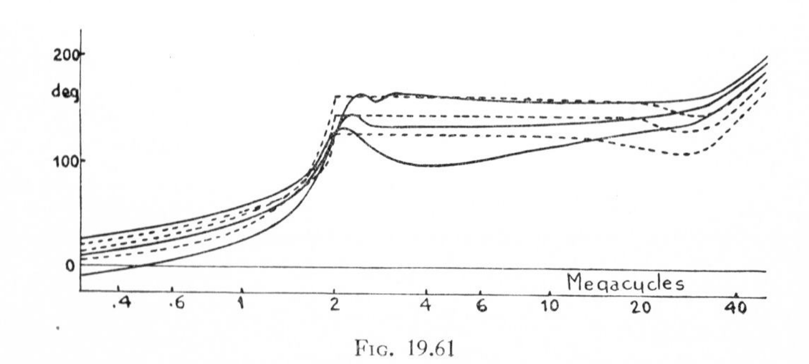

FIG. 19.61

octave slope to the overall characteristic. The remaining 3 or 4 db per octave required by the overall characteristic is contributed chiefly by the second interstage, whose slope is dampened considerably from the usual 6 db per octave by the parallel resistance in the circuit. For example, the slope of this interstage is exactly 3 db per octave at 6 mc, where the resistance and the capacity reactance are equal. The final horizontal step is obtained, roughly, by balancing the interstage slopes against the increases in loop gain due to the β circuit anti-resonance and to the removal of the local feedback on the last tube.

The collected results are shown in Figs. 19.58 to 19.61. The first pair of figures gives the gain and phase characteristics of the various forward circuit components plotted on an ordinary log frequency scale. Curves I, II, and III refer respectively to the first interstage, the local feedback, and the second interstage. The other figures give the overall loop characteristics for the mean and the two extreme settings of the regulator. The maximum feedback setting matches the theoretical curves of Figs. 19.45 and 19.46 quite closely. The others are amply stable but they depart somewhat from the theoretical curves because of the departures of the regulator characteristics beyond the band illustrated by Figs. 19.47 and 19.48.

INDEX

DATE DUE

GAYLORD			PRINTED IN U.S.A.